The Birds of Greece

George Handrinos
Triantaphyllos Akriotis

CHRISTOPHER HELM
A & C BLACK · LONDON

Line drawings by Stephen Message and George Handrinos

Christopher Helm (Publishers) Ltd, a subsidiary of A & C Black (Publishers) Ltd, 35 Bedford Row, London WC1R 4JH

0-7136-3929-6

A CIP catalogue record for this book is available from the British Library

Printed and bound in Great Britain by Cromwell Press Ltd, Melksham

CONTENTS

PREFACE

Why a book on the birds of Greece, and why now? There are many reasons one could cite. It would not be an exaggeration to say that the last book to cover all bird species in Greece dates as far back as 1905. This was O. Reiser's *Ornis Balcanica*, of which one volume (the largest in the series) was dedicated to Greece (Reiser 1905). Since then, the only other comparable publication appeared in 1969, when a group of German ornithologists, together with Prof. A. Kanellis of the University of Thessaloniki, produced *Catalogus Faunae Graeciae, Pars II: Aves* (Bauer *et al.* 1969a). Although a significant summary of all that was known up to that time on Greek birds, this book was in fact more of an annotated checklist, with limited details on distribution but no other information on topics such as population size, habitat preferences and times of occurrence. Furthermore, it was published privately and has long since been out of print.

Since then dramatic changes in the status and distribution of many bird species have occurred, coinciding with a growing interest in the birds of Greece as the rich diversity of Greek birdlife has come to be appreciated. This involves both native Greeks and visiting ornithologists and birdwatchers. As a result of this, our knowledge of the status, distribution and other aspects of the life of birds in Greece has greatly expanded in recent years, filling in many of the gaps that existed up to 20 or 30 years ago.

Unfortunately, this information is published in such a wide variety of journals, magazines, conference proceedings and other publications that much of it remains undetected by all but those with a deep interest, sufficient patience and access to the facilities of a good library. There is no specialised ornithological library in Greece and no Greek scientific ornithological journal, where one would naturally expect to find much of this information. A modern book on the birds of Greece was much needed, both to put together all recent findings and to provide a backing for the increasing number of people interested in Greek birds.

In recent years we have also witnessed the increasing negative impacts of human activities on birds and their habitats. Rare species have become extinct, others, which were common up to 30 or 40 years ago, are now restricted to a small part of the country, whilst loss or severe deterioration of some of the best bird habitats is evident almost throughout the country. Agricultural, industrial and urban development as well as direct persecution through intensive or illegal hunting are some of the problems threatening the continued existence of healthy populations of a large number of bird species. These need to be addressed urgently if Greece is willing to conserve its nature and rich birdlife for future generations. No conservation strategy can be planned and implemented unless a sufficient body of knowledge is available to Greek government agencies, policy makers and conservationists alike.

Therefore, a single handy volume summarising all our knowledge on the birds of Greece up to the present has been long overdue and evidently needed. And when Robert Kirk of A&C Black Publishers contacted the first author (GIH) with the aim of writing a book on the birds of Greece there was no place for a second thought. We immediately set about this task and it took us more than three years of work to carefully review all the Greek ornithological literature, to go through several thousand bird reports, letters and other unpublished sources, generously provided by numerous people both in Greece and abroad, to compile the species texts, distribution maps and introductory sections, and to edit the whole product. Although written in English and aiming at an international readership, it will hopefully be a signigicant aid to bird study and conservation especially within Greece, where despite recent advances it would be no exaggeration to say that still only a few hundred people are able to tell the difference between a Chaffinch and a Sparrow.

Much of the material in this book is presented here for the first time. The bird distribution maps are the first to have ever been attempted in such detail and for all species recorded in Greece, including accidental visitors. We also include estimates for the breeding populations of all species regularly breeding in the country, not just the rarer or threatened ones. The times of occurrence of migratory species also appear for the first time as a complete set for all species concerned. We finally include brief details of information which has partly remained unpublished and partly been published in a fragmented form or as reports with fairly limited circulation: ringing recoveries, IWRB January waterfowl counts, local specialised censuses and so on.

The book in your hands is neither a field guide nor a comprehensive handbook of Greek birds. Our aim was simply to bring together within a single volume as much as possible of our current knowledge on Greek avifauna. In writing this book we have always had in mind a wide range of potential readers, both within Greece and abroad. This is a meticulous yet simple treatment hopefully written in such a way so as to be useful and attractive to someone with a serious interest in birds as well as being easily understood by the non-specialist who simply enjoys watching birds and would like to have a better understanding of Greek birdlife. Whether we have been successful in fulfilling our task is a question to be answered by others, but apart from anything else, the present book will show not only what we know but also what we do not know about birds in Greece. Many gaps will be apparent, either for individual 'difficult' species or for whole groups such as seabirds and woodpeckers, and by pointing out how little we know we hope to promote a special interest in these particular fields. With this in mind, we urge all our readers to keep supplying us with bird records: even data on the commoner species might be valuable for possible revisions of the present book in the future.

G.I. Handrinos
44, El. Venizelou St.
GR-16675 Glyfada
GREECE

Dr. T. Akriotis
Dept. Environmental Studies
University of the Aegean
Karantoni 17
GR-81100 Mytilini
GREECE

FOREWORD by Dr Luc Hoffmann

Both professionals and amateur ornithologists seeking information on the distribution and numbers of birds in Greece, or in the general composition of Greek birdlife were, until now, confronted with a difficult task. Considerable knowledge has been gathered during the last 100 years, firstly mainly by foreign visitors, then increasingly and now mainly by Greeks. But all this information is scattered in thousands of often small publications in hundreds of journals, like bricks on a building site with no architect to make sense of them.

This book changes the situation radically. George Handrinos and Triantaphyllos Akriotis are remarkable architects. They have patiently collected, sorted and classified all the available data, putting them in a perspective which gives the reader not only a cornucopia of information but also brings him an immediate and coherent understanding of the context.

This book will remain a milestone in Greek ornithology, filling a gap which has become an increasing impediment for all those concerned.

The Birds of Greece will also have another effect which may be even more important. By presenting the knowledge it also shows the gaps. I hope that the will to fill these gaps will give a new and vital impulse to Greek ornithology.

Dr Luc Hoffmann
Camargue, August 1996

ACKNOWLEDGMENTS

No such book could have been the work of only two authors. Without the help of hundreds of ornithologists and birdwatchers, either in the form of work already published or through unpublished material, this book would probably have never been written.

Very special thanks go to our friend Costas Papaconstantinou, whose own data, continuous help, fresh ideas and criticism, smoothed out many of our problems, particularly on the birds of the Peloponnese and population estimates. Alan Vittery and 'The Friends of the Ionians' have also made a very important contribution to our work by providing much needed data on the birds of the Ionian islands, as well as from other parts of the country. John Parrott, Stephanie Coghlan and John Gooders have very kindly allowed us to draw heavily from a final draft of their *Birds of Crete* (soon to be published by the BOU). Independently, Stephanie Coghlan, a passionate lover of Crete, has supplied us with additional data and information through a large network of mainly British birdwatchers who have visited the island in recent years.

We were indeed moved by the immediate response and interest shown by both foreign and Greek ornintHologists and birdwatchers in our request for data; they are so numerours that much to our regret it is impossible to mention them all here. We sincerely thank them all but we are particularly indebted to the following for supplying information.

C. Alivizatos
J.B. Andersen
R. Allen
E. Arfwidsson
C.N. Arnold
P. Atkinson
D. Atter
D.E. Balmer
K. Bannister
J. Barker
F. Barrault
P. Barthel
P. Barry
R.E. Batty
P. Belman
H.J. Böhr
A. Bonetti
K.S. Bovey
N. & A. Bowman
M. Broggi
R. Brooks
E. Callebaut
C. Carbone
P.A. Casales
G. Catsadorakis
J. Choremi
K. & M. Claydon
M. Cocker
T. Conzemius
F. Cotaar
A.J. Crivelli
N. Curry
P. de Fraine
B. de Schutter
M.C. Dennis
G. Dick
M. Dimaki
A. Dimitropoulos
P. Doherty
J. Drachman
P. Dragoumis
M. Dretakis
S.B. Edwards
L. Empeirikos
P.P. Evrard
E. Euthymiadis
D. Fisher
D. Förnzlar
M. Gaetlich
M. Ganoti
S. Gantlett
D. Gaunt
C.L. Gibson
O. Girard
A.G. Gosler
G. Goumbouros
V. Goutner
J. Grearson
X. Gremillet
D. Grigoropoulos
P. Grundy
H. Hafner
A. & J. Hakala
P.D. Hanson
P. Harris
H. Harrop
D. Hatzilacou
V. Hatzirvassanis
S. Hayhow
P. Heck
P. Henderson
S. Henning
P. Henry
J. & C. Henshall
M. Herremans
K. Hingley
M. Hodge
L. Hoffmann
G. Hourmouziadis†
M. Huguenin-Maurer
R. Hume
D. Iredale
D. Jackson
C.M. Jackson-Houlston
H. Jerrentrup
F. Johansson
A. Johnson
G. Jones
E. Kainadas
F. Katsigiannis
S. Kazantzidis
S. Keen
G. Kondylis
V. Kotriklas
D. Koukouras
J. Koutsis
N. Kroftt
A. Kyrkos
R.-M. Lafontaine
W. Laich
R. Lamberton
M. Langridge
P. Latsoudis
B. Lee
M. Leuenberger

M. & J. Lewis
J. van der Linden
K.S. Lodge
L. Logothetis
U. Lundgren
P. Mackinder
M. Malakou
S. Magioris
H. Märki
A.W. Martin
K. Mauer
L. Maumary
M.I. McDonald
D.V. McMillan
D. Mervyn-Jones
J. Metcalf
J. Millett
M. Mitchell
T. Naziridis
T. Nilsson
I.C.T. Nisbet
S.C. Norman
M. O'Meara
R.D. Oades
B. Pambour
C. Pantsoglou
E. Papaevangelou
D. Papandropoulos
H. Percy†
F. Pergantis
J. Peters
G. Petrakis
N. Petrou
K. Pistiolas
K. Poirazidis
G. Potter
J. Potts
J. Poulopoulos
G. Jeff Price
J.H. Rahder
J. Rallis
A. Ranner
M. Richardson
D. Ristow
A. & J.E. Roadhouse
L. Rose
Y. Roussopoulos
W. Scharlau
P. Schiermacher-Hansen
I. Schogolev
R. Scott
A. & R. Scott
E. Seitz
V. Sheridan
V. Spinthakis
C. Squires
G. Strömberg
B.J. Summerfield
G. Susic
W. Suter
J.J. Swift
M.J. Taylor
C. Thomas
J. Thorogood
D. Townsend
M. & F. Trubridge
A. Tsatsaronis
E. Tsirozidis
G. Tsounis
M. Ullman
C. Vagliano
J. Vane†
D. Vangeluwe
V. Vassiliadis
M. Versluys
A. Vittery
C. Vlachos
H. Vonk
V. Vousvaros
J.T. Wakenshaw
J. Walmsley
R. Wake
P.F. Whitehead
J.D. Wilson
M. Wink
J. Wittbrodt
C. Wormwell
S. Zoggaris

† Deceased

Many thanks go to Didier Vangeluwe and René-Marie Lafontaine of the Royal Institute of Natural Sciences in Brussels for helping GIH use the extensive library of the Institute and for providing copies of many old or obscure papers and publications. Antonios Kyrkos has also been a great help, locating information for us in foreign journals in the Alexander Library of the Edward Grey Institute at Oxford.

The work of the Hellenic Wildlife Hospital on the island of Aigina is now widely acclaimed and respected throughout Greece: we are very grateful to Maria Ganoti and Philippos Dragoumis for allowing us to use their archives on birds brought to them for treatment.

During the early stages of our work a request for data was published in many foreign journals at our request. For this we are indebted to the editors of *Birding World*, *British Birds*, *BTO News*, *Dutch Birding*, *Der Falke*, *Journal für Ornithologie*, *Limicola*, *OSME Bulletin*, *Vår Fågelvard* and *Winging It*. We do not subscribe to all the periodicals that we sent our request to, and there may be others in Greece that we have unintentionally omitted. We express our apologies for omitting any such periodicals.

Apart from ornithologists, many other scientists have greatly assisted us by providing suggestions, useful references or their own unpublished data in the introductory sections. Special thanks go to Prof. M. Arianoutsou of Athens University (vegetation), A. Katsaounis of the Ministry of the Environment and Dr P. Panayotidis of the National Centre for Marine Research (oceanography), Prof. G. Theodorou of Athens University (paleontology), S. Plessas of the Ministry of the Environment (geology), and A. Katsimardos and P. Xirakis of the National Meteorological Service (climatic data).

Without the photographs and illustrations this book would certainly have been much poorer and less appealing. Our task in choosing the photographs was particularly difficult due to the large amount of excellent material provided by many photographers. For kindly allowing us to use their work, we would very much like to thank: T. Adamakopoulos, Prof R.F. Chandler, D. Koukouras, A. Limbrunner, L. Logothetis, Dr N. Petrou, V. Spinthakis, Dr T. Schultze-

Westrum, J.-F. and M. Terrrasse and E. Zouzis. We are particularly grateful to Sabine Schnabel-Makatsch, for allowing us to use photographic material from the files of her late parents, Wolfgang and Ilse.

Special thanks also go to Steve Message for his delightful ink drawings, and to Mary Dafopoulou for help in designing some of the maps in the introductory section. Dawn Balmer, Antonios Kyrkos and Dr Jeremy Wilson made significant improvements to the English and helped with their useful comments.

Bird conservation in Greece owes a lot to Dr Luc Hoffmann, a world famous conservationist and lover of Greek nature: we are both lucky to know him personally and really proud in having him introduce this publication to our readers.

This book would probably have never been finished without Robert Kirk of A & C Black. His incredible patience with our long delays and his encouragement and ideas throughout the long process of completing the manuscript has made it all possible.

Last but not least, we would like to express our deep thanks to Maria Aloupi for her invaluable support and endless other help in the preparation of this book, and to Maria Handrinos for her continuing support (and suffering) not only during work on this project but also for more than 20 years of tolerating her husband's absence from home while pursuing birds.

INTRODUCTION

For a country of its size, Greece possesses a rich diversity of bird species, albeit most of them represented by relatively small populations. The checklist of Greek birds today numbers 422 species, of which 15 are included here for the first time. The aim of the present book is to summarise all current knowledge on the birds of Greece. The species accounts and distribution maps form the main body of the work. These two, however, might not have been enough by themselves to give an adequate all-round picture of the character of Greek birdlife, especially to someone unfamiliar with the country. In order to fill in the picture as much as possible within the space limits of a single volume we have included a short introductory chapter. Following this Introduction, there is a section on the history of ornithology in Greece whilst the rest of the introductory section can be divided into two parts: the first, dealing with the country itself, serves as a background (geography, climate, vegetation) for the second part which deals with birds, their habitats and conservation. At the end of the book we include nine appendices with additional information which we think readers will find useful.

Sources of Information

For the species accounts, distribution maps and introductory chapter, a large volume of material from various sources has been used. In addition to our own data, collected in the course of field work or general birdwatching over the last 25–30 years, this includes the following.

Published Sources

All items included in the *Bibliography of Greek Ornithology* (Handrinos & Akriotis 1996), a total of 1,005 titles from 1833 up to 31 December 1994. In a few exceptional cases we have also consulted earlier books, mainly those published by early travellers and explorers of Greece. We have also taken into account more recent material, published in 1995. Furthermore, works such as regional handbooks covering Greece and treatments of the avifauna of regions adjacent to Greece were consulted. Two of these, the *Handbook of the Birds of the Western Palearctic* (Cramp *et al.* 1977–94) and the *Handbuch der Vögel Mitteleuropas* (Glutz *et al.* 1966–), were used extensively and on numerous occasions were an invaluable source of information. Readers may like to refer to these two works for more general information on particular species. We were also privileged enough to have had access to the manuscript of the *Birds of Crete* (Parrot *et al.* in press).

During the course of the preparation of this book, the *Atlas of European Breeding Birds*, organised by the European Bird Census Council, was due to be published and thus was not available for us to use. It includes data on Greece but only on a relatively coarse 50x50 km grid, so we do not think we missed a great deal of new information.

All published material, including the 1,005 titles in Handrinos & Akriotis (1996) was critically reviewed. Many of the titles that we consulted do not appear here because they contain superseded information, information proved erroneous in the light of more recent findings, or because they contain material irrelevant to this work.

Expedition Reports, Checklists of Birds Seen and Personal Communications

Birdwatching reports and checklists were mainly supplied by foreign birdwatchers visiting Greece. Since the early 1970s the first author (GIH) has collected 482 such reports from more than 350 people, comprising more than one and a half million individual bird records pertaining to various parts of the country and various times of the year. In addition, several Greek ornithologists and birdwatchers supplied information verbally or in written form.

To sort out, analyse and evaluate such a bulk of data has been a long, laborious and often delicate task, particularly when dealing with first records of species new to Greece, additional records of rarities or observations from previously unexplored parts of the country. A special effort to cull as many errors as possible was made and by applying strict judgment criteria some of this material had to be rejected.

Dissertations, Theses and Other Unpublished Work

Unpublished written work supplied by Greek ornithologists and birdwatchers and involving specific studies on particular areas, sites (especially wetlands) or species (e.g. pelicans, birds of prey). Included in this category are also several unpublished reports and studies dealing with the management and conservation of certain important bird areas such as National Parks and Ramsar sites. Information in these works derives mainly from field work carried out during the last 10–15 years.

Waterfowl Counts and Ringing Recoveries

Two sets of partly unpublished data were particularly useful. The IWRB January waterfowl counts were used to give population estimates of wintering waterfowl, while ringing recoveries give an indication of the origin of ringed birds found in Greece. Both sets of data are partly unpublished, so in both cases we deliberately give only brief summary information. There are still under 100 ringing recoveries of birds ringed in Greece, and only a small proportion of these have been recovered abroad. Thus the ringing recovery data refer mainly to birds ringed abroad and found in Greece.

Throughout the book sources of information are cited in one of the following three ways.

(i) Author's name(s) and year of publication for literature (books, papers, reports and other publications). All these are listed in the Bibliography towards the end of the book.

(ii) For all unpublished data (personal communications, letters, private reports etc.) the initials and surname(s) of the observer(s) appears in brackets (with no date). All names in this category are listed alphabetically in the acknowledgments section.

(iii) No citation appears for our own data or information that could be described as common knowledge.

The Species Accounts

The aim of the species' text is to give a complete account of the status and distribution in Greece of each species in as few lines as possible. We do not, as a rule, include data such as on feeding ecology, breeding biology and behaviour, except for species particularly well studied in Greece or where we otherwise thought that a mention would be of interest to our readers.

The English and scientific name of each species is followed by a phrase describing its status in Greece. The main species account follows, in which breeding status is usually described first, followed by wintering and/or migratory status. Whenever relevant information is available, species accounts include the following.

a. Distribution and abundance
b. Habitat
c. An estimate of the total breeding population of the species in Greece
d. Timing of movements
e. Ringing recoveries
f. Subspecies occurring in Greece

We have sometimes deviated from this order, giving priority to a smoother flow of the text. For species whose status is known to have changed significantly since the 19th century we also include information on their past distribution and abundance. For accidental visitors details of all records available are given.

In describing the distribution of a species, islands lying close to the mainland (e.g. Thasos and Evvoia) are presumed to have the same avifauna as adjacent parts of the mainland (subject to habitat availability) and are not mentioned separately except where necessary. The Peloponnese is considered as part of the southern mainland, rather than an island.

The terms rare, scarce, fairly common, common and very common used throughout the species account section are obviously subjective, as are the terms widespread and local. Rare refers to a species one does not normally expect to see in an ordinary day's birdwatching. Scarce refers to a species one expects to see once or twice a year when out in the field, say, about once a week during the appropriate time of year. Fairly common is used to describe a species which one expects to see on several days in the right time of year and in the right habitat but which may be missed during a short visit to a site known to hold the species. Common and very common refer to two levels of abundance for species which one cannot easily avoid! The term abundant appears in the main species accounts when needed for added emphasis but it is not used in the species status phrase because we felt that there was little difference between it and 'very common'. Indeed, because the species status phrase applies to the country as a whole and because practically every species is absent from or rare in some part of the country, strictly speaking no species qualified for a term referring to an exceptionally high abundance. We have refrained from using the term uncommon due its ambiguous meaning, though we initially planned to use it as an intermediate between scarce and fairly common and the resulting gap between scarce or fairly common was rather wide so that it was sometimes difficult to decide which one of the two alternative terms should be used.

The timing of movements is generally given in ten-day periods (early, mid and late parts of each month). The relevant dates are best known and mainly refer to central parts of the country. It is likely that in all cases movements are slightly earlier in the south and slightly later in the north in the spring (and vice versa in the autumn) and a difference of a few days may be assumed for all migratory species. This difference is usually of a smaller magnitude than the margin of error resulting from insufficient knowledge or from variation from year to year. In some cases there is a special mention where this north–south difference is more marked or more well known. One must bear in mind that the dates given are the best as far as we can tell but that there are often significant differences from year to year.

The timing of movements of resident species or those occurring as summer or winter visitors is often difficult to define as there is often a through-passage of migrants that move between wintering and summering grounds entirely outside the country, coinciding or overlapping with the arrival and departures movements of birds spending the whole winter or summer in Greece. For example, are the first Swallows one sometimes sees in early March local breeders or birds destined for further north? Passage movements may not be discernible at all when a species is present all year round, especially if the local population is high and through-migrants few. In some cases it was possible to get round this problem by considering parts of the country where the species does not normally occur year-round or during the whole winter or summer period. For some species (e.g. Blackcap, Stonechat) the situation is especially complicated and it is not even known whether birds occurring in different (geographically or altitudinally) parts of the country during different parts of the year are passage migrants, winter visitors, summer visitors or resident. Whenever not otherwise specified, 'winter' refers to the October to March period, 'summer' to the May to August period, 'autumn' to the (August–) September to October period and 'spring' to the March to May period.

Breeding population size is given for all breeding species. With few exceptions, there is a general lack of bird census and population monitoring work in Greece and thus it is almost always hard to estimate and sometimes even to guess the size of Greek populations. We have attempted to give rough estimates of breeding populations for each species by taking into account the geographical spread, habitat availability and abundance in suitable habitat. We judged these were better than no estimate at all but obviously one may expect a relatively high degree of inaccuracy. Furthermore, it was not possible to be very precise and as a result the upper and lower limits given are often wide apart.

In Tucker & Heath's (1994) book one may find population estimates for a large proportion of Greek species. Rather than repeating these data, which one may easily find in such a recent and widely available publication, we have deemed preferrable to give our own estimates. In most cases, sizes of Greek populations in Tucker & Heath are themselves rough estimates, thus there was no particular advantage in using them. However, we refer to their estimates when they differed considerably from ours. In the few cases (e.g. pelicans) in which reliable estimates or censuses existed already we used these rather than our own. In general we give breeding population estimates as a number of breeding pairs but it is well known that many species are partly or wholly polygamous and in such cases the term 'pairs' may be considered synonymous with 'territorial males' or 'territories occupied'.

Wintering populations are given for only a few species, mainly waterfowl, using data from the IWRB Midwinter Counts for the 1982 to 1992 period. These counts cover not only waterfowl but a wide variety of species, including raptors, herons and waders. However, it is mainly duck, swans and Coot that are covered adequately, with a significant proportion of the Greek wintering population within the boundaries of the sites counted. For other species (e.g. Hen Harrier) it is pointless to use these counts as an estimate of the total wintering population.

As an indication of the maximum abundance to be expected for some species we give the largest number ever recorded. One should be aware, however, that this may refer to two quite distinct situations: either the largest flock (e.g. of migrating herons) ever recorded or the largest number counted within an area, within which the species may have been scattered uniformly or in small aggregations (e.g. waders at a wetland site). In the latter case, actual flock size will usually have been much smaller than the total counted in the area.

Ringing recoveries provide useful information on the likely origin of migratory species occurring in Greece. For reasons already mentioned we did not attempt a detailed analysis of these. In most cases we present only a summary of the countries of ringing for birds ringed abroad and found in Greece. However, one should bear in mind that the country of ringing does not always correspond with the country of origin: birds may have been ringed whilst on passage (e.g. Turtle Doves in Italy) or wintering (e.g. ducks in western Europe) and found in Greece in a different year or migratory season because, for example, they followed a different route or selected a different wintering area, after an intervening period at their summer or winter quarters. Furthermore, the relative numbers from different countries are not always meaningful in showing the main provenance of populations occurring in Greece since the effort of ringing different species in different countries may vary considerably.

Races occurring in Greece are mentioned only where a form other than the nominate occurs.

The Problem of Unusual Records

Critical evaluation of Greek bird records was first performed by Reiser (1905), who very carefully scrutinised those obtained in the 19th century, and then by Bauer *et al.* (1969a), who similarly examined records up to 1969. Many of the more recent records appear in Tsounis & Handrinos (1987) and Handrinos (1992b).

Despite the growing interest in ornithology in Greece, the country still lacks an official body for the checking of records of rare species (a rarities committee). In fact there is neither a checking system for unusual records of commoner species (e.g. at unusual places or in unusual times of year) nor an official recording scheme with, for example, regional and local recorders who collect and check records.

The first author (GIH) has been actively involved in the collection and filing of records of accidental visitors or rare species as well as other observations in Greece during the last two decades. Analysis and evaluation of such records is being done in consultation with an informal group of competent Greek ornithologists. In cases of doubt or disagreement foreign experts are also consulted, while in recent years the Guidelines for Rarities Committees, as approved by the Association of European Rarities Committees, have been closely followed. A very conservative policy is adopted and only those records fully documented with photos and/or detailed descriptions (preferably by at least two observers) are eligible for discussion and eventual acceptance or rejection.

Several records have been published during the last couple of decades, either by the observers themselves (often in foreign magazines and journals) or by ourselves in *Nature*, the Greek/English bulletin of the Hellenic Society for the Protection of Nature. Records accepted as valid are also published periodically in a summary form in the European News section of *British Birds* magazine, where GIH has acted as the official national representative for Greece for a number of years. In addition, a review paper summarising all records of birds new to

Greece in the 1969–1989 period has also been published (Handrinos 1994a).

During the preparation of this book an appeal for bird records from Greece was published in many foreign journals and magazines. This resulted in a large influx of bird observations and birdwatching reports, including many records of rare species or species new to the Greek list. Some of these records have been published in the last few years but a significant proportion appear here for the first time.

It must be stressed that any checking and evaluation procedure of bird records cannot be faultless. Undoubtedly, some genuine records may have been rejected and conversely some erroneous ones may have been accepted. This applies not only to recent years but probably also to the pre-1969 period. Although we accepted such records as they appear in Bauer et al. (1969a), it is not unlikely that several of them are not valid: one is struck by the number of rarities seen by some observers on brief expeditions (they must have been very lucky indeed!) or by the large number of records of some species in former times, not seen at all in the last 20–30 years or seen much less frequently, despite increased observer activity.

Nomenclature

We generally follow Cramp (1977–94) for the common and scientific names of birds. There are a few exceptions for taxa treated as subspecies in Cramp (1977–94) but for which the trend nowadays is to upgrade them to full species. Thus we treat Mediterranean Shearwater *Puffinus yelkouan* as separate from Manx (Atlantic) Shearwater *Puffinus puffinus*, Steppe Eagle *Aquila nipalensis* as separate from Tawny Eagle *Aquila rapax*, Pacific Golden Plover *Pluvialis fulva* as separate from American Golden Plover *Pluvialis dominica* and Yellow-legged Gull *Larus cachinnans* as separate from Herring Gull *Larus argentatus*.

For plant names we follow Polunin (1980), for amphibians and reptiles Arnold *et al.* (1978), and for mammals MacDonald & Barrett (1993). With only a few exceptions, we use only the common name for birds on the Greek list but use both latin and common name (if one exists) for all other plants and animals.

Place Names

Modern Greek has inherited the ancient Greek alphabet, with the exception of three rarely used letters. Although most words in modern Greek have a root in ancient Greek and indeed a significant number of words in use in everyday language have remained unchanged since the time of Homer (9th century BC), there have naturally been significant changes since then. One form of change which is relevant here is the change in pronunciation of many letters. Although originally there was probably a one letter-one sound relation, nowadays many letters share the same sound. For example, 'eta', 'iota' and 'ypsilon', as well as two diphthongs ('eta-iota' and 'ypsilon-iota'), all have one common sound, 'ee' as in 'tree' but shorter. The reverse happens in the case of some other sounds for which a two-letter combination must be used (the sounds 'b', 'd', 'j' and 'g' of English), analogous, for example, to the two sounds of 'th' (as in 'the' and 'thin') in English. Therefore, the transcription of place names has not been easy and we had to choose between several alternative methods available.

We used the standard method used officially in recent times (e.g. in European Union official documents). This method is becoming more widespread and is a relatively simple rendering of the letters of the Greek alphabet. It is primarily phonetic but not entirely so. For example, 'sigma' is always transcribed as an 's' but in the transcribed word it should always be pronounced as an 's' as in 'sea', not like a 'z' as in 'rise'. The idea behind this is probably that there is no single rendering if one has to transcribe words so that they are readable by speakers of many different languages.

Some readers will thus find a different spelling from the one they are used to. We have kept anglicised forms for some place names known for their archaeological interest or which have appeared in that form repeatedly in past and recent ornithological literature, but in most cases we have used the modern spelling. Unfortunately foreign visitors will still be puzzled and frustrated by road signs or maps which use other ways of transcription or (in some cases) translation for a number of years to come but hopefully this will improve over the years.

Common changes between the method one would have used ten or 20 years ago and the new one adopted here are:

Old rendering	New rendering
ss	s
b, mb	mp
ph	f
dh, th	d
gh, gg	g

Furthermore, a number of place names also have one or more alternative names within the Greek language. Below is a list of such cases or of anglicised names used in this book and the various alternatives commonly used.

Name used here	Alternatives
Arogi (Lagoon)	Karatza
Athens	Athina, Athinai
Athos (Mt)	Agion Oros, 'Holy Mountain'
Attica	Attiki
Boeotia	Voiotia
Chania	Canea
Corfu	Kerkyra
Corinth	Korinthos
Crete	Kriti
Cyclades	Kyklades
Dodecanese	Dodekanisos, Noties (=Southern) Sporades
Doirani (Lake)	Doiran
Evvoia	Euboea
Faliron	Phaleron
Fanari (Lagoon)	Xirolimni
Filippoi	Philippoi
Hymmetus (Mt)	Ymittos
Idean Cave	Ideon Andron
Idi (Mt)	Psiloritis
Ileia	Eleia, Elis
Ioannina	Giannina, Yiannena, Jannina
Irakleion	Herakleion, Candia
Ismaris (Lake)	Mitrikoy, Metrikou
Kalamas (River)	Thyamis
Kalodiki (Marsh)	Margariti
Kefallinia	Cephalonia
Kerkini (Lake)	L. Kerkinitis
Kerkini (Mt)	Mt Beles
Kleisova	Klissova
Koronia (Lake)	Langada, Agiou Vasiliou
Lefkada	Lefkas
Lesbos	Lesvos, Mytilene (sometimes applied to whole island)
Limnos	Lemnos
Macedonia	Makedonia
Messolonghi	Mesolongi
Olympos (Mt)	Olympus
Orvilos (Mt)	Ali Botush
Ossa (Mt)	Kissavos
Parnitha (Mt)	Parnis, Parnes
Parnon (Mt)	Parnonas
Patras	Patrai, Patra

Peloponnese	Peloponisos, Morea, Morias
Penteli (Mt)	Pentelikon
Pindos (Mts)	Pindus
Piraeus	Pireefs, Pireas
Rhodes	Rodos
Rodopi (Mts)	Rhodope
Serres	Serrai
Strofades (Islands)	Strofadia
Thessaloniki	Salonica
Thessaly	Thessalia
Thira (Island)	Santorini
Thiva	Thebes
Thrace	Thraki
Timfi (Mt)	Gamila
Tymfristos (Mt)	Velouchi
Vistonis (Lake)	Buru
Voras (Mt)	Kaimaktsalan, Kajmakchalan
Zakynthos	Zante

The above list obviously cannot include all possible cases. Other examples could be the names of gulfs such as Amvrakikos (Gulf of Arta), Korinthiakos (Corinthian, Gulf of Corinth), Patraikos (Patraic, Gulf of Patras), Saronikos (Saronic) and Thermaikos (Thermaic, Gulf of Thessaloniki). Officially, Hellas (or Ellas) is often used instead of Greece and Hellenic instead of Greek.

Common in compound place names are words like 'agios' or 'agia' (also 'ayios' and 'aghios') (saint), 'ano' (upper, above), 'kato' (lower, below), 'megalos'/'megali'/'megalo' (large, greater), 'mikros'/'mikri'/'mikro' (small, lesser), 'neos'/'nea'/'neo' (new) and 'palios'/'palia'/'palio' (old).

Finally, one should bear in mind that there are rivers named Pineios in both Thessaly and the Peloponnese and the Mt Olympos (where the gods lived) lies on the border between Thessaly and Macedonia whereas the ancient site of Olympia (whence Olympic games) is in the west of the Peloponnese.

The Species Distribution Maps

Distribution maps are given for all 422 species recorded in Greece up to now. This is the first attempt ever made at such a level of detail and for the full set of Greek species. As could be expected, it was one of the most difficult and complex tasks in the preparation of the book, with a variety of problems ranging from lack of data from many parts of the country to presentation of information.

The first distribution maps of Greek bird species were prepared by the late W. Bauer for the Greek edition of Peterson's field guide (Peterson *et al.* 1981). These were of a very high quality but showed distribution only during the breeding season and that for a selection of only 83 species. Distribution maps covering the whole country have also appeared in Dr J. Hölzinger's recent work for a few species (e.g. Hölzinger 1986a, 1988a, 1988b, 1989a, 1995). These also show breeding distribution but they differ in being based on 10x10 km square grid, rather than using shading to cover whole areas. At a regional level, breeding distribution maps (36 species) have been published for the Peloponnese (Adamakopoulos *et al.* 1988) and for all species breeding on the island of Rhodes and in the eastern part of Crete (Sharlau 1989a, 1989b).

The maps in *Birds of the Western Palearctic* (Cramp *et al.* 1977–1994) were useful sources of information, even though they were not detailed enough for the purposes of this book. In fact GIH prepared the maps for Greece for Vols. V (in part) and VI to IX, whilst the two of us prepared the maps for all species for the forthcoming concise edition of this work.

To compile the species maps we used all possible sources of information. Even so, there was a considerable lack of data, often equally serious for the common and rare species alike. Much had to be assumed, especially for distribution on passage and in winter. In general, for a common species we assumed that it occurs in all areas where suitable habitat exists within its known broader range but we have been more conservative with local or uncommon species, not showing them present in an area unless there was positive evidence for their occurrence there. Through this process the geographical range of common species has probably been exaggerated in many cases whilst the opposite is almost certainly true for the less common species.

The maps do not show absolute or relative abundance but simply whether a species occurs regularly in a given area as a breeding species, winter visitor, passage migrant or resident. The term 'regularly' is rather subjective and not always easy to apply, especially with respect to distribution in winter and on passage. Furthermore, one must bear in mind that the distributions shown are applicable only to areas of suitable habitat. At any map scale, it is impossible to fully take into account the heterogeneity of bird distribution and habitat. In a mountainous country such as Greece, with contrasting habitat types often close together in a dense mosaic, this shortcoming is especially important. For these reasons, the maps do not depict the actual distribution of all species with the same degree of accuracy, e.g. both Sardinian Warbler and 'Black-headed' Wagtail are shown to breed on the island of Samos but the former is much more numerous and widespread than the latter.

For clarity of presentation but also often due to lack of information, in many cases we disregarded the effect of high mountains on bird (and habitat) distribution and bird movements. Among others, this means that:

(i) Montane species performing only limited altitudinal movements (in the majority of cases depending on snow cover) are shown as resident on high mountains; in fact there is virtually no bird living permanently above about 1500 m for at least a few weeks during the heart of winter.

(ii) For widespread species reaching up to about the treeline (e.g. Blackbird, Chaffinch) there are no empty spaces corresponding to high-altitude alpine areas from which such species are absent.

(iii) Many widespread species which mostly descend to low altitude in winter and are either rare or totally absent from high ground, appear as resident throughout.

Overall we are aware of the fact that the species maps are not perfect. But as with the species texts, they will at least serve as a baseline on which to build, making corrections and adjustments, and will hopefully stimulate an interest for more detailed investigation in the future.

Key to the Maps

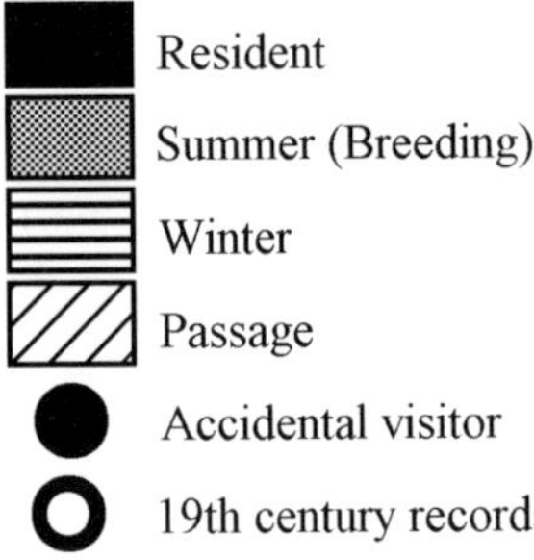

A BRIEF HISTORY OF GREEK ORNITHOLOGY

It is now generally accepted that ornithology and the science of zoology can trace their roots back to ancient Greece, when the great Aristotle (384–323 BC) changed the entire conspectus of knowledge by extending the study of philosophy into a new field, physical sciences. Although none of his nine books of *Historia Animalium* is devoted exclusively to birds, he described many species in detail and there is no doubt he spent many hours watching birds. Despite inevitable inaccuracies, his writings still remain the best ancient work on birds and form a sound basis for most later authors, even centuries after his death (Stresemann 1951, Pollard 1977). Further works exist from the Byzantine era and the period of Turkish occupation of Greece (1453–1821) but treatment of these is beyond the scope of this publication. The present chapter describes briefly the history of Greek ornithology in modern times, from the establishment of the modern Hellenic Republic at the end of the War of Independence (1821–1830) until today.

During these 160 years, ornithology in Greece has evolved through four distinct periods: 1830–1905; 1905–1950; 1950–1973; and 1973–1990.

First period (1830–1905): From Independence to Reiser

The first scientific treatment of Greek birds was published in Paris in 1833, as part of a multi-volume work presenting the results of the *Expedition Scientifique de Morée*. This expedition studied various aspects of natural history in the Peloponnese. In the Zoology section (Vol. III, 1st part) Dr I. Geoffroy Saint-Hilaire, Professor of Zoology and a medical doctor in Paris, published a list of 58 bird species, including the last records of Purple Gallinule for continental Greece (Geoffroy St-Hilaire 1832). A few years later, R. Jameson, a British military surgeon who lived on the island of Kythira for 30 years, published a list of birds from 'the Ionian islands generally' (Jameson 1837). In his work, Jameson unfortunately does not specify precisely which species were actually recorded on that island.

Between 1840 and 1860, the first two books on Greek birds were published, both in Germany. Heinrich Graf von der Mühle (= Graf Dumoulin) lived in Greece while on military service from 1834 to 1838. His *Beiträge zur ornithologie Griechenlands* (Mühle 1844) is the first checklist of Greek birds ever published, though some of his findings were seriously questioned later (Reiser 1905). *Die Vögel Griechenlands* by Dr Ritter A. Lindermayer, published in Passau (Lindermayer 1860), is also an important work. R.A. Lindermayer, a German medical doctor who also lived for many years in Greece (died in Athens in 1868), had already published a similar work in 1843 (Lindermayer 1843) as well as an account of the natural history of Evvoia, including birds (Lindermayer 1855). He adopted a much more critical approach in ornithology than von der Mühle, but despite this he also included some inaccuracies (Reiser 1905). *Die Vögel Griechenlands*, however, remains valuable both scientifically and historically.

In the meantime, Colonel H.M. Drummond-Hay published lists of birds seen or shot on Corfu and other Ionian islands, as well as on Crete and Macedonia (both still under Turkish rule at that time) (Drummond-Hay 1843a, 1843b, 1846) whereas Dr E. Frivaldszky, from Budapest, collected and observed birds also in Macedonia and Crete in 1833–1836 and 1841–1845. A summary of his work was published much later (Frivaldszky 1902) and includes the last record of Black Francolin in Greece (on Crete).

In 1858, another German, Dr Erhard (his Christian name is not known) published a list of the migrating and wintering birds of the Cyclades (Erhard 1858). This is the first publication on the avifauna of the central Aegean archipelago, but despite its significance it must be treated with much caution: some of the species he reports are highly improbable for the area and have never been reported again anywhere in the country (Rüppell's Vulture, Sooty Falcon, Desert and Hoopoe Larks etc.).

During the second half of the 19th century, two individuals dominate ornithological science in Greece. Theobald Johannes Krüper (1829–1921) studied zoology at the University of

Berlin, where he worked on his PhD thesis on the geographical distribution of European falcons. From 1852 onwards he dedicated his life to the collection and study of birds through a series of expeditions first to northern Europe and then to SE Europe. He came to Athens in 1858 and immediately went on to explore many areas of mainland Greece, the Ionian islands, the Cyclades and later, based on Smyrna (Izmir), he explored parts of Asia Minor. It was here in Smyrna that he discovered a new species of nuthatch, Krüper's Nuthatch *Sitta krueperi*, which was named after him. Upon his return to Athens (1872) he was appointed Curator and Director of the Zoological Museum of Athens University. Under his direction this modest institution (established in 1858) developed an important ornithological collection of mounted bird specimens and eggs collected by himself or his colleagues. An avid collector and dealer, he was supplying for years many European museums with bird skins and eggs from Greece, even just before his death in Athens in 1921. Dr T. Krüper contributed considerably to the early ornithology of Greece by publishing 15 papers from various areas and on various bird groups, particularly raptors. In his last years he also produced a detailed checklist of the birds of Greece, including passage migrants. This publication superseded the works of all earlier authors but unfortunately it was published in an obscure non-biological German journal and therefore never received the recognition it deserved (Krüper & Hartlaub 1875).

Otmar Reiser (1861–1936), Curator of Natural History at the National Museum of Bosnia-Herzegovina in Serajevo, was a pioneer of Balkan ornithology. A versatile biologist who studied not only birds, he published 140 scientific works and collected skins and eggs. His collection, totalling 9,226 skins and mounted birds, as well as 12,000 eggs, is now housed mainly at the Natural History Museum in Vienna and partly at the museums of Belgrade and Ljubljana (Matvejev 1986).

Early in his career, Reiser decided to explore Greece and embarked on three expeditions (in 1894, 1897 and 1898) studying and collecting birds and eggs in many regions, including the Ionian islands, Northern Sporades and SE Thessaly. Reiser's material from Greece consists of 1,617 skins and 488 eggs, but his most important contribution to Greek ornithology is the publication of *Ornis Balcanica: Part III: Greece and the Greek Islands (except Crete)* published in Vienna in 1905 (Reiser 1905). This book is a milestone in Greek ornithological literature and, almost a century after its publication, it is still used today as it contains carefully annotated observations including data on the breeding ecology of many species. He also published ten papers on Greek ornithology and commented critically on the work of earlier authors, very correctly rejecting many species from the Greek list. The thick-billed Balkan race of Reed Bunting *Emberiza schoeniclus reiseri* was named after him (type specimen is from Lamia).

A few more important papers published in this period include those of W.H. Simpson for the Messolonghi area (Simpson 1860a, 1860b, 1860c), T.L.H. Powys (= Lord Liford) for the Ionian islands and NW mainland (Powys 1860), H.J. Elwes and T.E. Buckley for northern Greece (Elwes & Buckley 1870) and C. Parrot, mainly for the Peloponnese (Parrot 1905, 1908).

The publication of *Ornis Balcanica* marks the end of the first period in the history of Greek ornithology, a period in which, through exploration and collecting, scientific ornithology was born in Greece.

1905–1950: From Reiser to Makatsch

The first two decades of the 20th century were a period of political turmoil and wars both in Greece and across Europe. Following the Greco-Turkish War, the Balkan War and the First World War, Thessaly, Ipeiros, Macedonia and Thrace became once again Greek territory and in 1923 Greece attained its present borders, with the exception of the Dodecanese. Some of the most important ornithological publications of this period were made by British Army officers of the Allied Forces during their stay in Macedonia, particularly in the Axios valley. These include the papers of A.G.L. Sladen (1917, 1918), G.V.H. Clarke (1917), F.N. Chasen (1921), W.E. Glegg (1924) and J.M. Harrison (1918, 1925). Chasen (1921) reported the last documented case of Great Bustards breeding in Greece, and Glegg (quoting Sladen) the only proof of Ospreys nesting in Greece (Glegg 1924).

In 1920, Prof. E. Stresemann published his *Avifauna Macedonica* and J. Gengler his

Balkanvögel, but despite their general significance neither book contains much material for Greece (Stresemann 1920, Gengler 1920). Later in this period, important contributions to the avifauna of Macedonia include the works of E. Kattinger, who collected birds from this area as well as from the islands of Thasos and Samothraki (Kattinger 1934, 1935, 1938) and the paper of W.H. Thorpe, P.T. Cotton and P.F. Holmes who explored Lakes Prespa, Ohrid and Malik and their surroundings (Thorpe *et al.* 1936).

Other ornithologists turned their attention to the islands. One could mention A. Laubmann's paper on the birds of the Ionians (Laubmann 1927), a few works on Cretan birds (e.g. Lynes 1909a; Meinertzhagen 1920; Schiebel 1925, 1926; Meiklejohn 1936; White 1939) and the works of Italian scientists on the island of Rhodes (at that time under Italian rule) such as those of T. Salvadori and E. Festa (1913), A. Ghigi (1929) and later by E. Tortonese and E. Moltoni (1947). However, the major publication regarding the ornithology of the Greek islands at that period is a paper by O. von Wettstein (1938). Although primarily an herpetologist, von Wettstein visited most of the Aegean islands in 1934 and 1935 observing and collecting species (a total of 363 specimens). He published an annotated list and he was the first to give an overall account of the distribution of birds in the Aegean (Wettstein 1938). Moreover, both Prof. G. Niethammer and E. Stresemann published several important papers on the birds of Crete (e.g. Niethammer 1943a; Stresemann 1942b, 1943). Prof. G. Niethammer also produced a major paper on the birds of the Peloponnese (Niethammer 1943b).

It was during the late 1940s that for the first time Greek scientists began to show an interest in birds. Prof. C. Hatzissarantos and A. Kanellis produced their *Checklist of the birds of Greece, with their common names* (Hatzissarantos & Kanellis 1947/48). It was the first checklist since Reiser's book and although published in *To Vouno*, the bulletin of the Hellenic Alpine Club (a non-scientific publication), it certainly triggered interest in birds among many Greek nature lovers.

The last part of the second period in the history of Greek ornithology, however, is marked especially by the appearance of a German ornithologist, whose contribution to our knowledge of the birds of Greece has been invaluable. Wolfgang Makatsch (1906–1983) studied biology, botany and geography in Leipzig and Munich and soon turned to ornithology. In 1938 he came to Yugoslavia and then Greece, where he was employed as a teacher at the German School of Thessaloniki. He immedialely started exploring and studying the birds of central Macedonia, a systematic work which he continued even during the German occupation of the country, having been recruited by the German Army in an anti-malaria programme. He got his PhD at the University of Thessaloniki (Makatsch 1943a) and in 1950 he published *Die Vogelwelt Macedoniens* (Makatsch 1950). This is a detailed account of the birdlife of this important area and one of the most significant publications in the history of Greek ornithology, complementing Reiser's (1905) book, which dealt with southern Greece. W. Makatsch, always accompanied by his wife Ilse, continued his research on Greek birds for many more years, producing a total of 32 papers on several parts of Greece and on the breeding biology of many species, particularly gulls and waders, including important contributions on species such as Collared Pratincole (Makatsch 1952), Spur-winged Plover (Makatsch 1962), Audouin's Gull (Makatsch 1968b, 1968c, 1969a, 1969b) and Fan-tailed Warbler (Makatsch 1978). He was also a fanatical egg-collector and amassed probably the largest collection of eggs from Greece, now housed at the Museum für Tierkunde in Dresden, but he was also one of the first ornithologists to be alarmed by habitat destruction and the decline of the populations of many species in his time. Together with T. Krüper and O. Reiser, Dr W. Makatsch stands out as one of the most eminent figures in the history of Greek ornithology.

1950–1973: From the War to *Catalogus Faunae Graeciae*

After the end of the Second World War, interest in Greek birds started to increase again. Although German ornithologists still played the leading role, scientists from other countries also appeared during this period, some of them studying other aspects of bird biology, such as zoogeography, migration and ecology.

The Aegean Sea, with its numerous islands, prompted many people to study the patterns of bird migration across this part of the Mediterranean. The results of such studies were published in several papers, notably those of R.E. Moreau (1960, 1961), D.K. Ballance and S.L.B. Lee

(1961), R. Vaughan (1960), R. Kinzelbach and J. Martens (1965), M.B. Casement (1966), D. Hafemann (1967), I.C.T. Nisbet and T.C. Smout (1956, 1957) etc.

F. Peus published two important papers on the birds breeding on some of the major Greek mountains (Peus 1954, 1957), H.J. Böhr a major paper on the avifauna of Corfu (Böhr 1962), while in a series of travels to Greece, a Swede, B. Flach, added several new species (mostly vagrants) to the Greek list and published the first data on the birds of the Evros Delta, then still in a pristine state (Flach 1955a, 1955b, 1956, 1959, 1960, 1961). Others were involved in the study of single species. For example, E. Curio produced the first detailed paper on the breeding ecology of Semi-collared Flycatcher (Curio 1959) and R. Vaughan worked on Eleonora's Falcons (Vaughan 1961). In 1957, A. Lambert compiled an updated checklist of the birds of Greece (Lambert 1957), whereas R.J. Raines published another important work, on the summer distribution of birds in NE Greece (Raines 1960), updating and complementing Makatsch's book.

The 1960s was a very important decade in the history of Greek ornithology, in terms of publication activity as well as in terms of significant discoveries. It was mainly in this period that the importance of wetlands in northern Greece was identified and breeding colonies of many waterbirds were discovered for the first time, e.g. of Dalmatian and White Pelicans, Spoonbill, Glossy Ibis, Mediterranean and Slender-billed Gulls and Black and Whiskered Terns. These findings were published in several papers of which the most important are those of B. Sage (1966), P. Conradty and G. Hohlt (1967), W. Bauer, O. von Helversen, M. Hodge and J. Martens (1969a, 1969b), W. Bauer and G. Müller (1969), M. Kraus, P. Conradty, G. Hohlt and E. Bauer (1969), J.-F. Terrasse, M. Terrasse and M. Brosselin (1969), and a few by W. Makatsch who was still very active during this period. The Swiss, P. Géroudet, also published several papers with important observations from various areas, including the only major treatment on the birds of the large L. Karla which was drained in that period (Géroudet 1962a, 1962b, 1962c, 1963, 1964, 1973).

Between 1953 and 1961 G.E. Watson, an American biologist from Yale University, visited the Aegean islands and parts of the mainland to study and collect specimens. He published 12 papers (Watson 1960, 1961a, 1961b, 1961c, 1962a, 1962b, 1962c, 1962d, 1962e, 1963, 1968, 1973) but his major contribution to Greek ornithology is his PhD Thesis titled *Ecology and Evolution of Passerine Birds on the Islands of the Aegean Sea* (Watson 1964), a very important work which is still useful and has inspired many Greek biologists to study bird ecology. Watson was also the last ornithologist to collect birds in Greece on a large scale (a total of 3,444 specimens of which 2,026 are passerines, now housed at Yale Peabody Museum) but unfortunately he published almost nothing on his non-passerine material.

Dramatic changes to the Greek countryside, mainly related to agricultural development, started to become obvious in the 1950s and intensified in the 1960s. Wetland drainage, clearing of lowland forest, increase in hunting pressure and other threats to birds and nature in general, all taking place at an increasing rate, alarmed a small circle of people, who in 1951 established the Hellenic Society for the Protection of Nature (HSPN), the first environmental NGO in Greece. HSPN eventually became a forum for Greek and foreign ornithologists and a valuable contact for international organisations such as IUCN, WWF etc. German ornithologists were again very active in Greece during this period and one of the leading figures was W. Bauer (1930–1991). He and several of his colleagues, i.e. H.J. Böhr, O.V. Helversen, M. Hodge, J. Martens, V. Mattern and others, working closely with Prof. A. Kanellis, not only published several important papers on their own but they also amassed a large amount of unpublished ornithological data from many other foreign birdwatchers visiting Greece. Compilation of these data resulted in the publication of *Catalogus Faunae Graeciae: Pars II: Aves* (Bauer *et al.* 1969a) and its two supplements (Bauer & Hodge 1970, Bauer *et al.* 1973). *Catalogus Faunae Graeciae*, written in German and edited and published by Prof. A. Kanellis, is another landmark in the history of Greek ornithology and, though primarily an annotated checklist, it was actually the first national book on Greek birds, which among others, clarified the status of several vagrant/accidental species, listed the various races occurring in Greece and included a full (at that time) bibliography on Greek birds.

It was also in the late 1960s that more specialised projects began such as the IWRB Midwinter Waterfowl Counts, started in 1969 by experts of the Station Biologique de la Tour du Valat in Camargue, and bird ringing, mostly of White Storks, by Germans with rings from the Radolfzell ringing scheme.

1973–1990: The Fledging of Greek Ornithologists

This last period is so recent that the term history is not applicable in the same sense as to earlier periods. It could be said that during these 20 or so years, ornithology gradually passed on to Greek hands as a growing number of Greek people became more aware of the pleasure of watching and studying birds. Prof. A. Kanellis (1908–1992), mainly through the activities of the HSPN and the help of foreign environmental organisations or eminent figures such as Dr Luc Hoffmann of WWF, has played a key role in popularising ornithology and educating Greek people with regard to birds and their conservation needs. Although Kanellis was not actually a field ornithologist, he published many articles on the subject. His major contribution in this period was the translation into Greek of Peterson's *Field Guide to the Birds of Europe* (Peterson *et al.* 1981).

Most bird studies in this period focused mainly on the conservation of species and their habitats, particularly wetlands. As a result of such efforts Greece enlisted 11 wetlands in the Ramsar list (ratified in 1975) and in the early 1980s the Greek Government started to implemetnt measures for the better regulation of hunting and conservation of wetlands and other important bird areas.

A small group of Greek ornithologists, who since 1977 had already formed an ornithological section within HSPN, realised the need for an independent organisation dealing with the study and conservation of birds. The Hellenic Ornithological Society (HOS) was officially established in 1982 and since then matters have evolved rapidly. Though still in its infancy and numbering only a handful of members, within five years HOS became one of the most active NGOs in the country and carried out a number of important research and conservation projects. These included the establishment, in 1985, of a ringing scheme, which, in 1989, developed into an independent organisation, the Hellenic Bird Ringing Centre (HBRC).

In the last 10–15 years scientific ornithology has been embodied mainly through research projects either in the form of postgraduate studies or of projects aiming at the conservation of species or habitats and largely funded by international bodies such as ICBP (BirdLife International) and the European Union. Several of these works appear in relevant sections of this book but at least three long-term projects are worth a special mention. The IWRB Midwinter Waterfowl Counts started in 1969, were interrupted in 1976 and resumed again in 1982. Since then, this census remains the most long-lived monitoring project in Greece and it is the most systematic survey of the populations of waterfowl, waders and raptors in major wetlands throughout the country (Handrinos 1989a). Another long-term project has been the study of a colony of Eleonora's Falcons off NE Crete by Dr D. Ristow, Prof. M. Wink and their colleagues: since 1979 they have published at least 18 papers on the breeding ecology of this Falcon, including such diverse topics as ringing recoveries and DNA analyses. The International Pelican Research and Conservation Programme, led by Dr A.J. Crivelli and his Greek colleagues since 1980, is another important long-term project. Although aiming mainly at the study of the ecology and the conservation of the Dalmatian Pelican, it also covers White Pelican in Greece as well as in neighbouring countries.

A final project worth mentioning here is Dr J. Hölzinger's recent series of expeditions to Greece with the purpose of mapping the breeding distribution of various species. Many of his results, concerning especially passerines in montane areas but on the whole covering a wide spectrum of species and regions, have appeared in *Kartierung mediterraner Brutvögel* in the last ten years and include very important contributions to our knowledge of birds in Greece.

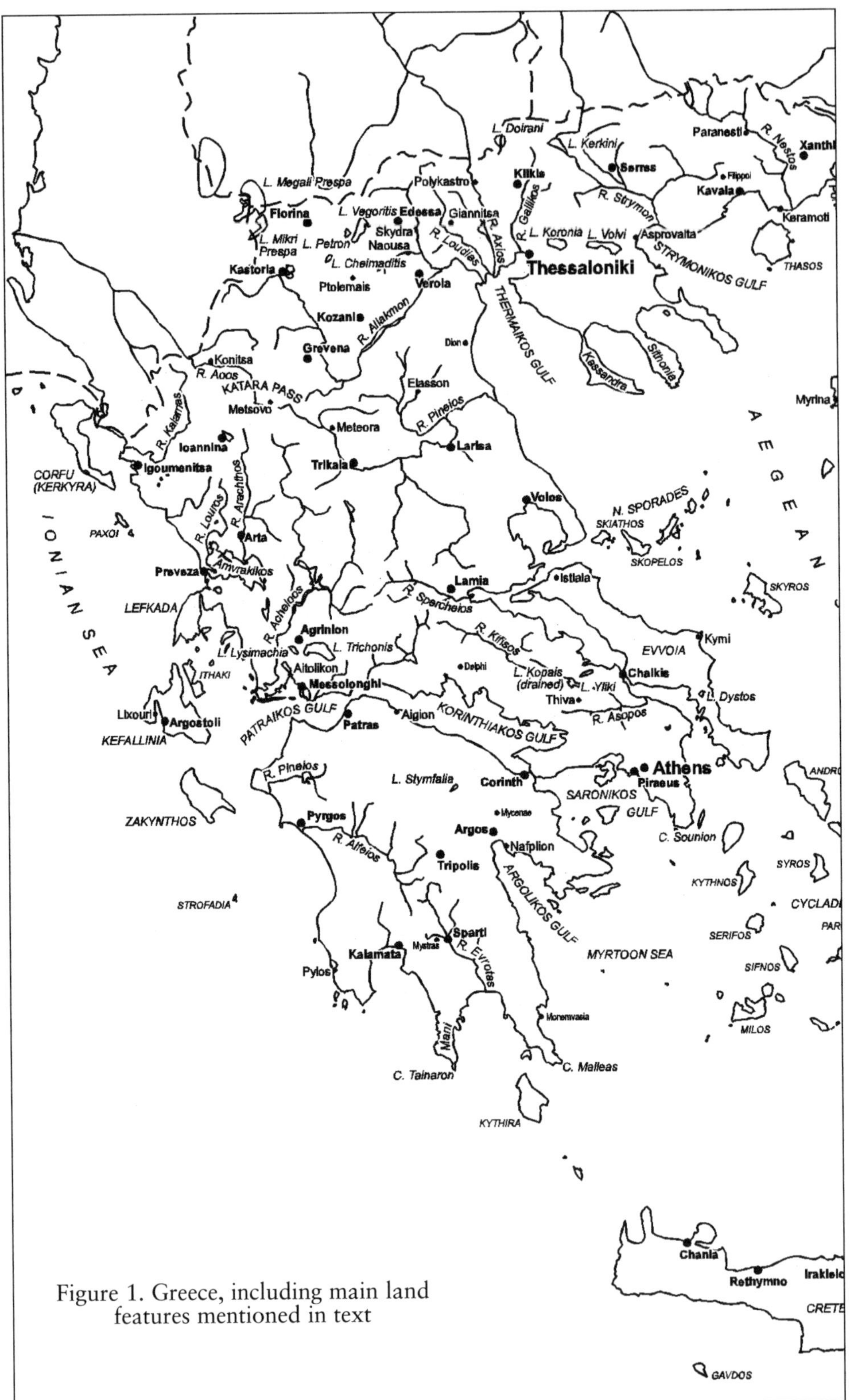

Figure 1. Greece, including main land features mentioned in text

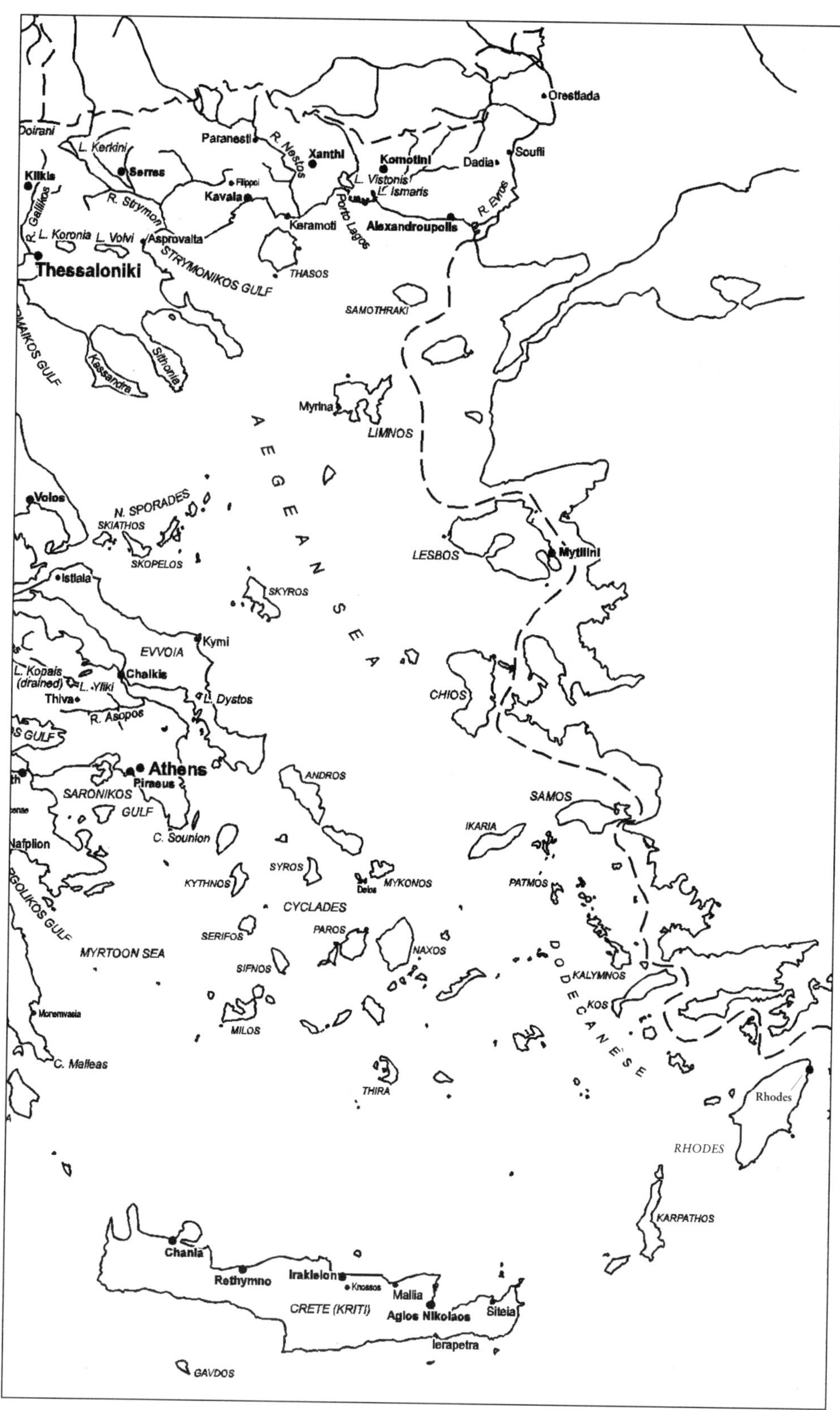
Orestiada
Doirani
Paranesti
R. Nestos
Xanthi
Komotini
Dadia
Soufli
L. Kerkini
Serres
Kilkis
Filippoi
L. Vistonis
L. Ismaris
Kavala
R. Strymon
R. Evros
R. Gallikos
Porto Lagos
Keramoti
Alexandroupolis
L. Koronia
L. Volvi
Asprovalta
Thessaloniki
STRYMONIKOS GULF
THASOS
SAMOTHRAKI
Kassandra
Sithonia
Myrina
LIMNOS
A E G E A N S E A
Volos
N. SPORADES
SKIATHOS
SKOPELOS
LESBOS
Mytilini
Istiaia
SKYROS
Kymi
EVVOIA
L. Kopais (drained)
L. Yliki
Chalkis
Thiva
L. Dystos
CHIOS
R. Asopos
Athens
Piraeus
ANDROS
SARONIKOS GULF
SAMOS
Nafplion
C. Sounion
IKARIA
SYROS
KYTHNOS
Delos
MYKONOS
PATMOS
CYCLADES
SERIFOS
PAROS
MYRTOON SEA
NAXOS
SIFNOS
KALYMNOS
D O D E C A N E S E
KOS
Monemvasia
MILOS
C. Malleas
THIRA
Rhodes
RHODES
KARPATHOS
Chania
Rethymno
Iraklelon
Knossos
Mallia
CRETE (KRITI)
Aglos Nikolaos
Siteia
Ierapetra
GAVDOS

GEOGRAPHY

Greece, a peninsula itself, forms the southern tip of the Balkan Peninsula. In the north it borders on Albania, Former Yugoslav Republic of Macedonia (FYROM), Bulgaria and Turkey. The coordinates of the four extreme points of Greece are:

North (near the village of Ormenion)	41°45'01''N– 26°13'51''E
South (island of Gavdos)	34°48'02''N–24°06'46''E
East (island of Strongyli)	36°06'17''N–29°38'39''E
West (island of Othoni)	39°51'11''N–19°22'41''E

Greece has a total surface area of 131,957 km^2, with 105,834 km^2 on the mainland and the remaining 26,123 km^2 the islands. It is second only to Norway among European countries in length of coastline, with a total length of 15,021 km of which the majority (*c.* 11,000 km) pertains to the islands.

The long and irregular coastline of mainland Greece is dominated by the presence of many large and small peninsulas such as those of Chalkidiki (Athos, Sithonia and Kassandra) and of the Peloponnese (Argolis, Neapolis, Mani and Messinia), as well as by numerous inlets, bays and gulfs, islets, straits, coves, promontories etc. The majority, if not all, of the islands have a similarly jagged coastline. Most of the coasts are steep-sloping and rocky but gently sloping coasts with sandy beaches are also not uncommon, as in much of Thrace and the western Peloponnese.

Throughout the Mediterranean tides are weak. In Greek seas the highest tides are observed in certain closed gulfs and inlets, such as the Thermaikos and Evvoikos, where the water is funnelled from a broad entrance into a narrowing head. The maximum difference between high and low water in these areas is under one metre. However, on many coasts there is a noticeable non-cyclical lowering and raising of sea level due to a seiche effect. In the northern Aegean coast for example, when a strong northerly wind blows continuously for a number of days, sea water piles up towards the south, causing a lowering of water level. When the wind drops a backward wave tends to cause a rise in water level again. If this is assisted by winds which have veered to southerlies, as is often the case, this rise in sea level is even more marked. Such fluctuations in sea level are evident within coastal wetlands even at a distance of several kilometres from the sea.

Greece is a mountainous country. The average altitude is nearly 500 m, with 39% of its total area lying below 200 m, 28% lying between 201 and 500 m and 30% lying between 501 and 1500 m. A total of 3875 km^2 (2.9%) lie above 1500 m, of which 500 km^2 are above 2000 m.

Two major mountain ranges dominate the mainland. The first is the Pindos range, in essence a southern extension of the Dinaric Alps, forming a chain which runs along the Adriatic coast, down former Yugoslavia, Albania and Greece as far as Cape Tainaron in the southern Peloponnese and bending eastwards to continue as the mountains of Crete and farther east as the mountains of southern Asia Minor. The Pindos range is the backbone of the Greek peninsula, on a north–northwest to south–southeast axis, and dominates much of Ipeiros and western Thessaly. Further south it breaks up into the more isolated but still high mountains of Sterea Hellas (Agrafa, Tymfristos, Vardousia, Giona, Parnassos) and of the Peloponnese (Chelmos, Taygetos etc.).

The second major Greek mountain range runs from west to east along the border of Greece with Bulgaria and is dominated by the Rodopi range and mountains such as Kerkini, Falakron and Orvilos. There is also an intermediate group of high massifs, like an offshoot of Pindos, running from NW Macedonia southeast to Pilion, Evvoia and the Cyclades. This group is dominated by high mountains such as Voras, Tzena, Pieria, Olympos and Ossa. Figure 2 shows the outline of Greek mountains (areas above the 1000 m contour) and the main peaks higher than 2000 m. The highest point in the country is the summit of Mytikas, on Mt Olympos, at 2917 m. This is the the second highest peak in the Balkans, only a few metres lower than the summit of Mus Ala on Mt Rila in Bulgaria (2925 m).

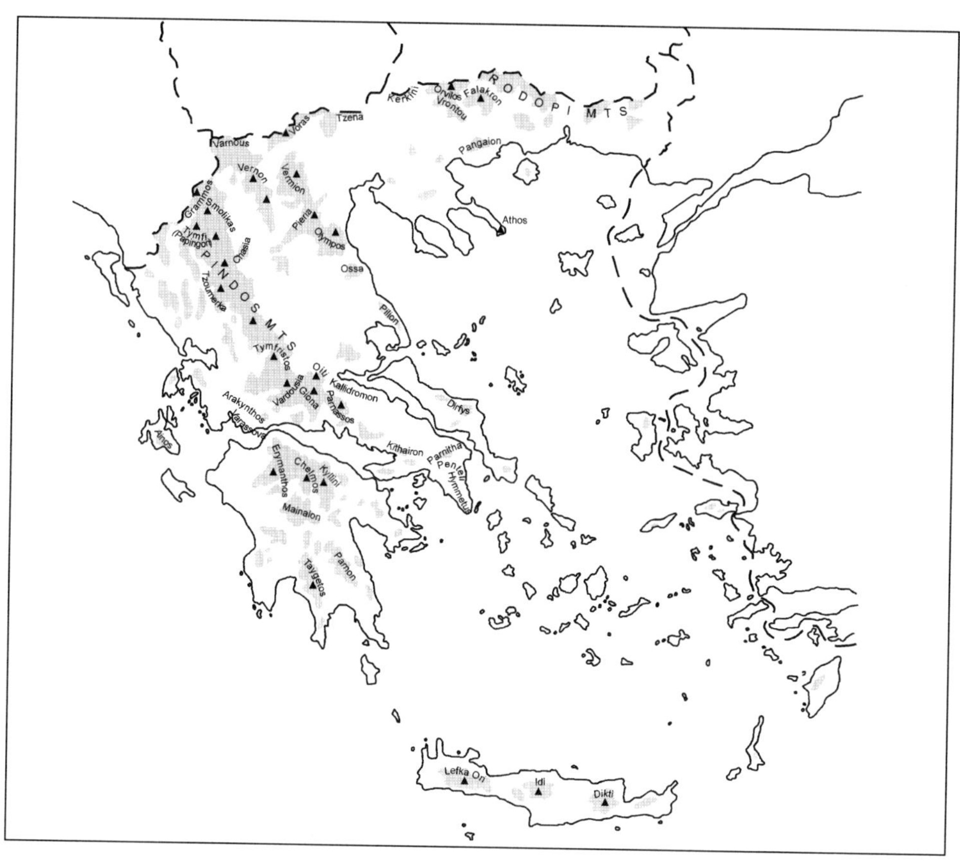

Figure 2. Main mountains and mountain ranges, areas above 1000 m (grey shading) and main peaks above 2000 m (triangles).

Between these mountain ranges and isolated massifs, numerous river valleys have been created by a dense network of fast-flowing streams or larger rivers. The Pindos range plays the dominant role in separating the catchment of rivers flowing into the Ionian and Adriatic from those flowing eastwards into the Aegean. There are no true plains (in the strict sense of the geophysical term) in Greece but instead a few larger and many smaller river basins, as well as flat coastal areas of recent alluvial deposits. Therefore, Thessaly, the largest 'plain' in the country, is in fact the basin of the R. Pineios, much broadened over millennia, whereas the coastal plains of Macedonia and Thrace were formed by the alluvial deposits of large rivers such as the Axios, Strymon, Nestos and Evros.

There are about 20 principal rivers in Greece, though some of the larger ones have their sources in adjacent countries (Axios, Strymon, Nestos and Evros). Only one, R. Aoos, has its sources in Greece and flows out of the country and into Albania. Among the main features most Greek rivers share is that they drain large catchment areas within a short distance from their source and that they create large deltaic formations, a phenomenon common in closed seas with limited tides such as the Mediterranean. Aliakmon (297 km) and Pineios (205 km) are the longest rivers entirely within Greece, followed by the Evros whose length within Greece is 204 km (NSSG 1994).

Wherever basins and depressions are closed, water flowing into them has created lakes and/or marshes, such as those of Aitolia (Lysimachia, Trichonis, Ozeros and Amvrakia), western Macedonia (Prespa, Vegoritis, Cheimaditis, Petron) and Lakes Koronia and Volvi. Most of the marshes surrounding these lakes have now been reclaimed for agriculture. Trichonis is the largest Greek lake (9700 ha), followed by Volvi (6800 ha) and Vegoritis (4300 ha).

The islands are one of the most distinctive features of the country. Greece has 9,838 islands and islets, a record number in the Mediterranean, with 8,110 in the Aegean, a true archipel-

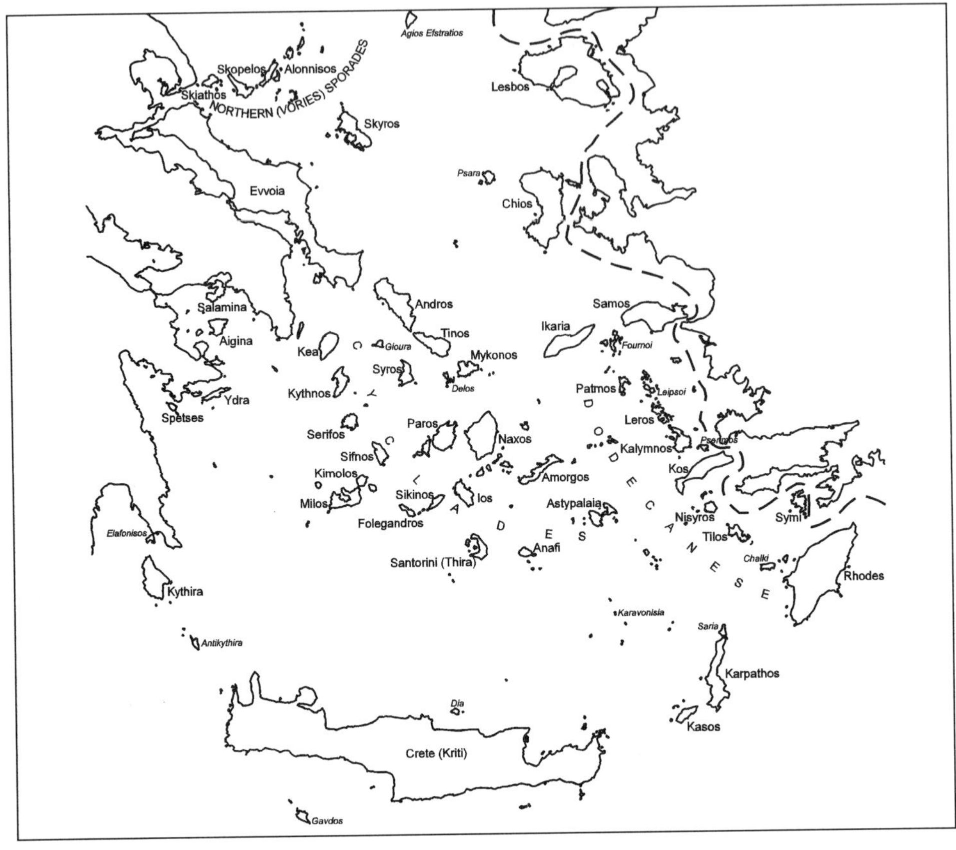

Figure 3. Map of the central and southern Aegean.

ago, and 1,315 in the Ionian. Only 217 are inhabited. The islands range in size between islets of less than 1 km^2 to Crete, with 8336 km^2, but the majority of those inhabited vary between 70 and 150 km^2. Most of the Aegean islands are in fact the tops of mountains, which were progressively submerged during the early and middle Pleistocene. A map of the islands of the Aegean appears in Figure 3.

Geological actions through the ages have created deep underwater trenches, making Greek seas the deepest in the Mediterranean: *c.* 68 nautical miles south–southwest of Cape Tainaron the sea reaches a depth of 5121 m, the deepest part of the Mediterranean, whereas the deepest part of the Aegean Sea (4452 m) lies *c.* 49 nautical miles E of Cape Prasso on the island of Rhodes (NSSG 1994).

The total population of Greece (1991 census) is 10,259,900 of which 28.3% is rural and 71.7% urban or semi-urban. According to another classification, 67.7% of the total population live in the lowlands, 20.3% in hilly areas and 12% in mountainous areas (NSSG 1994). This distinction, together with the fact that all the major urban centres (with more than 10,000 inhabitants), over 80% of all industrial activities and 90% of all activities associated with tourism and recreation are carried out in low-lying, mostly coastal areas indicate that the Greek economy is strongly oriented towards the sea and coasts. This has serious effects on the coastal and locally the marine environment whilst montane areas are much less heavily influenced.

The distribution of the total area of Greece into basic categories of land use is shown in Table 1 on the next page.

Table 1: Basic categories of land use in Greece (NSSG 1986, Anon 1992)

Land use	Area (ha)	%
Forest	3,359,190	25.5
Partly forested land	3,153,880	23.9
Pasture/grazing land	1,693,040	12.8
Farmland	3,945,200	29.9
Urban and industrial zones	489,310	3.7
Other (Bare, rocky etc.)	246,490	1.9
Water	308,630	2.3
Total	13,195,740	100.0

Administratively, the country is divided into 51 areas called 'nomoi' (singular = 'nomos'), further subdivided into 147 local districts ('eparcheia'). The whole country was traditionally composed of ten geographical regions ('diamerisma'), which for administrative reasons have recently been increased to 13 ('periphereia') (Figure 4).

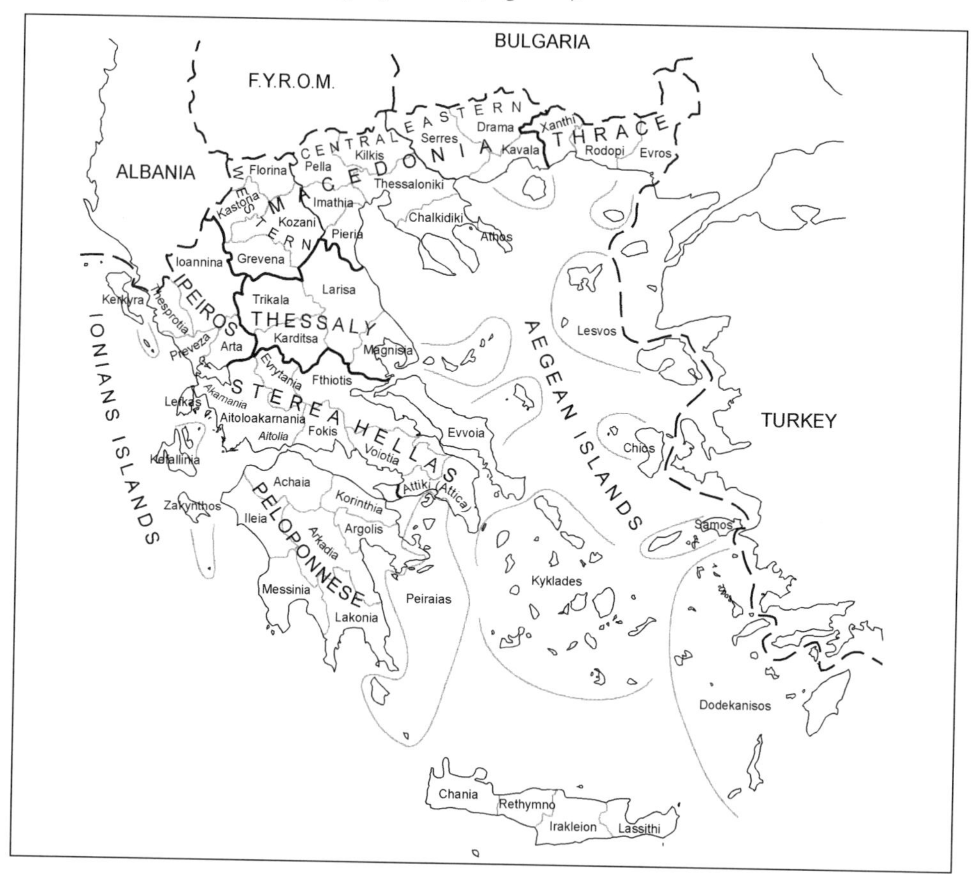

Figure 4. Administrative divisions of Greece.

CLIMATE

A comprehensive description of Greece's climate may be found in Polunin (1980). For more detailed coverage we referred to Mariolopoulos (1938, 1953). We have used the above and data obtained directly from the Hellenic National Meteorological Service (mainly 1930 to 1975 period) to provide here a short summary.

Broadly speaking, the climate of Greece is Mediterranean with a hot and dry summer and a cool and wet winter. However, significant local variations exist. It is only in southern and coastal areas, including most of the Aegean and Ionian islands, where one may find a typical Mediterranean climate whereas in northern areas and on the mountains the climate tends towards the central European type, with cold and snowy winters and more summer rainfall.

In winter the general pressure conditions over Greece (and the eastern Mediterranean) are dominated by two high pressure systems: the Siberian anticyclone, extending over southern Russia and the northern Balkans and the Azores anticyclone, extending over a large part of N Africa. Moreover, the Mediterranean, a closed and relatively warm sea, aids the passage and development of low-pressure systems. As a result, depressions originating in the Atlantic or the western Mediterranean come predominantly from the west and proceed eastwards. The contrast in temperature and pressure between the cold northern and central Balkans and the warm Mediterranean may be so great that winds of force 9 or 10 are quite common in the Aegean at this time of year following the passage of depressions.

In summer, the Azores anticyclone moves to the north and the Siberian anticyclone withdraws to the east. The intense heat of the Middle East generates a more or less permanent low pressure system, connected to the south Asian summer monsoon, which draws in dry continental air over the eastern Mediterranean. Consequently summers are dry and the wind blows almost exclusively from a northerly direction. This northerly wind, the 'meltemi', can be very strong and especially over the Aegean is a dominant feature of summer weather. The strong relief of the country, with fairly high mountains close to the coast, influences local wind patterns, deflecting or funelling and strengthening winds so that many regions have their own distinctive wind characteristics.

The same mountainous relief has a profound influence on precipitation, which shows a varied pattern, both geographically and seasonally. The highest total annual precipitation is observed in the western part of the country. The Pindos range acts as an effective barrier to the predominantly westerly rain-bearing winds thus the eastern mainland and the western Aegean islands receive much less rainfall. Total annual precipitation increases again in the eastern Aegean and may also be high on eastern coastlines, especially where high ground lies close to the sea (e.g. coast of Thessaly and Evvoia). Most of Macedonia and Thrace receive intermediate amounts of rainfall but inland basins tend to be drier. Some of the high mountains receive a high annual precipitation, which may reach 1800 mm in the Pindos range, 1600 mm in Sterea Hellas, 1400 mm on the mountains of the Peloponnese and 2000 mm on Lefka Ori of eastern Crete. Of course much of it falls as snow.

In general, the seasonal precipitation regime is that found throughout the Mediterranean: rain and, on rare occasions, snow are limited to late autumn, winter and early spring, whereas summers are dry. December is usually the wettest month. However, this pattern is closely matched only in southern and coastal Greece. In the summer half of the year depressions are rare in the Mediterranean and tend to move across the warm middle parts of the European continent. Northern parts of the country are regularly influenced by the southern extremity of cold fronts moving eastwards across Europe. Thus, summer precipitation is more frequent there and the development of thunderstorms is further promoted by the presence of mountains. As a result, in the north and on the higher mountains even in the south precipitation is more evenly distributed throughout the year, often with the main peak earlier in November and a secondary peak around May/June.

The periodicity of rainfall is often more important than the total annual amount and it has a profound influence both on the vegetation and on the river systems. This is the key reason why western and northern Greece generally have more well developed vegetation and more surface water, whereas southern parts of the country are less well vegetated and with very few and small rivers, which usually dry up in summer.

Temperature is influenced by latitude and altitude, by distance from the sea and by the obstructing effect of high mountains lying between a given area and the sea. In winter, the temperature may vary from cold in the interior of the mainland and on high mountains to mild with little or no frost in coastal areas and islands. In summer, the overall pattern of temperature is more uniform, being warm to hot throughout, diminishing only with increasing altitude. However, in some coastal areas and most Aegean islands the high summer temperatures are tempered by the proximity of the sea and the strong cool and dry 'meltemi' wind.

January is usually the coldest month and July the hottest. Frost and snow are frequent in January and February in northern Greece, where mean January temperatures lie mainly within the 1–5°C range. Snow may cover the ground for quite long periods. However, deep snow is relatively rare in the lowlands of Macedonia and Thrace because northerly winds blowing from the interior of the Balkans tend to be dry. It is much commoner in parts of the country which experience a combination of humidity and cold, e.g. the central and southern Pindos range, eastern Sterea Hellas and the northern Peloponnese. Southern and coastal areas are virtually frost-free with mild temperatures, averaging 5–13°C in January. The hottest months of the year are July and August, with mean temperatures around 24–29°C in the lowlands. Figures 5, 6, 7 and 8 show the distribution of mean annual precipitation, average surface temperatures for January and July and dominant wind direction for the country.

In his classical treatise on the climate of Greece, Mariolopoulos (1938) has identified five main climatic regions in Greece, summarised below, whilst Tables 2 and 3 show some important temperature and precipitation data for selected weather stations in the five climatic regions.

The montane region: Covers all the main ranges and massifs including Rodopi and the high mountains of the Peloponnese, with an overall climate very similar to the central European type. Rain falls throughout the year with maxima in May/June and October. Above 1000 m snow may lie almost continuously from late autumn up to early March but above 2000 m the first snow usually falls in late October and may lie until at least mid May. Snow patches may last near the summits of the highest mountains until July or later. In many areas snow depth may well exceed 1 m, with drifts even deeper. There are no weather data available from this region but Florina in NW Macedonia and Tripolis in the Peloponnese, both above 600 m, are indicative of conditions prevailing at higher altitude, especially when compared with the nearest low-lying stations (e.g. Trikala and Kalamata respectively).

The northern mainland: Extends over the interior of Ipeiros, Thessaly, Macedonia and Thrace. In this region the climate is intermediate between the Mediterranean and the central European types. Its main characteristics are the large annual temperature range (>20°C between hottest and coldest month), a short dry season (1–2 months) and some rainfall throughout the year. Serres in central Macedonia, Orestiada in NE Thrace and Trikala in the interior of Thessaly are examples from this region. It is interesting to note that July temperatures are not very different from those much further south whereas winter temperatures are much lower and very low absolute minima have been recorded, equalling or exceeding those recorded at the intermediate altitude stations of Florina and Tripolis. The region is also characterised by a low number of sunny days.

The Ionian region: This type dominates on the Ionian islands and coastal parts of the western mainland. This area has a mild winter climate and a high annual precipitation, with a marked though short (2–4 months) dry season. Examples from this region are Corfu and Kalamata. Despite this being the wettest part of the country, rainfall tends to be heavy but of short duration, as indicated by the high number of sunny days.

The Aegean region: Covers the southeast part of the mainland and the Aegean islands, including most of Crete. It has a considerably drier climate than western Greece but with cooler winters at corresponding latitudes. On the mainland (e.g. Athens) summers are very hot, with mean July temperatures often well above 25°C, but in the Aegean (e.g. Naxos) the sea has a strong tempering effect and summer temperatures are cooler. The region has a generally low total annual rainfall, with a long dry season, lasting up to six months. However, in the eastern Aegean islands (e.g. Samos) the rain-shadow effect of the mountains of the mainland has diminished and precipitation is relatively high. Northerly winds charged with moisture over the Aegean also give a wetter climate to the east coast of the mainland and parts of northern Crete, especially where mountains lie close to the coast (e.g. Kymi).

Southern Crete: In this region (southern and southeastern Crete) the climate is intermediate between Mediterranean and semi-desert. Rainfall is low, winters are very mild and summers are long, hot and dry. Ierapetra is one of the mildest parts of the country in winter. Open-air cultivation of tropical fruit crops (such as banana) is possible here, given irrigation.

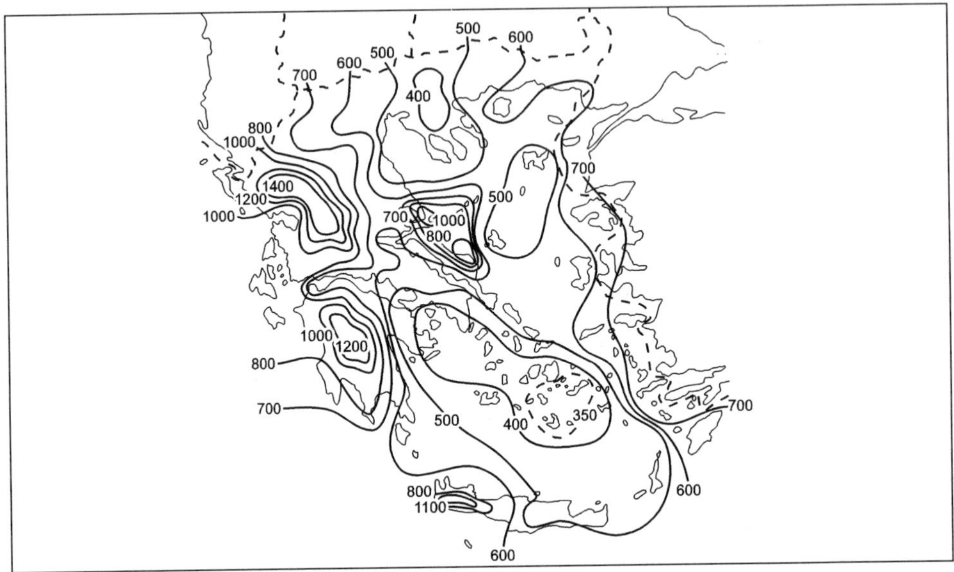

Figure 5. The distribution of mean annual precipitation (mm) (source: Hellenic National Meteorological Service).

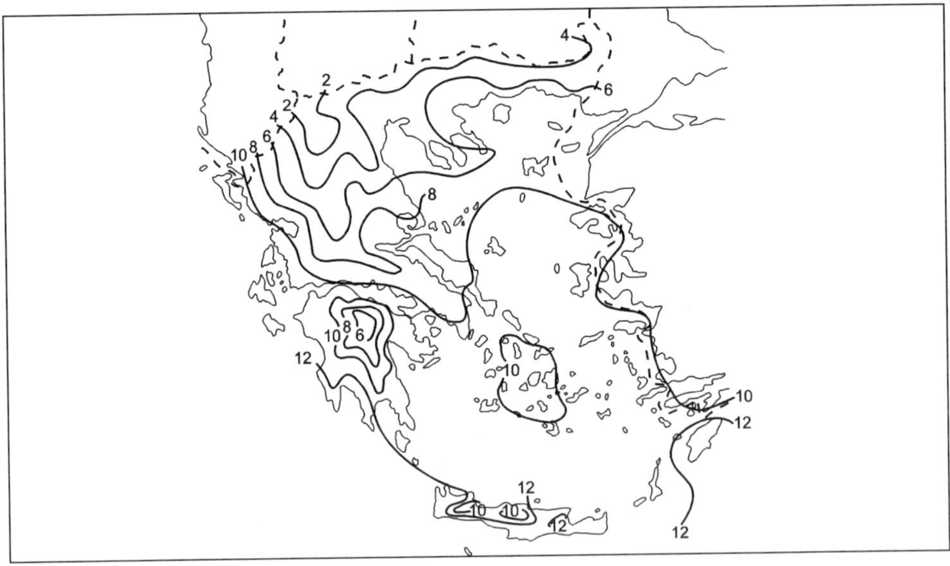

Figure 6. The distribution of average surface temperatures (C°) in January (source: Hellenic National Meteorological Service).

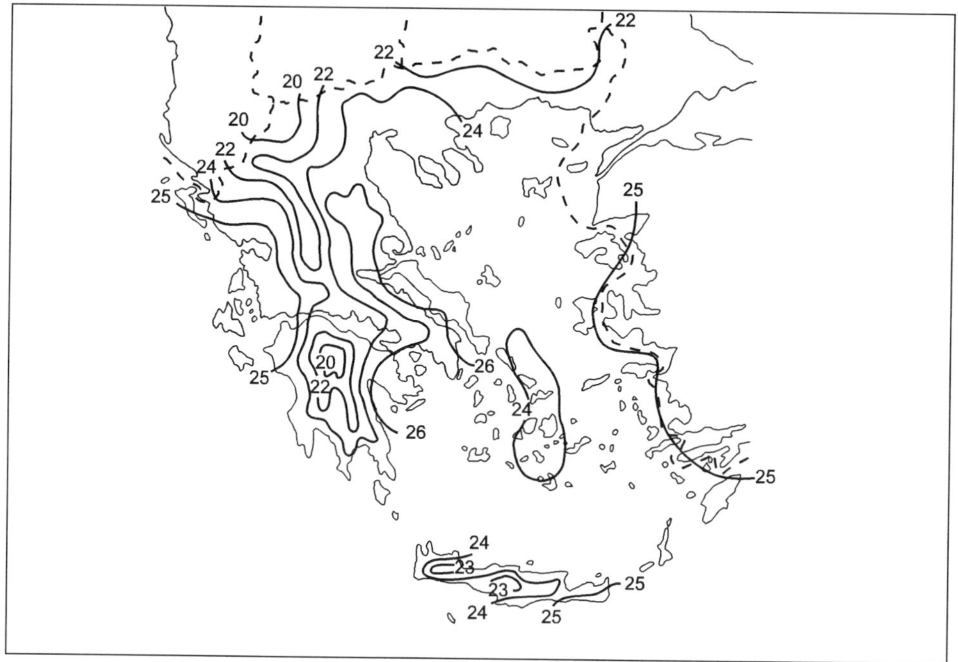

Figure 7. The distribution of average surface temperatures (C°) in July (source: Hellenic National Meteorological Service).

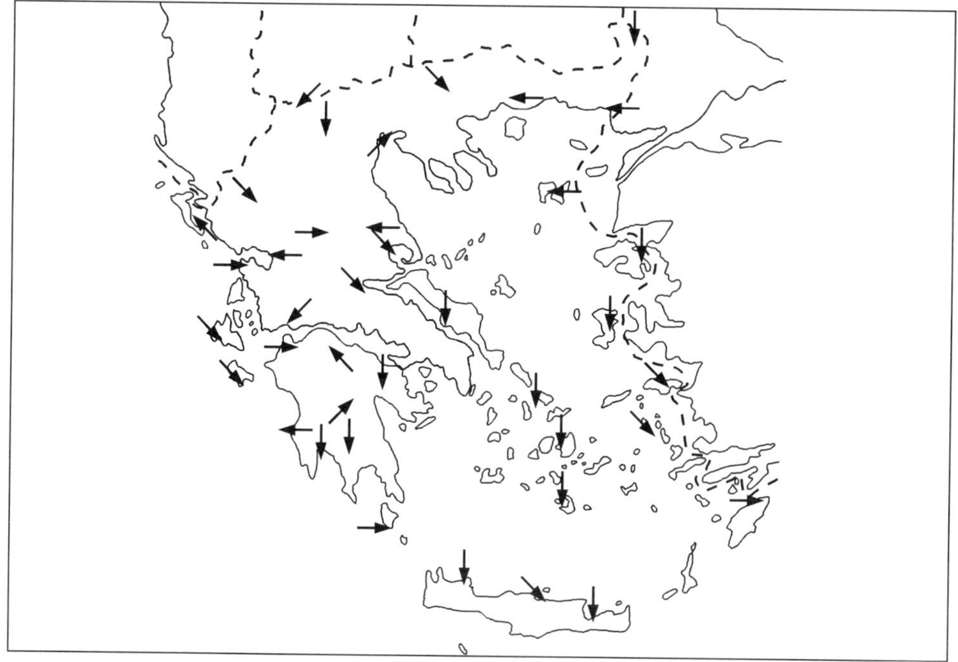

Figure 8. Dominant wind directions (source: Hellenic National Meteorological Service).

Table 2: Temperature (C°) data for selected weather stations (source: Hellenic National Meteorological Service)

Station	Altitude (m)	Average January Min	Average January Max	Average July Min	Average July Max	Annual Minimum Avrg	Annual Minimum Absolute	Annual Maximum Avrg	Annual Maximum Absolute
Florina	650	-3.4	4.3	14.5	28.8	-12.2	-21.0	34.6	38.0
Tripolis	661	1.3	9.2	15.1	30.2	-5.3	-17.0	35.8	40.8
Serres	32	0.0	8.5	18.1	33.0	-7.7	-23.0	38.2	42.4
Orestiada	43	-0.6	6.2	17.2	31.5	-9.3	-20.0	36.5	40.8
Trikala	112	1.4	9.6	19.7	34.3	-5.3	-16.8	39.5	43.7
Corfu	2	5.9	13.9	19.1	31.0	-0.5	-4.5	35.5	40.2
Kalamata	6	6.4	16.4	18.8	31.5	0.8	-4.0	37.2	43.0
Athens	136	4.8	12.8	20.7	32.8	-1.7	-10.4	37.7	42.1
Kymi	222	5.4	11.6	21.0	28.6	0.0	-6.0	34.2	40.0
Naxos	9	9.5	14.6	21.8	27.0	4.5	0.3	31.7	38.0
Samos	48	8.1	13.7	22.1	30.0	1.8	-4.3	34.2	38.7
Ierapetra	16	8.8	16.3	22.8	32.2	–	2.0	–	44.0

Table 3: Precipitation and other weather data for selected weather stations (source: Hellenic National Meteorological Service)

	Year				Wettest Month[5]			Driest Month[5]		
	Total Pptn[1]	Dry months[2]	Sunny days[3]	Snow Cov[4]		Total Pptn	Rain days		Total Pptn	Rain days
Florina	785	0	84.6	38.8	December	95.5	13.1	August	32.6	5.1
Tripolis	897	2	104.9	–	December	175.5	15.4	August	13.7	3.2
Serres	554	1	62.0	6.9	December	75.0	10.6	August	19.9	4.4
Orestiada	580	1	95.6	17.5	November	74.7	9.3	August	22.4	4.0
Trikala	781	2	86.5	8.8	November	113.1	11.1	August	12.3	3.0
Corfu	1276	3	122.9	0.0	December	236.5	18.3	July	6.2	2.5
Kalamata	833	3	124.6	0.1	December	187.4	17.1	July	2.4	1.5
Athens[6]	414	5	124.6	1.0	December	69.8	14.1	August	2.5	1.3
Kymi	1116	3	128.4	3.0	December	193.4	13.7	August	18.0	1.6
Naxos	390	6	138.3	0.0	December	80.0	13.7	July	1.7	0.5
Samos	918	4	153.0	0.0	December	210.2	15.0	July	0.2	0.4
Ierapetra	548	6	139.2	–	January	147.3	16.1	July	0.0	0.0

1 Total annual precipitation (mm).

2 Number of months with less than 25 mm of average total monthly precipitation.

3 Average number of days in a year with less than 1.5/8 cloud cover

4 Average number of days in a year with ground covered by snow

5 Month with the highest (wettest) and lowest (driest) total precipitation; total precipitation (mm) and number of days with rain for corresponding month.

6 Inland station (Nea Filadelfia)

VEGETATION

The vegetation of the country is treated in great depth and detail in a number of botanical books. We especially recommend Polunin's (1980) work. Our description here is intended to give a brief account of the natural vegetation of the country so as to act as a background for the understanding of bird habitats in the chapter that follows.

Climate usually plays the dominant role in determining the general character of the natural and semi-natural vegetation cover of any given area. However, geology can also play a very important role. Geologically, Greece is a complex and varied country, as expected from its mountainous character and a recent geological history. Siliceous metamorphic and sedimentary rocks (sandstones, shales, schists etc.) are commonest in the Pindos and in Macedonia and Thrace. Such rocks erode quickly to give a relatively thick layer of soil. Since they are not water-permeable or are permeable only to a limited degree, rainwater is retained in the deeper layers of soil and acts like a reservoir for plants during the dry season. Limestone (mostly Mesozoic) is the dominant bedrock over large parts of the central and southern mainland and Crete. Several of the high mountains of Sterea Hellas and the Peloponnese are almost solid limestone. Limestone behaves in a very different way from siliceous rocks. Its main constituent, calcium carbonate, is soluble to rainwater carrying small amounts of acid (in its simplest form dissolved carbon dioxide) but it contains little other material. Thus chemical weathering tends to dissolve away the stone without leaving much behind. Soil formation is a much slower process than in the case of most siliceous rocks and this means that limestone often has a poor soil and vegetation cover. Furthermore, rainwater can percolate through cracks in limestone and enlarge them by dissolution. Surface run-off and storage of water in deeper layers of the soil is thus virtually non-existent, streams and rivers are rare and underground drainage is the rule. When water flowing underground meets an obstruction (such as non water-permeable rocks) it is forced to come to the surface as springs. In some cases whole rivers may dissapear down sink holes and reappear many kilometres away.

Forest

In the early 1960s the forest coverage of Greece was estimated at 19.63% or 2,512,400 ha (Anon 1964). However, according to the latest and so far the most accurate inventory, forested land occupies 3,359,186 ha or 25.5% of the country (Anon 1992). The higher figures of the latter inventory may partly be due to a slightly different definition of what 'forest' is but at least in some cases there seems to have been a real increase in forest coverage due to regeneration as a result of a decreasing human population and lessening grazing pressure in the mountains.

One may be surprised by the high forest coverage for a Mediterranean country. However, as already pointed out, much of Greece has a continental or transitional climate and a significant proportion of its total area lies at a relatively high altitude, with the associated cooler and moister conditions than those found in Athens, the islands and most other places popular among tourists. On the other hand it must be stressed that the greatest proportion of forest is of inferior quality, with low and stunted trees growing as it does on poor and shallow soil, and much of what appears as 'forest' in statistics is not comparable with well developed forests in other parts of the world. Yet true, closed high forest is not lacking and in the particularly well studied forests of the Rodopi range spruce may reach a height of almost 60 m and beech almost 45 m.

Table 4: Composition, area and percentage of Greek forests (Anon 1992)

FOREST TYPE	AREA (ha)	%
Deciduous		
Oak (*Q. frainetto, Q. petraea, Q. cerris* etc.)	1,471,839	43.8
Beech (*Fagus sylvatica, F. orientalis*)	336,640	10.0
Oriental plane (*Platanus orientalis*)	86,579	2.6
Sweet chestnut (*Castanea sativa*)	33,081	1.0
Birch (*Betula pendula*)	1,437	0.0
Sub-total	1,929,576	57.4
Coniferous		
Aleppo, Calabrian pine (*Pinus halepensis, P. brutia*)	567,731	16.9
Fir (*Abies cephalonica, A. alba*, hybrids)	543,308	16.2
Black pine (*P. nigra*)	281,692	8.4
Scots pine (*P. sylvestris*)	20,955	0.6
White-bark pine (*P. heldreichii*)	8,300	0.2
Mixed fir + black pine	4,762	0.1
Norway spruce (*Picea abies*)	2,754	0.1
Umbrella pine (*P. pinea*)	108	–
Sub-total	1,429,610	42.6
Grand total	3,359,186	100.0

Greek forests are predominantly deciduous (57.44% of all forest) but a significant proportion (42.56%) is coniferous (Table 4 and Figure 9). Deciduous forest is dominated by oaks (76.3%), of which 12 species occur in Greece. The commonest forest-forming species are Hungarian *Quercus frainetto*, Turkey *Q. cerris*, sessile *Q. petraea* and white oak *Q. pubescens*. Beech (European *Fagus sylvatica*, eastern *F. orientalis* or their natural hybrid *F. moesiaca*) forms 17.4% of deciduous forest, whereas the rest consists of oriental plane *Platanus orientalis* (4.6%), sweet chestnut *Castanea sativa* and other species.

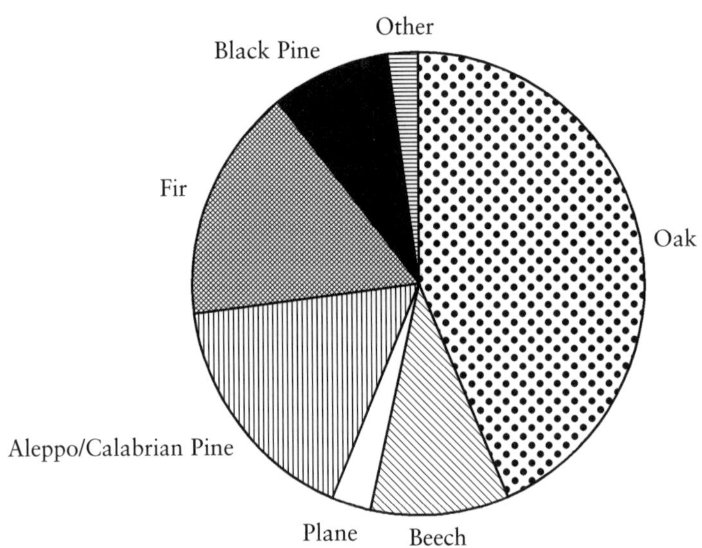

Figure 9. Percentage distribution of forest types.

Aleppo *Pinus halepensis* and Calabrian pines *P. brutia* are the commonest type of coniferous forest, occupying 40% of this category, followed by firs (38%), mainly Greek *Abies cephalonica* but also silver *A. alba* and hybrids between the two (*A. borisii-regis*). Black pine *P. nigra* forms 19.7% of coniferous forest and the rest consists of other pine species and a tiny percentage (0.2%) of Norway spruce *Picea abies*.

Generally speaking, northern (Thrace, Macedonia and Ipeiros) and central mainland Greece (Sterea Hellas, western Thessaly) have the highest forest coverage, depending on relief, local climate, local soil conditions and human impact. Deciduous oak forests are widespread but the most extensive tracts occur in Macedonia and Thrace. In southern parts of the country they are usually found at medium altitudes (300–1000 m) whereas in the north they occur down to sea level. Beech is a more or less montane species, and in most cases it forms a belt above the warmth-loving oaks, at about 700–1500 m. At its upper limit it often forms mixed forest with conifers. Its southernmost limit is on Mt Oxya in Sterea Hellas (38°45'N). Most beech forests occur in the northern Pindos and parts of central and eastern Macedonia. Sweet chestnut woodlands occur locally in various parts of the country, at medium altitudes (300–1500 m) and on acid soils. The largest areas of sweet chestnut occur on Mt Athos.

Forest on the mountains of Sterea Hellas and the Peloponnese is almost exclusively of Aleppo pine on the lower slopes, with Greek fir above about 700 m. Eastern Sterea Hellas, Evvoia and the northern Peloponnese have the highest percentage of Aleppo pine forest of the country whereas the islands of Lesbos, Thasos and the district of Evros have the most extensive tracts of Calabrian pine. Black pine forest occurs on many mountains, from Mt Taygetos northwards, but is especially important in the northern Pindos. Norway spruce and silver birch *Betula pendula* forest occur only on Mt Rodopi, although small populations of the latter also occur on a few other mountains of north-eastern Greece.

Maquis, Phrygana and Pseudosteppe

The bushy vegetation that covers much of Greece today has largely resulted from the destruction of forest. However, the first destruction of forest goes well back into prehistory and it is difficult to imagine the landscape of, say, the Cyclades in those times. Fires are a common feature of Mediterranean habitats during the dry season, and although nowadays they are usually the direct or indirect result of human action, natural fires started by lightning are not rare. After fire, many Mediterranean woody plants can quickly regenerate from rootstocks surviving underground but some loss of soil is inevitable when thunderstorms arrive after the dry season. Grazing by goats, which weakens the bushes, and fires repeating at frequent intervals have the cumulative effect of a significant loss of soil and an ever decreasing rate of regeneration after each fire episode. Once soil has been removed, the development of the original vegetation is practically impossible: more or less permanent desertification is the end result. It has been estimated that 86,000,000 m^3 of top-soil are lost each year over the whole country (Kotoulas 1989). The barren, stony landscape of many areas and the development of the relatively large deltas of Greek rivers are testimony to the amount of erosion taking place.

When fires are not very frequent, or the bedrock can easily erode and rapidly produce more soil, or where the local climate is more humid, maquis develops. This is 1–2 m high and composed of sclerophyll bushes such as Kermes oak *Quercus coccifera*, lentisc *Pistacia lentiscus*, *Philyrea*, junipers *Juniperus phoenicea* and *J. oxycedrus*, broom *Calycotome* and, on acid soils, heaths *Erica*. In slightly damper or cooler areas species such as the strawberry trees *Arbutus unedo* and *A. adrachne*, holm oak *Q. ilex*, Myrtle *Myrtus communis* and laurel *Laurus nobilis* are commoner. In the lowlands of northern parts of the country and at medium altitudes further south this bushy vegetation contains a proportion of deciduous species such as various oaks, oriental hornbeam *Carpinus orientalis*, flowering ash *Fraxinus ornus*, turpentine tree *Pistacia terebinthus*, smoke tree *Cotinus coggygria* and Judas tree *Cercis siliquastrum*. In still cooler and moister situations deciduous species predominate. The term 'shiblyak' is used to refer to this type of deciduous bushy vegetation.

When fires are frequent or the soil has been largely lost or goat grazing is intensive, phrygana develops, and in more extreme cases pseudosteppe. Phrygana (the Greek equivalent of the French garrigue) is a low woody vegetation, up to 50 cm in height, composed of shrubs such as *Sarcopoterium spinosum*, *Coridothymus capitatus*, *Cistus* and Jerusalem sage *Phlomis fruticosa*. Pseudosteppe contains fewer woody plants and a high proportion of grasses and other herbaceous species. Asphodel *Asphodelus*, an unpalatable plant to grazing animals, is typical of pseudosteppe. Extensive tracts of pseudosteppe occur especially in the drier parts of the central and northern mainland (interior Thessaly and Macedonia) whereas phrygana is commonest in the south and on the islands.

The total area covered by these vegetation types is not known. What appears as 'partly forested land' in Table 1 is probably mainly maquis and phrygana, perhaps with scattered low evergreen trees, whereas 'pasture/grazing land' is mainly phrygana and pseudosteppe, as well as high-altitude or wet lowland meadows and pasture.

Alpine Zone

The higher zones of mountains have traditionally provided good summer pasture for huge numbers of sheep and goats. Flocks were moved to the lowlands for the winter and taken back to the mountains towards the end of May. This practice still takes place today though it has been declining in recent years. The upper limit of forest on mountains high enough to have one is around 1800 m. However, on many mountains forest does not reach as high as this, while bushes and scattered trees (e.g. of the particularly hardy white bark pine *Pinus heldreichii*) are often found at up to 2000–2200 m. Thus in most cases the limit of forest is considerably lower than the limit of tree growth and this suggests that in all probability forest has been destroyed at higher altitude to provide grazing land. Because of this, much of what we call here for convenience the 'alpine' zone, is not strictly speaking identical with the true alpine zone of the Alps or other high mountains.

Meadows of tall grass and herbs, later grazed to a short turf, occur on mountains with a siliceous bedrock and high summer rainfall, especially in the northern Pindos and on mountains along the northern border of the country. On limestone anywhere in the country and on the mountains of the southern Pindos, the Peloponnese and Crete short shrubs resistant to grazing, such as *Daphne oleoides* and thorny *Astragalus*, *Juniperus communis* and *Berberis* predominate. Rare plants and butterflies are an additional attraction of the alpine zone to those with a wider interest.

Wetland Vegetation

Conditions in wetlands may vary as much as in terrestrial ecosystems and vegetation is correspondingly diverse. However, this variation is not so much dependent on geographical location, as is the case with land vegetation, as on the constancy of water supply, water temperature, dissolved nutrients and other local factors.

Streams and small rivers are often dominated by the presence of oriental plane *Platanus orientalis*, ubiquitous along fast-flowing water with a stony bed. Slow-flowing rivers have lines of willows *Salix*, white poplar *Populus alba,* narrow-leaved ash *Fraxinus angustifolius* and alder *Alnus glutinosa* on their banks. In the natural state these must have formed patches of riverine woodland in the wider floodplain, long cut and converted to farmland or grazing meadows. Wide tracts of riverine woodland must have also existed in river deltas before these were largely converted to farmland. Patches of this habitat are still to be found at a few sites such as the Nestos and Axios Deltas, L. Kerkini, L. Mikri Prespa, the Amvrakikos and Messolonghi. These tiny remnants are composed of the above tree species, often with the addition of elms *Ulmus*. The trees are often clothed with climbers such as wild vine *Vitis* and hop *Humulus lupulus* and there is a dense undergrowth of brambles *Rubus* and other bushes, so that an impenetrable and jungle-like tangle is often created.

Most Greek lakes are more or less eutrophic and have belts of reeds *Phragmites* growing around their margins. In deeper water there are often floating beds of water lilies *Nymphaea alba* or *Nuphar lutea*, water chestnut *Trapa natans* and pondweeds *Potamogeton*. In some lakes, especially Kerkini and Ismaris, these form extensive carpets, covering a significant proportion of the surface of water. Few lakes have steep-sloping banks and lack fringing reedbeds (e.g. L. Vegoritis and some artificial lakes) whilst some are the exact opposite, being almost completely covered by reedbeds (e.g. L. Cheimaditis, L. Dystos and many of those that have now been drained).

Freshwater marshes and meadows are relatively rare nowadays, having largely been converted into agricultural land. Beds of *Phragmites* and locally *Typha* (mainly *Typha domingensis*) occur in marshes which are more or less permanently flooded, and mixed swards of *Scirpus*, *Cyperus*, *Carex*, *Juncus*, yellow flag *Iris pseudacorus*, water plantain *Alisma plantago-aquatica* and various grasses on damp or seasonally flooded soil.

A large proportion of marshes and lakes are spring-fed and this is especially the case in limestone country: amidst a very dry landscape, springs gush water that has been carried over long distances, creating oases of lush green reedbeds and clear water. As a rule, such marshes and lakes do not have strong fluctuations in water level between dry and wet season and are thus important in maintaining aquatic bird populations in parts of the country with little or no summer rainfall. On the other hand, they often show marked cycles of high and low water over periods of many years, depending on the long-term periodicity of rainfall. Whole lakes may almost dry up for a number of years. Such examples are L. Stymfalia in the Peloponnese and L. Dystos in Evvoia, as well as many of the lakes that have now been drained (e.g. Kopais).

Coastal lagoons are often called brackish but this term is slightly misleading because their salinity is not constantly brackish but usually fluctuates from brackish or almost freshwater in winter and spring to saline or hypersaline in summer. In most, a very dense growth of submerged *Ruppia* develops in the warm water during the summer. Coastal lagoons often adjoin areas of saltmarsh and when not too saline they may have a fringing belt of reeds.

Saltmarshes commonly occur on flat land near the coast. They may be flooded by sea water at high tide all year round or by rain water in the winter half of the year. Even when never flooded by sea water, salt water is present underground. In summer, water evaporates from the surface and salt water is continuously drawn up from below to replace it, often creating a salt crust on the surface.

Under very saline conditions saltmarshes exist in the form of short (usually less than 30 cm) and sparse halophytic vegetation, dominated by such plants as the perennial *Arthrocnemum*, *Halocnemum* and *Halimione portulacoides* or the annual *Salicornia*. The vegetation is often in the form of low mats, with a significant proportion of bare mud in between. The mud is wet and slippery in winter but dries and cracks in summer. In less strongly saline conditions a dense low carpet is formed. Rushes such as *Juncus acutus*, with its characteristic spiky clumps, and then *Juncus maritimus*, forming dense meadow-like beds, appear as one moves inland towards lower salinity. In shallow channels or hollows, in the shallow margins of lagoons and in sheltered muddy bays, where there are strong fluctuations in water level and salinity, beds of pure *Scirpus maritimus* tend to develop. Tamarisks *Tamarix* form thickets or occur as scattered bushes in the transitional zones between saltmarsh and fresh water.

AN OUTLINE OF GREEK BIRDLIFE

Birds have been inhabiting Greece for millions of years. Paleornithological studies based on rather limited material have traced fossil bird remains as far back as the upper Miocene (5–6.5 million years ago) at sites mainly in Attica (Pikermi), Evvoia and Samos (G. Theodorou). These include storks *Ciconia* spp., pheasants *Phasianus* spp., cranes *Pliogrus* spp. and an ostrich, *Struthio karatheodoris* F. Major, 1888. Remains of the latter were excavated at Pikermi and on Samos and bones were dated from the Lower Pliocene.

Excavations from several sites on Crete have provided material from the Pleistocene which belongs to at least 67 bird species. The majority are identical to modern birds but some of them are either extinct altogether or do not occur in Greece or Crete anymore, whereas a few are very rare or accidental today. Weesie (1982) has described a new species of endemic island owl of the genus Athene, *Athene cretensis*, a bird similar to the Little Owl, but with larger wings and longer legs, reflecting an adaptation to a mainly terrestrial life. The same author has also identified remains of Brown Fish Owl *Ketupa zeylonensis*, a species not found in Greece anymore, remains of Tengmalm's Owl, White-backed Woodpecker and Bullfinch, all boreal species now confined to northern Greece, as well as fossils of species such as the Gannet, Red-breasted Goose and White's Thrush, which are either very rare or accidental in Greece today (Weesie 1987). Another species that may have existed up to 2,500 years ago (or later?) is Bald Ibis *Geronticus eremita*. Desfayes (1987) has presented evidence, even though circumstantial, that the legendary birds of Lake Stymfalia could be identified as this species, which probably bred in the Peloponnese in early antiquity.

In historical times, the only other species which are known to have become extinct are Black Francolin, reported for the last time on Crete in 1844 (Frivaldszky 1902) and not seen since then in Greece, and Purple Gallinule, last reported from two sites in southern Peloponnese (and perhaps elsewhere) in the 1830s (Geoffry Saint-Hilaire 1833; Reiser 1905).

Since 1833, when the results of the *Expedition Scientifique du Morée* were published (Geoffrey Saint-Hilaire 1833), the number of bird species recorded in Greece has increased considerably, mainly as a result of more extensive ornithological research rather than due to actual changes in status.

The number of bird species recorded in Greece up to 31 December 1995 is 422. A further 49 species mentioned in the literature or reported by various observers have been ommitted from the Greek list (see Appendix C). Some of them have been rejected purely for technical reasons (such as lack of supporting field data etc.) though their occurrence in Greece is very likely. Moreover, the large number of accidental visitors added to the Greek list in recent decades clearly indicates that increased observer activity will certainly add more species of this category in the near future.

Table 5 summarises the current status of the 422 bird species in Greece. One must bear in mind that whenever trying to calculate simple statistitics for such complex multi-dimensional information as timing of occurrence and regularity of breeding, it is inevitable that results will be subjective, rules arbitrary and distinctions between categories not clear-cut.

Table 5: Summary of the current status of the birds of Greece

STATUS	NON-PASSERIFORMES	PASSERIFORMES	TOTAL
REGULARLY BREEDING			
Resident	81	73	154
Summer visitors	44	45	89
WINTER VISITORS	47	8	55
PASSAGE MIGRANTS	34	13	47
NON-BREEDING VISITORS	5	–	5
EXTINCT	1	–	1
ACCIDENTAL VISITORS	40	31	71
TOTAL	252	169	422

Breeding Species

More than half (243, or 58%) of all species recorded in Greece have a permanent and regular breeding population in the country. Two of them, Woodcock and Pygmy Owl, have not actually been proven to nest but almost certainly do so. Marmora's Warbler is included as a resident species but, although reported a number of times, some doubt still remains about its occurrence since no good description, photographs or other solid evidence has yet come to light. One species, Red-legged Partridge, has been introduced successfully in recent years whereas Ring-necked Parakeet, not included in the list, may be on the way to establishing permanent populations (see Appendix D). Pheasant is presumed to have been introduced in ancient times.

Species not included as breeding birds are:

(i) Six species, Bittern, Baillon's Crake, Dotterel, Caspian Tern, Short-eared Owl and River Warbler are treated here as winter visitors or passage migrants but have been seen in suitable habitat during the breeding season, singing, displaying or otherwise showing signs of possible breeding.

(ii) At least ten more species used to breed, at least irregularly, in the past but have not done so since 1970: Red-necked Grebe, Shoveler, Marbled Teal, Osprey, Black Francolin, Purple Gallinule, Crane, Little and Great Bustards and Rook. Black Francolin has become extinct but the remaining species have been recorded in more recent times as accidental or irregular visitors or occur regularly in winter or on passage. Red-necked Grebes and Rooks may even still nest occasionally in the north.

(iii) Five species, Black-necked Grebe, Cattle Egret, Red-crested Pochard, Pied Wheatear, and Rose-coloured Starling, occur mainly as winter visitors or passage migrants but breed irregularly, either every few years or almost annually but not at fixed localities. For most of them Greece is at the edge of their global range and conditions in the country may not be suitable for breeding every year.

(iv) For four species, Greater Flamingo, Fieldfare, Spectacled Warbler and Willow Warbler, there have been recent breeding cases but it is not known yet whether these represent casual breeding attempts or a range expansion, with the establishment of more or less permanent populations.

The majority of breeding species are resident or partial migrant (154) and the rest (89) are mainly summer visitors. However, in both categories there is a significant proportion of species in which populations breeding further north in Europe or western Asia occur also as winter visitors or passage migrants (e.g. Buzzard and Swallow). In fact in many cases, breeding species are far more numerous and widespread outside the breeding season. Only 118 resident or partial migrant and 66 summer visitors are commoner or as common during the breeding season as during passage or in winter, whereas 36 of them are much more numerous in winter (e.g. Sparrowhawk and Song Thrush) and 23 on passage (e.g. Garganey and Sedge Warbler).

In an attempt to estimate and evaluate in quantitative terms the avian diversity of the Balkan Peninsula as a unit, Vasic (1994) used the number of species/$\log_e$ area ratio as an index. With *c.* 300 breeding species in the Balkans (486,000 km^2) this species density index is 22.93 whereas for Italy (301,278 km^2) the same index calculated by Massa (1982) is 20.30. Vasic (1994) also concluded that the Balkan Peninsula has one of the two richest avifaunas of Europe, the other one being that of the Iberian Peninsula. With 243 species regularly breeding and a further 13–17 possibly or occasionally doing so, Greece, a small-sized country indeed holds a relatively rich avifauna in terms of the total number of breeding species present. For a simple comparison, Italy, a much larger country, has 240 breeding species (Meschini & Frugis 1993), Romania, also much larger, has 256 (Weber 1994) and Bulgaria, fewer than 255 (Boev & Simeonov 1985).

In his study Vasic (1994) also attempted to assess the geographic variability of avian diversity within the Balkan Peninsula. By using a complex set of criteria he divided the area into 24 different territories/regions, each one dominated by similar biomes or landscape types. With this simplified approach he has shown that Macedonia and Pindos, with 219 and 208 breeding species respectively, are the two peak regions regarding avian diversity. From there southwards, the number of breeding species decreases to e.g. 153 in Sterea Hellas, 104 in the Peloponnese and 85 on Crete. These results, similar to those described by Massa (1982) on the faunistic gradient of the Italian Peninsula, show that in the Balkans bird density declines with latitude, contrary to the global faunistic gradient, in which diversity increases with decreasing latitude (Vasic 1994). This is probably a result of lower habitat diversity and insularity as one moves from northern Greece southwards to Crete.

Tsounis & Frugis (1989) attempted to classify the breeding birds of Greece according to the faunal types proposed by Voous (1960). They listed 20 out of Voous's 24 faunal types, with 218 species (88%) belonging to nine such types, dominated by the Palearctic type (72), Holarctic (23), European (23), Europian/Turkestanian (23) and Mediterranean (20).

For a number of species Greece is the southernmost limit of their breeding range within the Western Palearctic, though very few of them may also breed in the extreme southwest part of it (Caucasus, NE Turkey etc.). There are at least 20 species in this category (Appendix E) of which Goosander, Fieldfare (Hölzinger 1986, Schmid 1992) and perhaps Pied Wheatear (Hölzinger 1989) are especially worth mentioning since their populations in Greece are also isolated.

The distribution of several other species breeding in Greece is also interesting in terms of zoogeography as well as of conservation. Seabirds are a good example, with several species either breeding nowhere else in the eastern Mediterranean or even if they do, Greece holds a large or the largest part of their regional population. For Storm Petrels and probably Sandwich Terns Greece has the only breeding colonies in the eastern Mediterranean whereas for Cory's and Mediterranean Shearwaters, Shag, Mediterranean and Audouin's Gulls Greece holds the largest populations in the eastern Mediterranean (Tucker & Heath 1994). For a large number of species the importance of Greece on a regional scale is second only to that of Turkey, which, however, is a much larger country and with a wider spectrum of habitats. Typical examples in this category are species such as the four European vultures, some of the eagles and falcons, Stone Curlew, Collared Pratincole and many passerines (e.g. Rock and Blue Rock Thrush, Olivaceous, Olive-tree, Subalpine and Rüppell's Warblers, Woodchat Shrike, Chough, Cretzschmar's and Black-headed Bunting) (Tucker & Heath 1994).

Moreover, Greece holds globally important breeding populations of two species, Dalmatian Pelican and Eleonora's Falcon. L. Mikri Prespa hosts the largest colony of Dalmatian Pelicans outside the former U.S.S.R., with *c.* 400 pairs in 1994, whereas the largest world population of Eleonora's Falcons breeds in the Aegean archipelago: 2,873 pairs or *c.* 65% of the global population (Walter 1978a, 1978b, 1979; Tucker & Heath 1994). Interestingly, both species and particularly Dalmatian Pelican show positive population trends (Tucker & Heath 1994).

Winter Visitors

A total of 55 bird species may be termed winter visitors. For many of them (e.g Pintail, Dunlin) there is also a significant passage through the country, whereas some may breed irregularly (see above) and for some (e.g. Curlew and other waders) very small numbers may be seen even during the summer. The majority of winter visitors are non-passerine.

The geographical location of Greece, the mild climate and the relative abundance of some rich habitat types (wetlands, olive groves etc.) are the main reasons for the importance of Greece as a wintering area. This is particularly true for three groups of birds: waterfowl, thrushes and seed-eating passerines (finches, buntings etc.).

The significance of Greek wetlands for wintering waterfowl has been assessed and widely recognised since the early 1960s (Sevastos 1976; Kanellis 1980; Athanassiou 1987; Handrinos 1988b, 1989a). The IWRB Midwinter Waterfowl Counts, which started in Greece in 1969 interrupted in 1976 and resumed again in 1982 (Handrinos 1989) have clearly shown that despite its small size Greece is one of the most important countries in the eastern Mediterranean, as far as wintering populations of Anatidae, Coot and other waterbirds are concerned. Several of the 11 Greek Ramsar sites hold internationally important populations of swans, geese, ducks and Coot, as well as other waterbirds such as Dalmatian Pelicans, Pygmy

Cormorants and Great White Egrets. (Crivelli 1980; Crivelli *et al.* 1991a; Handrinos 1989b, 1991, 1993b, 1995; Handrinos & Goutner 1990; Naziridis *et al.* 1992).

Figure 10 shows the total January counts for Anatidae and Coot in Greece (1969–1994). Data for the 1982–1992 period show that the average population of swans, geese ducks and coots wintering in Greece is 345,000. These numbers represent counts at an average of 35 sites, but both Athanassiou (1987) and Handrinos (1989a) have shown that 90–94% of the total wintering population of these birds occurs in the 11 Greek Ramsar sites. Coot, Wigeon and Pochard are the most abundant wintering waterfowl species, followed closely by Teal, Pintail and Mallard.

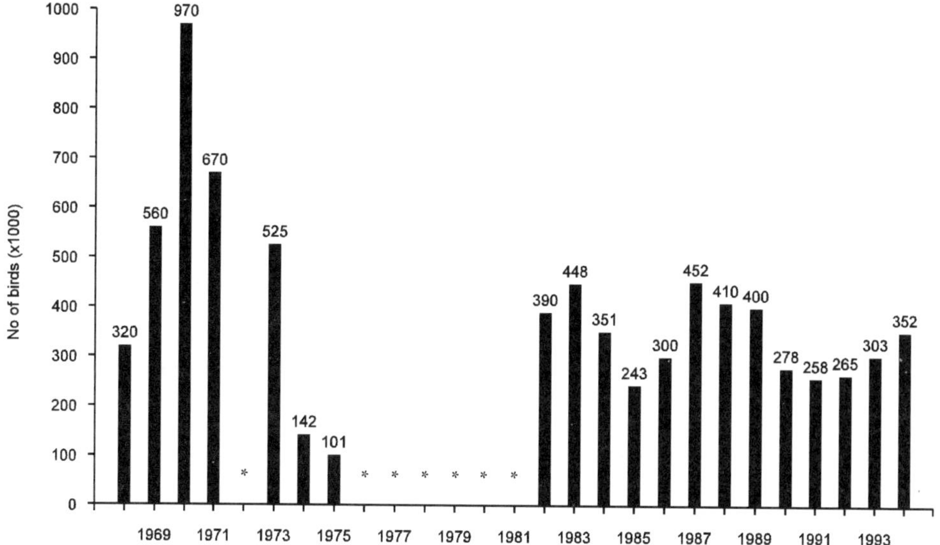

Figure 10. Totals (x 1000) of duck and Coot counted in main Greek wetlands (1968–1994). Years when no counts were made are marked *.

A few other wintering waterfowl species (Mute Swan, Shelduck etc.) are present in smaller numbers but even for these Greece is a very important area on a regional scale. Among the less common waterfowl the more or less regular, though in small numbers, occurrence of species such as Lesser White-fronted and Red-breasted Goose, both of them now globally threatened, is another important aspect of Greece's diversity in wintering waterfowl.

Besides waterfowl, Greek wetlands are important wintering areas for many other waterbird species, such as Dalmatian Pelicans (Crivelli *et al.* 1991a), Cormorants and Pygmy Cormorants (Handrinos 1993b), Greater Flamingos (Handrinos 1989b), grebes and herons, particularly Great White Egret, whose wintering population in Greece is increasing (Naziridis *et al.* 1992).

Data from the IWRB Midwinter Counts, show that Greece is not very important for wintering coastal waders (Smit 1986). However, although average January populations are relatively small, occasionally quite high concentrations can be recorded, perhaps reflecting regional weather patterns or temporary availability of good feeding and roosting sites. As an example, the national average wintering population of Dunlin in the 1982–1992 period is 6,900 birds but in January 1989 a record 18,588 were counted. Dunlin, Redshank, Curlew and Avocet are the most numerous (on average) wintering wader species. Lapwings are also common, although their overall wintering population is difficult to estimate, as happens with other non-coastal waders (Golden Plover, Snipe etc.).

Only a few passerines can be regarded as purely winter visitors (e.g. Meadow Pipit, Redwing, Great Grey Shrike and Brambling) but for many others which do nest in Greece (e.g. Skylark, Robin, Chaffinch etc.) their population is greatly augmented in winter by immigrants from further north. The relatively mild winters of most of the country, with temperatures rarely below freezing for long, mean a generally snow- and ice-free ground, suitable for seed-eaters. Large, often mixed, flocks of finches, larks and buntings form on arable land, whereas olive groves and maquis provide excellent feeding conditions for thrushes, Robins, Blackcaps, Starlings and other fruit-eating birds. The number of birds involved is not easy to estimate but many of the commoner species probably number at least several tens of millions each. Olive groves on marginal land, where olives are often left unpicked, are particularly rich and may harbour astonishing numbers of Song Thrushes and Blackbirds in mid and late winter when other sources of food are scarce. Such birds may eat their day's fill within minutes of sunrise and spend most of the rest of the day quietly sitting in dense evergreen bushes along roadsides or streams. Meadow Pipits and White Wagtails are also common birds of open spaces in winter.

The large number of wintering birds, as well as other prey, attract significant numbers of birds of prey. Sparrowhawks and Hen and Marsh Harriers occur in relatively large numbers in winter, and Peregrines are not rare, especially near wetlands. Buzzards are another common species of bird of prey in winter.

Many waterbirds and passerines are strongly affected by cold weather spells. During and immediately after such weather conditions, wintering populations are greatly augmented, though data are either lacking or incomplete to quantify the numerical increase. The best examples are provided by waterfowl and particularly swans and geese. The record number of Mute Swans wintering in Greece (7,557) in 1994 was the result of such cold weather movements (Handrinos 1995; Rose 1995), as was the record number of White-fronted Geese, with 40,000 counted in the Evros Delta alone, on 3 March 1985 (Handrinos 1991). Northern Greece often experiences cold conditions long enough for freshwater and even brackish lakes and lagoons to freeze and at such times mass movements of waterfowl and frost-sensitive species such as Snipe, Woodcock and Lapwing occur and their numbers greatly increase in milder parts of the country. Cold weather may also cause large influxes of passerines such as Skylark, Redwing and Brambling.

Passage Migrants

A total of about 47 non-breeding species occur mainly during the annual spring and autumn migration. Again, for a number of these the distinction between passage migrants and winter visitors is not straightforward and many (e.g. Sanderling, Ruff) occur almost throughout the non-breeding season, though reach their peak numbers when on passage. Only 25 species (e.g. Red-footed Falcon, White-winged Black Tern, Pied Flycatcher) are pure and regular passage migrants.

The study of bird migration has advanced little in Greece. There are still many gaps in our knowledge regarding the timing and direction of movements, intraspecific variation (population, age and sex differences) and other aspects of migration. Relevant publications are still few and inadequate, both in the older literature (see e.g. Casement 1966; Lynes 1909a, 1909b; Mitchell 1968; Moreau 1953, 1960; Moreau & Moreau 1963; Nisbet 1967; Steinfatt 1954/55; Stresemann 1942a, 1943, 1944; Wettstein 1938) and in the more recent (see e.g. Catsadorakis 1983; Handrinos 1987c; Klockenhoff & Krapp 1978; Magioris 1987b; Meininger 1990; Spinthakis *et al.* 1993; Vagliano 1985a).

Generally speaking, the geographical location, shape and relief of Greece favour the orientations of migratory movements on a north–south axis. The elongated massif of the Pindus range, which runs along the full length of the mainland, the relatively narrow valleys of the main rivers cutting between high mountains, the long and jagged coastline, the numerous islands in both the Aegean and Ionian Seas, the three prominent peninsulas of the southern Peloponnese and the position of Crete between the mainland and the African coast are among the most important geographical features influencing the movements of migrants over Greece. On a wider scale, it is important that whilst movement to and from the north are unhindered, to the south lies the Mediterranean which must be crossed by migrants moving to and from Africa. The nearest part of N Africa is Cyrenaica in Libya but some species probably make use of the Nile valley on their way to sub-Saharan Africa, crossing southeastwards, whilst a few wintering mainly in W Africa have to make the crossing towards the southwest, at one of the widest parts of the Mediterranean.

The overall size of Greece is so small that it is hard to speak of migratory corridors. Most migration takes place on a broad front and there are no true 'bottlenecks'. However, many species which migrate by day at a low altitude seem to follow coastlines and other land features which facilitate their movements. Raptors such as harriers, which are able to make long sea-crossings, do nonetheless use thermals and tend to follow chains of islands or move along peninsulas whenever they can. Long-lived birds which tend to occur in flocks and are thus characterised by 'traditional' knowledge (e.g. Glossy Ibis, Cormorants) also seem to use local landmarks to a significant extent. Yet other species probably overfly the whole of the country at a high altitude and some of them (e.g. Crane, Sedge Warbler in the autumn, Grasshopper Warbler, perhaps Dotterel) are seen only rarely and irregularly on the ground.

Most migratory species (especially herons, waders and passerines) are nocturnal migrants and their directions of movements are even less well known than those of day migrants. There is only sporadic information from radar observations (e.g. Casement 1966), prey analyses of Eleonora's Falcon (e.g. Ristow *et al.* 1986) and liming and trapping studies (e.g. Choremi & Spinthakis 1990) for such movements. The offshore movements of seabirds and waterfowl also still remain very poorly known and it is generally believed that for many species (e.g. Garganey, Mediterranean Gull, marsh terns) the actual numbers involved are much larger than existing data show.

As in Cyprus (Flint & Stewart 1992), Sicily (Iapichino & Massa 1989) and probably other parts of the northern Mediterranean coast, spring passage is generally more evident than autumn passage, involving a wider variety of species and often larger numbers of individual birds. This may be due to a combination of reasons such as:

(i) In spring, migrants arrive in Greece after having made a long sea and perhaps desert crossing, and are more in need of rest and refuelling than in autumn.

(ii) The weather in spring is much more variable. Cloud, rain and strong northerly winds are often interspesed with fine, calm, warm weather or with light southerly winds at intervals of one to three days. This may force migrants to make frequent stops. 'Falls' of large numbers of migrants are frequent at this time of the year and migration tends to take place in waves. By contrast, the generally hot and sunny autumn weather, with winds from a more or less constant northerly direction, help southward moving migrants make an easy and fast journey to N Africa.

(iii) The amount of food and suitable habitat is much greater in spring, after the winter rains, than in the autumn. This is especially true for many aquatic birds but probably affects all species to a varying degree. In autumn the landscape is scorched, small wetlands have dried up and it may be difficult for migrants to find even drinking water. Nevertheless, many passage migrants (e.g. Red-backed Shrike, Willow Warbler and Spotted Flycatcher) are far more numerous in autumn than in spring.

Most autumn migrants move across Greece from early or mid August to late October or early November, whereas return movements start mainly from mid March and last up to mid May. Of course there are exceptions and for some species passage begins earlier or tails off later, e.g. several waders are already on autumn passage before mid July or on spring passage as late as early June and Hoopoes and House Martins may appear as early as mid February. For many species there are additional difficulties in defining the beginning or end of passage movements because arrivals from outside Greece mix with local wintering, summering or resident populations. For example, many heron, duck and wader species wintering in Greece begin the movements to their breeding grounds from early or mid February, at a period when other populations of the same species may arrive in Greece from wintering areas further south, to continue their northward movements.

Non-breeding Visitors

Five non-passerine species occur practically all year round but without breeding or breeding irregularly. Four of them, Greater Flamingo, Eider, Great Black-headed Gull and Caspian Tern are species which reach adulthood at three or more years of age and immature birds may stay away from their breeding grounds during the spring and summer (Cramp 1977–94). Furthermore, Greater Flamingos may not breed every year and adult birds may also spend the summer away from normal breeding sites, whilst there is at least one documented breeding attempt in recent years. Caspian Terns may have also bred in Greece, whilst the fifth species, Cattle Egret, has definitely bred at least once.

Accidental Visitors

The number of species recorded as accidental visitors to Greece (up to 1995) is 71 (17% of the total number of species). All species recorded fewer than ten times since 1950 are included under this heading. Obviously this is an arbitrary distinction from irregular visitors and we have used it cautiously and with some exceptions. The crucial number of valid records is often difficult to assess and species such as Corncrake or Grasshopper Warbler, which are difficult to detect and rarely recorded, may actually occur relatively often and were treated as rare passage migrants rather than as accidentals. One species, Black Grouse, has not been seen in the last 20 years despite increased observer activity and is very unlikely to make long distance movements but it is so distinctive that the probability of confusion seems remote.

Since the publication of *Catalogus Faunae Graeciae* (Bauer *et al.* 1969a), the number of additions to the Greek list has considerably increased with species mainly from this category. In these 26 years, 34 accidental species new to Greece have been recorded, whilst another four had been seen before 1969 but records had either remained unnoticed or were re-evaluated later (Handrinos 1994). This increase is mainly the result of better observer effort from an ever increasing number of foreign and Greek birdwatchers and only to a very small extent due to changing patterns of occurrence or changes in the status of these species in their countries of origin (Handrinos 1994). The number of species recorded in Greece by various authors since the 19th century appear in Figure 11 below.

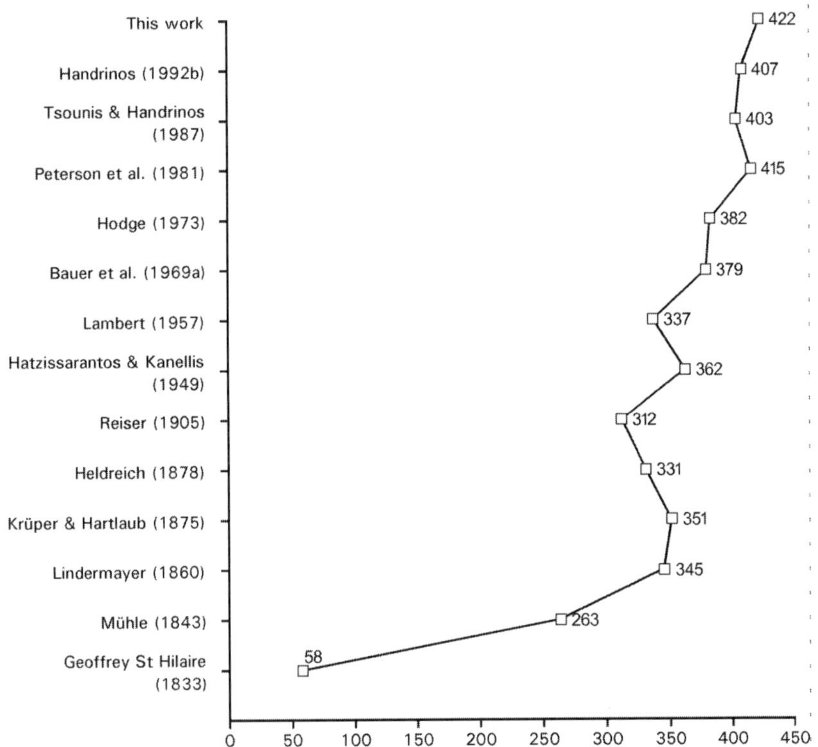

Figure 11. The total number of bird species recorded in Greece between 1833 and 1995.

The majority of species in this category are birds of Palearctic origin, many of them (Black-shouldered Kite, Laughing Dove, Finsch's Wheatear etc.) breeding in countries or areas adjacent to Greece such as Turkey and NE Africa, and a few (Black-throated and White's Thrush, Pine Bunting etc.) of Siberian origin. Nine species (Baird's Sandpiper, Spotted Sandpiper, Laughing Gull etc.) are of Nearctic origin.

Records of accidental visitors are widely distributed throughout the country but the large majority are from the coast and/or the islands which, in general, are very suitable areas for vagrant birds (Dymond *et al.* 1989). The Aegean islands and Thrace are the regions with the highest proportion of such records but this probably reflects a combination of high probability of occurrence of vagrant birds and of comparatively high observer activity in these areas.

BIRD HABITATS IN GREECE: A PROFILE

Despite its small size, Greece has a rich variety of habitat types which, in turn, host a diverse flora and fauna not found in many other European countries. This diversity is probably the result of a complex combination of interacting factors of which at least two are the most important.

a) A series of relatively recent geological events, such as the creation of most Greek mountains, submergence of large areas of land in the Aegean region and the rapid formation of river deltas have resulted in or contributed to the formation of a rugged relief, varied landscape and the fragmentation of land masses into numerous islands and peninsulas.

b) The geographical location of Greece, which includes two distinct and contrasted climatic zones, the Mediterranean and the continental, with a transitional zone between the two and with many local modifications depending on topography and other local features.

Such fundamental abiotic factors form an ideal background for the development of a wide range of natural landscapes, habitats, microhabitats and ecological niches.

There are apparently very few, and maybe no other, European countries which possess such diverse and complex natural habitats, terrestrial, marine or freshwater, ranging from the boreal-type primeval forests of Mt Rodopi to the palm grove of the near endemic *Phoenix theophrasti* at Vai (NE Crete) or from the windswept summits of Mt Olympos (2917 m) to the Ionian trench off SW Peloponnese, where the Mediterranean reaches its maximum depth. This diversity of habitats is further emphasised by the strong relief and small size of the country. In simplified terms this means a rich array of habitats within a relatively short distance of each other. The distance between Mt Rodopi and the coast of the Aegean Sea is only 80 km. Yet, there is a unique zonation of habitats within these 80 km, ranging from submerged *Zostera* and *Posidonia* beds off the mouth of R. Nestos to the virgin tracts of old, mature Norway spruce *Picea abies* on the slopes of Mt Rodopi.

It is not surprising, therefore, that Greece is one of the richest countries in Europe in numbers of plant and animal taxa. By contrast, species tend to be found in small populations due to fragmentation and limited overall area of suitable habitats.

The first serious attempt for a uniform classification of areas with natural or near-natural habitats in the countries of the European Union started in 1985 (CORINE Biotopes project) and resulted in the publication of an extensive typological list of 1,260 detailed habitat types, grouped in seven higher classes and 44 generic habitat types (Devillers *et al.* 1991). The inventory also produced a list of 6,095 sites (biotopes) throughout the EU Member States, of which 300 are in Greece. Although the Greek data in CORINE are still far from complete, Greece together with Spain, rank as the countries with the highest diversity both in habitats and species and particularly those of conservation interest.

A more recent inventory, completed as part of the implementation of the 'Habitats' Directive 92/43/EC, produced similar results: Greece has 115 out of the 226 main habitat types listed in this Directive, of which 31 represent 42% of the 73 habitat types of conservation priority (Dafis *et al.* 1994).

However, not all habitat types or sites of conservation interest in Greece are important for birds. Many of the sites included either in CORINE or in the 92/43/EC Directive have either little or relatively limited ornithological significance, particularly as far as rare, declining or threatened species are concerned. This is because species may be threatened or rare because of reasons other than habitat scarcity (e.g. vultures need extensive areas with large number of livestock) alone or may depend on particular combinations of common habitats (e.g. Lesser Spotted Eagles may need trees for nesting or roosting and grazing land or rice fields with plenty of reptiles, rodents and frogs for feeding).

This chapter gives, in a summary form, the profile of the most important habitats and their birds.

Wetlands

The most recent and so far the most complete inventory of Greek wetlands was published in 1994 (Zalidis & Mantzavelas 1994). This inventory lists a total of 378 sites, with 269 (71%) on the mainland and 109 (29%) on the islands. They cover a total surface of *c.* 200,000 ha, of which 97,000 ha (48%) are in Macedonia and Thrace, 98,600 ha (49%) in the rest of the mainland and only 7500 ha (3%) on the islands. Almost half (180) of the wetland sites listed are coastal (lagoons, coastal marshes, river deltas and river mouths) whereas the rest are freshwater lakes, reservoirs, rivers and natural springs (Table 6).

Table 6: Greek wetland sites, their type and total surface area (Zalidis & Mantzavelas 1994)

Wetland type	No of sites	Total surface (ha)
River Deltas	12	68,000
River Mouths	42	4,200
Lagoons	60	28,700
Marshes	75	5,830
Lakes	56	59,700
Reservoirs	25	35,820
Springs	17	133
Rivers	91	(4,268) (length in km)
TOTAL	378	202,600

In simplified terms, Greek wetlands offer a wide spectrum of important habitats, ranging from coastal mudflats to montane oligotrophic lakes, which function as breeding, wintering and stopover sites for large numbers of birds throughout the year. Birds in wetlands are influenced by a complex of interrelated biotic and abiotic factors, including the impact of human activities. The composition of bird assemblages exploiting the various types of such habitats may vary considerably in both space and time. Generally speaking, the large wetland complexes of Thrace, Macedonia and Ipeiros are particularly important for breeding, wintering and migrating birds, whereas the numerous but scattered and smaller wetlands of the south and the islands function mainly as stopover sites for migratory species and to a lesser extent as wintering areas (Gaetlich & Dragoumis 1985).

However, no two sites are exactly the same and each tends to have its own distinctive character. Some Greek wetlands hold large and diverse bird populations throughout the year. In this respect, L. Kerkini ranks top of the list, with large breeding colonies of Cormorants, Pygmy Cormorants, Spoonbills and Whiskered Terns (the largest in Greece) as well as many herons species and possibly still the last Greek colony of Glossy Ibis. It also holds as many as 50,000 wintering waterfowl and is equally significant during both spring and autumn migration. Other wetlands of year-round importance include the Amvrakikos, Messolonghi, the Axios Delta and the complex of Porto Lagos lagoons and L. Vistonis. In contrast, L. Mikri Prespa is world known for its breeding colonies of pelicans (both species), herons, cormorants and other species but it is very poor in wintering bird populations since it usually freezes over for long periods in winter.

The importance of any given wetland may change over the years. In most cases this is the result of habitat degradation caused by human activities which has particularly affected breeding species. This is probably best illustrated by the case of the Evros Delta, which due to habitat degradation and destruction by man during the last 30 years has almost totally lost its former significance as a breeding site for many rare species though still remains one of the most important wetlands for wintering waterfowl in the eastern Mediterranean. Of course other sites have lost all of their waterbirds due to complete drainage!

The ornithological importance of many Greek wetlands and their birds has drawn the interest of many Greek and foreign ornithologists and birdwatchers, to such an extent that our knowledge of Greek birds is clearly biased towards waterbirds, with little attention being paid to other groups. Even so, we are still far from knowing everything about waterbirds and their habitats, even for fairly simple and yet important aspects such as detailed studies on how different species exploit specific habitat types through the seasons, the feeding ecology of waterfowl and turnover rate and habitat use by waders during migration.

Allowing for the limited amount of existing data, certain types of wetland habitat seem to be of particular interest in respect of both diversity of species and the populations involved either throughout the year or during parts of their annual cycle. Such habitats include:

Coastal lagoons, particularly those dominated by submerged beds of *Ruppia*, an important food for wintering waterfowl. Such lagoons are found mainly in Thrace and parts of Macedonia, the Amvrakikos, Messolonghi and the western Peloponnese. Wigeon, Mute Swans and Coot are the main *Ruppia* feeding species but other species of *Anas*, Pochard, Shelduck, Flamingos, Avocets, Redshank, Dunlin and Curlew are also common in winter. Fish-eating birds such as grebes, Red-breasted Mergansers, cormorants, herons and pelicans, are also regularly attracted to coastal lagoons in large numbers in winter. In summer, coastal lagoons function as the main fishing ground for some of the largest colonies of Common, Little and Gull-billed Terns in the country.

Shallow freshwater lakes with extensive reedbeds and other marshy vegetation. This habitat is important for the breeding and wintering of many species of waterfowl, grebes, cormorants, herons and other waterbirds. Carpets of floating vegetation are important as nesting sites for marsh terns whilst herons find suitable roosting and fishing sites. Rodia Marsh in the Amvrakikos, with an area of 2000 ha, is the largest reedbed in Greece and one of the largest in the Mediterranean.

Saltmarshes and other flat coastal zones with halophytic vegetation are an important habitat for breeding species such as Spur-winged Plover, Ruddy Shelduck, Collared Pratincole, Kentish Plover, Stone Curlew, Black-headed Wagtail and some gulls and terns. Saltmarshes are equally important as roosting and feeding sites for wintering or migrating waterfowl and waders, including the globally threatened Slender-billed Curlew. Saltmarshes exist in most coastal wetlands but the largest expanses are in the Amvrakikos, where about 5200 ha were estimated in the 1970s (Szijj 1980) (this has now declined significantly).

Wet meadows and wet pasture. This is a rapidly declining habitat not only due to direct drainage and reclamation for agriculture but also due to hydrological changes resulting from water extraction and flood control works. Wet meadows, rich in amphibians, insects, seeds and other sources of food are an important feeding habitat for many herons, ducks and waders or species such as the Glossy Ibis, whose dramatic decline in Greece is almost certainly due to loss of this habitat.

Riverine woodland is another type of habitat that has largely been destroyed already and the last remnants are also disappearing or degrading due to direct cutting but especially due to over-exploitation of water for human needs and consequent drying of the soil and inability of seedling trees to establish. Such woodlands provide nest sites to many colonial waterbirds (Cormorants, Pygmy Cormorants, Spoonbills, Glossy Ibises, herons etc.), as well as raptors such as White-tailed Eagle and Black Kite. The Nestos Delta riverine woodland is the only site where Pheasants have existed since ancient times.

Two distinct wetland habitats are worth mentioning. Both are man-made and both are quite rich in birds. Rice fields are an excellent freshwater marsh substitute for many bird species. They occur in various parts of the mainland, usually near river mouths but also inland. The fields are ploughed and sown in April and May and kept flooded until September, when they are drained and harvested. The stubble stays water-logged and often partly flooded during the winter. Herbicides are widely used to control weeds but use of insecticides or other chemicals poisonous to birds seems to be rare. Thus in summer rice fields offer abundant supplies of insects (e.g. dragonflies, midges) and frogs, and in autumn and winter there is often a significant amount of left-over rice seeds. One serious drawback of rice fields is the heavy disturbance caused by ploughing, sowing and herbicide spraying during late spring and early summer, coinciding with the breeding season of many species. Thus few birds actually nest there preferring adjacent marshes or trees and using rice fields only for feeding. White Storks, Collared Pratincoles, marsh terns, Mediterranean Gulls, Gull-billed Terns, Black-winged Stilts, Redshank and various small species of heron are some of the species that use them extensively for foraging during the breeding season. Huge flocks of Spanish Sparrows are a common sight (and a serious problem) towards late summer, as the grain ripens. In winter, Great White Egrets, Grey Herons, Snipe, Lapwings, Curlews, Hen and Marsh Harriers, Chaffinches, Bramblings and Reed and Corn Buntings are regular and often very common, whilst various ducks of the genus *Anas* appear to use them at night. Large numbers of Ruff and Black-tailed Godwit also occur on passage. The largest areas of rice fields occur in Macedonia, in the Spercheios Delta etc.

The other type of man-made wetland habitat is saltpans or 'industrial salinas' (in Natura 2000 terminology), with a total area of about 2400 ha. These host large colonies of gulls and terns and function as feeding and resting sites for many other species both in winter and during migration. The attractive feature of saltpans for breeding gulls and terns is mainly the lack of disturbance, something which is becoming increasingly difficult for them to find. The Messolonghi saltpans today host the largest Greek colony of Gull-billed Terns, as well as good numbers of nesting Little and Common Terns, Avocets and Stone Curlew; Alyki Kitrous Lagoon (Kitros saltpans) until recently held the largest colony of Mediterranean Gulls outside Russia and now the only Greek colony of Slender-billed Gulls, whereas Messi Lagoon (Messi saltpans) hosts large numbers of Flamingos all year round and it is the only site in Greece where they have attempted to breed. On migration, saltpans are often rich in waders such as Kentish Plover, Curlew Sandpiper, Little Stint, Dunlin, Redshank, Ruff and Black-tailed Godwit. Avocets are almost exclusively found in this habitat, especially during the breeding season, now that natural saline lagoons are rare.

A relatively rare habitat type is tidal mud- and sandflats. The largest areas of such flats occur in the Thermaikos Gulf, along the coast of Thrace (e.g. Porto Lagos, Evros Delta) and in the northern Evvoikos Gulf (e.g. Spercheios Delta). Typical birds are similar to those found on the far more extensive tidal mudflats of the Atlantic coast of Europe and include Grey Plover, Curlew, Redshank, Dunlin and Shelduck.

A very important factor affecting birds in most wetland habitats is the seasonal lowering of water level or complete drying up. Drying up is a great aid to many fish-eating species, which find concentrated supplies of fish (and amphibians) in gradually shrinking pools, as well as to other waterbirds, which can get access to bottom-living invertebrates and submerged plants or their seeds in the shallow water or exposed mud. A deeper, though at first less obvious, consequence of drying up is through its effect on the species composition of the marsh or lake. For example, marshes and shallow lakes which dry up in summer have no fish; fish may compete with birds for the same food sources and thus similar-looking sites may present an entirely different set of conditions to birds. Temporary waters are usually richer in insects (midges, mosquitoes, dragonflies etc.) and frogs and toads and attract species such as Night and Squacco Heron, White Stork, Glossy Ibis and Collared Pratincole.

Forest

The distribution and composition of bird communities in Greek forest and woodland clearly depend upon the type of forest itself but also on other ecological and biogeographical factors, with regional and seasonal variations sometimes quite pronounced. In contrast to e.g. wetland birds, our knowledge of the distribution and particularly the ecology of forest and woodland bird species in Greece is still very limited. This is particularly true for certain difficult groups such as woodpeckers and owls but also many passerines.

A large proportion of forest and woodland species are sedentary, rarely wandering far from their breeding territories, though sometimes (e.g. in very hard winters) they may descend to lower forested areas. These include all ten woodpecker species occurring in Greece and species such as Hazel Grouse, Capercaillie, Jay, Nuthatch, tits and treecreepers. Others are summer visitors (e.g. flycatchers, warblers) and some possibly regular altitudinal migrants (e.g. Wren, Firecrest), though for the latter the situation is often confused by wintering populations of the same species from outside the country.

During the breeding season, broadleaved deciduous woodland is probably the richest terrestrial habitat in bird species diversity. The species composition is similar to that of deciduous woodlands throughout Europe, with several species of tits, woodpeckers and warblers, as well as one or two species of flycatcher, *Accipiter* hawks, thrushes, Nuthatch, Short-toed Treecreeper, Jay, Golden Oriole, Chaffinch and Hawfinch being more or less consistently present. Blue Tit is usually the most numerous species. Higher-altitude coniferous forest and the small patches of broadleaved evergreen woodland existing today usually hold fewer species and lower densitities but are still quite rich. In contrast, low-altitude woodland of Aleppo *Pinus halepensis* and Calabrian pine *P. brutia* is usually very poor in both number of species and overall populations. In many cases one finds only Blackbird, Olivaceous and Sardinian Warbler, Great Tit and Chaffinch breeding in pure woodland of this type but diversity increases markedly with increasing altitude or where the habitat is more varied, with some admixture of broadleaved trees or at the edge of woodland, where it adjoins open habitats.

Since most woodlands and forest occur in montane and submontane areas, often under deep snow for many months each winter, they are one of the least important habitats for winter visitors. It is mainly at lower altitudes that Robins, Wrens, Dunnocks, Chiffchaffs, Chaffinches and thrushes appear in winter or local populations increase with the arrival of immigrants. Bullfinch may be the only woodland winter visitor which is rare at sea level and more numerous at intermediate altitude.

From a zoogeographical or ecological perspective, certain forest areas are particularly interesting. The forests of Mt Rodopi, dominated by Norway spruce *Picea abies* and with an admixture of black *Pinus nigra* and Scots pine *P. sylvestris*, beech *Fagus*, oak *Quercus* and other woody species (silver birch *Betula pendula*, hazel *Corylus*, rowan *Sorbus aucuparia* etc.) are the southernmost distribution limit in Europe of boreal species such as Hazel Grouse and Nutcracker. They are also the only area or one of the very few areas in the country where species such as Capercaillie, Tengmalm's Owl, Woodcock, Willow Tit and Ring Ouzel breed.

The Forest Reserve of Dadia, an area dominated by black and Calabrian pine forest and open oak woodland, is renowned for its diverse community of breeding birds of prey (a total of 20 species) though most of them are not strictly forest species. For example, Golden and Short-toed Eagle and vultures use this forest for nesting but they usually forage in adjacent farmland, wetlands and pasture. The case of Dadia is a good example of how valuable for birds old, lowland areas of forest surrounded by a variety of other habitats can be, particularly when the latter are still largely unaffected by human activities.

As most of the islands in both the Aegean and, to a lesser extent, in the Ionian are devoid or very poor in woodland, wherever they occur, insular woods are an important asset to the diversity of bird habitats in these areas. The extensive pine woodlands and the patches of deciduous oaks of Lesbos hold both Nuthatch and Krüper's Nuthatch, a rare combination, whereas the recent discovery of Black and White-backed Woodpeckers in the fir forests of Mt Ainos (Vittery 1994) makes Kefallinia the only Mediterranean island and one of the very few islands throughout Europe where the two species co-exist.

Maquis, Phrygana and Pseudosteppe

Unquestionably, the most typical and usually most numerous species of maquis is Sardinian Warbler. Locally other *Sylvia* species such as Rüppell's and Subalpine Warbler partly or completely replace it. Black-eared Wheatear, Cirl Bunting and Blackbird are other regular species during the breeding season. However, it is in the winter half of the year that species diversity and abundance reach a peak. Many plants produce berries which appear to be an important food source for wintering Robins, Blackcaps, Song Thrushes and at times Redwings and Fieldfares, while insects and other invertebrates are also available for wintering Wrens, Dunnocks and Chiffchaffs. The dense evergreen cover of the maquis also provides excellent cover for the night. Large roosts of thrushes and sometimes finches are often located in patches of tall maquis on hillsides overlooking plains with extensive olive groves or other forms of cultivation where the birds feed during the day.

It is often difficult to draw the line between phrygana and maquis, as intermediates or mixtures of the two may occur ('open maquis'). Phrygana is poor in berry-producing plants but it can be extremely rich in grasshoppers and bush-crickets (Orthoptera) in the spring and there may be good seed production suitable for finches and buntings. Characteristic breeding species include Stonechat, Cretzschmar's Bunting, Linnet, Nightjar, Long-legged Buzzard, Kestrel and Short-toed Eagle. In winter, Woodlarks, Meadow Pipits, Cirl Buntings, Linnets, Chaffinches and, locally, Hen Harriers are regular. Both maquis and phrygana tend to be rocky. Even relatively small rock outcrops have their own breeding pair of Rock Nuthatch and Blue Rock Thrush, and in winter Black Redstarts are rarely missing.

Pseudosteppe is rather species-poor. Birds of open ground are typical and include various larks, Tawny Pipit and Wheatear during the breeding season and Meadow Pipit in winter.

Mountains

As in the case of woodland birds, there are still many gaps in our knowledge regarding the vertical distribution, the ecology or the precise habitat requirements of mountain birds in Greece. A few papers published long ago seem to be still valuable (Niethammer 1943; Peus 1954, 1957; Watson 1964) and in recent years the studies of Dr J. Hölzinger (Hölzinger 1986a, 1988a, 1988b, 1989a, 1990a, 1990b, 1990d, 1992d, 1993c, 1994) have been an important contribution to the subject.

The number of purely montane bird species, i.e. species that depend exclusively on high-mountain ecosystems, is small. Fewer than ten species belong to this category, of which the most characteristic are Shore Lark, Alpine Accentor, Wallcreeper, Snowfinch and Alpine Chough. However, the range of many species at lower altitudes extends up to alpine areas. One could include species such as Wheatear, Black Redstart, Linnet, Chough and Rock Partridge but it is difficult to make a precise list because both the species involved and the character and definition of 'high mountain' or 'alpine' areas varies a lot geographically.

Many species tend to occur at a higher altitude in the south than in the north. Usually this is a relatively small difference, reflecting the similarity of conditions in the middle zone of mountains in the south with low altitude in the north. Robins, Chaffinches and other woodland species are examples in this category. The reverse is the case in other species (e.g. Sardinian Warbler), which reach up to high altitude in the south but are restricted to low altitude in the north, presumably for the same underlying reasons.

In the case of a few species, however, the difference is much greater and often inexplicable on purely ecological factors. Ortolan Bunting is a good example, reaching down to sea level in Macedonia and Thrace but found only above the treeline in Sterea Hellas and the Peloponnese. However, there are always exceptions, and on Crete Ortolan Buntings range from sea level to 1200 m (Parrott *et al.* in press)! Wheatears occur only at high elevations over much of the mainland but both in the northern mainland and on many islands of the Aegean they are common down to sea level. Skylark is another peculiar example, breeding both at sea level and at high plateaus and the alpine zone but entirely missing from intermediate elevations. Presumably the explanation lies mainly in historical and zoogeographical considerations and involves competition of newly arriving species with already established populations of related species.

Mountain bird communities are also influenced by human activities and land use. The numerous flocks of sheep and goats grazing in high-altitude pastures in summer, attract vultures and Golden Eagles which do not necessarily nest in such high areas. Unusual food sources (e.g. at shepherds' huts or rubbish dumps) may also attract even coastal or marine species such as Yellow-legged Gull, whose flocks are quite often seen scavenging in high mountain areas.

Hunting may also affect the vertical distribution of certain birds. Rock Partridges, though a real montane species, have progressively withdrawn to the highest and most inaccessible zones of rocky mountains due to hunting pressure, whereas in areas with no hunting (e.g. Mt Athos) they also breed at sea level (Watson 1964, Hölzinger 1988b). Similarly, on Crete Chukars remain common in higher areas whereas their population in the lowlands has been much reduced.

Another important feature of many Greek mountains is that they rise abruptly from flat lowlands or the sea. Mytikas, the highest peak of Mt Olympos (2917 m), lies at a distance of only 18 km from the sea, Lefka Ori, on Crete (2452 m), is at 8 km and Mt Athos (2033 m) is even closer, at 4 km. The close proximity of mountain and lowland is important to some species, particularly birds of prey such as vultures and Peregrine, which may nest and roost in mountains and forage in the lowlands. This combination as well as the high diversity of habitats available over such small distances (rocky gorges, cliff faces, high-altitude bare or grassy meadows, fast-flowing streams, forest etc.) contribute towards a very rich avifauna.

Farmland

Agricultural land occupies about 30% of Greece's total area, a low figure by the standards of most other European countries. The majority (66.24%) is arable land (mainly winter cereals but also cotton, maize, sugar beet and tobacco), followed by orchards (25.93%), vineyards (4.41%) and vegetable crops (3.42%). Fruit trees (citrus, peach, apple etc.) comprise 14% of orchards and other trees (almonds, hazel, pistachio, walnut etc.) a small percentage, but the highest proportion (73% or 663,000 ha) is occupied by olive trees, a figure which does not take into account isolated olive trees (NSSG 1986).

The main crops grown vary regionally due to local differences in relief, climate, soil quality etc. In general, the large plains of Thessaly, Macedonia and Thrace are used to grow cereals, sugar beet, cotton and other industrial crops whereas vineyards are dominant over large parts of the Peloponnese, Crete and other hilly areas. Citrus plantations, mainly orange, exist mainly in the Peloponnese, Crete and parts of Ipeiros while western Macedonia is a major area for peach, apple, pear, cherry and other fruit production. Olive groves are also restricted to certain areas, especially the southern mainland, the Ionian islands, Crete and the island of Lesbos, being rare or absent from much of Macedonia and Thrace.

Animal husbandry is an important sector of Greece's rural economy. Goats and sheep are the most numerous among free-grazing stock, with fewer cattle and very small numbers of pigs and other animals. With the exception of the few large plains of the country, farmland and pasture are strongly intermingled and often used alternately or in combination. Fallow fields are used for grazing and so is stubble and the remains of crops after harvesting. Flocks of grazing animals are almost invariably led and tended by herdsmen while grazing and taken back to a safe place at night. Thus the practice of leaving hedges to retain stock is virtually unknown. However, bushes and trees are often found along the edge of fields for a variety of reasons such as to provide shade in summer, because there are ditches (much of farmland is on flat low-lying country) or because rocks and large stones have been moved there from the middle of the field and cannot be ploughed.

Over the country as a whole, field size tends to be small, commonly only a fraction of a hectare, and areas of cultivation are also generally small, occupying valley bottoms and the less steep hill slopes. This means that cultivated land often borders on natural habitats on steep slopes, rocky ground or watercourses. As crops themselves may vary a lot from one field to the next (e.g. cornfield, olive grove, vineyard), a complex landscape is created, beneficial to many birds and other wildlife. For this reason, pure farmland birds are difficult to define and most species of farmland depend to a lesser or greater extent on this mixture of fields, bushes and groves.

Typical arable-land breeding birds include Lesser Kestrel, Quail, Crested, Calandra and Short-toed Larks, Lesser Grey Shrike, Hooded Crow, House and Spanish Sparrows, and Corn and Black-headed Buntings. Most are adversely affected by intensive cultivation and are either less common (e.g. Black-headed Bunting) or nearly absent (e.g. Lesser Kestrel, Lesser Grey Shrike) from such land. In winter, flocks of Skylarks, finches and buntings are widespread and on damp or partly flooded fields Lapwings, Golden Plover and Black-headed Gulls are quite common. In late April and early May one cannot miss parties or fairly large flocks of Red-footed Falcons perched on telegraph wires and hawking for insects. White Storks, Black-headed and Yellow-legged Gulls are the three species most commonly seen following the plough.

The cultivation of olive trees is not only a significant contribution to the rural economy but also an important type of habitat for many birds. The role of olive groves for birds is still not well studied (see e.g. Pergantis 1981, Wietfeld 1981). Olive groves (especially those with old trees and dense undergrowth) act as a substitute of natural evergreen forests and many bird species are clearly associated with this habitat, including southeast European specialities such as Olive-tree Warbler and Sombre Tit as well as more widespread species such as Olivaceous

Warbler, Blackbird, Short-toed Treecreeper and Scops Owl. Moreover, outside the breeding season olive groves function as a feeding habitat for many more species, ranging from Eleonora's Falcons hawking over the groves for insects to Robins, Starlings and thrushes feeding on the olives.

The Marine Environment

The Mediterranean is an oligotrophic sea and overall plankton production is generally small due to scarcity of nutrients. Its waters are relatively static with little mixing, deep sea marine life does not flourish and at depths of more than 120 m the Mediterranean is virtually sterile (Margalef 1984, UNEP/UNESCO/FAO 1988).

The eastern Mediterranean and Greek seas are more strictly oligotrophic than the western Mediterranean, which can easily explain why Mediterranean seabird populations are larger in the west than in the east (Guyot 1993; James 1984; Thibaut 1993; Sultana 1993). Despite much available nesting habitat (at least in the Aegean), lack of food resources is a serious limiting factor. Greece holds the largest populations of breeding seabirds (including both pelagic and coastal species) in the eastern Mediterranean despite the fact that due to the lack of detailed surveys their numbers and distribution are still poorly known.

Cory's Shearwater is the most numerous pelagic species, with an estimated population of at least 5,000 pairs, mostly in the Aegean. Mediterranean Shearwater appears to come second but its breeding population is not known. Storm Petrels have been discovered breeding only recently and even if they breed in all areas where they are suspected to do so, their total population is certainly not more than a few hundred pairs.

Shag, Audouin's and Yellow-legged Gull are three species with a mainly marine coastal distribution. Shags and Yellow-legged Gulls occur on practically all rocky coasts, in fact the latter regularly breeds also in wetlands and forages some distance inland. Audouin's Gulls are much more local.

Small uninhabited rocky islets in the Aegean offer optimum nesting habitat for another species which, though not a seabird, is one of the most typical birds in the area. The Aegean holds 57–65% of the world population of Eleonora's Falcon (Walter 1978a, 1978b, 1979), a colonial raptor, whose late nesting period coincides with the mass autumn migration of small birds over the Aegean, the main prey of the falcons and their chicks during this period.

Information on the distribution and population of seabirds outside the breeding season is even more limited and the overall picture still very incomplete. Counts of gulls and terns in coastal wetlands are regularly carried out within the framework of IWRB Midwinter Counts but numbers possibly occurring offshore are not known. Mediterranean Shearwaters have been observed moving in large numbers but we do not know where the main fishing and nesting grounds of these birds are. It is also possible that larger numbers of Black Tern, Little Gull, Gannet and skuas than those recorded near the coast move offshore but we still know very little about such movements and it will probably be a long time before we have a fairly good picture.

BIRD CONSERVATION PROBLEMS IN GREECE

For thousands of years the Greek landscape has been modified by man. Little by little forest was destroyed over much of southern coastal areas and the islands, and following the loss of soil, vegetation structure was permanently changed. Already in classical times the hills surrounding Athens were described as bare and rocky, much as they are today. The drainage of the huge L. Kopais, the largest Greek lake (*c.* 20,000 ha), by the Minyans (14th century B.C.) is a remarkable engineering feat and one of the first works on such a scale in antiquity. Years of war, from ancient times up until the 20th century, and heavy exploitation of natural resources throughout Greek history, all had an impact on the landscape, fauna and flora. However, it is mainly during the last 200 years that habitat degradation accelerated and spread to relatively untouched parts of the country.

During the War of Independence against Turkish occupation (1821–1830) large areas of forests and olive groves were burnt in the Peloponnese and elsewhere in the south. After Independence (1830), the ever growing needs of the nation to develop its economy led to more intensive forest exploitation and expansion of agricultural land through wetland drainage and clearance of lowland woods, presumably seriously affecting the numbers and distribution of many Greek birds. Moreover, the increasing use of shotguns, especially after the Second World War and the succeeding Civil War (1945–1949), also started to take a heavy toll on bird populations; even more recently the increased use of agrochemicals has been responsible for the decline of many birds.

For many species (e.g. large eagles and vultures) the decline was so obvious already in the early 1950s, when compared to ten or 20 years earlier, that both Greek and foreign ornithologists of that period were alarmed. It was during the Seventh I.U.C.N. Technical Meeting in Athens (11–19 September 1958) that the need to protect the rare and declining birds of Greece was expressed for the first time (Hatzissarantos & Kanellis 1959, Makatsch 1959).

In 1977, Prof. A. Kanellis published the first Greek *Red Data List* of birds (Kanellis 1977). It was followed by the similar lists of Müller (1980) and Tsounis & Frugis (1987) and finally *The Red Data Book of Threatened Vertebrates of Greece* (Karandeinos & Legakis 1992), by far the most complete work on the subject to date. This Greek *Red Data Book* includes a major section on birds in which, following I.U.C.N criteria and guidelines, 99 bird species and one race (*Emberiza schoeniclus reiseri*), i.e. 24% of Greek avifauna, are listed. The full list of the *Red Data Book* birds in Greece is given in Appendix G and the main categories are summarised in the following table.

Table 7: Number of bird taxa in the main categories of the Red Data Book (Handrinos 1992b)

Category	No of taxa
E: Endangered	25
E1: immediate danger	13
E2: non immediate danger	12
V: Vulnerable	23
R: Rare	20
I: Indeterminate	6
E: Extinct	6
K: Insufficiently known	20
TOTAL	100

The *Red Data Book* provided a good opportunity to inspect, analyse and identify the major threats and reasons for decline of Greek birds. As expected, the vast majority of the 100 taxa listed are threatened directly or indirectly by human activities, particularly habitat destruction and/or alteration, illegal hunting, disturbance and pesticides. However, for most species conservation problems are interlinked and may involve a combination of threats. This is best illustrated by the fact that large waterbirds and raptors comprise 51% of bird species listed in the *Red Data Book*, these two groups being much more affected by both habitat changes and illegal hunting than other groups of birds (Handrinos 1992b).

Habitat Changes

The modification and, quite often, the destruction of natural habitats in Greece is clearly connected with agricultural practices and to a lesser extent with other human activities such as tourism and industrial development.

Owing to lack of data on bird populations in the past (e.g. prior to 1970), it is very difficult to make an adequate assessment of the long-term impact of habitat changes on the status and distribution of birds. The case of wetlands is the best example of this. In modern times, mass wetland drainage in Greece started in 1889, when L. Kopais was drained for agriculture, 32 centuries after the initial though temporary drainage achieved by the ancient Minyans. Many more lakes and marshes had the same fate over the next few decades. Wetland drainage took place particularly after 1922, when almost a million Greek refugees arrived from Asia Minor at the end of the Greco-Turkish War. The need for more agricultural land and the problem of malaria prompted the drainage of huge wetland areas, such as L. Giannitsa (20,400 ha with surrounding marshes), L. Achinos (12,000 ha), the marshes of Filippoi (20,000 ha) etc. It has been estimated that before 1930 in Macedonia alone wetlands occupied 157,200 ha, of which 115,100 ha (73.2%) have now totally disappeared due to drainage (Psilovikos 1990). At a national level, wetland loss in the 20th century has been estimated at 61% (Handrinos 1992a) or 63% (Psilovikos 1992), ranging from 33% in the Peloponnese to 95% in Thessaly (Handrinos 1992a). Even these figures, however, should be considered as minima because, for example, many areas which were not permanently flooded are not included in the calculations. Although data are limited and scanty there can be little doubt that most, if not all, of these wetlands were important for many species during the breeding season as well as in winter (Handrinos 1992a). A typical example is L. Karla, in Thessaly (average size *c.* 14,000 ha) where on 3 and 4 March 1964, a time when drainage was nearly complete, 430,000 waterfowl were counted (Hoffmann 1964), a remarkable figure considering that the national average number of wintering waterfowl in recent years (1982–1992) has been 345,000. It has also been suggested that the dramatic decline of the populations of geese wintering in Greece is clearly connected with wetland loss and degradation and can partly explain the absence of geese not only from individual wetlands but from whole regions (e.g. Ipeiros) as well (Handrinos 1990).

The last major wetland to be drained was Agoulinitsa Lagoon in the western Peloponnese (*c.* 3000 ha) whose drainage was completed by 1973. Since then, wetland drainage has been abandoned as a state policy but even today many wetlands, particularly coastal sites (river deltas etc.), are still suffering from the side effects of past drainage schemes, such as serious changes in water regime, reduction of freshwater inflow, saltwater intrusion and progressive salinisation of the soil. These are typical problems of most Greek wetlands nowadays. Their consequences affect the natural vegetation and thus overall conditions for birdlife and in many cases have a serious adverse impact on feeding conditions for wintering waterfowl (Handrinos 1992a).

In recent years, the ever growing need for fresh water to irrigate farmland, occasionally combined with series of dry years and worsened by mismanagement practices has become another serious problem, expected to become even worse in the future. In many lakes wide fluctuations of water level due to pumping for irrigation are causing serious problems to many breeding populations of waterbirds, either due to flooding of nests (e.g. at L. Kerkini) or to drying up (e.g. L. Ismaris).

In many wetlands housing development, usually unplanned and illegal, and other constructions such as fish ponds and infrastructure works also have a serious negative impact on local breeding birds, since they usually destroy large areas of natural habitat (e.g. saltmarshes) that had largely escaped from destruction up to now. The dramatic decline of the populations of Black-winged Stilt and Collared Pratincole in the Amvrakikos is the result of such habitat loss for the creation of large fishponds (Pergantis & Roussopoulos 1994).

Forest or tree-nesting species have also suffered from habitat loss and degradation, particularly in the decades just before and immediately after the Second World War. However, reduction of forest coverage appears to have been taking place already in the middle of the 19th century and though statistics from that period are debated, it has been estimated that in 1830–1840 (when Greece was about half the size of today) forests may have covered up to 41% of its surface (Grispos 1973), a significantly higher figure than today.

The greed for more agricultural land has been the main reason for the clearance of lowland woodlands including large areas of riverine forest. The most striking example is the forest of Kotza Orman in the Nestos Delta. Up to 1946, this riverine forest was one of the largest and best preserved in SE Europe, covering an area of 7200 ha. By the mid 1950s, at least 4500 ha had been clear-cut and replaced by farmland and poplar populations, and today only small patches remain. Although its wildlife was never properly recorded, it was virtually impenetratable and rich in large mammals, including wolves *Canis lupus* and wild boar *Sus scrofa*, as well as holding a dense population of Pheasants of the nominate race, *P. c. colchicus* (Papaioannou 1953). Up to the mid 19th century Pheasants were also present in the dense riverine forests of the Acheloos Delta (Reiser 1905) and probably existed in similar habitats elsewhere within their former range. The loss of riverine forests or dry lowland oak woodland was detrimental to the survival of large raptors such as White-tailed, Lesser-Spotted and Imperial Eagles, which were still locally common up to fairly recent times (e.g. Makatsch 1950). Makatsch (1943b) points out that the disappearance of Lesser Spotted Eagle from parts of western Sterea Hellas coincides with the clearance of the deciduous woodlands of that region at the turn of the century.

Fires are a common phenomenon in Mediterranean forest ecosystems, particularly pine woodlands, but in recent decades the problem of forest fires in Greece has spread and intensified. Between 1974 and 1994 a total of 74,900 ha of non-cultivated land, including 17,500 ha of forest, were destroyed by fire (General Secretariat of Forests, unpubl. data). There is still no study to assess the impact of this loss to birds, which must be especially serious on islands where available habitat for forest and woodland birds is limited.

Forestry practices are also posing threats to many birds, at least on a local scale. The conversion of maquis or old deciduous woodland to commercial pine plantations (quite often of introduced tree species) has a negative effect on many species such as raptors, owls, woodpeckers and hole-nesting passerines since it transforms a biologically diverse habitat into a monoculture. Construction of new forest roads has also intensified in recent decades. Between 1951 and 1985 the total length of such roads has been increased by 150% (Kotoulas 1989). Forest roads may seriously affect populations of many birds through habitat fragmentation and by facilitating illegal hunting, even in remote areas.

Changes in agricultural practices have caused the decline of many bird species. Intensification of arable farmland in the form of monocultures of industrial crops and increased field sizes took place mainly after the 1960s. This has encouraged the widespread removal of bushes and trees from field margins, especially in central and northern parts of the mainland. Through a series of voluntary or compulsory land consolidation schemes, which are still going on, thousands of hectares of farmland have been converted into vast treeless expanses. Such changes have largely been responsible for the dramatic decline and disappearance of the Grey Partridge over much of its former range, as well as for the reduction of the population of several passerines (Lesser Grey Shrike, Black-headed Bunting etc.). At the other extreme, abandonment of traditional agricultural practices on many Aegean islands and upland areas of the mainland has negatively affected species such as Rock Partridge and the Chukar. Abandonment of terraced fields and small scale cultivation has limited the food and sources of drinking water for both species (Papaevangelou 1980).

With 5,831,000 goats (1991 census) in the whole country, it is not surprising that overgrazing, probably since ancient times, has seriously modified the natural landscape in many regions. About 82% of the goat population occurs in hilly and mountainous areas. Grazing by goats seems to be the most important factor in preventing regeneration of forest after fire. The large number of free-grazing goats, as well as sheep and a smaller number of cattle may have both negative and positive effects on the birds. Large flocks of grazing stock may benefit species such as raptors and in most areas are the only food source for vultures. On the other hand, uncontrolled grazing by cattle is a major threat to ground-nesting birds in some areas. In the Evros Delta whole colonies of Avocets, Collared Pratincoles and other species have been destroyed by trampling on a number of occasions (Goutner 1983a). The dramatic decline of the population of Spur-winged Plover in the same wetland is also mainly due to trampling, and similar losses have also been recorded in the Nestos delta, the main stronghold of the species in Greece (Tucker & Heath 1994).

Pesticides

Intensification of agriculture during the last decades has resulted in much higher inputs of agrochemicals, including both artificial fertilisers and pesticides. Although long-term data do not exist, pesticide use in Greece is considered to be small to moderate. The average annual use of pesticides (all types) throughout the country in the years 1987–1989 was 15,112 tonnes, of which 48% was fungicides (Min. of Agriculture, unpubl. data).

The impact of pesticides on birds has not yet been studied in Greece and only quite recently a few papers examining existing problems have been published. DDT, DDE and most other organochlorines have been banned since 1972 but several pesticides banned in other countries (e.g. Lindane) are still in use (Voiklis 1990).

Crivelli *et al.* (1989) found that concentrations of DDE in Dalmatian Pelican eggs collected at L. Mikri Prespa between 1984 and 1986 were among the highest in waterbirds in the Mediterranean region. However, although a 15–20% decrease in eggshell thickness was recorded, no impact on their breeding success was observed. Substantial concentrations of DDE and PCB have also been found in the eggs of Cory's Shearwaters from a colony off NE Crete (Ristow *et al.* 1992), whereas other studies from the same colony have also recorded high levels of other contaminants such as mercury and cadmium (Renzoni & Massa 1993). In contrast, pesticide residues in eggs of Eleonora's Falcons from the same site were found to be remarkably low (Ristow *et al.* 1980). Apart from fish-eating birds, pesticides seem to have a serious impact on other groups of birds, particularly insectivorous species. Aerial spraying of olive groves against the Olive-fruit Fly *Dacus oleae* is still practised in many areas and appears to be lethal to many passerines, either directly by poisoning them or indirectly by killing all insect food available. Mass deaths of Swallows, tits, warblers and other passerines as well as of Eleonora's Falcons have been recorded on many occasions (e.g. Vagliano 1977) but there are still no proper studies to assess the full scale of the problem. Similar cases are also known from areas of intensive agriculture and pesticide use seems to be one of the major causes for the dramatic decline of Grey Partridge.

Hunting

As in most countries bordering the Mediterranean, hunting is quite popular in Greece. In the post war years the number of licensed hunters has greatly increased from 165,340 in 1962 to 314,430 in 1982. In 1993 there were 291,000 licensed hunters (*c.* 3.5% of the total Greek population) but the actual number may be higher (probably as many as 500,000) as the use of shotguns without a licence is not uncommon. In the country as a whole there are about 2.2 licensed hunters/km^2 but locally hunter density far exceeds this figure (e.g. 11.8 on Corfu and 8.0 on Zakynthos). Bird shooting has always been a highly controversial issue between hunters and conservationists and despite some slight improvements since the early 1980s, the overall situation still remains far from ideal.

In theory, existing legislation on hunting is quite satisfactory, particularly since 1985, when improvements were made in accordance with the 79/409/EC Bird Directive. This was a turning point for hunting practices in Greece, with a significant reduction of the list of huntable species. At present (31 December 1995), the open season runs from 20 August to 28 February, with a further restriction regarding waterbirds (hunting closed until 15 September) and an even more limited open season for Chukars and Rock Partridges. Hunting is allowed only with the use of shotguns (e.g. falconry, traps of any kind and use of attracting devices are illegal) and there are daily bag limits for all species. A full list of all huntable species is given in Appendix I.

Hunting is permitted throughout public land (which is the majority in Greece) except for protected areas such as National Parks. There are also more than 600 permanent Game Reserves, where hunting is forbidden and which cover a total of more than 900,000 ha. The total size of all areas closed to hunting is over 1,300,000 ha.

There is one type of licence for all species (including mammals) so it is not possible to know precisely the proportion of hunters shooting mainly wildfowl, Quail or other game. Such preferences are generally dictated by the local availability of huntable species. For example, hunters on the Ionian islands rely almost exclusively on migrants (Quail, Turtle Doves etc.), in the Aegean both on migrants and on Chukars, whereas on the mainland Woodcock, thrushes and wildfowl are common game species. With the long-term decline of resident species such as partridges, the majority of Greek hunters are increasingly depending on birds such as thrushes and wildfowl.

Generally speaking, most hunters respect the opening and closing dates of the hunting season and illegal shooting is not a problem in most protected areas and Game Reserves. Shooting at any bird which comes within range is a problem, though it is gradually getting less frequent than it used to be in the past. A striking example is the case of the former spring hunting season, from 15 April to 15 May. This was intended for shooting Turtle Doves on spring migration but large numbers of other species, including birds of prey, herons, Glossy Ibis, Golden Oriole, Bee-eater and Roller were also shot (Knightbridge & Akriotis 1982). Spring hunting was permanently banned in 1986. Protected species may be shot for a number of reasons. The overall population decline of many bird species, including migrants, induces a stronger hunting pressure on what remains. In many cases shooting of protected species is caused by the inability of hunters to identify their target and this is a serious problem for protected species which look like huntable ones. Moreover, species such as shrikes or Golden Orioles are often still shot because, although now protected, many locals ignore or refuse to accept such limitations for species they used to hunt for many decades. Overall, the problem of illegal shooting is most serious on the islands and the Peloponnese and becomes progressively less so towards the northern mainland.

Problems regarding hunting in Greece boil down mainly to ineffective law enforcement. With fewer than 1,500 state and private (employed by hunters' organisations) specialised game wardens, effective control of hunting is practically impossible. In many areas, such as many of the islands in the Cyclades, there are no game wardens at all and hence hunting there is actually not controlled. It is extremely difficult to evaluate in an objective and scientifically sound way the overall impact of hunting, both legal and illegal, on the birdlife of Greece. There are no bag statistics, virtually no other useful information and the subject has never been investigated in depth.

According to the *Red Data Book*, at least 33 bird species have been or are still affected negatively by hunting but with the extent and quality of existing data it is not possible to be absolutely certain of this. Tucker & Heath (1994) have also pointed out the difficulties of assessing the effect of hunting on bird populations on the European scale, though from both works it is quite clear that hunting and persecution are the second most common threat both in Europe and in Greece. Present day hunting has nothing to do with the old, traditional hunting for the pot: the greatly improved standards of living, increased leisure time, modern guns, a much larger number of cars and an ever improving and spreading network of roads mean that more and better equipped hunters penetrate into formerly remote and inaccessible areas.

Perhaps the best example of how much shotguns have affected birds in Greece is the case of raptors, especially the larger species. Full legal protection of all raptor species was introduced in Greece as late as 1979 (Decision no 180755/8-7-79; Min. of Agriculture), following more than a century of deliberate shooting and poisoning. Eagles and large falcons were among the main target of Man since Krüper's (1860) times: he reported that Golden Eagles were shot for a large reward. Such long-term persecution, certainly accelerated by habitat changes and other causes, was detrimental for the survival of several lowland species such as White-tailed and Imperial Eagle, which already in the first post war years had been exterminated over much of their former range (Bijleveld 1974, Vagliano 1977, Hallmann 1985a, Handrinos 1992b). Even today, large areas or even whole regions such as the Peloponnese and many large islands are devoid of eagles or other large raptors, even though there is suitable nesting and feeding habitat for them. It is certainly not a coincidence that these areas have on average higher densities of hunters than others.

Large waterbirds have also suffered from the long-term effects of hunting. Both pelican species were considered pests until as late as 1977 and during the 1950s and 1960s a premium was paid for killing them. Pygmy Cormorant and Great White Egret are still victims of illegal and indiscriminate shooting and this is one of the reasons for their decline (Jerrentrup *et al.* 1988). Large numbers of herons and Glossy Ibises were also shot during the spring hunting season, along with large numbers of other species which nowadays have small or declining populations (e.g. Roller and Bee-eater).

Since the late 1980s an indication of the impact of hunting has come from the Hellenic Wildlife Hospital, the only Greek NGO dedicated to the treatment and rehabilitation of wild birds and other animals. Their data show that from an average of 1,000 birds handled each year, a minimum of 60–70% are birds wounded or killed by shotguns, and that protected species (mainly diurnal and nocturnal birds of prey and large waterbirds such as swans, storks and herons) represent an average of 70% of all birds handled. Rates of arrival of new birds increase dramatically during periods of cold weather (when it is known that hunting also intensifies) and there is a clear correlation between the origin of wounded birds and hunting pressure, with a predominance of parts of the south and the islands where bird shooting is particularly popular.

Widespread use of airguns (illegal for bird shooting) by youngsters takes a heavy toll on smaller birds in inhabited areas and is one of the reasons for the decline of Lesser Kestrel in Aitolia (Roussopoulos & Pergantis 1994). Indiscriminate and unlicensed use of shotguns is another problem. Pelicans, Pygmy Cormorants and herons are still shot by fishermen in some wetlands and many shepherds would readily shoot an eagle when given the chance. In recent years there has also been a sudden increase in the use of tape recorders, ultra-sound devices, decoys and other attracting devices (all illegal) for hunting thrushes, Quail or other species, a practice which is locally becoming a serious problem.

One of the major problems with hunting is the disturbance it causes, often a more serious problem than the actual killing, particularly in areas or sites such as wetlands with dense concentrations of both hunters and birds. This is due to the fact that many such sites hold significant populations of a wide variety of species, both game and protected. Even when legally practised, hunting may severely interfere with daily activities of birds such as feeding and resting and may prevent them from using large areas of otherwise suitable habitat. At times of cold weather this disruption may significantly increase mortality rates. This was evident in the case of swans in 1985 (Jerrentrup & Handrinos 1987) and 1993 when large numbers died of starvation, primarily due to the icy conditions but with the situation made much worse by the presence of hunters who prevented them from feeding normally. Disturbance by wildfowlers is also a problem for Dalmatian Pelicans nesting in the Amvrakikos since the hunting season is still not over when nesting begins (D. Hatzilacou).

Recently lead-poisoning was investigated for the first time in Greece (in the Evros Delta). High ingestion levels (up to 53% for diving ducks) were recorded (Pain & Handrinos 1990). Lead-poisoning is a matter of concern not only for waterfowl but also for rare raptors such as White-tailed, Spotted and Imperial Eagles wintering in Greek wetlands and feeding on waterfowl containing lead either in the stomachs or in their flesh.

Trapping

The taking of birds with methods other than guns is a long tradition in Greece, which goes back to antiquity. Liming and trapping with nets was commonly practised by Ancient Greeks both for consumption and as a sport, their methods having apparently little changed since then (Pollard 1977).

In more modern times and before the spread of use of shotguns, trapping of birds for consumption was widely practised in certain areas, especially in the Mani peninsula (southern Peloponnese) and islands such as Santorini and Chios. The main target were Quail on their southward migration. These were pickled and kept in jars for consumption during the winter. In the Mani peninsula Quail were caught mainly with hand-held nets from mid August to mid October (Kassis 1980). Elsewhere, lime was widely used to catch Red-backed Shrikes and other passerines. Quantitative data from this period are lacking and it will never be known how many birds were taken annually using these methods. Bird (1935) reports that in the autumn of 1933, 15,000 Quail were killed in one day on the island of Syros alone, though he does not specify whether these were trapped, shot or both. Mass capture of migrating Quail and other birds largely died off in the early 1960s due to the decline of Quail populations, the introduction of modern shotguns and new legislation forbidding the use of all kinds of trapping devices for taking birds.

Until recently, the overall attitude of Greek people towards birds was not a particularly friendly one. Instead, birds, like other components of the environment, were mainly regarded as a resource for potential exploitation. Thus, besides the trapping of large numbers of migrating birds to complement an often protein-poor diet, over much of rural Greece it was common (and in many places still is) for children to kill and catch birds more as a pastime than for any other reason. Methods varied enormously and included a variation of the fall trap, using slabs of stone and a worm or olive as bait to kill thrushes, nooses, spring traps and frames covered with netting set so as to fall on birds feeding underneath.

Nowadays, over most of the country lime and rarely nets or other traps are used illegally on a small scale with the relatively benign purpose of trapping birds for cages. The three most popular species are Goldfinch, Greenfinch and Siskin but all species of finch and bunting, as well as Calandra Larks are regularly trapped. No one knows the total number of birds caught each year but there has definitely been a marked decline in recent years.

The situation on the island of Chios is very special and certainly worth mentioning. Capture of passerines during the autumn migration, mainly using lime, is a traditional activity on this island and has only recently come to light thanks to the efforts of local conservationists. It was found that practically all the villages in the southern part of the island were involved. The tradition goes back many centuries and the preparation of lime, from the fruit of the Assyrian plum *Cordia myxa*, is a family ceremony in which even young children participate. It has been estimated that up to 5,300,000 small birds may be trapped each autumn on Chios, particularly Goldfinches, Greenfinches, Willow Warblers and Blackcaps (Choremi & Spinthakis 1990, Spinthakis *et al.* 1993). Efforts to enforce the law have brought a slight improvement but tradition is hard to break and it will probably take many years before all trapping stops.

Poisoning

The use of poisoned baits to control populations of carnivorous mammals (wolves, jackals, foxes etc.) has been detrimental to raptor populations in Greece. The widespread use of strychnine on the mainland was practised officially by the Forestry Service for many decades and was not banned until 1981, when vulture and eagle populations in central and northern parts of the country had nearly collapsed (Hallmann 1985a, Handrinos 1985c). Since 1981, there has been effort to reduce the use of such baits (now containing cyanide) and in 1992 even stricter criteria and controls were introduced, with a tendency towards a complete ban. Nevertheless, there is still illegal use of poisonous baits, mainly by shepherds, and at least locally this is still a serious threat to vultures and large eagles. The extermination of a small, local population of Black Vulture from the Tempi Valley in the mid 1980s can be safely attributed to illegal poisoning (Hallmann 1992), whilst as recently as spring 1995, seven Black Vultures (*c.* 10% of the total Greek population) were found poisoned near Dadia Forest Reserve. One of the most important reasons that Crete still holds good populations of Lammergeier and Griffon Vulture, as well as Golden and Bonelli's Eagles, is certainly due to the fact that poisoned baits have never been used there as large carnivorous mammals do not exist on the island.

Damage Caused by Birds

Though not of immediate concern from the point of view of conservation of threatened species, damage caused by birds may at times be a serious problem, adversely affecting public opinion and hindering the application of conservation measures designed for other species.

The amount of damage caused by birds to crops has been a matter of debate between conservationists and hunters in recent years. The former argue, for example, that the damage done may be overestimated and that there is no excuse for widespread and uncontrolled hunting of possible pest species. The latter believe that many species formerly regarded as pests (e.g. Hooded Crow) and for the killing of which the Ministry of Agriculture would pay a bounty in the past, have increased and there is no reason to protect them. The truth is that neither side can present concrete evidence that significant damage is or is not done.

The commonest complaints by farmers include the consumption of fruit (e.g. cherries) by corvids, of olives by Starlings and of cereal grain by sparrows (House and Spanish). Less frequently geese are accused of damage, especially to winter cereals in the case of large flocks of White-fronts in winter and to bean fields in the case of the small resident population of Greylags of L. Mikri Prespa. Geese are nowadays so much reduced in numbers that problems caused by them can usually be solved easily by the application of local measures. Huge flocks of Starlings and sparrows have the potential to afflict serious damage to olives and cereals respectively but corvids are probably unjustly accused in most cases since all except Rooks and Jackdaws are rarely found in large enough numbers to do significant damage and only Jackdaws are present in Greece during the fruit production season.

Fish-eating birds are the only other group which may pose a threat to human interests. Generally, problems are localised but where they exist they may be serious. Pelicans were widely persecuted in the past and sometimes still are but even though, following protection, they have been increasing in recent years they are still too uncommon over most of their range to be a problem. Herons were also widely considered as competitors of fishermen but they rarely consume significant quantities of commercially important fish. Overall, it is Cormorants which seem to do most damage to commercially important fish stocks and as their wintering population has been speading and probably increasing in recent years complaints may be expected to become more frequent in the future.

LEGISLATION AND OTHER PROTECTION MEASURES

During the second half of the 19th century and until 1929 there was no specific legislation dealing with bird or wildlife conservation in Greece, except for a few obscure police or administrative rules and decisions regulating, for example, possession of shotguns. The first as far as known of such decisions was issued by the Police Department of Piraeus on 23 October 1849 and dealt with '...the protection of birds useful to agriculture...'.

The first hunting legislation came into force significantly later: Forestry Law No. 4173/29 was published in the Official Journal on 19 June 1929. It includes 15 articles (200–214) on hunting regulations. These were later (in 1939) incorporated into Law No. 1926/39, where the idea of protecting certain bird species against hunting was intoduced for the first time: the relevant article listed birds such as the swallows, Cuckoo and Nightjar, but even today it is very difficult to identify all the species on the list because common names were used and some were confusing or ambiguous. Nevertheless, the very same list was transferred to subsequent amendements and modifications of the hunting law, particularly the Forestry Code No. 86, issued in 1969. This list survived until 1976, when with two ministerial decisions a much longer list of protected species was adopted and this was further increased through two more decisions issued in 1977 and 1979.

Throughout this 60-year period the legal protection of birds was dominated by the concept of huntable and non-huntable species, with extremely few and vague provisions on habitat conservation. This situation changed drastically in 1985, when the 79/409/EEC Bird Directive was adopted (by the Joint Ministerial Decision 414985/85), so that today Greece shares the same bird protection legal framework with the other state-members of the European Union.

Moreover, Greece has ratified nearly all the international conventions relating to the conservation of birds and their habitats, including the Ramsar Convention, the Convention of International Trade in Endangered Species (CITES) and the Convention of European Wildlife and Natural Habitats (Bern Convention). Although so far implementation of most of them has not been very successful, the situation has gradually been improving, particularly since 1981 when Greece joined the then European Community.

Greece was among the first European countries to recognise the need for specially protected forested areas through provisions and regulations of the first Forest Code (Law 4173/1929). A few years later, the idea of preserving certain areas of outstanding beauty and natural interest was initiated by the Forest Service and the Hellenic Alpine Club, and in 1937 Law 856/1937 came into force, recommending the establishment of five National Parks. Mt Olympos was the first National Park to be established (1938) and since then, nine additonal ones have been established covering a total area of 95,000 ha (Kassioumis 1990). In the course of the last decades many more areas have been identified as important to nature conservation and have been designated as protected, although the actual legal status for most of them is both vague and complex. The latest and most advanced environmental legislation came into force in 1986 (Law 1650/1986).

The first effort to identify Greek sites of ornithological interest was carried out in the early 1980s and resulted in a list of 93 main and 43 additional (secondary) important bird areas (Hallmann 1982). This list was further improved through the CORINE project and later with support from ICBP, IWRB and RSPB culminating in the publication of Grimmett and Jones (1989). This last work lists a total of 113 Important Bird Areas for Greece and was recently translated into Greek by the Hellenic Ornithological Society (HOS 1994). Despite the need for updating, this list still remains a valuable source of data, both for conservation reasons as well as to those who would like to visit Greece for birdwatching. Unfortunately, inclusion of a site in this list does not automatically confer protection and does not have legal significance. Special legislation has to be passed for each site and up to now only a few of the 113 sites are protected.

According to Kassioumis (1990), who analysed in detail the whole set of protected areas in Greece, there are 99 areas designated as such which can be divided into six major categories. They cover a total surface of 360,000 ha or 2.72% of the total surface of Greece and this corresponds to 0.37 ha per thousand people (Table 8). Figure 12 shows the location of National Parks, Ramsar wetlands and a selection of Important Bird Areas which are of greatest interest to visiting birdwatchers.

Table 8. Summary of protected areas in Greece (Kassioumis 1990).

Type of protected area	No of areas	Area (in ha)
National Parks	10	95,000
Aesthetic Forests	19	35,000
Protected Natural Monuments	51	16,500
Hunting Reserves	7	10,500
Ramsar Wetlands	11	100,000
Others	2	105,000
TOTAL	99	360,000

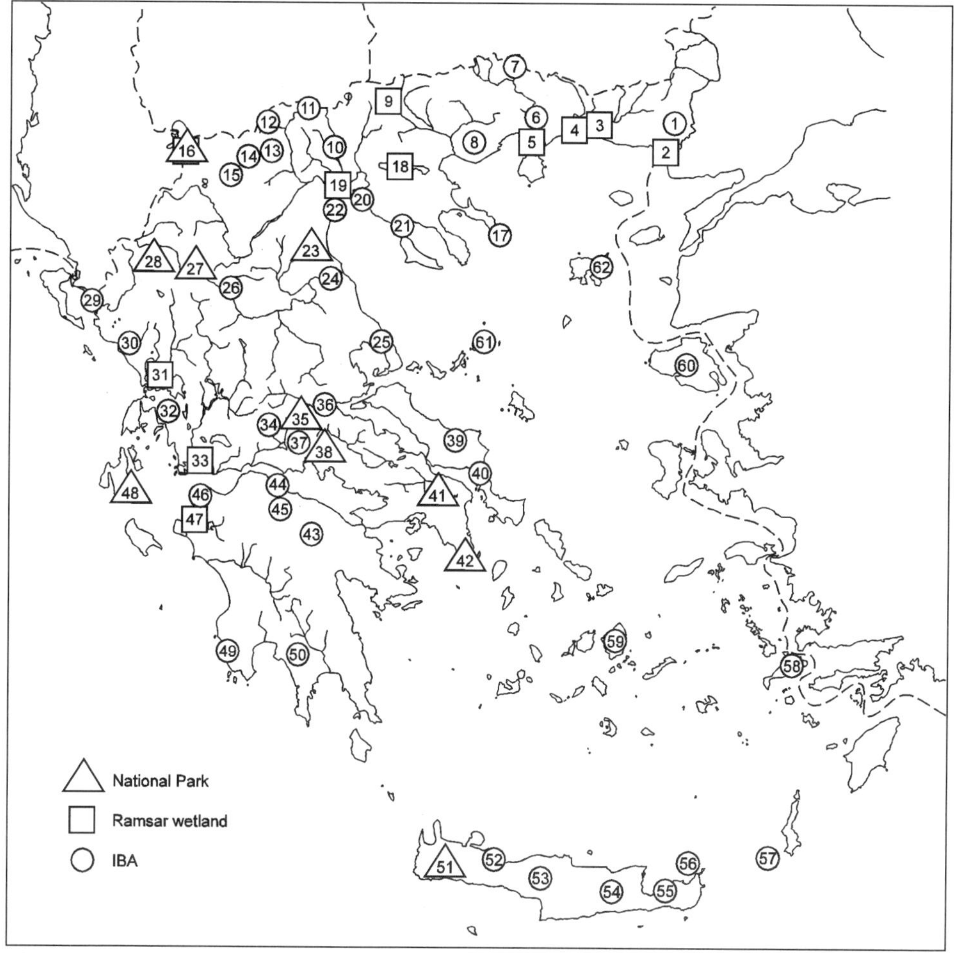

Figure 12. National parks, Ramsar wetlands and a selection of Important Bird Areas.

Key to Figure 12 (IBA numbers in brackets)

1 Dadia Forest Reserve (002)
2 Evros Delta (001)
3 L. Ismaris (Mitrikou) (003)
4 Porto Lagos, L. Vistonis and Thracian Lagoons (004)
5 Nestos Delta and Keramoti Lagoons (007)
6 Nestos Gorge (009)
7 Central Rodopi Mts (010)
8 Mt Pangaion (014)
9 L. Kerkini (012)
10 R. Axios (inland) (018)
11 Mt Tzena (028)
12 Mt Voras (029)
13 L. Agras (031)
14 L. Vegoritis and L. Petron (033)
15 L. Cheimaditis and L. Zazari (034)
16 L. Prespa (Lakes Mikri and Megali Prespa) (032)
17 Mt Athos (027)
18 Lakes Volvi and Koronia (022)
19 Axios, Loudias and Aliakmonas Delta (019)
20 Epanomi Lagoon (021)
21 Agios Mamas Lagoon (025)
22 Alyki Kitrous Lagoon (039)
23 Mt Olympos (040)
24 Mt Kato Olympos, Mt Ossa and Pineios Delta (048)
25 Mt Pilion (068)
26 Antichasia Mts and Meteora (045)
27 Pindos National Park (area of Valia Kalda) (044)
28 Vikos/Aoos National Park (Mt Tymfi and Mt Smolikas) (042)
29 Kalamas Delta (051)
30 Acheron Gorge and Delta (053)
31 Amvrakikos Gulf wetlands (055)
32 Akarnanika Mts (058)
33 Messonghi and Aitolikon Lagoons, Acheloos Delta (060)
34 Mt Vardousia (061)
35 Mt Oiti (064)
36 Spercheios Delta (065)
37 Mt Giona (062)
38 Mt Parnassos (063)
39 Mt Dirfys (071)
40 L. Dystos (072)
41 Mt Parnitha (088)
42 Cape Sounion National Park (not an IBA)
43 L. Stymfalia (081)
44 Aigion Lagoon (076)
45 Vouraikos Gorge (078)
46 Kalogria/Strofylia/Lamia Lagoons (075)
47 L. Kotychi (074)
48 Mt Ainos (not an IBA)
49 Divari Lagoon (Pylos or Yalova Lagoon) (084)
50 Mt Taygetos (083)
51 Samaria Gorge National Park (Lefka Ori) (091)
52 L. Kourna, Almyros Delta and beach of Georgioupolis (092)
53 Mt Idi (095)
54 Mt Dikti (099)
55 Mt Thrypti and Mt Ornon (100)
56 Dionysiades islands (101)
57 Island of Kasos (102)
58 Mt Dikios, Cape Louros and Psalidi Lagoon (112)
59 Mts Dias, Mavrovouni and Koronos (106)
60 Gulf of Kalloni (incl. Kalloni Saltpans) (109)
61 Outer Northern Sporades islands (107)
62 Chortarolimni and L. Alyki (108)

Management of national parks and other types of protected areas is, however, still far from satisfactory. As a result of an inflexible structure in the administration, there is still a lack of a special state nature conservation agency. The main authority charged with nature conservation and management of most protected areas has been the General Secretariat for Forests and the Natural Environment (Ministry of Agriculture) but in recent years (since 1986) the situation has become more complex because the Directorate for the Environment (Ministry of the Environment, Physical Planning and Public Works) has taken over the coordination of the overall implementation of environmental policies. This complicated and unclear system of administration has added difficulties to a situation already suffering from ineffectiveness, institutional difficulties, financial restraints, legal problems, lack of public awareness, deficiency of public involvement in the management of protected areas and often limited political commitment to conservation (Kassioumis 1990).

Lack of enforcement or ineffectual application of legislation relevant to the protection of birds or their habitats is still a principal problem. Even in protected areas and despite national and international legislation, the interests of birds are very often neglected, in favour of 'development' projects and other harmful actions. This is best illustrated by the case of Environmental Impact Assessments which, although obligatory since 1990, have so far been applied in such an inappropriate way that they are either ineffective or have the opposite effect to what was intended. As a rule, they have been used more as an excuse or cover-up, than as a potentially important means to minimise impacts from development projects.

Apart from legal and administrative measures, active management of bird populations is hardly practised. So far, the main efforts have focused on re-stocking the declining populations of certain game birds. Each year an average of 73,000 Chukars, 85,000 Pheasants and 7,500 Quail, all captive bred, are released into the wild both by the General Secretariat for

Forests and the Natural Environment (Ministry of Agriculture) and by Hunters' Clubs in an effort to reduce hunting pressure on wild populations and to establish viable populations in areas where these species were exterminated or have strongly declined.

A few other examples that could be mentioned, all on a much smaller scale, include the construcion of artificial nesting platforms for White Storks (carried out by the Public Power Corporation), the establishment of a feeding place for vultures in Dadia Forest Reserve (since 1989) and the experimental construction of new nesting sites for the Dalmatian Pelican or reinforcement of existing ones at Lakes Mikri Prespa and Kerkini.

In recent years, and especially since the early 1980s, protection of birds and their habitats has been greatly supported by international and national NGOs as well as by individual conservationists. Often working in an adverse environment and with serious constraints (financial, administrative etc.), organisations such as the Hellenic Ornithological Society and the Hellenic Birg Ringing Centre (the only Greek NGOs dealing solely with bird study and conservation), as well as the Hellenic Sosiety for the Protection of Nature, the Hellenic Wildilife Hospital, the Hellenic Zoological Society, WWF (Hellas), the Goulandris Natural History Museum, the Greek Biotope and Wetland Centre and several others have been active in this field. Their contributions range from basic research projects to educational campaigns and court actions and through a series of victories and setbacks they are gradually improving the overall situation regarding bird conservation in Greece.

BIRDWATCHING IN GREECE

Greece is nowadays one of the most popular tourist destinations in the Mediterranean. Each year an average of 10,000,000 tourists from all over the world come here to enjoy the sun, the sea, the numerous archaeological sites or historical monuments and, of course, the warm hospitality and friendliness for which Greeks have been famous since antiquity. The vast majority of these tourists rarely wander far from the beach allowing themselves no more than fleeting glimpses of the country itself. To those who are willing to walk off the beaten track the Greek countryside offers a rewarding experience. It is not known how many visitors come to Greece to enjoy nature in general, to photograph flowers or butterflies or to hike in the mountains but no doubt the majority of these eco-tourists are birdwatchers.

There are many reasons why Greece is an ideal place for birdwatching.

(a) Despite the increasing human encroachment and general degradation of its natural environment, it still holds large areas of undisturbed and unspoilt habitats, some of them in almost pristine state. Even though not all of them are full of birds, the natural and often wild landscape is appealing even to the most demanding of visitors. Moreover, due to the small size of the country and the rugged topography, one can very easily explore the birds of a coastal lagoon and those of an alpine meadow within the same day.

(b) There is a good number of bird species which are unusual, rare or even totally absent from western or northern European countries. Although many of them occur, often in larger numbers, in other adjacent countries, Greece is the only member state of the European Union in the eastern Mediterranean, so citizens of all EU member states enjoy advantages such as no need for visas, ease of currency exchange etc. Birdwatchers either travelling alone or in organised groups will find all types of accommodation, travel facilities and food quite readily available anywhere in the country and (as these lines are being written) at very reasonable prices. In some remote parts of the mainland and some faraway islands conditions may be rather primitive but this usually goes with a rich birdlife so on balance this is not necessarily a disadvantage.

(c) The Greek list of bird species today comprises 422 species and is increasing every year. During the last 25 years 44 new species have been added (16 of them are first published in this book) and almost all have been recorded by visiting birdwatchers. Although Greece is a small country, large areas are still unexplored by ornithologists, so the chances of making new discoveries are high, even during a short visit. Greece also hosts many races not present in western Europe, so for the most advanced birdwatchers or for those interested in studying subtle differences in plumage colours, voice etc., it is an ideal place. Besides birds, there is also a rich flora (6,000 species) and fauna in general, including butterflies and reptiles.

(d) With rare exceptions, the weather is excellent throughout the year, with clear sunny skies frequent even in the heart of winter, a great advantage for bird photography as well as observation.

What are the drawbacks that a visitor may face when on a birdwatching holiday in Greece? There are certainly some which are beyond control (such as unexpected weather or unwillingness of some birds to cooperate) but also some which can be dealt with reasonably easily, should the birdwatcher be patient and sensible enough to make an effort.

One of the major problems foreign (and Greek!) birdwatchers face when in Greece is the lack of road signs showing access to bird sites (lakes, marshes, gorges etc.). Even protected areas such as National Parks and Ramsar wetlands are very poorly or not at all signposted and though access to them through asphalted or reasonably passable unmade roads is relatively easy, time may be lost trying to locate the best way to reach them. However, for many of the best and most popular sites this is now a minor problem which can easily be overcome with a good map and some guidance by the locals (many Greeks, especially younger people, speak at least some English or German).

One should also pay attention to signs (usually in Greek and English) near military camps or bases prohibiting the use of cameras. This is particularly true for areas close to the borders, where military authorities may (on rare occasions) not even tolerate the use of binoculars, telescopes or very detailed maps.

Many foreign birdwatchers have commented on the fact that throughout the country the majority of birds are very shy and difficult to approach, thus presenting serious problems to bird photographers. Such behaviour is probably the long-term result of hunting and persecution, not only in Greece but in the whole of the wider region. Bird shooting is a popular activity in Greece so birdwatchers are advised not to lose their temper, even in cases where a hunter may spoil a pleasant afternoon's birdwatching.

It should be noted that birdwatching in Greece is a welcome, free and unrestricted activity (particularly since most of the land is state-owned). However, those interested in bird photography should be aware that Greek legislation (Joint Ministerial Decision No. 414985/85) does not allow disturbance of nesting birds, including photography or filming at the nest.

Finding Birds

Despite its ornithological importance, both in terms of species richness and habitats available, Greece still lacks a detailed book on how and where to watch birds. Details of the most important birding areas may be found in several books dealing with the subject on a European level (Nisbet 1975, Gooders 1970, 1988, 1994). Although containing little material on birds, some recent publications are quite useful for those interested in Greek nature, particularly mountaineers or trekkers: Adamakopoulos *et al.* (1986, 1988), Dubin (1993) or Tsounis and Sfikas (1993) are especially useful, the latter being the first guide of its kind to be published in Greece. Kautzky's excellent book on the Greek mainland is also recommended (Kautzky 1993). Nikos Petrou, one of the foremost Greek wildlife photographers, has published a lavishly illustrated book on Dadia Forest Reserve and another on L. Kerkini (Petrou 1994, 1995), both areas renowned for their birdlife, and these might interest those planning a visit these.

Very good descriptions of the best birdwatching sites are to be found in *Important Bird Areas in Europe* (Grimmett & Jones 1989). Although not a birdwatching guide, it is a very useful publication since it lists 113 Important Bird Areas in Greece with their coordinates, a brief habitat description and the most important species occurring in each one of them. However, it must be noted that (a) several of the areas listed are much less suitable for birdwatching than others for a number of reasons such as inaccessibility or due to the fact that they are only seasonally important, (b) that some of the sites included in the list no longer qualify as Important Bird Areas due to degradation and (c) that a few good sites (e.g. Tigkaki Lagoon on the island of Kos, a well known birdwatching site) are not included at all.

April is probably the best time of year to visit Greece. It is the peak of the migratory season and in addition to resident species, most of the summer visitors have already arrived and also some winter visitors may still be present May is better for some waders and for some passerines of southern distribution (e.g. *Hippolais* warblers and Black-headed Bunting). May, June and July are also better for higher altitudes whereas late March and early April may be best for many southern areas and islands for those with an added interest for wild flowers.

Finally, we would like to urge visiting birdwatchers to try new areas as well as the most popular and well known. Much of the country still remains ornithologically little known and such exploration can be both useful and exciting.

ABBREVIATIONS

The following abbreviations are used in the species accounts.

References

BoC	*Birds of Crete*	Parrott *et al.* (in press)
BWP	*Birds of the Western Palearctic*	Cramp (ed.) (1977–94)
CFG	*Catalogus Faunae Graeciae*	*Bauer et al.* (1969a)
CP	Costas Papaconstantinou	pers. comm.
RDB	*Red Data Book*	Handrinos (1992b)
VME	*Handbuch der Vögel Mitteleuropas*	Glutz *et al.* (1966–)
WIWO 90	WIWO Report: 1987 expedition to NE Greece	Meininger (1990)
WIWO 95	WIWO Report: 1990 expediton to Messolonghi	De Nobel (1995)

Other

IWRB MC IWRB Midwinter Counts

We use the term 'Messolonghi' to describe the whole wetland complex of the Messolonghi and Aitolikon Lagoons and the Acheloos and Evinos Deltas; the phrase 'Porto Lagos complex' for the coastal wetlands of the western part Thrace, i.e. from Lafri Lagoon, L. Vistonis and Porto Lagos in the west to Elos and Ptelea Lagoons and L. Ismaris in the east; 'the Amvrakikos' for the wetlands along the northern shores of the Amvrakikos Gulf.

Greece is a mountainous country with many spectacular massifs. Above: the summit of Astraka (2436 m) on Mt Tymphi, Ipeiros (T. Adamakopoulos); below: a typical alpine meadow in the northern Pindos range (N. Petrou).

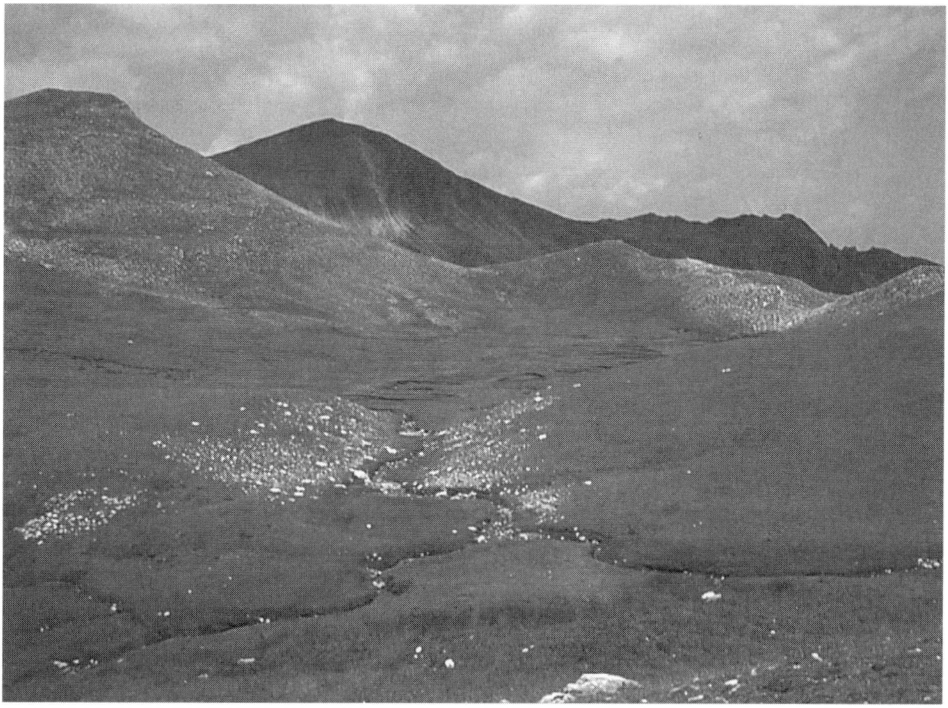

Two of the major forest types of Greece. Above: Greek Fir *Abies cephalonica* in Mt Oiti National Park (G.I. Handrinos); below: open deciduous oak *Quercus* woodland on Mt Ossa (G.I. Handrinos).

Two contrasting examples of montane forest in Greece. Above: the mixed primeval forests of the Rodopi Mts (K. Poirazidis); below: open *Juniperus* woodland on Mt Idi, Crete (G.I. Handrinos).

Wetland habitats in Greece. Above: flooded saltmarsh in the area of Messolonghi; below: reedbed with water lilies in the Louros Delta, Amvrakikos (both G.I. Handrinos).

Coastal wetlands are important breeding sites for many bird species. Above: Tsoukalio Lagoon in the Amvrakikos (G.I. Handrinos); below: Mediterranean Gulls at a colony in the Axios Delta (W. Makatsch).

Freshwater wetlands, a decreasing habitat, are very important for many breeding and wintering or migrating birds. Above: Lake Ismaris, Thrace, with Glossy Ibis (G. I. Handrinos); below: Spoonbill at Lake Kerkini (A. Limbrunner).

Most of the islands in the central Aegean are covered with low, xerophytic vegetation (phrygana). The island of Naxos (G.I. Handrinos).

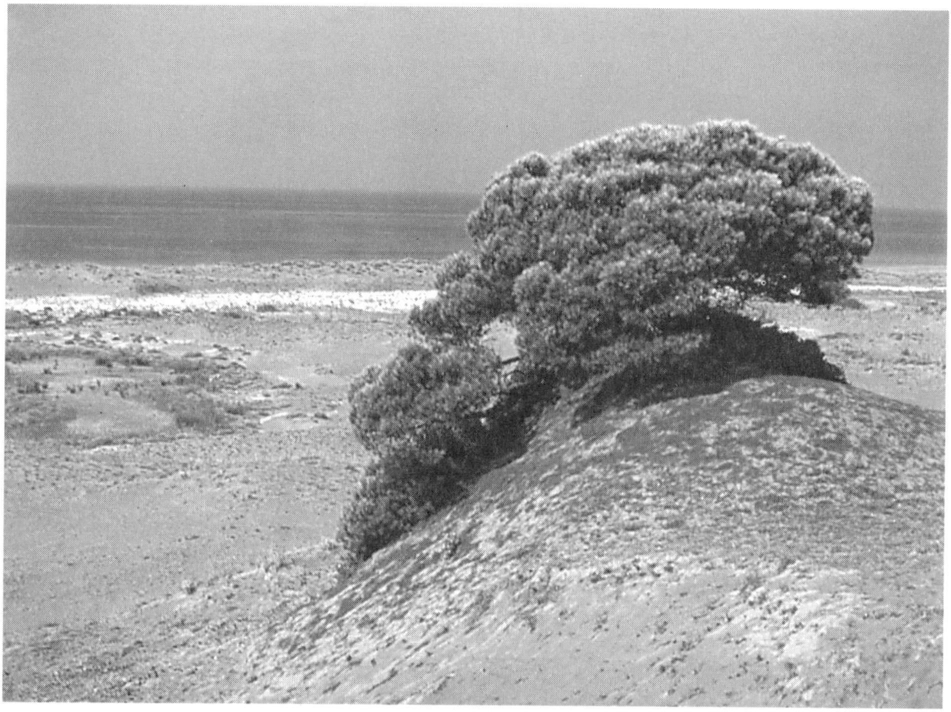

Some of the most extensive sand dune areas in Greece are found along the northwest coast of the Peloponnese (G.I. Handrinos).

Farmland is locally an important habitat for many bird species in Greece. Above: a traditional rural landscape in W. Macedonia; below: olive grove (both G.I. Handrinos).

Lake Mikri Prespa, NW Macedonia, is the only site in Greece and one of the very few in Europe where both European pelican species nest. Above: White Pelicans; below: Dalmatian Pelicans copulating (both J.-F. and M. Terrasse).

Lake Kerkini, Macedonia, has the largest breeding colony of Pygmy Cormorants in Greece (both A. Limbrunner).

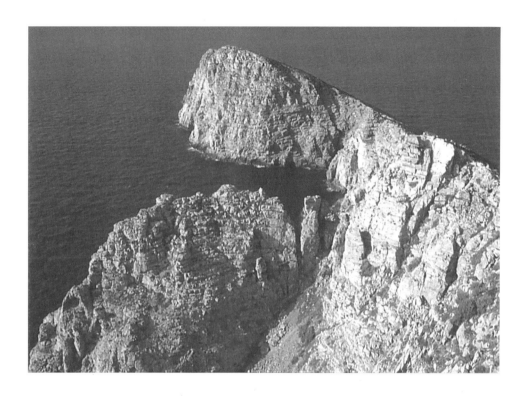

The Aegean Sea is the world's stronghold for breeding Eleonora's Falcons. Above: Typical nesting habitat, off Crete (G.I. Handrinos); below: light-phase adult (T. Schultze-Westrum).

Greece holds the largest breeding population of Audouin's Gull in the eastern Mediterranean. Above: Typical nesting habitat on a rocky islet (T. Schultze-Westrum); below: nest with eggs (W. Makatsch).

Greek wetlands attract large numbers of wintering waterfowl, including many uncommon and/or rare species. Above: four Bewick's Swans, Lake Kerkini, 23 January 1994; below: a mixed flock of White-fronted and Red-breasted Geese, Evros Delta, 3 March 1985 (both G.I. Handrinos).

Waders in Greece. Above: Curlew Sandpiper, a common passage migrant (R.J. Chandler); below: Spur-winged Plovers at a nest in NE Greece (A. Limbrunner).

Two of the rarest breeding birds of Greece. Above: White-tailed Eagle (A. Limbrunner); below: Glossy Ibis (J.-F. and M. Terrasse).

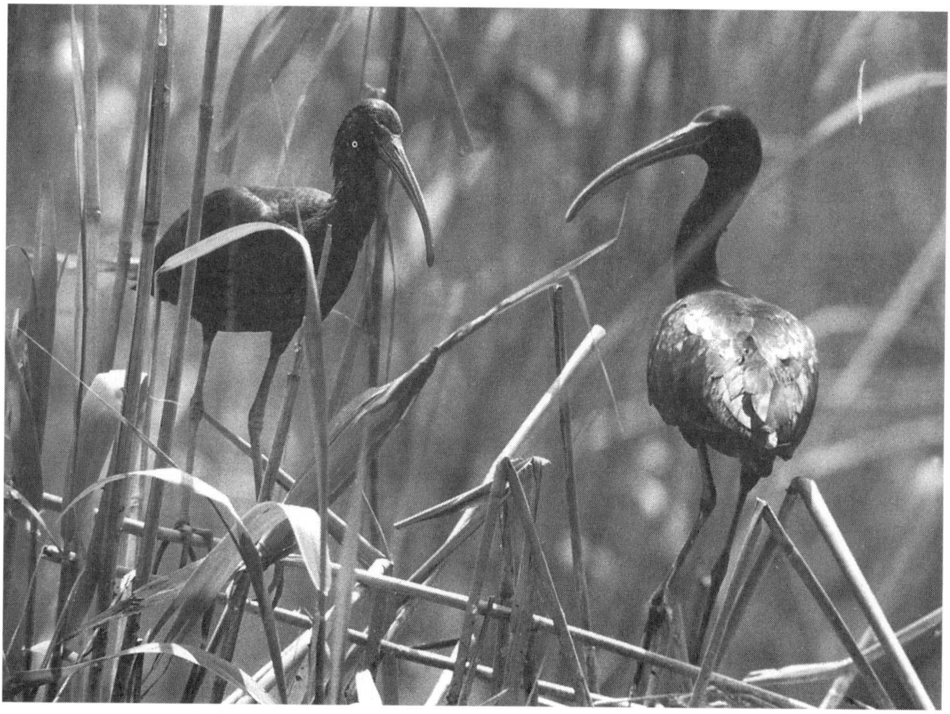

Greece is particularly rich in raptor species, including several with a restricted distribution in Europe. Above: Levant Sparrowhawk at its nest in northern Greece; below: a group of Griffon and Black Vultures in Dadia Forest Reserve, Thrace (both A. Limbrunner).

The first proof of Great Spotted Cuckoos nesting in Greece: Asvestochori, near Thessaloniki, 26 May 1978 (A. Limbrunner).

The first Capercaillie nest discovered in Greece: Mt Chaindou, near Xanthi, 22 May 1981 (D. Koukouras).

Masked Shrike at nest in an olive tree, NE Greece (A. Limbrunner).

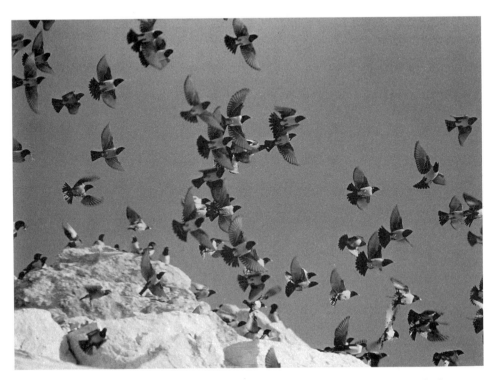

One of the first breeding colonies of Rose-coloured Starlings discovered in Greece. Vafiochori, Macedonia, 1987 (A. Limbrunner).

The first documented breeding attempt of Greater Flamingos in Greece. Two of the three eggs which had been laid are just visible. Messi Lagoon, Thrace, June 1992 (N. Petrou).

Prassoudha, off the east coast of Evvoia. A typical Greek rocky islet of the Aegean where the first nesting colony of Storm Petrels in the eastern Mediterranean was discovered in 1986 (G.I. Handrinos).

Two of the least common Greek passerines: Fan-tailed Warbler (above) and Rufous Bush Robin (below), both at Divari Lagoon, SW Peloponnese (both I. Makatsch).

Conservation problems of Greek birds. Above: dead passerines collected after aerial spraying of olive groves with insecticide on the island of Lesbos (P. Zouzis); below: Blackcap and Robin limed on the island of Chios (V. Spinthakis).

Greece offers many challenges to birdwatchers. Above: an adult male Pied Wheatear, a very rare recent breeding species in Greece (R.J. Chandler); below: Cream-coloured Courser, an accidental species, Kalogria Lagoon, NW Peloponnese, 21 April 1995 (L. Logothetis).

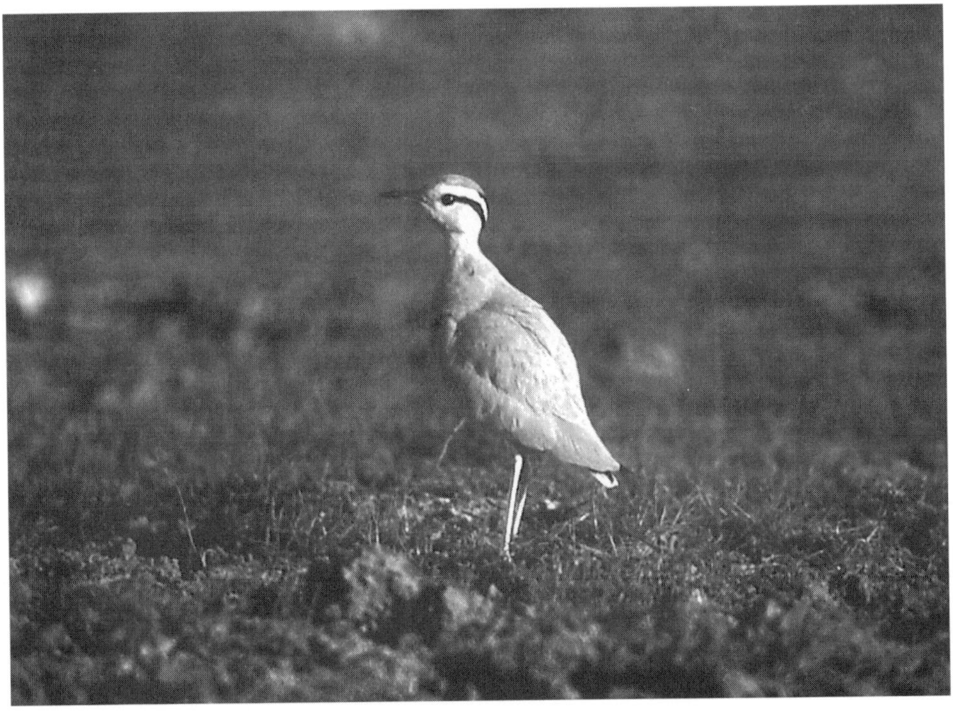

Red-throated Diver *Gavia stellata*

Fairly widespread but scarce winter visitor

In the past listed as an accidental (*BWP*) or very rare and irregular winter visitor (Lambert 1957), Red-throated Diver has in recent years turned out to be regular though scarce in winter. Since 1835, when first recorded off Chalkis (Lindermayer 1860), there have been about 40 published records, nearly all in winter. Most records come from the N Aegean coast, with half of all records from the Thracian coast, as well as a few from the coast of western Greece, south to the Aigion Lagoon in the Peloponnese, and only four records from inland (L. Doirani and L. Volvi). It has not been recorded on any of the islands, except for one at Tigkaki Lagoon (Kos) on 3 October 1975 (Kumerloeve 1977). Data from the IWRB MC (1982–1992) give an average of four birds, a maximum count of 17 (1991) and a maximum site count of 16, at L. Vistonis (13 January 1991). However, many more birds may be present each year on coasts outside those covered by the IWRB MC. Red-throated Divers are present in Greece mainly from November to March but the earliest record is on 3 October (see above) and the latest of four birds at Asprovalta on 4 May 1986 (S. Henning).

Black-throated Diver *Gavia arctica*

Fairly common but local winter visitor

Much commoner than Red-throated Diver, Black-throated is a regular visitor in winter. Data from the IWRB MC (1982–1992) give an average of 15 birds and a maximum count of 241 (1993), but many more birds are probably present outside areas covered by the counts. Black-throated Divers are usually recorded singly or in small parties (2–6), but on 17 January 1993 at least 231 birds were counted in less than 8 km of coastline just west of Kavala. In the same area, 38 were seen together on 22 January 1984 and at least 42 birds were present off the Kalamas Delta on 11 January 1992. Black-throated Divers winter mainly inshore and in coastal wetlands. The largest numbers are found in eastern Macedonia and Thrace, from Asprovalta eastwards to the Evros Delta, as well as in the Thermaikos Gulf and the larger wetlands on the Ionian coast, i.e. the Kalamas Delta, the Amvrakikos and the area of Messolonghi. They are less often recorded on inland freshwater lakes (e.g. L. Volvi, L. Kerkini, L. Prespa, L. Kastoria and L. Vegoritis). So far there is only one record from the Cyclades, on the island of Milos in March 1989 (Magioris 1992a) and none from Crete (*BoC*). Outside the strict winter period, Black-throated Divers have been recorded mainly in the spring, as late as mid May, and then they often turn up inland. Between 2 March and 9 May 1987 a total of 51 birds was recorded at sea off the wetlands of Thrace, with a maximum of 12 together (WIWO 90). Most of these were seen flying east, an indication of passage movement but probably mainly attributable to birds wintering in Greece since insignificant numbers winter south of the Mediterranean (*BWP*). There are also three summer records, one at L. Kastoria on 19 August 1972 (E. Callebaut), one immature off Kalochori on 19 July 1981 (Hendriks & Mölicker 1982), and two near Igoumenitsa on 12 June 1991. Three Black-throated Divers ringed in Sweden, Finland and Russia have been recovered in Greece in winter.

Great Northern Diver *Gavia immer*

Accidental

There are three records of Great Northern Diver, all in winter: two at L. Doirani on 20–21 November 1968 (Dangel 1973), two also at Doirani on 31 December 1969 (Johnson & Hafner 1970), and one immature seen in the harbour of Keramoti on 3 January 1994 (W. Laich).

Little Grebe *Tachybaptus ruficollis*

Widespread and locally common resident

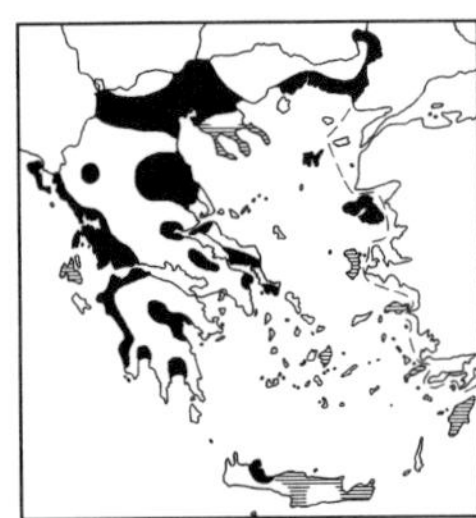

Little Grebes have a widespread breeding distribution on the mainland, wherever suitable habitat exists. They are the only species of grebe nesting on some of the larger Aegean islands: Corfu, Crete, Limnos, Lesbos and, at least in some years, on Naxos (S. Zoggaris). The population increases in winter, particularly during cold spells, presumably due to birds coming from further north in the Balkans or the rest of Europe. There appears to be no significant passage through the country, other than movements made by local birds or winter visitors. At all times of the year Little Grebes are found in freshwater habitats with plenty of emergent vegetation, and they regularly occur even in the smallest of wetlands which can hold no more than one breeding pair. In winter they frequently occur in more open situations, such as saline lagoons and sheltered bays and inlets on the coast next to lagoons or river mouths. In northern parts of the country Little Grebes are quite often observed on the coast when freshwater lakes and marshes freeze.

Great Crested Grebe *Podiceps cristatus*

Fairly widespread and locally common resident, common and widespread winter visitor

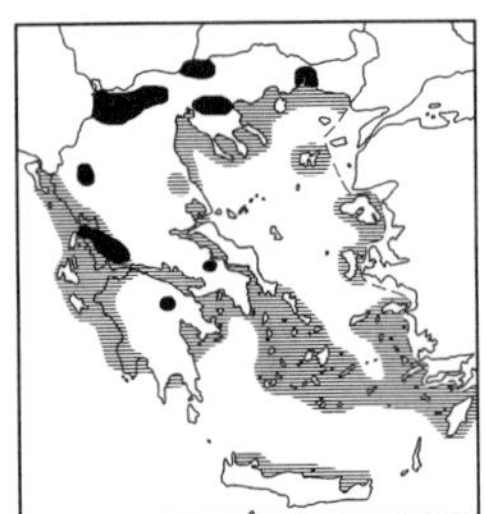

Great Crested Grebes nest in most freshwater wetlands of the country but they are regular and fairly numerous only in Macedonia and Thrace, where more suitable habitat exists. Elsewhere, breeding is in the form of relatively isolated populations, e.g. at L. Stymfalia in the Peloponnese, with *c.* ten pairs in 1994 (V. Spinthakis) and L. Paralimni in Sterea Hellas, with one or two pairs in some years. The size of the total breeding population is not known but on some lakes they are quite numerous, e.g. there are about 30 pairs breeding on the small L. Zazari in NW Macedonia.

The species is much more widespread and common in winter. Small numbers occur on almost all shallow coastlines and larger concentrations form on lakes and lagoons. Data from the IWRB MC (1982–1992) give an average of 13,700 birds, but since they also commonly occur on sea coasts, not covered by the MC, the total wintering population may be 25% or even 50% larger. The maximum IWRB MC was in 1990, with at least 21,100 birds, of which at least 15,000 were at L. Volvi alone. This lake is the most important site for the species, regularly holding large wintering concentrations, e.g. 11,000 in 1984, 10,000 in 1982 and 9,080 in 1985.

Red-necked Grebe *Podiceps grisegena*

Former breeding species, now rare and local winter visitor

Red-necked Grebes used to breed in the Nestos Delta up to the early 1960s, but following drainage and land reclamation over much of the area, this small breeding population (*c.* ten pairs) ceased to exist (*CFG*; *BWP*). A recent record of a pair possibly nest-building at L. Ismaris (8 May 1991) (P. Atkinson), suggests that perhaps isolated pairs may still nest occasionally in NE Greece. Today the species is recorded only as a winter visitor from November onwards, with birds frequently staying as late as the end of April. There are five records in August but none in the other summer months. The great majority of records are from E Macedonia and Thrace, from Asprovalta eastwards to the Evros Delta, particularly the Nestos Delta and the L. Vistonis/Porto Lagos complex. There are few records from the Ionian coast (Amvrakikos, Aitolikon and Araxos Lagoons). Data from the IWRB MC (1982–1992) give a national average of 12 birds. The maximum site count is of 66 at Aitolikon Lagoon on 18 January 1986 (Joensen *et al.* 1987), a doubtful record since such large numbers have never been recorded, even in NE Greece, and the species has never been recorded on any offical counts at that site. Wintering Red-necked Grebes frequent mainly inshore coastal waters and brackish coastal lagoons.

Slavonian Grebe *Podiceps auritus*

Widespread but rare winter visitor

Although probably overlooked among the tens of thousands of Black-necked Grebes wintering in Greece, Slavonian Grebes are certainly very rare winter visitors, with a limited distribution. First recorded on 8 May 1962 at Porto Lagos (Raines 1962) with, since then, fewer than 20 records, almost all from winter (November to February), and only one earlier in the autumn, on 30 September 1977 also at Porto Lagos (Magerl & Francis 1979). Most of the records are from the coastal wetlands of Macedonia and Thrace but there also exist three inland records from L. Koronia, L. Mikri Prespa and L. Volvi in Macedonia, and three from western Greece, two from the Amvrakikos and one from the Aigion Lagoon (D. Papandropoulos). All Greek records refer to single birds.

Black-necked Grebe *Podiceps nigricollis*

Common and widespread winter visitor, rare and irregular breeding species

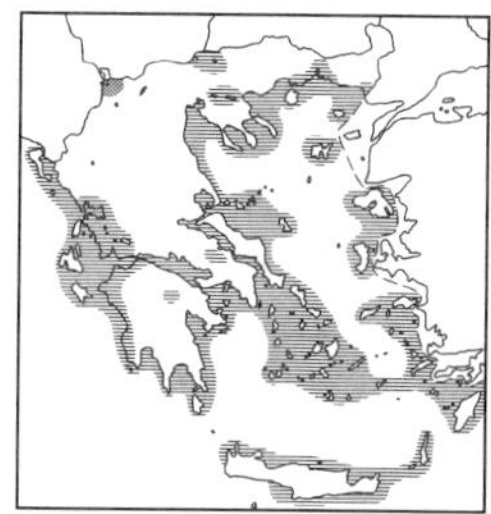

Black-necked Grebe is one of the commonest waterbirds in Greece in the winter, particularly in the major coastal wetlands of Thrace, Macedonia and Ipeiros, where it is locally very common. It also winters on the coast of practically the whole mainland and most islands both in the Aegean and the Ionian Seas. It is found mainly in shallow waters on the coast and in coastal lagoons or lakes, and less often on fresh water far from the sea. Data from the IWRB MC (1982–1992) give an average of 2,500 birds, (maximum 5,754 in 1989) but the total wintering population is very much higher as birds are present in large numbers outside counted areas. Wintering populations are present in Greece mainly from early November to early April and in smaller numbers to early May. In the L. Vistonis/Porto Lagos complex, regular coverage throughout the spring period showed maximum numbers in early April (a peak of 5,621 at L. Vistonis on 2 April 1987), with a lot of birds still present up to late April and numbers declining rapidly in May (WIWO 90). However, the early April peak does not necessarily suggest spring migration and may well be explained by the shift of birds wintering along the coastline to a freshwater habitat as the breeding season draws closer.

Black-necked Grebe has been listed as a breeding species in Macedonia and Thrace (Raines 1962; Lambert 1957; *CFG*) but in fact the only site where breeding has been reported at all regularly in recent decades is L. Mikri Prespa. Here nesting was first confirmed in 1972 (five adults with three young seen) (Géroudet 1973) and the species is today described as an occasional breeder with 3–10 pairs (G. Catsdorakis). A few pairs are present annually in some freshwater wetlands (e.g. L. Ismaris, L. Kerkini, L. Vistonis and Kalodiki marsh in recent years). Although there is no proof of breeding from such areas yet, they may occasionally do so, e.g. one pair with nest was found at L. Pikrolimni, Kilkis, on 25 May 1984 (Hölzinger 1992e). The species has also been seen at L. Stymfalia (Peloponnese) in late August 1987 (CP), where it probably bred in the past (*CFG*).

Cory's Shearwater *Calonectris diomedea*

Widespread and locally common summer visitor

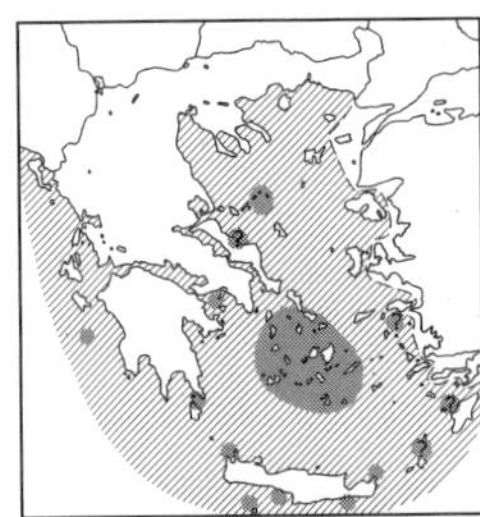

Although common in both the Ionian and the Aegean Seas, Cory's Shearwaters remain rather poorly known. The total population breeding in Greek territory has been tentatively estimated at *c.* 5,000 pairs (Tucker & Heath 1994), of which 900 pairs are found on the Dionysiades islets off NE Crete (D. Ristow). Since the 1970s this Cretan colony has been extensively studied by Dr D. Ristow, Prof. M. Wink and their colleagues. Thanks to their work many aspects of the breeding biology and ecology of the species have come to light: at the Dionysiades colony eggs are laid at the end of May; the chicks fledge in about 90–100 days, i.e. by mid October, and most birds have left the colonies by late October. Ringing has shown a high degree of site fidelity. Young birds return to their breeding colony at the age of three or four years and begin nesting at the age of five to seven years (see e.g. Ristow & Wink 1980; Ristow *et al.* 1990; Ristow *et al.* 1991; Wink *et al.* 1982c).

Cory's Shearwaters are mainly summer visitors to Greek waters. They are present mainly from mid March to late October but small numbers may be seen also during winter, e.g. two off Cape Sounion on 8 November 1991, three off Piraeus on 11 November 1989, and flocks of up to 80 birds off Chalkis in late December 1980 and 1982. There are very few data on their migratory movements but at the western end of the Gulf of Corinth more than 80 birds per hour have been recorded passing in April (CP). The largest number ever recorded in Greece is of *c.* 2,500 birds off Gouves, N Crete, on 22 April 1989 (*BoC*).

Mediterranean Shearwater *Puffinus yelkouan*

Common and widespread resident

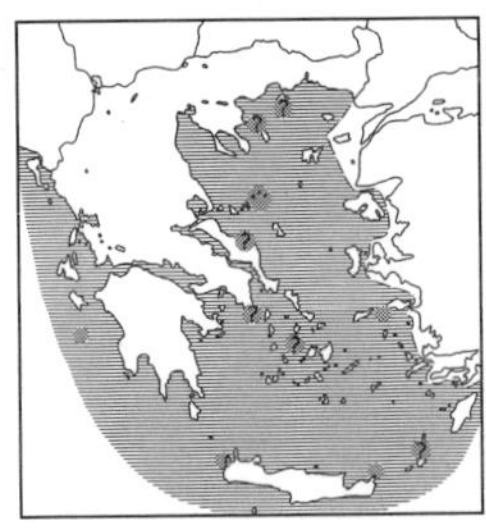

Mediterranean Shearwaters can be seen all year round in Greek waters, but remain a very poorly known species: their breeding population and range are even less well known than those of Cory's Shearwater and their overall pattern of occurrence is still not fully understood. As a breeding species they appear to be much less common and more localised than Cory's Shearwaters, although their population is extremely difficult to estimate. They breed in the Aegean Sea, where the bulk of the population is found, and also in the Ionian Sea, where they are much less numerous. During the breeding season they are often seen in the vicinity of groups of small islands such as the Northern Sporades, the Cyclades, and the Saronikos and Argolikos Gulfs, e.g. 'a few thousand' were seen between Serifos and Sifnos on 28 June 1983 (Dragoumis 1984). All of these areas (and many more) are potential breeding sites.

The species is more numerous during spring migration, from early March to early May, with peak numbers usually at the end of March and early April, e.g. *c.* 2,500 off Cape Sounion on 3 April 1977 (P. de Fraine), *c.* 1,500 off Siteia on 29 March 1991, *c.* 2,500 off Aposelemis river mouth, N Crete, on 22 April 1984 (*BoC*) and flocks of 5 to 100 birds (probably well over 2,000 in total) moving south along the Aegean coast of Evvoia on 19 April 1980. A further remarkable record is of *c.* 4,000 birds (the largest number ever recorded in Greece) off Asprovalta on 2 May 1984 (S. Hayhow). In winter they are recorded in small parties or larger flocks mainly in central and northern parts of the Aegean, less often farther south, e.g. there are only two winter records from Crete (*BoC*). The Strymonikos Gulf (from Asprovalta east to Kavala) seems to be particularly attractive as a winter feeding area. The Balearic race *P. y. mauretanicus* also occurs in Greek waters, but so far there are only two documented records: 'some' among *c.* 1,000 *P. y. yelkouan*, off the Nestos Delta and Porto Lagos from 12 November to 14 December 1976 (P. Doherty), and four *c.* 10 km NW of Patras on 26 September 1990 (CP). One adult male shot off the island of Karpathos on 22 September 1963 has been claimed as a Manx Shearwater *Puffinus puffinus* (formerly *P. p. puffinus*) (Kinzelbach & Martens 1965). The specimen was measured and identified at the Zoological Museum A. Kønig, Bonn, but its identification is very doubtful since the separation of single *P. puffinus* from *P. yelkouan* is extremely difficult, many of the latter being almost identical to *P. puffinus* (Reiser 1905; *CFG*; *BWP*; J. Borg *per* R. Ristow). So far, there is only one ringing recovery of Mediterranean Shearwater, an adult bird ringed in Malta in May and found dead on the coast of Attica in July of the same year.

Storm Petrel *Hydrobates pelagicus*

Rare and local summer visitor

Storm Petrel was first recorded in Greece in the 19th century, when 'several' were seen off Crete on 19 June 1843 (Drummond-Hay 1843b). Since then there have been fewer than 30 records, mainly of single birds, and all but one, which was recorded off the coast of Ipeiros in December 1857 (Powys 1860), from May to September. Almost all records are from the Aegean Sea, from Crete northwards to Thasos, but mainly in the Cyclades and particularly around the island of Paros. There is only one 20th-century record from the Ionian Sea.

Breeding of Storm Petrels in Greece was first confirmed in 1982, when a small party of hunters and fishermen found eggs and chicks on Prassouda, a small rocky islet off the east coast of Evvoia. Nesting was confirmed again in 1983 (Akriotis & Handrinos 1986) but no visits have been attempted to this islet since then and the size of the colony has not yet been assessed. The migration and patterns of seasonal occurrence of Storm Petrels in Greece are still poorly known, as they are for the whole of the eastern Mediterraneann (*BWP*; Akriotis & Handrinos 1986). There is a lack of winter records from Greek waters suggesting that the entire population winters elsewhere, although the Aegean is then much less frequently visited by people likely to notice them. Since many of the Greek records are of birds seen during the breeding season (May to early August) and suitable nesting habitat is readily available in both the Aegean and the Ionian Seas, it is very probable that more colonies are yet to be discovered in Greece (Akriotis & Handrinos 1986).

Gannet *Sula bassana*

Rare and irregular winter visitor and passage migrant

Since May 1853, when two juvenile birds were seen in the Cyclades (Erhard 1858), Gannets have been recorded fewer than 20 times. Most records are from May to mid June and from early August to mid September, with single records from December, January, early March and April. In the majority of cases single birds in juvenile, immature and sub-adult plumage have been seen. Adult birds have been seen only on three occasions. The geographical distribution of records does not produce any clear pattern, and although most of them are from the Aegean, there is a cluster of seven records from the central Ionian islands and the Patraikos Gulf. The seasonal distribution of records suggests birds on passage or non-breeding birds spending part

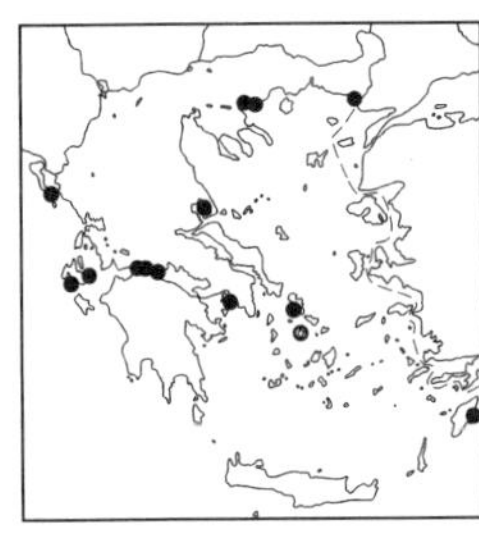

of the summer in Greek waters but this pattern could also be due to observer bias towards the summer half of the year. The picture is far from clear and Gannets may in fact be much more common than existing records suggest (Paterson 1993), and western Greece may be on the edge of their normal wintering range (CP). The species is recorded almost annually in recent years, which can be attributed both to increased observer activity and to the continuous increase of the breeding population of the species in western Europe (*BWP*).

Cormorant *Phalacrocorax carbo*

Fairly widespread and locally common resident, common and widespread winter visitor

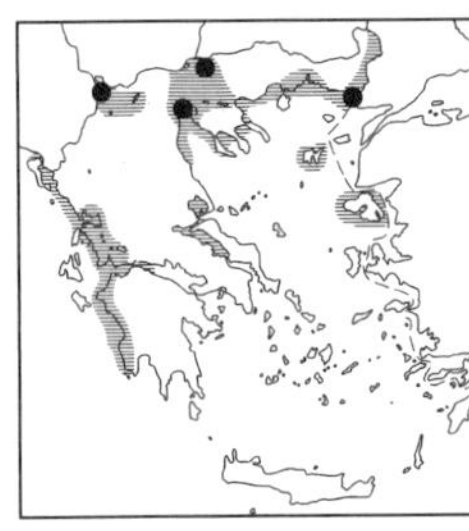

Cormorants were first proved to breed in Greece in 1944, when a small colony of six pairs was discovered in the Axios Delta (Makatsch 1950). However, the species was possibly breeding at L. Artzan and L. Doirani already before the Second World War (Sladen 1918; Makatsch 1950). In 1971 there were only two known colonies (at L. Mikri Prespa and the Evros Delta), with a total population of 540–570 pairs (*BWP*), whilst in the early 1990s there were four colonies, all in Macedonia and Thrace, with *c.* 600 pairs. Thus the total population appears to have remained stable in recent times. However, in 1995 the L. Kerkini colony had increased to 900–1,000 nests.

Cormorant is much more widespread and numerous in the winter, occurring not only in wetlands on the mainland but, in small numbers, also along the coast of much of the mainland and the larger islands. In winter, it frequents both inland and coastal lakes, lagoons and rivers, as well as sheltered bays and shallow marine waters. Data from the IWRB MC (1982–92) give an average of 5,900 birds (counted in the main wetlands only), a maximum of 12,200 in 1983 and a maximum site count of 6,000 in the Evros Delta on 5 February 1988 (Handrinos 1993b). L. Kerkini, the L. Vistonis/Porto Lagos complex and the Nestos Delta hold a large proportion of the wintering population, with the Evros Delta and the area of Messolonghi also attracting significant numbers (Handrinos 1993b). The species seems to have become more widespread in recent years, reaching further south and spreading to a wider variety of habitats than used to be the case up to the mid 1980s. A total of 10,000 birds counted at L. Karla (now drained) on 22 March 1939 (Dathe & Profft 1940) is the highest number ever recorded in Greece. There are 41 recoveries of foreign-ringed Cormorants in Greece so far. Most had been ringed in Denmark (9), the Ukraine (8) and Germany (7), with fewer from Sweden, Estonia, Poland, the Czech Republic, Hungary, Moldavia, Croatia and Yugoslavia. Cormorants nesting and wintering in Greece belong to the continental race, *P. c. sinensis*.

Shag *Phalacrocorax aristotelis*

Fairly common and widespread resident

Shag is not a very well known species and its numbers and distribution in Greek waters still remain largely unknown (*RDB*). By far the largest numbers breed in the Aegean Sea, where the species is widely but rather thinly distributed from Thasos and Thasopoula in the north, south to the Dodecanese and Crete. In the Ionian, Shags are scarce and very local, breeding at a few scattered localities on or around Kefallinia, Ithaki and Zakynthos (D. Papandropoulos, A. Panou; CP). Most breeding sites are on inaccessible steep slopes, sea-cliffs and uninhabited rocky islets. The size of the Greek population is very difficult to assess. In the northern part of the Dodecanese alone there are thought to be *c.* 70 pairs (Papaconstantinou *et al.* 1995) and around the island of Lesbos, where it is fairly common, there are at least 15 pairs. The species has been listed as 'vulnerable' in the past (*RDB*) and the total breeding population estimated at 200–400 pairs (Tucker & Heath 1994). This estimate now seems too low and there may if fact be over 1,000 pairs. In winter and outside the breeding season Shags, particularly immature birds, disperse along the coasts but they are still largely confined to rocky coasts, not far from their breeding sites. Shags breeding in Greece belong to the Mediterranean race, *P. a. desmaresti.*

Pygmy Cormorant *Phalacrocorax pygmeus*

Scarce and local resident, locally common winter visitor

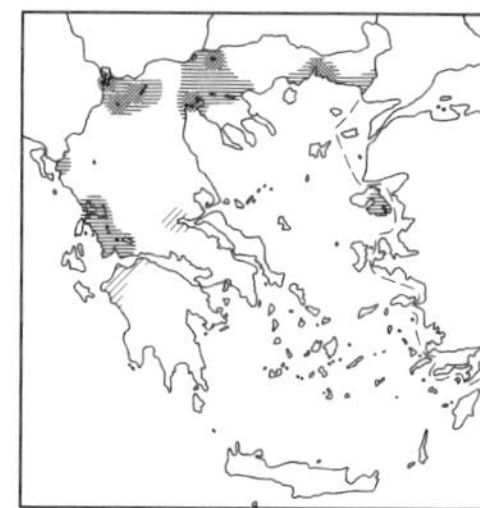

Listed in the past as a fairly common winter visitor (Lambert 1957, Raines 1962), Pygmy Cormorant was first discovered breeding in Greece in 1967, at L. Kerkini and L. Ismaris (Kraus *et al.* 1969), as well as in the Evros Delta (Bauer & Müller 1969), with a total population of *c.* 120 pairs. In the mid 1970s, there were five colonies with *c.* 500 pairs in total, the majority of them at L. Mikri Prespa, which alone held up to 650 pairs in 1971 and 400 pairs in 1973 (*BWP*). In the 1960s Pygmy Cormorants ceased breeding at a few sites (e.g. the Evros and Axios deltas), following drainage, but recently they have been found breeding irregularly at L. Petron, L. Kastoria and Porto Lagos (G. Catsadorakis). In 1993, the total Greek population was 557–590 pairs, mainly at L. Mikri Prespa and L. Kerkini (Naziridis & Papageorgiou in press).

Pygmy Cormorants are much more widespread and numerous in winter though again restricted mainly to Thrace and Macedonia, being very rare in western and southern Greece, and normally not reaching further south than the area of Messolonghi. Data from the IWRB MC (1982–92) give an average of 2,640 birds, a maximum count of 5,626 in 1986 and a maximum site count of 4,200 at L. Kerkini, on 15 January 1984. At L. Kerkini, however, maximum numbers are usually recorded in November to early December, outside the counting period in January (T. Naziridis). This lake, together with the L. Vistonis/Porto Lagos complex and the Nestos Delta, are the key wintering sites for Pygmy Cormorant in Greece (Handrinos 1993b). Most winter visitors arrive from early November onwards and leave between late March and mid April, a few birds remaining until early May. At L. Kerkini, birds arrive at their breeding colonies in mid March (T. Naziridis). In autumn small flocks have been seen in some of the wetlands of NW Peloponnese (Araxos and Kotychi lagoons) (CP). Only stragglers reach most of the Aegean islands, with only four records from the Northern Sporades and Cyclades (*CFG*, Magioris 1987a) and two records from Crete (*BoC*). Nevertheless, small numbers winter regularly on Lesbos. So far there are only four ringing recoveries of Pygmy Cormorants in Greece, all ringed in the Danube Delta and found in Macedonia and Thrace in winter (Handrinos 1993b).

Pygmy Cormorants

White Pelican *Pelecanus onocrotalus*

Scarce and local summer visitor and passage migrant

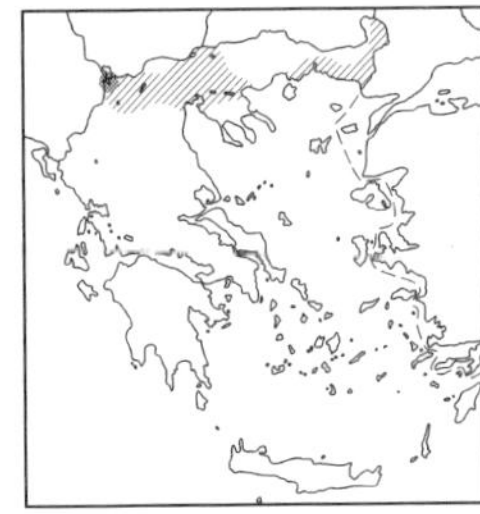

Nesting of White Pelican in Greece was first confirmed in 1968, at L. Mikri Prespa, when *c.* 35 adults and at least two chicks were seen (Brosselin & Molinier 1968), but probably the species bred earlier at this site (Bodenstein & Kroymann 1967). L. Mikri Prespa is still the only nesting site of the species in Greece, with a population of 40–150 pairs (Crivelli *et al.* 1991b; Hatzilacou 1992) and a maximum of 210 pairs in 1981 (Cramp 1983). Since 1983 this colony has been extensively studied and many data on the breeding biology and feeding ecology of the species have been collected (Hatzilacou 1992; Crivelli *et al.* 1991b). White Pelicans arrive at the breeding colony from mid March onwards, but mainly in April. Most eggs hatch in late May to early June, after a 31-day incubation period. The fledging period lasts 11–12 weeks and brood size is 0.50–0.73 chicks/breeding attempt (Hatzilacou 1992). White Pelicans nesting at L. Mikri Prespa feed not only on this lake but also fly long distances, sometimes more than 100 km daily, to feed elsewhere in western and central Macedonia, e.g. L. Kastoria, L. Cheimaditis, L. Kerkini and the Axios Delta (Crivelli 1984; Hatzilacou 1992, 1995; Pyrovetsi 1989).

On spring passage, White Pelicans are more widespread and can be seen in all the major wetlands of Thrace and Macedonia, in varying numbers. Such birds are presumably heading for the large colonies in the Danube Delta. On 23 April 1968, at least 1,200 were counted in the Evros Delta (Bauer & Müller 1969), the largest number ever recorded in Greece. Much smaller numbers are usually seen today, with flocks not normally exceeding 100 birds. On autumn passage the species is more numerous and up to several hundred birds may be seen together (e.g. at least 850 at L. Kerkini in October 1994). In autumn the species is also more widespread and a few stragglers regularly appear on the coast of some Aegean islands such as Lesbos, Rhodes, the Cyclades and Crete. Such birds are frequently caught and tamed, and act as a tourist attraction. Very few birds (the maximum is 16 at L. Kerkini in 1993) occasionally winter in Greece. The wintering areas of White Pelicans breeding in Greece and other breeding areas in the Western Palearctic are still not known (*BWP*; Crivelli *et al.* 1991b) but are believed to be in southern Sudan and/or Ethiopia (Crivelli *et al.* 1991b).

White Pelicans

Dalmatian Pelican *Pelecanus crispus*

Fairly common but local resident

During the 19th century and the first decades of the present century, Dalmatian Pelicans were reported nesting at several wetlands throughout the country, such as L. Giannitsa (now drained), L. Artzan (now drained), the Axios Delta, the coast of Ipeiros, the area of Messolonghi, the Pineios Delta (Peloponnese), and possibly even in Attica (Elwes & Buckley

1870; Powys 1860; Reiser 1905; Sladen 1918; Laubmann 1927; Simpson 1860c; *CFG*). As late as 1962, 40–50 pairs were still nesting in the Evros Delta but this colony was later destroyed by local fishermen (Bauer & Müller 1969). Today, Dalmatian Pelicans nest only at two sites: L. Mikri Prespa, where breeding was first confirmed in 1968 (Brosselin & Molinier 1968), and the Amvrakikos, where 18–20 pairs were first found nesting in 1967 (Bauer *et al.* 1969b), though this colony probably existed as early as 1857/58 (Powys 1860). The total Greek population (1990–93) is estimated at 200–260 pairs (Tucker & Heath 1994), with an average of 162 pairs at L. Mikri Prespa (1983–93) and of 37 pairs in the Amvrakikos (1987–91) (Crivelli *et al.* 1991c; G. Catsadorakis, D. Hatzilacou). Since 1990 the population at L. Mikri Prespa has been increasing, with a record number of *c.* 400 pairs in 1994 (G. Catsadorakis).

The species is now subject to detailed, long-term studies ('International Pelican Research and Conservation Programme', see e.g. Crivelli 1980, 1987; Crivelli & Vizi 1981; Crivelli *et al.* 1991c). The first adults arrive at their nesting sites in early February but most arrive in mid March. The mean first egg date is 7 March (L. Mikri Prespa) and 2 March (Amvrakikos), the incubation period averages 31.4 days, the fledging period is 12–13 weeks and the mean brood size is 0.86–1.03 chicks/breeding attempt (Hatzilacou 1992). By mid September the majority of birds have left the nesting colonies. In winter, Dalmatian Pelicans may be found in most of the major wetlands of Thrace, Macedonia and Ipeiros, as far south as NW Peloponnese and the Spercheios Delta. L. Kerkini, the complex of L. Vistonis/Porto Lagos and the Amvrakikos are of primary importance for the wintering population. Data from the IWRB MC (1982–1992) give an average of 421 birds, a maximum count of 705 in 1983 and a maximum site count of 470, at L. Kerkini, on 23 January 1983. In the winter of 1995 a total 1,260 birds was counted in the whole country.

There is still little published information on the distribution of Dalmatian Pelicans during both spring and autumn migration. In the Porto Lagos area, between 1 March and 21 May 1987, a maximum of 220 birds was counted on 15 March (WIWO 90), whereas there are records of 600 in the Evros Delta in mid August 1962 (Raines 1962), 600 at L. Kerkini in October 1980 (Hallmann 1981) and a remarkable count of 1,200, also at L. Kerkini, on 3 October 1994, the largest number ever recorded in Greece. During winter dispersal or migratory movements Dalmatian Pelicans are occasionally recorded singly or in very small numbers on some of the Aegean islands such as Lesbos and Crete. Ringing has shown that Dalmatian Pelicans from Bulgaria winter in Greece and Turkey and that some birds of Greek origin also move to Turkey in winter (Crivelli 1987).

Dalmatian Pelican

Bittern *Botaurus stellaris*

Widespread but scarce winter visitor and passage migrant

There is no definite proof that Bitterns have ever bred in Greece. Sladen (1917) listed the species as comparatively common in the Axios floodplain and noted that 'its booming note is often heard'. Since then 'booming' males have been heard on a few occasions, e.g. at the Araxos Lagoon in June 1942 (Niethammer 1943b), the Evros Delta in the middle of May 1955 and in 1973 (five, and six to eight males respectively) (Flach 1955a; *BWP*), the Spercheios Delta on 22–23 April 1968 (Bauer *et al.* 1969b) and L. Lysimachia on 12 May 1976 (G. Tsounis). Birds were also seen in suitable habitat during the breeding season on three occasions prior to 1969 (*CFG*). There has been a scattering of possible breeding records in recent years too, e.g. at L. Ismaris (5 May 1987) (WIWO 90) and the Rodia Marsh in the Amvrakikos (June 1987) (CP).

Bitterns seem to be regular and widespread, though not numerous, winter visitors to western and northern parts of the country. They are not recorded frequently but this is to be expected from their secretive habits and many are probably overlooked. At times of cold weather, exhausted individuals turn up in remarkable numbers throughout southern Greece and many of the islands, in all kinds of habitat and sometimes in unlikely places, such as the streets of central Athens. They are scarce but regular on spring migration, from late March to early May, but much less often recorded in autumn. In most cases, whether in winter or in spring, single birds are observed, but small parties may be seen on migration and a flock of 13 was seen coming in from the sea at Plakias Bay, Crete, on 4 May 1989 (*BoC*).

Little Bittern *Ixobrychus minutus*

Common and widespread summer visitor and passage migrant

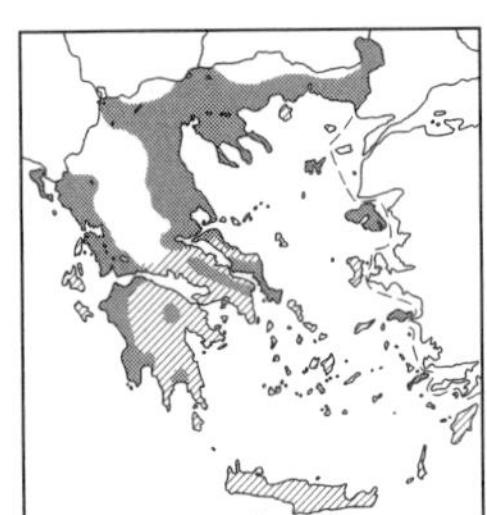

Little Bittern is widely distributed as a breeding species, though limited by its special habitat requirements. Owing to its secretive habits, its precise distribution is still not very well known but it is common in Thrace, Macedonia and Ipeiros, where large reedbeds occur at a relatively high density. It is also locally common in the Peloponnese (e.g. in Achaia, Ileia and L. Stymfalia). Data from the islands are still limited but it definitely breeds on Limnos and Lesbos and almost certainly on Corfu, Samos and Kos. The size of the total Greek population is not known but the estimate of 600–700 pairs (Tucker & Heath 1994) is probably too low. Breeding birds can be seen even in rather small patches of reedbed, canals with reed belts on the banks, and other situations offering cover and rich fishing in nearby open water. Although they feed on a large variety of prey, one of their commonest prey items is mosquito fish, *Gambusia affinis*, a North American species widely introduced to freshwater and brackish marshes all over the country.

Little Bitterns are even more widespread during migration, both in spring and in autumn. It is quite common to hear the calls of birds flying overhead in the early part of the night. Spring movements occur from early April to early June, with the main passage from late April to mid May, while in autumn movements occur from mid August to late September or early October, mainly in late August and the first half of September. In spring, when marshes and pools are easily available after winter rains, the species is common in wet areas throughout the country. In autumn, when suitable habitat is scarce, it is very often found in totally unsuitable places, such as olive groves and roadsides. Many of these birds can be caught by hand and are probably starved or dehydrated. There is only one apparently reliable winter record, of a male collected at L. Giannitsa in January 1931 (Kattinger 1935).

Night Heron *Nycticorax nycticorax*

Common but local summer visitor, common passage migrant and rare wintering species

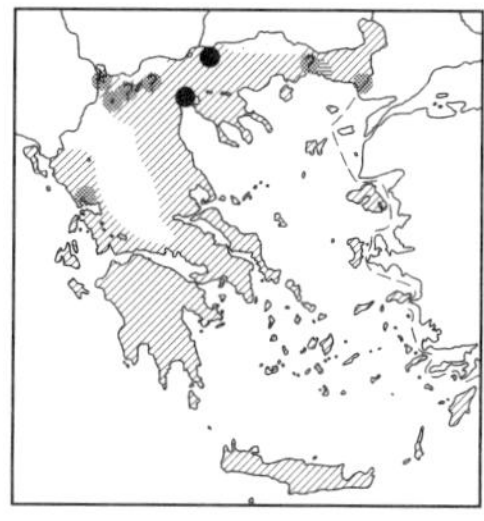

Night Herons were first discovered breeding in Greece in 1957 when one colony (*c.* 10 pairs) was found in the Gallikos–Axios Delta and another one (30–40 pairs) at L. Koronia (Reiffenstuel 1958). A few years later (1967) colonies were also found at L. Kerkini, along the course of the R. Strymon, L. Vistonis (Kraus & Conradty 1965; Kraus *et al.* 1969), the Amvrakikos, near Trikala (Bauer *et al.* 1969b) and, the largest, in the Evros Delta, with 550–600 pairs (Bauer & Müller 1969). In 1973, the total Greek population was 1,500–1,600 pairs (*BWP*), whereas in a census in 1985–86 the population had declined dramatically to 492–591 pairs (Crivelli *et al.* 1988), in four main and a few small colonies. No census has been made since then but there are indications that the population is still slowly declining.

As a passage migrant Night Heron is much more widespread and can be seen in every suitable site on both the mainland and the islands, although information on the numbers involved and the pattern of movements is still limited. On Crete, passage is between the end of March and mid May, with a peak around mid April. Most records are of singles or of flocks of up to 70 (Plakias, 8 April 1990) (*BoC*). On the mainland birds arrive from early April onwards but the main passage period is from mid April to early May. The end of the passage period is difficult to determine because many non-breeding birds stay to spend the summer away from breeding colonies. Like most other species of heron, Night Herons usually migrate in flocks of up to 100 birds, and although movements occur mainly at night, migrating flocks may occasionally be seen in daylight, especially coming in from the sea. In the Axios Delta most of the birds leave the breeding colonies by mid July (S. Kazantzidis) but autumn departures and through-passage mainly take place from early September to mid October.

In recent years, small numbers of Night Herons have increasingly been recorded wintering at three sites: the Axios Delta, L. Kerkini and Porto Lagos, with a total population ranging from 50 birds (1971) to 154 (1988). This phenomenon is probably related to a population increase outside Greece and to a series of mild winters in the 1980s (Naziridis *et al.* 1992). Up to now there are 13 recoveries of Night Herons in Greece, of birds ringed mainly in Yugoslavia (5), with smaller numbers from the Czech Republic, Slovakia, Hungary, Croatia and the Ukraine.

Squacco Heron *Ardeola ralloides*

Common but local summer visitor, common and widespread passage migrant

Although recorded as probably nesting at L. Artzan (now drained) since the 1910s (Sladen 1918), the first substantiated case of Squacco Herons breeding in Greece was much later, when on 20 May 1961 large numbers of adults in full breeding plumage were seen at the Evros Delta (Raines 1962). In 1962 breeding was confirmed at L. Ismaris, in 1963 at L. Dystos and in the next few years colonies were found in the Amvrakikos, at L. Kerkini, L. Kastoria, the Nestos Delta and the Evros Delta (Bauer *et al.* 1969b). Before 1970 the total population was estimated at 1,400 pairs (Crivelli *et al.* 1988). Later counts (mid 1970s?) suggest *c.* 2,050–2,200 pairs in nine main colonies, an increase attributed to better censusing rather than true population change (*BWP*). In a census in 1985–86 the population was found to have dramatically decreased to a total of 201–377 pairs (Crivelli *et al.* 1988).

On spring migration, Squacco Herons occur throughout the country, including the islands. The first birds arrive at the end of March but the peak period is in late April and early May, numbers declining thereafter. Significant numbers are still on passage in late May but a few of the late birds may stay longer to spend the summer at non-breeding sites. In autumn, passage is on a much smaller scale, mainly during the whole of September, the last birds leaving by the middle of October. On both spring and autumn migration Squacco Herons are usually seen singly when feeding but in small parties or flocks of up to 30–50 birds when gathering to roost in the evening or resting during the day. Like other heron species, migrants may sometimes be seen in unusual places, such as rocky coasts or by small pools within large areas of unsuitable habitat.

Cattle Egret *Bubulcus ibis*

Rare and irregular visitor and breeding species

Since the beginning of this century (Reiser 1905), Cattle Egrets have been recorded in Greece on about 36 occasions (Goutner *et al.* 1991; Pasquali 1982; Vittery 1994; *BoC*; M. Dretakis), though in some of these cases the same individual may have been involved. So far, most records are from L. Kerkini (7–9), the Thermaikos Gulf (6) and Crete (10), the rest being spread over a wide area from the Ionian, i.e. the islands of Kefallinia and Zakynthos (Vittery 1994; P.F. Whitehead), to the southeastern Aegean (Samos and Kos). In 25 cases, singles were involved. In 1978 an adult was seen at a mixed heronry in the Axios Delta and at the same site an adult with three recently fledged chicks were seen on 5 August 1991. This was the first confirmed breeding of Cattle Egrets in Greece (Goutner 1991).

Western Reef Heron *Egretta gularis*

Accidental

There are four records of Western Reef Heron, all of single birds: one (white morph) at Porto Lagos on 17 August 1981 (Handrinos 1994a), one (dark morph) at Kleisova Lagoon on 20 August 1983 (Tsounis 1984), one (dark morph) at Porto Lagos on 2 May 1986 (Mighell 1986) and one (white morph) on the island of Paxoi from 13 to 19 May 1992 (Vittery 1994).

Little Egret *Egretta garzetta*

Fairly common and widespread resident, common and widespread passage migrant

Until the late 1950s Little Egret was listed as a summer visitor and passage migrant (Reiser 1905; Makatsch 1950; Lambert 1957), with only a few winter records (*CFG*). Nesting was confirmed for the first time in 1962, at L. Ismaris, followed by the discovery of colonies at L. Karla and L. Dystos in 1963 (Bauer *et al.* 1969b; *CFG*). In 1967 colonies were also found in the Amvrakikos (120–140 pairs), the Evros Delta (120–150 pairs) and L. Kerkini (*c.* 340 pairs), with smaller colonies at two or three other sites (Kraus *et al.* 1969; Bauer *et al.* 1969b; *CFG*). In 1972 there were nine large and several smaller colonies, with a total population of *c.* 1,500 pairs (*BWP*). In a census in 1985–86, the population had declined to 1,055–1,232 pairs (Crivelli *et al.* 1988). No counts have been made since then but it appears that the species has declined still further, with only five main colonies in 1994.

During both spring and autumn migration, Little Egrets can be seen practically all over Greece, both on the mainland and on the islands. The spring passage, which is on a larger scale, begins in mid March and peaks from mid April to early May. It appears that breeding adults pass earlier than younger birds, many of which spend periods of up to a few weeks at stopover sites. Some birds are still on the move until the end of May and such late birds, presumably immatures, may stay at non-breeding sites for longer, as long as water conditions allow. Migrants may be seen singly or in flocks of 5–50, which disperse when feeding during the day and reassemble in the evening to roost. Autumn migration is less pronounced and takes place mainly from late August to early October. A relatively small number of Little Egrets winter in Greece, especially in southern and western coastal wetlands. Data from the IWRB MC (1982–1992) give an average of 465 birds, a maximum count of 1,155 (1989) and a maximum site count of 466 in the Amvrakikos (1989). So far, there are only five ringing recoveries of Little Egrets in Greece: two of birds ringed in Croatia, one ringed in Rumania and two ringed in the Ukraine.

Great White Egret *Egretta alba*

Rare and local resident, widespread and locally common winter visitor

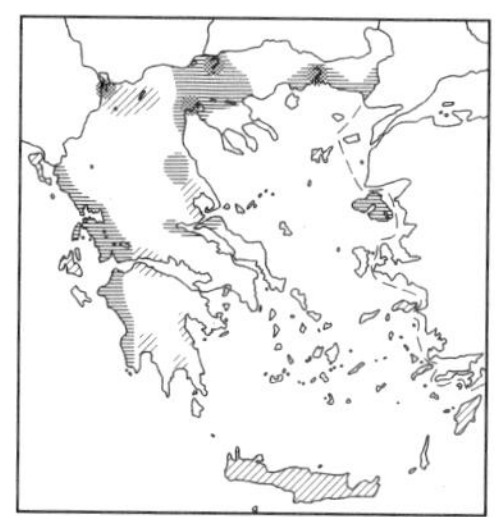

Although at least 12 adult Great White Egrets in full breeding plumage were seen in the Evros Delta on 20 May 1961 (Raines 1962), the first breeding colony of the species in Greece, estimated at 5–10 pairs, was found in 1968, at L. Mikri Prespa (Bauer & Hodge 1970). In 1971, Great White Egrets were breeding only at L. Mikri Prespa (12–15 pairs) (*BWP*), where only five pairs remained in 1983 (Catsadorakis 1986). In 1988 the total Greek population was estimated at 11–15 pairs, with 7–10 pairs at L. Mikri Prespa, at least three pairs at L. Kerkini, one or two pairs in the Axios Delta and possibly one pair at L. Vistonis (Jerrentrup *et al.* 1988). No census has been made since then but the species has probably declined still further, with no breeding at L. Kerkini in 1994 (N. Petrou).

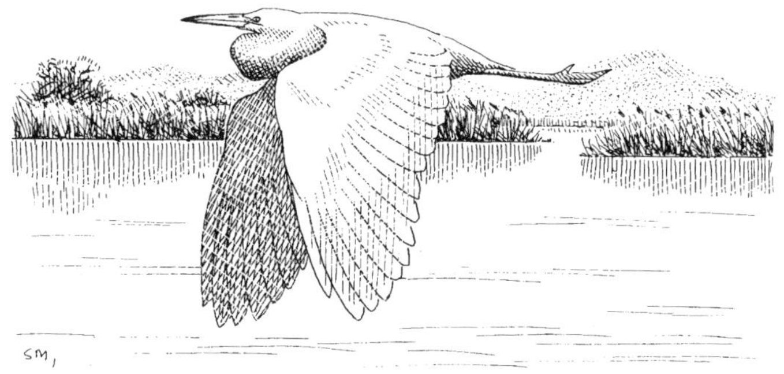

Great White Egret

Since the early 1980s the population of Great White Egrets wintering in Greece has increased significantly, both at a site to site level and nationwide. In some wetlands in Macedonia and Thrace (e.g. L. Kerkini, L. Vistonis/Porto Lagos complex and L. Volvi) they are very numerous and even outnumber Grey Herons. The increase is also apparent on the island of Corfu (X. Gremillet) and in the Peloponnese as far south as Divari Lagoon, which may in the near future become an internationally important site for the species (CP). Data from the IWRB MC (1982–1992) give an average of 1,030 wintering birds, a maximum of 1,875 in 1987 and a maximum site count of 1,072 at L. Kerkini (1982). The actual number of birds wintering in Greece may, however, be significantly higher: during the day birds are very often spread out on farmland, by ditches and elsewhere away from large areas of open water and thus are easily missed. Both spring and autumn passages are relatively insignificant. Great White Egrets are regular but very rare on Crete in the spring, where usually singles are seen, especially in early April. They are even rarer in autumn, mainly in mid September, although a flock of 40 was seen at L. Kournas on 21 September 1989 (*BoC*). They are also uncommon on passage on the island of Kefallinia (A. Vittery). Seven Great White Egrets ringed in the Ukraine and one ringed in Austria have been recovered in Greece.

Grey Heron *Ardea cinerea*

Common and widespread resident

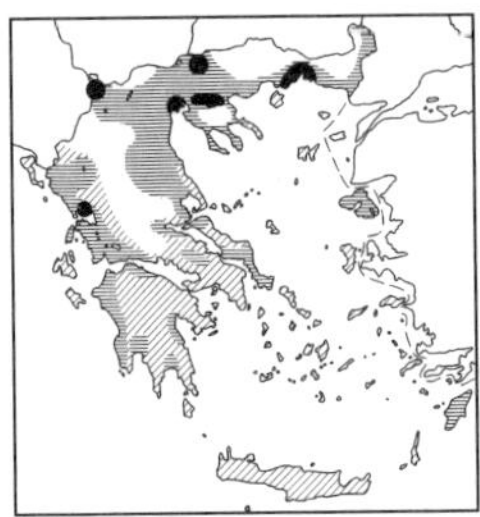

Although usually outnumbered by Little Egret, Grey Heron is one of the commonest species of heron in Greece. Furthermore, it seems to have been increasing in recent decades. Before 1970 the total breeding population was estimated at 200–250 pairs, whereas in 1985–86 it had risen to 572–600 pairs (Crivelli *et al.* 1988), a significant increase even accounting for some colonies probably missed in the earlier period. Breeding of Grey Herons is restricted to northern and western parts of the mainland, where more suitable habitat is available. The species is more widespread in winter, occurring throughout the mainland and on many of the larger islands. The IWRB MC (1982–1992) give an average of 507 birds but this figure is definitely an underestimate since the species is not counted satisfactorily, being widely dispersed over large areas and present at many sites not covered by counters.

During both spring and autumn passage Grey Herons are also widespread and common all over the mainland and the islands, particularly along the coast. In spring, migratory movements may be detectable as early as late February and may continue to the end of May, peak numbers occurring between about 5 and 20 April. Migration usually takes place singly or in small parties, though flocks of 20–50 are not uncommon and sometimes still larger flocks are recorded. On 26 April 1986, a flock of 120 was seen flying in from the sea on the southern coast of Crete, and *c.* 200 were counted within 45 minutes, flying southwest to northeast on the northern coast of the island on 15 April 1989 (*BoC*). Autumn movements take place usually from mid or late August to mid October. A flock of at least 100 on Crete at the end of September 1985 (*BoC*) is the largest number ever recorded in the autumn in Greece. Ringing recoveries show that winter visitors and passage migrants mainly come from eastern Europe: out of a total of 15 recoveries in Greece, seven were of birds ringed in Poland, two in Russia, two in the Ukraine and singles in Sweden, Estonia, the Czech Republic and Bulgaria.

Purple Heron *Ardea purpurea*

Rare and local summer visitor, fairly common passage migrant

Apparently commoner and more widespread in the 19th century and early in this century (Reiser 1905; *CFG*), today Purple Herons have a rather restricted and patchy breeding distribution. They breed in almost all of the main wetlands of Thrace, Macedonia and Ipeiros, but after the drainage of L. Karla they are now absent from Thessaly. Odd pairs may still breed as far south as Messolonghi and L. Dystos. Purple Herons do not breed on any of the islands, while in the Peloponnese they may possibly nest only at L. Stymfalia (V. Spinthakis). Before 1970 the population was estimated at 600–650 pairs, but during a census in 1985–86 only 105–140 pairs were recorded (Crivelli *et al.* 1988) and the population is probably still declining.

Like all species of heron, Purple Herons migrate through Greece on a broad front and can be seen throughout the mainland and the islands. Spring passage takes place between late March and early May, with a peak in mid April. In the early 1960s migrating flocks of 20–50 or even up to 120 birds were seen in Thrace (Bruch & Stickel 1965) but today isolated individuals or groups of 2–5 birds are more usual. Autumn passage is less obvious, perhaps mainly because most of the smaller wetlands have dried up after the summer drought, and mainly occurs during September, with some birds observed as late as early October. On migration, Purple Herons can be seen in freshwater or brackish wetlands with plenty of reedbeds or other similar vegetation. They can very often be seen taking off at dusk calling as they do so. Single birds may rise from different parts of a marsh. They form small flocks as they spiral higher and higher and finally disappear out of sight. In seasonal marshes which dry up in the summer and thus have no fish, migrant birds very often feed on tadpoles of green toad, *Bufo viridis*, perhaps the most widespread and numerous amphibian in Greece. There are only two recoveries of Purple Heron, of single birds ringed in Hungary and the Netherlands and found in Greece on passage.

Black Stork *Ciconia nigra*

Rare and local summer visitor and passage migrant

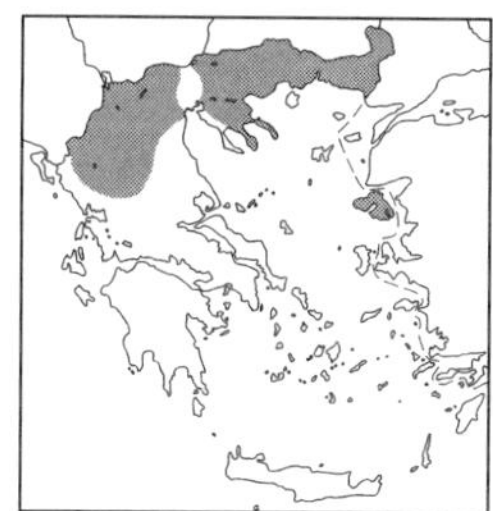

Existing data suggest that Black Storks were scarce or uncommon birds even during the 19th century (Powys 1860; Glegg 1924; Reiser 1905; *CFG*), although eggs collected from a nest on Mt Parnassos (Makatsch 1950) indicate that their distribution was wider than today. Today Black Storks nest in Thrace, Macedonia, Ipeiros and as far south as northern Thessaly, as well as on the island of Lesbos. The total breeding population, previously estimated at under 20 (*BWP*) or at 30–40 pairs (Tucker & Heath 1994), is probably significantly higher, with probably at least 50 and perhaps as many as 80 pairs. Listed as 'endangered' in the *RDB*, it now seems more appropriate to assign Black Stork to the 'vulnerable' category. At least 10–12 pairs nest in Dadia Forest Reserve (Petrou 1994), all in black *Pinus nigra* or Calabrian pines *P. brutia*. Woodland of the latter species is also their nesting habitat on the island of Lesbos (Tsounis & Dimitropoulos 1992b) but elsewhere on the mainland (Meteora, Kato Olympos etc.) nests on rocky cliffs and gorges are also known.

Outside their breeding range and the nesting season Black Storks are very rare. Though they migrate via the Bosphorus, a few birds seem to fly south over the Peloponnese, the Cyclades and Crete. A small group of 11 birds (six adult and five juvenile) flying south at a great height over Kaiafas Lagoon on 8 September 1984 is the largest number ever recorded in the Peloponnese. There are also single September records from the Aigion Lagoon and the island of Ithaki (CP). A noteworthy record is of a flock of *c.* 40 birds flying south down the east coast of the Kassandra Peninsula, Chalkidiki, on 20 September 1991 (N. & A. Bowman). On a few occasions Black Storks have been recorded in winter and a group of five birds was seen in Dadia Forest Reserve on 10 January 1992 (Petrou 1994).

Black Stork

White Stork *Ciconia ciconia*

Widespread and locally common summer visitor and passage migrant

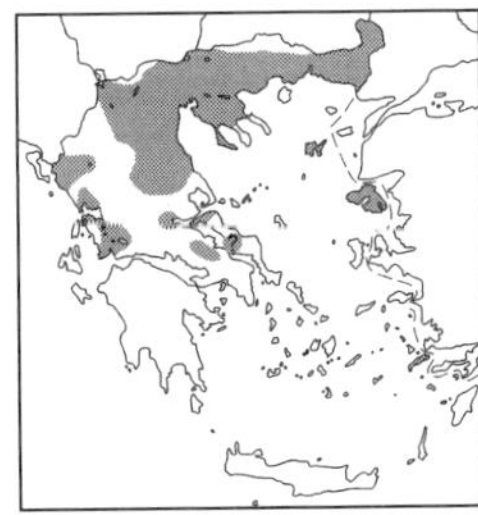

Still a common and familiar sight in many parts of Thessaly, Ipeiros, Macedonia and Thrace, White Storks were much more widespread in Greece until the 19th century or the early decades of this century. They are now extinct from the Peloponnese, southern Evvoia, Attica and from a few other areas on the mainland further north. Today the southernmost breeding sites on the mainland are at 38°25' N, but on the Aegean islands at least one pair still nests as far south as the island of Kos, in the Dodecanese. They also nest on Lesbos and on Limnos (a remarkable locality due to its distance from the mainland) but not on any other island. The highest known nest in Greece was recorded at 1,040 m at Ano Vrontou, Serres (Hölzinger & Kunkele 1986). The total breeding population has been slowly but steadily declining, though no complete census has ever been made. In the Nestos Delta, a decline of 40–50% has been reported between 1970 and 1985 (Jerrentrup 1989). In 1958 there were *c.* 9,000 pairs in the whole of the country and in 1968–70 *c.* 2,500 pairs (*BWP*), whereas a census in the mid 1980s revealed no more than 1,500 pairs, with at least 680 pairs in Macedonia and Thrace (Hölzinger & Künkele 1986). This is in contrast with the 2,000–2,500 pairs estimated in Tucker & Heath (1994) for the total Greek population.

The first White Storks arrive in early to mid March, though several records of much earlier arrivals exist (mid and late February). In late February 1942, near Porto Koufos, Chalkidiki, about 3,000 White Storks were seen during a storm (Kummer 1981), one of the largest numbers ever recorded in Greece on passage. In the spring of 1987 in NE Greece, peak passage was in late March (WIWO 90). Most birds leave Greece from mid August to early September. A flock of 7,200 birds at the Evros Delta on 21 August 1965 is the largest number ever recorded on migration (Bauer 1970). It is still not known whether the White Storks of southern Thessaly and Sterea Hellas move north–northeast to the Bosphorus, directly eastwards over the central Aegean to Asia Minor (Martens 1966), or southwards to Crete and N Africa. Nevertheless, there are almost annual records of flocks migrating over the Aegean islands and Crete (Vagliano 1984; Magioris 1987a). In mid August 1993, a flock of more than 200 was reported in Argolis, moving south, and more than 300 appeared on Mykonos after a storm in late August 1994 (J. Rallis). These might be birds from the Greek population or coming from further north, and it is not known whether they intentionally use this route or whether they somehow get disoriented. White Storks ringed as nestlings in Greece have been found in the Near and Middle East and all along the eastern half of Africa, from Egypt south to Natal. A few have also been recovered in the Arabian Peninsula, and one bird from Thessaly was killed in Andhra Pradesh (India) in January. Exceptionally, single birds winter in Greece.

Glossy Ibis *Plegadis falcinellus*

Rare and local summer visitor, fairly common and widespread passage migrant

Breeding of Glossy Ibis in Greece was first confirmed in 1960, when a colony of at least 2,000 birds was found in inaccessible reedbeds in the Evros Delta (Raines 1962). In the next few years, more but smaller colonies were discovered: at L. Kerkini (*c.* ten pairs) in 1965 and in the Amvrakikos (*c.* 150 pairs) and L. Ismaris (*c.* 40 pairs) in 1967, when two colonies (totalling 700–800 pairs) were also present in the Evros Delta (Kraus & Conradty 1965; Bauer & Müller 1969; *CFG*). In 1971–73 there were at least six colonies in the whole country, with a total of 1,100–1,500 pairs, the largest colony being that of the Evros Delta (1,000–1,200 pairs in 1971 and 400–500 in 1973) and at L. Kerkini (400 pairs in 1972) (*BWP*). Since then, the population crashed to 50–71 pairs in one colony in 1985–86 (Crivelli *et al.* 1988). In 1994 the only colony (at L. Kerkini) numbered 5–15 pairs, and in 1995 no nesting was recorded (N. Petrou).

Glossy Ibis

Glossy Ibis are still common on spring passage, from late March to mid May and with peak movements in early and mid April. They migrate on a broad front over both the mainland and the islands, mainly following the coastline. Although flocks of many tens and occasionally hundreds can still be seen, overall numbers have definitely declined in the last 25–30 years. On 1 April 1991 in NE Crete, a total of 555 birds, in flocks of 30–60, were counted in two hours, all birds heading east along the coast (*BoC*). At least 1,000 were seen flying north between the island of Samos and the Turkish coast on 3 June 1974 (C. Vagliano). A flock of 1,800 birds at Kleisova Lagoon, Messolonghi, on 10–11 April 1990 (WIWO 95) is the largest number recorded in Greece in recent times, while in the past up to 3,000 could be seen in one day in the Evros Delta (Bauer & Müller 1969). Between 1 March and 21 May 1987 a total of only 174 birds in 14 groups was counted in the wetlands of NE Greece, with a peak of 105 birds at Porto Lagos on 12 April. At least 65% of the 174 birds were heading east–northeast (WIWO 90). Glossy Ibis are much less common on autumn passage, something which is in agreement with recent findings that those breeding along the northwest coast of the Black Sea cross the northern Balkans into the Adriatic in autumn (I. Schogolev). Exceptionally Glossy Ibis have been recorded in winter. There is a total of four ringing recoveries of birds from abroad found in Greece: one is from Hungary and the other three from the Ukraine.

Spoonbill *Platalea leucorodia*

Rare and local resident

Data existing since 1843 suggest that the range of the Spoonbill in Greece during the 19th century was not significantly different from that of today (Reiser 1905; Makatsch 1950; *CFG*). In fact, although possibly breeding in earlier times too, the first Greek colony was discovered in 1965, with *c.* 30–40 pairs at the Evros Delta (Bauer & Müller 1969) and a few more at L. Ismaris (Kraus & Conradty 1965). In 1971, the total breeding population was estimated at 200–240 pairs in five colonies, the largest at L Kerkini (*c.* 100 pairs) and L. Mikri Prespa (60–80 pairs) (*BWP*). In a census in 1985–86 the total Greek population was found to be 113–172 pairs, in the same colonies as before (Crivelli *et al.* 1988). The species has declined still further and today the total population is estimated at *c.* 120 pairs, with no nesting any longer at L. Mikri Prespa and L. Ismaris, and with only very few pairs in the Axios Delta.

Spoonbills are less common during the winter. Data from the IWRB MC (1982–1992) give an average of 29 birds, a maximum of 149 (1993), and a maximum site count of *c.* 100 in the Amvrakikos (1973). In most wetlands they occur irregularly, except for the Kalamas Delta, where an average of 50 birds are present every winter. There is very little information on their movements through Greece during spring and/or autumn migration. In the spring of 1987, only a few birds were counted in the wetlands of Thrace, with peaks of 46 (end of March) and 65 (29 April) (WIWO 90). Between 1986 and 1991, only one bird was seen on Crete (6 April 1991) (*BoC*) and since Erhard's work (1858) there have been no records from the Cyclades (Magioris 1987a, 1992). Flocks of *c.* 520 at L. Kerkini on 3 October 1994 (CP) and of 112 at Messolonghi on 1 September 1980 (Walmsley 1980) are the largest numbers recorded during autumn passage. So far there are five recoveries of Spoonbills in Greece, three of birds ringed in Austria (L. Neusiedler) and two in Hungary.

Greater Flamingo *Phoenicopterus ruber*

Fairly widespread and locally common non-breeding visitor

Greater Flamingos were first recorded in Greece in the 1830s (Geoffroy Saint-Hilaire 1832). Until 1982, there were fewer than 30 records, mainly of singles or of very small flocks, from various parts of the country and from all seasons (Handrinos 1989b). Since the spring of 1983, when a flock of *c.* 200 was seen at Drana Lagoon, in the Evros Delta (3 May 1983), Greater Flamingos have been reported in increasing numbers in most Thracian wetlands, from the Evros Delta westwards to Keramoti Lagoon. Today they are present all year round in the area, with the largest numbers in winter. Their numbers and arrival/departure dates vary considerably from year to year. The population usually builds up from September and peaks in January–February. However, large numbers may have arrived already by mid autumn, e.g. 5,800 were counted between Alyki Kitrous Lagoon and L. Ismaris (including L. Kerkini) on 2 October 1994. Most birds have left by late April but in recent years a few tens to a few thousand (up to 2,500) have been staying all through the summer. So far, at least three or four breeding attempts have been made at Messi, a hypersaline lagoon east of Porto Lagos, with nest-building observed in 1986 (Anon 1986), 1989 and 1991. In June 1992, four birds were seen sitting on nests, and a week later at least three eggs were photographed on the nests (N. Petrou).

Greater Flamingos

Data from the IWRB MC (1982–1992) give an average of 1,910 birds. The maximum year count is 6,350 (1995) and the maximum site count is 3,280 at Ptelea Lagoon (17 January 1994). Outside NE Greece, Greater Flamingos occur regularly on the larger eastern Aegean islands, i.e. Limnos, Lesbos, Samos and Kos, with most records from the winter and spring. For example, 200–250 are present each winter at Kalloni Saltpans on Lesbos. In February 1995 there were 950 at L. Alyki and Asprolimni on Limnos in February, rising to 1,100 in March, dropping to *c.* 180 in June and July and disappearing in August, when the two lagoons dried up. Since the late 1980s Greater Flamingos have also become increasingly regular, though in small numbers, at coastal sites of Macedonia (Axios Delta, Alyki Kitrous Lagoon etc.), Thessaly, Sterea Hellas and Evvoia (Messolonghi, Spercheios Delta, Livari Lagoons) and the Peloponnese (Aigion and Divari Lagoons). Recently a few have also been recorded from the island of Syros (S. Magioris). In January only 5–10% are immature (first-winter) birds but later in the spring this proportion increases to 10–15% (Marteijn & Meininger 1988).

Greater Flamingos clearly prefer shallow brackish, saline or hypersaline lagoons. They frequently occur in active saltpans, especially in areas deprived of suitable natural habitat (e.g. the Aegean islands). They generally avoid freshwater wetlands, though they sometimes use them during migration. For example, on 1 October 1993, 300 were seen at L. Koronia (M. Dennis), where they are not normally present during the winter. There are five ringing recoveries of birds found in Greece. Four of these had been ringed in the Camargue (S France) and one in Iran, indicating that Greater Flamingos wintering in Greece originate from both Asiatic and west Mediterranean populations (Marteijn & Meininger 1988).

Mute Swan *Cygnus olor*

Rare and local resident, locally common winter visitor

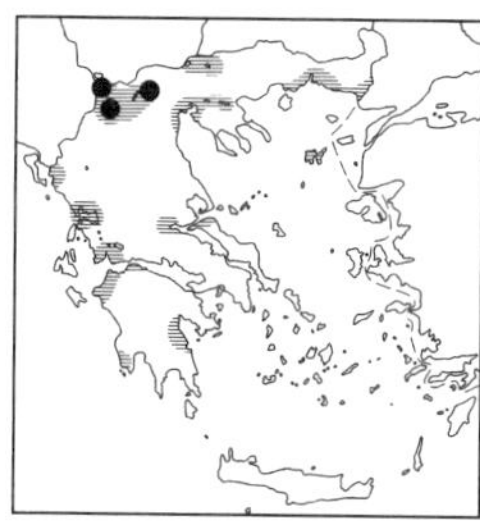

In the 19th century Mute Swans were reported breeding in several wetlands in Boeotia, Evvoia and Akarnania (Lakes Kopais, Yliki, Paralimni and Dystos, the Spercheios Delta and possibly L. Trichonis) (Lindermayer 1860; Reiser 1905). In the earlier part of the 20th century breeding was recorded only at L. Doirani (one nest, 31 May 1938) (Makatsch 1943a, 1950). Today, wild Mute Swans breed fairly regularly only at L. Mikri Prespa (one pair, 1983–85) (G. Catsadorakis). One pair nested at L. Vistonis in 1987 (C. Pantsoglou). Mute Swans also nest at Lakes Kastoria and Agras but these are feral birds, introduced from the Netherlands in the late 1960s.

Outside the breeding season, Mute Swans are winter visitors, mainly from mid October to mid March. In normal winters they are present in moderate numbers, mainly in northern Greece (particularly the Evros Delta), but in severe winters there are large influxes and the birds spread all over the country. Such influxes occurred in 1985, 1993 and 1994 and in these years they reached many Ionian and Aegean islands, from Corfu in the northwest to Crete and Rhodes in the south and east, turning up in unusual habitats such as mountain river valleys and rocky coasts. Data from the IWRB MC (1982–1992) give a national average of 613, and a maximum year count of 3,820 in 1993. The Evros Delta, with an average of 566 birds (1982–1993) and peak counts of 2,015 (January 1987) and 2,360 (January 1994), is the key site for the species in Greece, followed by L. Ismaris together with the four nearby Thracian lagoons (Handrinos in press). Although present in a variety of wetland habitats, birds wintering in Greece clearly prefer coastal sites and especially brackish lagoons, rich in submerged vegetation (primarily *Ruppia* spp.). Regardless of cold-weather movements and influxes, it appears that Mute Swans have become increasingly regular and have been spreading their range in recent years. Since the mid 1980s, they have become annual visitors to areas where they were only stragglers in the past (e.g. the Peloponnese). A similar trend, though to a much lesser extent, is also recorded in summer, with birds now oversummering at several sites where they never did so up to ten years ago. This phenomenon is in accordance with the recent increase of Mute Swan populations in the Western Palearctic and particularly in SE Europe (Handrinos in press). Surprisingly, so far there are only two recoveries, both of birds from Chernomorski Reserve on the northwest coast of the Black Sea and found in Greece in the winter (Handrinos in press).

Bewick's Swan *Cygnus columbianus*

Accidental

There are eight records of Bewick's Swan, all in winter. The species was first recorded in Greece on 5 February 1934, when one adult was shot near the harbour of Kavala. It was mounted and kept in the collection of a local school but the specimen was later destroyed dur-

ing the war (G. Hourmouziadis). The next three records of Bewick's Swans are all from the Evros Delta: one adult in December 1968 (Bauer & Müller 1969), six on 16 January 1969 (M. Hodge & A. Johnson) and one adult on 4 February 1988. The most recent records are mainly from L. Kerkini, with two adults on 27 November 1991, one adult on 16 April 1993, four adults with one juvenile on 23 January 1994 and, presumably the same birds, four adults on 19 February 1994 and three on 3 March 1994 (T. Naziridis). On 23 January 1994, when five were present at Kerkini, four adults were also seen at L. Kastoria (G. Catsadorakis).

Whooper Swan *Cygnus cygnus*

Scarce and local winter visitor

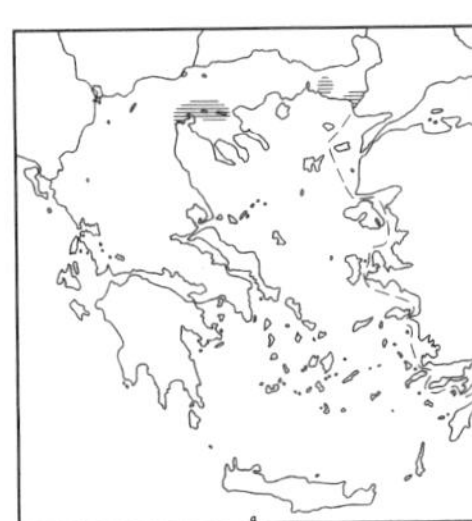

The numbers and distribution of Whooper Swans in Greece are clearly related to cold-weather phenomena outside the country. In normal winters, small numbers occur irregularly in Thrace, particularly the Evros Delta, whereas during cold spells (e.g. 1963, 1985 and 1993) numbers increase and the birds spread all over Greece. In such cases (e.g. 1993) small numbers of Whooper Swans have reached as far south as the northern coast of Crete, Rhodes, Kos or the Ionian islands (e.g. Corfu and Kefallinia). Data from the IWRB MC (1982–1993) give a national average of 14 birds, which compares with an average of 65 in the 1967–1978 period. The two largest counts are both from the Evros Delta: 400 on 16 January 1969 (M. Hodge & A. Johnson), rising to 1,500 on 2 February of the same year (Bauer & Müller 1969). In a few cases, family parties may delay their departure until late spring, e.g. nine were still present at L. Ismaris on 11 May 1987 and six on 18 May 1993. Whooper Swans wintering in Greece prefer coastal brackish or saline lagoons, sheltered bays and oligotrophic or eutrophic freshwater lakes (Handrinos in press).

Bean Goose *Anser fabalis*

Rare and irregular winter visitor

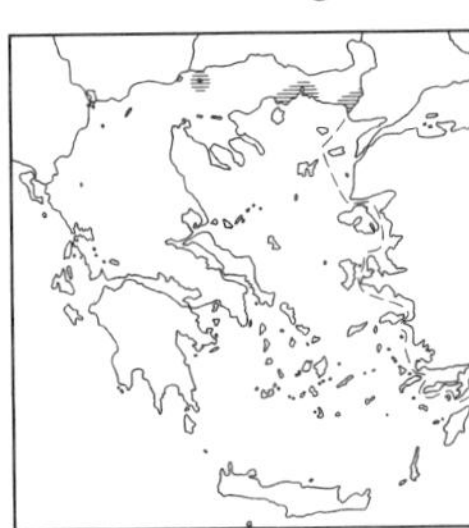

Bean Geese are rare winter visitors, with fewer than 20 records since the middle of the 19th century. However, they may have been commoner in the past. In 1846 they were reported as very numerous in Macedonia (Drummond-Hay 1846) and around the same period they were found to be common on the western coast, particularly in the Acheloos Delta (Powys 1860). In recent decades they have been seen mainly in hard winters and almost all records are from eastern Macedonia and Thrace, especially the Evros Delta. Maximum numbers recorded include *c.* 500 (December 1963) and *c.* 300 (winter 1962/63), both in the Evros Delta (Bauer & Müller 1969), *c.* 400 at L. Doirani on 4 February 1969 (Dangel 1973) and a few hundred on the island of Limnos in January 1942 (Kummer 1981). Since 1980 there have been only eight records in northern Greece, ranging from three (January 1988) to 69 birds (March 1985) (Jerrentrup & Handrinos 1987). One was also seen at Aigion Lagoon (Peloponnese) on 2 January 1994 (CP). A few shot birds examined appear, on the basis of bill structure and colour, to belong to the so called 'intermediate' type, *A. f. fabalis/rossicus*, though more data are needed to confirm this for all Bean Geese wintering in Greece.

White-fronted Goose *Anser albifrons*

Fairly common but local winter visitor

Records of White-fronted Geese during the 19th century are contradictory: they were reported as being common in Ipeiros, Akarnania and Macedonia (Powys 1860; Glegg 1924) but others considered them very rare (Heldreich 1878; Drummond-Hay 1846). Nevertheless, they were then seen or collected in more southern areas than today: the Peloponnese and Evvoia (Lindermayer 1860), Messolonghi, the Spercheios Delta and Attica (Reiser 1905). Their numbers and distribution are clearly influenced by the severity of the winter. Depending on weather conditions in the northern Balkan countries, they arrive in Greece usually in early–mid November and depart again in mid to late February or early March. They are the most widespread and numerous of all goose species in Greece. They winter mainly in eastern Macedonia and Thrace and they are most regular in the Evros Delta, which occasionally holds the entire wintering population. In severe weather, small groups or singles regularly reach as far south as the Spercheios Delta, NW Peloponnese and the northern Aegean islands such as Limnos (Kummer 1981) and Lesbos. Data from the IWRB MC show strong annual fluctuations, the total ranging from 45 birds (1984) to peaks of 35,470 (1969) or 16,500 (1965), though the more recent average (1982–1992) is 448 birds. In cold-weather spells, numbers may increase dramatically, e.g. during and just after the severe weather of February 1985, 55,000–60,000 were seen in Thrace (1 to 3 March 1985), with 35,000 in the Evros Delta, more than 20,000 at L. Ismaris and 2,500 at L. Kerkini (Jerrentrup & Handrinos 1987). Wintering White-fronted Geese feed on both natural grassland and arable land (winter cereals or stubble fields).

The fact that White-fronted Geese are now very rare in western Greece whilst they are still regular in Macedonia and Thrace agrees with the suggestion that birds wintering in north-eastern Greece belong to the Pontic population of Bulgaria and Rumania, rather than the more westerly Pannonic population of the plains of Hungary (Ogilvie 1978). The birds wintering in the Evros Delta are quite clearly connected with those wintering in Rumania and Bulgaria but those of L. Kerkini may originate from flocks wintering in Hungary (D. Vangeluwe). However, at least some intermixing of the regional populations does occur, as two ringing recoveries suggest: one found at L. Doirani on 13 February 1962 had been ringed in Britain on 9 March 1959, whilst another found at Ptolemais on 26 January 1967 had been ringed in the Netherlands on 28 January 1965. The only other ringing recovery of the species is of a bird ringed in the Taymyr Peninsula on 30 July 1991 and shot at the Nestos Delta on 18 December 1992.

Lesser White-fronted Goose *Anser erythropus*

Rare and irregular winter visitor

Nowadays, Lesser White-fronted Goose is a rare and irregular winter visitor. There are fewer than 30 documented records since the 19th century. The species was first recorded in Greece on 18 February 1859, when a pair was collected for the Zoological Museum of Athens University. There are further records prior to that date but they are poorly documented and therefore not accepted (Handrinos & Goutner 1990). Earlier this century Lesser White-front appears to have been much more numerous. It was seen in 'large flocks' at L. Koronia and the Strymon valley (Harrison 1918) and shot birds were frequently on sale in the market of Thessaloniki (Kattinger 1934). In recent decades it has been recorded only in eastern Macedonia (L. Kerkini and Nestos Delta) and Thrace. Most records and the largest numbers are from the Evros Delta, where maximum numbers recorded include 1,630 (21–22 February 1963), 480 (18–19 January 1973), 155 (15 January–17 February 1965) and 116 (20–21 January 1988) (Handrinos & Goutner 1990). L. Ismaris is also an important site, with 70 birds on 19 January 1984 and 40 on 24 January 1974, whereas recently it has been seen at L. Kerkini, with a maximum of 26 on 22–25 January 1988 (Handrinos & Goutner 1990). Most records are from late December to early March. However, this may partly reflect a bias of observations towards midwinter: at L. Kerkini they may arrive from early October (T. Naziridis) and a flock of 85 was seen in the Evros Delta on 30 March 1973 (W. Suter). Lesser White-fronts are almost always seen in mixed flocks with White-fronts, in the Evros Delta feeding on both natural grassland and fields of winter wheat. A single recovery of a bird ringed in Swedish Lappland and recovered in Macedonia (7 February 1956) may suggest that at least part of the Greek population is, or used to be, of Fennoscandian origin.

Lesser White-fronted Geese

Greylag Goose *Anser anser*

Rare and local resident, scarce winter visitor

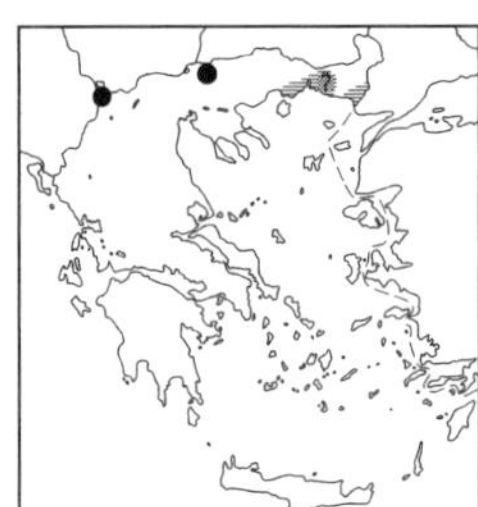

As in the case of the White-fronted Goose, 19th-century records of Greylag are confusing. It was reported as common or even numerous in Ipeiros, Akarnania and Macedonia in the winter (Powys 1860; Drummond-Hay 1843a) but other authors thought it was rare or at least not common (Drummond-Hay 1846; Glegg 1924). Reiser (1905), however, gives records from many southern areas (e.g. Evvoia, the Peloponnese, Attica) and islands (e.g. Kythira and the Cyclades), where they are now extremely rare. The species was first discovered breeding in Greece in 1917 at L. Artzan (now drained) in Macedonia (Sladen 1918) and later (1938) in the Axios Delta (Makatsch 1950). In both cases single pairs were involved. During the 1960s, 40–50 pairs nested in the Evros Delta (Bauer & Müller 1969) and single pairs at L. Ismaris and L. Kerkini (Kraus *et al.* 1969). Another small population was discovered at L. Mikri Prespa in 1968 (Terrasse *et al.* 1969) and this still survives and today holds the largest breeding population, with 20–60 pairs (G. Catsadorakis). Today there are also an estimated 2–5 pairs at L. Kerkini and, until 1984, 1–5 pairs at L. Ismaris, where a single pair may still nest.

The wintering population, though fluctuating according to cold spells, has significantly declined since the 1960s. IWRB MC (1982–1992) data give an average of 289 birds but the maximum year and site count is of 7,300 in the Evros Delta in 1965, when only this site was counted. Maximum year counts have been much lower since the 1980s, e.g. 936 in 1982 and 835 in 1987. L. Ismaris also has a record count of 3,000 on 24 January 1974 (Hafner & Hoffmann 1974), but in recent years, L. Kerkini has been the most important site, with maxima of 890 on 16 January 1982 and 542 on 27 January 1987.

There are very few data on either the breeding or wintering ecology of Greylag Geese in Greece. At L. Mikri Prespa, a National Park since 1974, they sometimes cause damage to crops by eating the young shoots of peas *Pisum* and beans *Phaseolus* in the spring. In winter (Evros Delta) they usually feed on winter wheat or stubble fields, though according to the locals the tubers of *Scirpus maritimus* are their most important food. Several shot wintering birds which have been examined show the characteristic pink bill of the Eastern race, *A. a. rubrirostris*. On 29 December 1988 and 14 January 1989 two birds with white collars (from L. Neusiedler, Austria) were seen at L. Kerkini (T. Naziridis, G. Dick). Apart from Turkey, the

Greek breeding population of Greylag is the southernmost in Europe and is isolated from those of Bulgaria and Yugoslavia (*BWP*; Rutschke 1987).

Brent Goose *Branta bernicla*

Accidental

Although single Brent Geese and a small flock were reported in the Axios–Aliakmon Deltas on 20 April 1946 (J. Vane), the only documented record of the species is of one dark-bellied *B. b. bernicla* bird in the Evros Delta, in January 1966 (Bauer & Müller 1969).

Red-breasted Goose *Branta ruficollis*

Scarce and local winter visitor

Red-breasted Geese are rather irregular in their appearance. There have been about 40 records since 1846, when the species was first recorded in Macedonia (Drummond-Hay 1846). All records are from mid December to early March but mainly from late January to mid February. Most observations are from eastern Macedonia and Thrace. However, in the past singles were recorded at L. Giannitsa (December 1922 and February 1929) and Sarigiol Marshes, near Ptolemais (January 1946), in Macedonia (both sites now drained) and in recent years singles have been shot or seen at Marathon (1982), the Spercheios Delta and Megalo Livari Lagoon (1985) and the island of Kefallinia (December 1992). The Evros Delta is the most important site, with 22 records. The largest numbers recorded in the Evros Delta include *c.* 2,000 on 2 March 1985 (Jerrentrup & Handrinos 1987), *c.* 300 in March 1957 (Coombes 1957), 80 in March 1954 (Watson 1961a) and 80 on 28 January 1989. Outside the Evros Delta, the largest number recorded is a flock of 61 at L. Ismaris in February 1985 (Jerrentrup & Handrinos 1987). The occurrence of Red-breasted Geese in Greece is clearly connected with severe winter weather, birds certainly originating from the large flocks wintering in Rumania and Bulgaria. In most cases they are seen in mixed flocks with 'grey geese', particularly White-fronts. In the Evros Delta they feed on natural grassland, fields of winter cereals and in shallow water.

Red-breasted Goose

Ruddy Shelduck *Tadorna ferruginea*

Scarce and local partial migrant

Ruddy Shelducks breed along the coasts of Macedonia and Thrace, particularly from the Nestos Delta east to the Evros Delta, with occasional pairs westwards to the Thermaikos Gulf, and on the larger eastern Aegean islands, i.e. Limnos, Lesbos, Samos and Kos. They mainly breed in coastal wetlands (brackish lagoons, saltpans etc.) but their nests may be located in remote areas of sand dunes, inland cliffs and rocky offshore islets. The total breeding population, previously estimated at under 200 pairs (*BWP*) or 30–60 pairs (*RDB*; Hallmann 1982) now probably numbers not more than 15–40 pairs. It seems, however, to be an erratic species, e.g. in 1988 an exceptional number of 36 pairs was censused on the island of Limnos (Hölzinger 1991) but none was seen there in 1994 (P. Dragoumis), and there were only about 12 pairs in 1995.

Outside the breeding season Ruddy Shelducks have been recorded irregularly on the mainland, mainly in winter. The largest numbers have been recorded in the Nestos Delta in winter: 150 (15 January 1973) (Johnson & Carp 1973), 80 (12–21 November 1976) (P. Doherty), 76 (19 February 1985) (Jerrentrup & Handrinos 1987) and 60 (17 January 1984) (H. Jerrentrup). Other large concentrations include 68 on 10 June 1979 and 23 on 22 April 1988 in the Evros Delta, and 25 at L. Ismaris on 7 September 1980. On the eastern Aegean islands Ruddy Shelducks are present practically all year round but they also make erratic movements, probably connected with the drying up or re-flooding of their strongly seasonal habitat.

Ruddy Shelduck

Shelduck *Tadorna tadorna*

Scarce and local resident, fairly widespread and locally common winter visitor

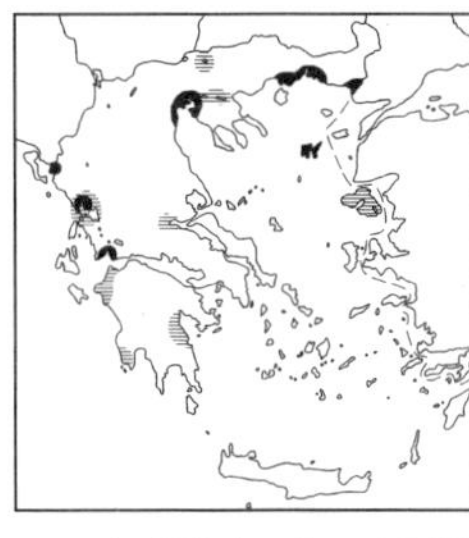

Shelducks nest in most coastal wetlands of Macedonia and Thrace, from the Alyki Kitrous Lagoon in the west to the Evros Delta in the east, with occasional single pairs on the Ionian coast, from Messolonghi north to the Kalamas Delta. A few pairs also nest on the island of Limnos. The Greek breeding population was previously estimated at 200–300 pairs (*BWP*) but it is now estimated at not more than 40–50 pairs, with seven pairs on Limnos in 1988 (Hölzinger 1991) and three to five there in 1995. During the moulting period the population breeding in Greece decreases, with birds probably migrating to the northeast (Black Sea) or east (Iran?) to moult (Walmsley 1980).

In winter, Shelducks are present in moderate numbers, mainly in Macedonia and Thrace but also in W Greece, the Peloponnese, the Spercheios Delta and some large islands (especially Limnos and Lesbos). Their numbers increase further during severe winter weather. There is only one record from Crete, of a male shot at Agia on 10 December 1944 (Stresemann 1956).

Data from the IWRB MC (1982–1992) give a national average of 3,000 birds. In recent years, the maximum count for the whole of Greece is 10,502 (1989, not a hard winter), with 4,240 at Ptelea Lagoon. More than 6,000 were counted also at Ptelea Lagoon on 1 March 1985 and 5,000 at Messolonghi on 25 February 1963. Shelducks wintering in Greece prefer coastal wetlands with brackish or saline lagoons, saltpans and shallow bays but inland freshwater lakes are also used (e.g. L. Kerkini). Little is known of their feeding ecology in Greece but ostracods were present in 18 of 20 faeces collected from a tidal area at Nea Agathoupolis (Aliakmon Delta) (Walmsley 1980). There are only two ringing recoveries of the species in Greece, both of birds ringed at L. Tenghiz in Kazakhstan and found in Greece in winter.

Wigeon *Anas penelope*

Fairly widespread and locally very common winter visitor

Wigeon is the most numerous wintering duck in Greece and the country is the second most important wintering area for the species in the Black Sea–Mediterranean area after Turkey, holding 14% of the regional population (Rüger *et al.* 1986). Data from the IWRB MC (1982–1992) give a national average of 64,000 birds, as against 84,600 for the 1968–1976 period. The maximum MC for the whole country is of 225,500 (1970), with a maximum site count of 70,000 in the Axios Delta (1970), although the record count for a single site was at L. Karla (now drained), where 120,000 were counted on 3 February 1964 (Hoffmann *et al.* 1964). Wigeon occur mainly from early November to late March, probably with a small passage in the autumn (no counts available). They prefer coastal brackish or saline lagoons or shallow marine waters in sheltered bays but their distribution is strongly influenced by disturbance caused by hunters. In the Amvrakikos they are known to feed mostly on submerged vegetation in shallow water, especially *Ruppia*, *Zostera* and algae (*Ulva*, *Enteromorpha*) (Joensen & Madsen 1985). At least two wetlands (Evros Delta and Amvrakikos) qualify as sites of international importance for the species (Monval & Pirot 1989). There are four recoveries of ringed birds found in Greece, three from Russia (Kandalaksa Reserve and Astrakhan Reserve) and one from the Netherlands.

Gadwall *Anas strepera*

Scarce and local resident, fairly common winter visitor

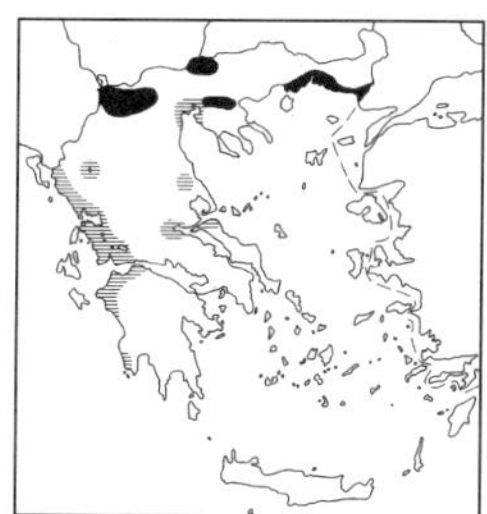

Nesting of Gadwall in Greece was first confirmed at Porto Lagos in May 1961 (Raines 1962), though the species was recorded as possibly breeding at L. Karla in 1894 (Reiser 1905). Today Gadwalls are known to breed locally in many parts of Macedonia and Thrace, with a population estimated at 100–200 pairs in the 1970s (*BWP*) and at probably not more than 50 pairs in more recent times. The species is not very numerous in winter either, with a national average of 850 (1982–1992) as against 2,035 in the period 1968–1976. The maximum midwinter count is of 6,073 birds (1968) and the maximum site count is of 3,860 in the Evros Delta (1989). Greece never held large concentrations of wintering Gadwall and today no Greek site qualifies as a wetland of international importance for the species, though the Evros Delta and the Amvrakikos used to do so. The Evros Delta is still the most important wintering site for the species in Greece. Winter visitors occur in small flocks in the shallow parts of large wetlands, both freshwater and brackish. There is only one ringing recovery in Greece, of a male ringed at Speichersee, München, Germany.

Teal *Anas crecca*

Very common and widespread winter visitor

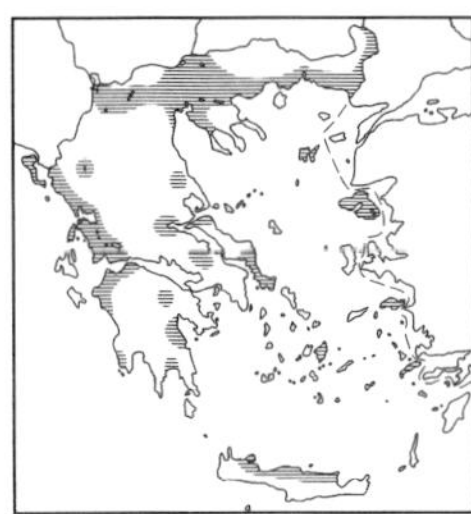

One of the commonest and most widespread wintering ducks in Greece, Teal occur mainly from early November to early or mid March. Data from the IWRB MC (1982–1992) give a national average of 38,000 birds, as against 53,000 for the 1968–1976 period. The maximum winter count is 96,940 (1970) and the maximum site count is 45,000 in the Amvrakikos (1969). The largest known count other than the MC was on 3 February 1964 when at least 60,000 were counted at L. Karla (now drained) (Hoffmann *et al.* 1964). On the basis of recent counts, L. Kerkini and the Evros Delta do not qualify as wetlands of international importance, as they did in the past, but the Amvrakikos is still listed as such (Monval & Pirot 1989). Teal occur in a variety of wetlands both coastal and inland but in general very little is known about their winter ecology.

A small passage is obvious from late August to mid October but records of the species at this time of the year are scanty and it is not possible to evaluate accurately the number of birds involved. An interesting record is of a flock of at least 1,000 birds seen moving west at a great height (probably more than 2000 m) at Agia Fotia, E Crete, on 29 August 1979 (D. Ristow & M. Wink). Unfortunately, as with many other late summer and early autumn records the possibility of confusion with Garganeys, much commoner at this time of the year, cannot be ruled out. There are 27 ringing recoveries in Greece of birds ringed breeding, wintering or on passage through much of central, northern and eastern Europe, west to Britain and Switzerland, north to Finland and east to the Caspian Sea.

Mallard *Anas platyrhynchos*

Fairly widespread but scarce resident, very common and widespread winter visitor

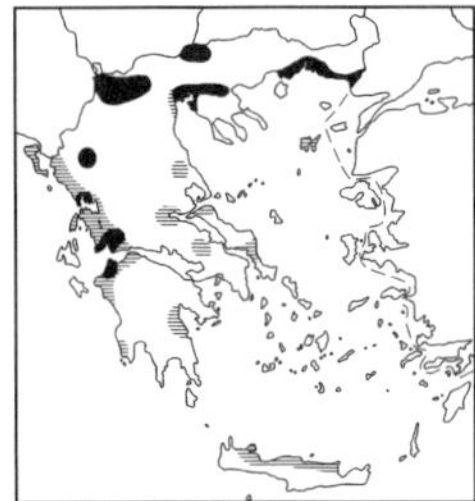

Mallard is the commonest breeding duck in Greece, nesting in most of the wetlands of the mainland and very locally or irregularly on some of the islands such as Crete, Lesbos and Limnos. The total breeding population is small and probably lies in the 100–1,000 pairs range. The species is much commoner and widely distributed in winter, with a national January average of (1982–1992) 23,000 as against 37,400 for the 1968–1976 period. The maximum year count is 71,920 (1970) and the maximum site count 37,200 at L. Kerkini (1982), although the highest number ever recorded in Greece is 92,000 at L. Karla in 1964 (Hoffmann *et al.* 1964). In the 1968–1976 period, L. Kerkini and the Evros Delta used to qualify as sites of international importance but today none of the Greek wetlands does so. There are no population counts during autumn and spring migration but Mallard are certainly much less numerous then than in winter. Breeding Mallard occur in richly vegetated freshwater or brackish wetlands, both coastal and inland, whilst in winter they occur in a wider variety of habitats but again mainly freshwater or brackish. In many areas they spend most of the day at sea due to hunting disturbance, flying inland in the evening to feed during the night. There are four recoveries of birds ringed in Russia, one in Sweden and one in the Ukraine, all found in Greece in winter.

Pintail *Anas acuta*

Common and widespread winter visitor and passage migrant

Pintail is one of the commonest wintering ducks in Greece, occurring mainly from early November (a few earlier on passage) to mid March. Data from the IWRB MC (1982–1992) give a national average of 28,000, as against 47,000 for the 1968–1976 period. The maximum year count is 95,430 (1969) and the maximum site count is 48,000 in the Amvrakikos (1969). However, the highest number ever recorded in Greece is of 80,000 at L. Karla (3 February 1964) (Hoffmann *et al.* 1964) and the record count for the whole country (incom-

plete census) is in 1964, when a total of 127,100 birds was counted. Greece holds on average 21% of the Black Sea/Mediterranean wintering population (Rüger *et al.* 1986). The Evros Delta and the Amvrakikos hold internationally important concentrations of Pintail, but two more sites (Kotychi Lagoon and the Thracian Lagoons) that used be internationally important until the 1970s do not qualify as such any more (Monval & Pirot 1989). Wintering Pintails show a strong preference for coastal brackish or saline lagoons, being much less numerous on freshwater lakes. Sixteen out of a total of 28 ringed Pintails recovered in Greece originate from the Astrakhan Reserve in the Volga Delta, three more from the north Caspian Sea and one from as far east as Naursum Reserve in Kazakhstan (51°30'N, 64°30'E). The remaining seven recoveries are of birds that had been ringed in Britain, the Netherlands and European Russia. There is not much information on the volume of spring or autumn passage through the country, though certainly very much smaller numbers are involved compared with wintering populations. Most wintering birds have left by late March but spring migrants may occasionally be seen through April and until early May. A record probably indicating autumn passage is of 522 birds at Georgioupolis (Crete) on 16 October 1988 (*BoC*).

Garganey *Anas querquedula*

Scarce and local summer visitor, common and widespread passage migrant

Garganeys breed in scattered localities throughout the country. Most breeding sites are in eastern Macedonia and Thrace but occasional isolated pairs are found elsewhere on the mainland, e.g. Messolonghi (Roussopoulos 1990) and Aigion Lagoon (CP), and on a few islands, e.g. Limnos (Hölzinger 1991) and possibly Crete (Malakou & Catsadorakis 1992). At all sites breeding is irregular and the total breeding population, although never censused, apparently amounts to no more than 20–30 pairs.

On migration, Garganeys occur in much larger numbers throughout the country. Passage runs from late February to early May, with peak numbers from late March to mid April, and then from early August to early October, with a peak in the first half of September. The largest known count is of *c.* 15,000 at L. Ismaris on 13 April 1992 (P.P. Evrard) and flocks of thousands are not uncommon elsewhere in spring, whereas in autumn generally smaller numbers are recorded. This pattern is in agreement with the situation in the Mediterranean in general, with a heavier spring than autumn passage (Monval & Pirot 1989). Flocks on the move are often seen at sea, especially in the vicinity of coastal marshes and lagoons, and are thus probably often overlooked. There have been no documented records from the December to early February period. There are 18 ringing recoveries of Garganeys found in Greece. Two of these had been ringed in Mali and another one in Nigeria, whereas the rest came from the Netherlands (5), France (3) and (singles) from Denmark, Sweden, Germany, Latvia, Croatia, Italy and the Volga Delta.

Blue-winged Teal *Anas discors*

Accidental

On 25 and 26 April 1986, a pair of Blue-winged Teal was seen and photographed at Kleisova Lagoon, Messolonghi. Both birds were shy and were not ringed or otherwise marked, which indicates that they were probably genuinely wild birds (Gaetlich 1986a; 1986b).

Shoveler *Anas clypeata*

Fairly widespread and common winter visitor and passage migrant

Shoveler have been found breeding in Greece on only three occasions: at L. Artzan (now drained) (Sladen 1918), probably near Chania (Crete) in 1942 (Stresemann 1943) and at L. Karla (now drained) in 1963 (*CFG*). They have also bred in the Albanian part of L. Mikri Prespa (Lamani & Zeko 1985), so odd pairs are not unlikely to breed occasionally in various parts of the country.

Otherwise, Shoveler are a common winter visitor and spring passage migrant, present mainly from October to mid or late April. They also occur on autumn passage (mid August to October), in smaller numbers than in spring, but both in spring and in autumn fewer birds are involved than in winter and it is not easy to separate passage movements from the arrival and departure of wintering birds. A remarkable spring record is of at least 10,000 at L. Ismaris on 13 April 1992 (P.P. Evrard). Data from the IWRB MC (1982–1992) give a national average of 11,000, against 14,000 in the 1968–1976 period. The maximum year count is 27,450 (1973) and the maximum site count is 18,000 in the Amvrakikos (1969). The highest number ever recorded in Greece is 40,000, at L. Karla on 3 February 1964 (Hoffmann *et al.* 1964), and the record count for the whole country (incomplete census) is also from 1964, with 73,650 birds. Greece is estimated to hold 12% of the Mediterranean–Black Sea population (Rüger *et al.* 1986) and the Amvrakikos qualifies as a site of international importance for the species. Wintering Shoveler are commonest in coastal wetlands, especially shallow brackish lagoons and, to a lesser extent, freshwater sites. So far, there are six recoveries of ringed Shoveler in Greece, two from the Netherlands and four from Russia (all ringed in Astrakhan Reserve, Volga Delta).

Marbled Teal *Marmaronetta angustirostris*

Former breeding species, now accidental

Marbled Teal was first recorded in Greece in the winter of 1857/58, at the marshes of Fanari (now drained) in the R. Acheron basin in NW Ipeiros (Powys 1860). In the same winter, one was seen in the Louros Delta also by Powys. Since then, there have been 12 more records, with one documented breeding record of one female with young at the mouth of R. Almyropotamos in Crete on 23 June 1925 (Schiebel 1926). Most other records are from Crete: singles at Kladissos river mouth on 16 May 1925 (Schiebel 1926), at Almyropotamos river mouth on 1–2 May 1937 (Pease 1940), at Platanias in November 1941 (Stresemann 1942b), at Agios Nikolaos on 27 June 1973 (G. Strömberg), at Georgioupolis on 21 August 1982 (D. Ristow), 20 at Plakias on 11 April 1984 (Handrinos 1993a) and two at Georgioupolis on 7 April 1991 (D. Townsend). The remaining records are of one at Kos in March 1964 (*CFG*), two in the Evros Delta on 6 May 1968 (Bauer & Müller 1969), one also in the Evros Delta on 28 April 1972 (Handrinos 1993a) and one at Kalandos Lagoon (Naxos) on 1 May 1984 (Broggi & Willi 1986). Seven of the records are from March to early May, suggesting that they refer to birds on spring migration (though one must bear in mind observer bias towards spring months), and in most cases refer to birds seen in very small island wetlands in the south Aegean, indicating an origin in N Africa.

Red-crested Pochard *Netta rufina*

Rare and irregular breeding species, regular but scarce winter visitor

Red-crested Pochards have nested in Greece only on a few isolated occasions. Breeding records are known from the former L. Artzan (Sladen 1918), the Loudias Delta (*CFG*) and probably L. Koronia (Makatsch 1950) and L. Stymfalia (Niethammer 1943b). The last docu-

mented breeding case is of three females with young at Aigion Lagoon in 1984 (Gaetlich & Dragoumis 1985). In 1967, *c.* 60 pairs of Red-crested Pochards from the Netherlands were released at L. Agras where they possibly bred for some years but their fate was not investigated further. Data from the IWRB MC (1982–1992) give a national average of only 165 birds, against 1,492 for the 1968–1976 period. The maximum year count is 4,650 (1970), of which 4,500 were counted at Agoulinitsa Lagoon in the Peloponnese (now drained). Such a dramatic decline is certainly due to the drainage of this site, which together with nearby Mouria Lagoon (also drained) and Kaiafas Lagoon (largely drained), were the stronghold of the species in Greece (Johnson & Carp 1973). Greece holds about 5% of the eastern Mediterranean population of the species (Rüger *et al.* 1986), although the actual size of this sub-population has not yet been accurately estimated (Monval & Pirot 1989).

Pochard *Aythya ferina*

Rare and local resident, common and widespread winter visitor

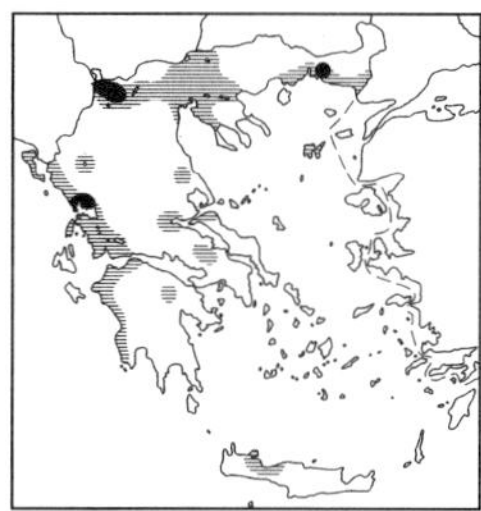

In the past, Pochards were reported as possibly nesting in Macedonia (Lakes Artzan, Koronia and Doirani) (Sladen 1918; Makatsch 1950; *CFG*) and as having nested on Crete in 1942 (Stresemann 1943). In more recent years, nesting was first confirmed in the Amvrakikos (Rodia Lagoon) in 1980 (Chwallek *et al.* 1981). Breeding has been regular in the Amvrakikos since then and further breeding records have been at L. Mikri Prespa in June 1986 (M. Huguenin-Maurer), L. Ismaris in June 1988 (V. Vassiliadis) and occasionally (since 1988) at L. Cheimaditis (G. Catsadorakis). The total breeding population is estimated at 5–15 pairs.

Pochard winter in Greece in large numbers from early or mid November to mid March. Data from the IWRB MC (1982–1992) give a national average of 45,000, compared with 39,200 for the 1968–1976 period. The maximum year count is 111,830 (1987) and the maximum site count is 50,000 at Porto Lagos and L. Vistonis (1987). Greece holds 6% of the total Black Sea–Mediterranean wintering population (Rüger *et al.* 1986). In the past, L. Ismaris together with the four adjacent Thracian lagoons, L. Koronia, L. Volvi and the Amvrakikos used to qualify as wetlands of international importance for this species but today only the Amvrakikos does so. In winter, Pochard occur on freshwater lakes and brackish lagoons or, less often, in shallow sheltered sea bays. At L. Vistonis they seem to feed almost exclusively on *Anodonta anatina* (WIWO 90). Preliminary analysis of the sex ratio of Pochards wintering in Greece (63 counts in 1988/89) has shown an average of 87,2% males (C. Carbone). Eight ringed Pochard have been recovered in Greece. Three of them are from Switzerland, one from France and four from European and Asiatic Russia, as far east as the Novosibirsk area at 53°47'N, 78°01'E.

Ferruginous Duck *Aythya nyroca*

Local and scarce summer visitor, widespread and fairly common passage migrant

Ferruginous Duck was formerly a widely distributed breeding species (Reiser 1905; *CFG*; *RDB*; Stresemann 1943). It is now confined to only a few wetlands of Ipeiros (the Amvrakikos only), Macedonia and Thrace, with occasional isolated pairs elsewhere on the mainland. The total breeding population, previously estimated at 400 pairs (Hallmann 1982; *RDB*), is estimated today at hardly more than 200–250 pairs and probably less. About half of these are estimated to breed in the Rodia marshes (Amvrakikos). Breeding birds clearly prefer richly vegetated freshwater wetlands but their breeding ecology and exact habitat requirements are not known.

Ferruginous Duck appear in Greece mainly in mid March, with passage going on up to late April or early May. The autumn migration through the country is poorly known but the main passage period is in mid October. There is no regular counting during the autumn passage but

larger concentrations are recorded then than on spring passage, e.g. more than 2,000 in the Spercheios Delta on 30 October 1988 (V. Vassiliadis). In late August 1941 and 1942 'huge flocks' were seen on the sea off Crete (Seer 1942) and more recent data from Crete suggest regular offshore passage in the autumn (*BoC*). In recent years Ferruginous Duck have also been seen regularly in the winter but in very small numbers. Data from the IWRB MC (1982–1992) give a national average of only 25 birds, but the species is probably overlooked due to its secretive habits, e.g. the extensive reedbeds of Rodia in the Amvrakikos are not surveyed in the winter. The maximum year count is of 108 (1988) and the maximum site count if of 93 at L. Kerkini (1988), which together with the Amvrakikos are the main wintering sites. The species is listed as a winter visitor in variable numbers (up to 300) on Crete (*BoC*).

Ferruginous Duck

Tufted Duck *Aythya fuligula*

Fairly widespread and common winter visitor

Tufted Duck occur in wetlands of the mainland from mid or late October to late March. They have a rather patchy distribution, with moderate numbers wintering in most of the major wetlands of Thrace and Macedonia, as well as in western Greece and the NW Peloponnese. Data from the IWRB MC (1982–1992) give a national average of 4,700 and of 5,800 in the 1968–1976 period. Wintering Tufted Duck prefer freshwater lakes or brackish coastal lagoons. At L. Vistonis they have been seen feeding on *Anodonta anatina* (WIWO 90). Counts of the sex ratio (small sample size) show that in the NW Peloponnese males comprise only 10–15% of the wintering population whereas in NE Greece this percentage may reach 40%. So far there are five ringing recoveries of the species, all found in Greece in winter, with two from Russia (Tjumen and W Siberia) and the rest from Finland, Switzerland and the Czech Republic.

Scaup *Aythya marila*

Rare and irregular winter visitor

Scaup was first recorded by Lindermayer (1860) at Messolonghi, though later authors have discarded this record (Reiser 1905; Makatsch 1950). Since then there have been about 30 records, all from January and February, except for one, of a single bird seen at L. Vistonis on 2 April 1987 (WIWO 90). The species has been seen mainly in brackish lagoons and inshore coastal waters both on the Ionian coast, from the Kalamas Delta south to Kalogria Lagoon,

and in the north Aegean/Thracian Seas, from Asprovalta east to the Evros Delta. There are also four records from the Thermaikos Gulf, at least four from Aigion Lagoon (CP) and one unusual record of ten birds on L. Vegoritis, a large oligotrophic lake of W Macedonia, on 24 January 1988. In most cases, small groups of one to five birds have been recorded, with larger numbers at Messolonghi (20 on 23 January 1988) and Aitolikon Lagoon (ten on 13 November 1984). The largest number, however, is of 700 at Aitolikon Lagoon on 18 January 1984 (Joensen & Madsen 1985), a surprising and perhaps dubious record, being one of the largest known counts of the species in the Mediterranean.

Eider *Somateria mollissima*

Rare and irregular non-breeding visitor

The first Greek record of the Eider was of a bird off Kalamata in April 1905 (Parrot 1908). Since then, there have been 19 more records, nine of them in winter, six in April and May, two in June and one each in March and October. All records are from inshore waters of the mainland, with only one from a (coastal) brackish/freshwater lagoon (L. Vistonis). Three of the records are from the Ionian Sea (Kalamas Delta, Cape Araxos and Kalamata) and two from the Thermaikos Gulf. All of the the others are from the coast of Thrace, with eight from the Evros Delta. This geographical distribution of records suggests a connection with the Black Sea wintering populations. Most records are of singles or of groups of up to eight but in three cases larger flocks have been seen: 32 in the Evros Delta on 16 February 1991, 25 at Porto Lagos on 25 October 1988, (R.-M. Lafontaine) and 18 off Alexandroupolis on 30 December 1983 (Alkemeier & Hennig 1988).

Long-tailed Duck *Clangula hyemalis*

Rare and irregular winter visitor

There has been a total of 16 records of Long-tailed Duck since the winter of 1855 when it was first recorded (Erhard 1858). All records are from December to early February except for two, both from L. Vistonis, in April 1964 and 13 May 1986. Apart from the first record of the species which was in Evvoia, one female seen at Messolonghi on 14 January 1991 and another female in the Amvrakikos on 21 January 1994, all other observations are from northern Greece and particularly Thrace, with six from the Evros Delta. Singles or parties of up to three have been seen. Most birds have been seen in shallow marine waters and coastal lagoons, with only one record from the inland freshwater L. Volvi.

Common Scoter *Melanitta nigra*

Widespread but rare winter visitor

So far there are fewer than 20 known records of Common Scoter in Greece. Eight of them have been in January and February, three in April and early May and one in August. The species was first recorded in January 1938 when an immature male was shot at Agoulinitsa Lagoon. Most records are of singles or twos, the largest numbers being of 16–17 males and three females at sea south of the island of Kefallinia in January 1983 (Joensen & Madsen 1985), nine at Porto Lagos on 12 January 1973 and seven also at Porto Lagos on 3 May 1970 (R. Scott). Common Scoter have been seen mainly in inshore coastal waters, with only two

records from inland freshwater lakes: L. Karla on 6 February 1946 (J. Vane) and L. Volvi in April 1968 (*CFG*). Three more records are from coastal brackish lagoons: two males and one female at Araxos in January 1989, one female shot at Aitolikon Lagoon in December 1990 (N. Petrou) and one at Messolonghi Lagoon on 14 January 1991. Common Scoter is one of those species wintering mainly at sea where it is probably overlooked, though certainly it is not common.

Velvet Scoter *Melanitta fusca*

Widespread but rare winter visitor

Velvet Scoter was first recorded in Greece in early February 1961, when a female was shot in the Axios Delta. Since then, it has been recorded 11 more times: two males in the Evros Delta on 4 February 1965 (Bauer & Müller 1969), 27 at L. Volvi on 15 January 1968, one immature male near Chalkis on 7 January 1982, two males and one female in the Nestos Delta on 22 January 1984, two females off the Alyki Kitrous Lagoon on 15 January 1989, one male at Araxos Lagoon on 2 February 1989, six in the Amvrakikos on 18 January 1990 and eight at the same site on 21 January 1991, 12 in the Evros Delta on 14 January 1992, five in the Amvrakikos on 21 and 22 January 1995 and three at the Keramoti Lagoons on 22 January 1995. With the exception of the L. Volvi record, and the one at Araxos (a brackish lagoon), all other observations are from inshore waters, where the species may occur more frequently but is probably overlooked. There is an additional unconfirmed record of 15 at sea off Sigri (Lesbos) in September 1994 (Brooks 1995)

Goldeneye *Bucephala clangula*

Scarce and local winter visitor

Apparently more widespread during the 19th century (Reiser 1905), Goldeneyes have in recent years been recorded annually at only a few sites, mainly in Macedonia and Thrace, i.e. from L. Kastoria and L. Megali Prespa in NW Macedonia eastwards to the Evros Delta. Single birds or small flocks are also occasionally recorded further south and west in Ipeiros and Sterea Hellas, e.g. two at L. Karterion on 5 January 1973, one pair at Messolonghi on 14 January 1985 (Pergantis & Handrinos 1992) and 25 in the Spercheios Delta on 17 January 1992. So far, there are no records from any of the islands in either the Aegean or the Ionian seas and there is only one recent record from the Peloponnese, of two immatures at Aigion Lagoon on 11 January 1993 (CP). Data from the IWRB MC (1982–1992) give an average of 140 birds, a maximum year count of 408 (1988) and a maximum site count of 154 at L. Doirani on 25 January 1988. Although most of the winter visitors are gone by mid March, some may stay until quite late in spring, e.g. one was seen in the Thermaikos Gulf on 14 March 1943 (Makatsch 1950), two in the Evros Delta on 20 April 1987 (WIWO 90) and a few at L. Trichonis in early March 1992 (G. Tsounis). Goldeneyes wintering in Greece are found mainly on freshwater lakes, brackish coastal lagoons and rarely in shallow coastal waters (e.g. in the Spercheios Delta).

Smew *Mergus albellus*

Scarce and local winter visitor

The numbers and distribution of Smews wintering in Greece are clearly influenced by weather conditions outside the country. In the 19th century they were reported as very numerous in Macedonia (Drummond-Hay 1846) and common in Ipeiros (Powys 1860), with records as far south as the island of Kythira (Jameson 1837). In recent years, they have occurred mainly in northern Greece, north of about 39°00'N, from the Kalamas Delta in the Ionian Sea eastwards to the Evros Delta. There have been very few recent records from the south of the country, e.g. singles were seen at Agoulinitsa Lagoon on 28 September 1967 (Kinzelbach 1969), at Messolonghi on 30 January 1989 and in the Spercheios Delta on 14 January 1990. The average total wintering population (1982–1992) is 36 birds, with a maximum year count of 318 (1993) and maximum site counts of 278 and 307 at L. Kerkini (1968 and 1993 respectively). In winter, Smews frequent similar habitats to Goldeneye, i.e. freshwater lakes and brackish coastal lagoons as well as, occasionally, freshwater canals and sheltered, shallow marine bays.

Red-breasted Merganser *Mergus serrator*

Fairly common and widespread winter visitor

Red-breasted Mergansers wintering in Greece are found almost exclusively in inshore coastal waters, sheltered, shallow bays and brackish or saline lagoons. The bulk of the wintering population is concentrated along the Thracian coast and the coast of western mainland Greece, with the Amvrakikos and the Porto Lagos area being the most important sites. Smaller numbers occur all round the coast of the mainland and some of the larger islands (e.g. Lesbos). Depending on the severity of the winter, stragglers may reach as far south as Crete (three records, *BoC*) or the other southern Aegean islands. In the Porto Lagos area and the Nestos Delta, during the spring of 1987, numbers were much higher in late March to early April than in early and mid March, perhaps suggesting migration of birds wintering on the Adriatic and Ionian coast (WIWO 90). Wintering birds begin arriving in late October and leave from late February onwards, with a few staying as late as the end of April or May. There are four summer records, all of single female-plumaged birds: Nestos Delta (4 August 1982) (Siblet 1986), Kamariotisa, on the island of Samothraki (July 1989) and Evros Delta (25 June 1992 and 5 June 1993). Data from the IWRB MC (1982–1992) show that the average wintering population is 271 birds, with a maximum year total of 386 and a peak site count of 294 birds in the Amvrakikos (January 1970). However, these are certainly underestimates of the total wintering population of the country since many suitable coastal areas, where Red-breasted Mergansers are known to occur, are not surveyed. There are two ringing recoveries of birds ringed in the Ukraine (Black Sea) and Finland, both found in Greece in winter.

Goosander *Mergus merganser*

Rare and local resident

Goosanders were first recorded in Greece in the middle of the 19th century, when a specimen was obtained in Evvoia (date not given) (Lindermayer 1860). As a breeding species they were first recorded on 4 June 1968, when two females with young were seen at Laimos, L. Megali Prespa (Bauer & Hodge 1970). The Prespa population still exists and appears to be stable, with three to eight pairs (G. Catsadorakis) nesting among rocks on the lake shore. It is the southernmost breeding population of Goosanders in the Western Palearctic, completely isolated from those breeding in central Europe (*RDB*). Outside the breeding season there are about 30 records, mainly from December to mid March but singles have been seen as late as

mid May. Most of these records are from the large freshwater lakes of Macedonia and Thrace, particularly Mikri and Megali Prespa, Kastoria, Koronia, Volvi, Kerkini and Vistonis, with only a few from inshore coastal waters (the Thermaikos Gulf, off the Evros Delta etc.). In most cases singles or up to eight birds are recorded, with maximum numbers of 26 at L. Mikri and Megali Prespa (21 January 1988) and *c.* 15 at L. Kerkini (3 February 1994). There is also an interesting record of a pair seen on the R. Strymon, near L. Kerkini, on 17 May 1992 (C. Thomas).

Goosanders

White-headed Duck *Oxyura leucocephala*

Rare and local winter visitor

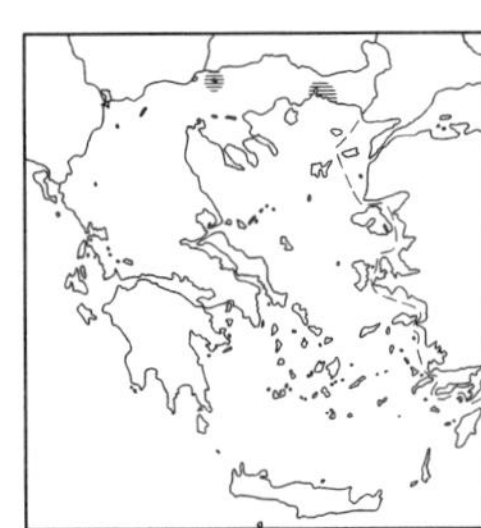

White-headed Duck was first recorded in Greece in the winter of 1857/1858 by Powys (1860). He found them common in Ipeiros and he believed they were resident in the Louros Delta (Amvrakikos). This is the only indication that White-headed Ducks ever bred in Greece and no nest has ever been found. Existing information shows that the species was apparently much more widespread in the 19th century, when specimens were collected as far south as Attica, the Spercheios Delta and Messolonghi (Reiser 1905, Naumann 1905). For more than 50 years there were practically no records at all until the species was recorded again, in 1960, in the Thermaikos Gulf (*CFG*). There is a report of White-headed Ducks possibly having bred in Greece in 1957/58 (*BWP*) but no more details of this record are known. Lambert (1957) listed the species as an 'accidental/vagrant' in Greece.

Today, White-headed Ducks are regular but very local and rare winter visitors. Since 1960 there have been about 30 records, all from December to early April, with half of them from January. With the exception of two, all these records are from Macedonia and Thrace, particularly lakes Vistonis, Ismaris, Koronia and Kerkini. Data from the IWRB MC show that the wintering population ranges between five (1993) and 423 birds (1990) (1982–1994 average=142). The largest number ever recorded in Greece is 850–900 birds at L. Vistonis on 12 December 1994 (F. Pergantis & D. Grigoropoulos). Between 1982 and 1985, White-headed Ducks were seen only at L. Ismaris but from 1987 onwards the entire wintering population shifted to nearby L. Vistonis. This lake is their main stronghold in Greece today, although in 1993 and 1994 a few were also seen at L. Kerkini. There is only one record from the islands, of one female shot on Lesbos in December 1991. In recent years, the species has also been recorded in the Evros Delta (one pair in February 1991 and one female in December 1993) and in the Kalamas Delta ('a few' in the winter of 1991).

White-headed Ducks arrive in Greece in early to mid November. In the spring of 1987, the last

White-headed Duck

birds left L. Vistonis in early April (WIWO 90). During the same study, White-headed Ducks were seen actively diving for food in daytime, in mixed flocks with Pochard, Tufted Duck and Coot. The other three species were diving for *Anodonta anatina* so it is reasonable to assume that this bivalve, abundant in Vistonis, was also the main food of White-headed Ducks (WIWO 90). Analysis of the stomach contents of two males and one female from L. Vistonis in the winter of 1993 was unsuccessful because all three stomachs contained only grit (Handrinos 1995). Owing to lack of data on their ecology in Greece, it is still not known why almost the entire wintering population prefers L. Vistonis and especially its southeastern part, where the birds are almost invariably seen. Since, however, it is well known that ducks are traditional in their use of habitat, it is possible that those wintering at L. Vistonis form a distinct sub-population unit, returning every winter to exactly the same part of the same lake. The origin of these birds is still not known but it is probable that they are part of the Turkish wintering population (e.g. of L. Burdur).

Honey Buzzard *Pernis apivorus*

Widespread but scarce summer visitor and passage migrant

Honey Buzzards have a wide though patchy distribution all over the mainland, being commoner in northern and central parts. They are uncommon in much of the Peloponnese (though data are limited) nesting as far south as Mt Taygetos (Grimmett & Jones 1989), but are fairly common in low or middle altitude Aleppo pine *Pinus halepensis* woodland and high-altitude fir *Abies* forest in the north-eastern Peloponnese, eastern Sterea Hellas and Evvoia. Nesting has also been confirmed on the islands of Skopelos (E. Kainadas) and Lesbos, in low altitude pine woodland. The total Greek population has been estimated at more than 200 pairs (Hallmann 1985a) but it is probably more and may well exceed 500 pairs.

In Dadia Forest Reserve, most Honey Buzzard nests are in pines *Pinus*, and one nest on the island of Skopelos was in an Aleppo pine. On Skopelos, one adult has been seen digging out a large nest of wasps *Vespula germanica* (E. Kainadas). Very little is known of the movements of Honey Buzzards in Greece. Passage migrants are more often seen during autumn than in spring and the largest numbers are seen in Thrace and the eastern Aegean islands, presumably due to the proximity of these areas to the migration corridor of the Bosphorus. The species arrives in Greece from late March or early April but migrants may be passing through until much later, e.g. 39 out of a total of 53 birds seen from 1 March to 21 May 1987 were in mid May, flying mainly in a westerly direction (WIWO 90). The main autumn passage is in mid September but starts from mid August and lasts until mid October. Though uncommon, Honey Buzzards are regular on Crete, mainly during the autumn migration period (Handrinos 1987b). Between about 20 August and 20 September flocks of up to 20 birds are regular in the northern Peloponnese, the majority juveniles (CP). Other reports indicate that numbers migrating over the southern Peloponnese and the island of Kythira may be much larger than older data show and that the Peloponnese–Crete flyway is perhaps quite important, at least in the autumn. Six Honey Buzzards ringed in Finland have been recovered in Greece, all in the autumn.

Black-shouldered Kite *Elanus caeruleus*

Accidental

There are only two records of the Black-shouldered Kite. The first is from the mid 19th century, reported by von der Mühle (1844), who not only mentions that two males (adult and juvenile) were collected in Greece in April (in the 1830s) but he also examined their stomach contents and found them containing mantids *Empusa fasciata* and various grasshopper species (*VME*). Later authors (Reiser 1905; *CFG*) have rejected this record because the original labels on the specimens, at that time in the Regensburg Museum, were lost. The second record is much more recent and refers to one adult above the village of Agia Triada in the Messara plain, Crete, in December 1987 (Handrinos 1994a).

Black Kite *Milvus migrans*

Rare and local resident, scarce winter visitor and passage migrant

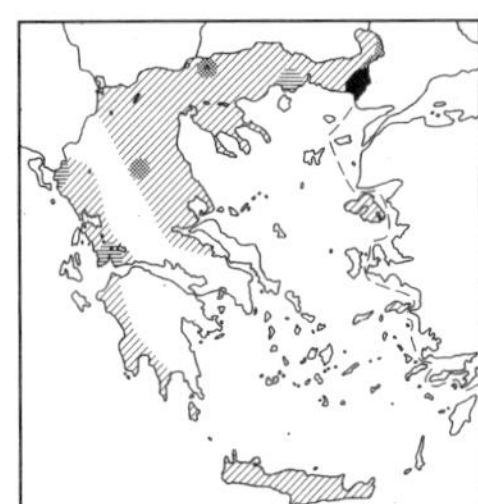

Although apparently never common in Greece, Black Kites had a much wider distribution in the 19th century and early this century than today, breeding as far south as Sterea Hellas (Reiser 1905). They were described as uncommon summer visitors in Macedonia by Glegg (1924) but there were at least 13 pairs in the Asvestochori oakwoods, close to Thessaloniki, in the early 1940s (Makatsch 1950). These were reduced to six in less than 20 years (Makatsch 1963), with none there today. There has been a marked decline in all other known breeding areas, e.g. in the Evros district where the population declined from 20–40 pairs in 1979 (Hallmann 1979) to not more than two or three since about 1990. Today, the total Greek population is estimated at 10–30 pairs, all in Thrace, Macedonia and W Thessaly (area of Meteora), nesting almost exclusively in patches of riparian woodland, in or close to wetlands.

Black Kites are rare and local in winter, when they are almost always found in or near wetlands. There is little information on their movements but they are commoner on autumn passage than in spring, both movements merging with the arrival and departure of local breeders (Handrinos 1987b). Most birds begin to arrive after the middle of March, whereas autumn migration begins around early August and lasts until early October. After breeding, large concentrations may form at favourable sites, e.g. a flock of 40 was seen at the rubbish dump of Soufli (Evros) on 12 August 1987 (J. Drachman). These concentrations presumably include birds from distant populations. The species is regular, though uncommon, during autumn passage in the western Peloponnese, the island of Kythira and Crete (Handrinos 1987b; Vagliano 1984), suggesting regular movements over southern Greece to Africa. Two specimens of race *M. m. aegyptius* have been reported as collected in Greece in the first half of the 19th century (Mühle 1844) but details are lacking and thus the records are difficult to confirm (Reiser 1905). There are three ringing recoveries of Black Kite, all from Germany, found in Greece on autumn passage.

Red Kite *Milvus milvus*

Widespread but rare winter visitor and passage migrant

There is no historical evidence that Red Kites have ever bred in Greece, though Reiser (1905) saw a pair at Velestino in Thessaly on 17 May 1894, one female was collected at Elasson, Thessaly, on 26 June 1952 (Peus 1954) and singles have been seen at Asvestochori near Thessaloniki on 28 May 1959 and Ouranoupolis (Chalkidiki) in May 1990 (S.C. Norman).

Since the mid 19th century there have been fewer than 40 records, mostly in winter, i.e. November to March. April seems to be also a peak month with seven records, whereas there are only four records between August and October. In April of both 1991 and 1992, up to five birds were seen along the R. Axios, probably suggesting a small scale migration (S. Kazantzidis).

In recent times, Red Kites have been seen in various parts of the mainland. At least ten records come from Akarnania and particularly the Messolonghi wetland complex, where small groups are sometimes seen, e.g. four on 19 November 1984, three on 28 February 1981 and three on 23 January 1994 (Pergantis & Handrinos 1992). Records from the islands include singles on Corfu on 28 September 1958 (Boness 1959), Rhodes on 20 April 1970 and on 18 April 1987 and Naxos on 24 March 1989. On Crete they have been recorded twice in autumn and on several occasions in spring, with the most recent record being of two at Kotsyfos on 12 April 1988, one at Falasarna on 16 April 1988 and one at Milatos on 24 March 1989 (*BoC*). There is only one ringing recovery in Greece, of a bird ringed in Slovakia, but Akarnanian records may suggest connection of these birds with the population breeding in southern Italy and Sicily.

White-tailed Eagle *Haliaeetus albicilla*

Rare and local resident

White-tailed Eagles were once widespread and locally common in all suitable areas of the mainland and perhaps on some of the islands (Reiser 1905; Powys 1860; Drummond-Hay 1843a, 1846). Up to the early 1940s there were at least five pairs around Thessaloniki (Makatsch 1950) and 10–12 pairs were nesting in the Evros Delta as late as the mid 1960s (Bauer & Müller 1969). Today, it is a critically endangered species with a population previously estimated at 3–8 pairs (Jerrentrup & Hallmann 1989) but in 1994 only one to four pairs survived. Outside the breeding season, White-tailed Eagles are regular but rare and local winter visitors mainly to the major wetlands of Macedonia and Thrace. Data from the IWRB MC (1982–1992), which are underestimates, give a national average of six birds, a maximum winter count of 14 (1968) and a maximum site count of ten in the Evros Delta (1976). There is only one record from Crete (Wilde 1980) and extremely few records from the Aegean islands, mainly during migration and probably of birds migrating along the Turkish coast (Handrinos 1987b), e.g. Kos in March 1964 (*CFG*) and Lesbos, with one juvenile on 9 May and one adult on 19 May 1994 (D. Jackson).

White-tailed Eagle

There are very few published data on the breeding biology and feeding ecology of White-tailed Eagle in Greece. All known nests are in trees, mainly in riverside forest and hill pines *Pinus*, less often in mixed woodland, but it is possible that in the past there were also nest sites on cliffs, particularly on the islands (Reiser 1905). Eggs are laid quite early, sometimes in early to mid February and clutches have been collected on 6 and 24 February (Reiser 1905). As elsewhere in their range, in Greece White-tailed Eagles often feed on birds (especially medium to large-sized waterbirds), fish and mammals but they also feed on carrion. The species is regularly recorded at the vulture feeding station in Dadia Forest Reserve.

Lammergeier *Gypaetus barbatus*

Rare and local resident

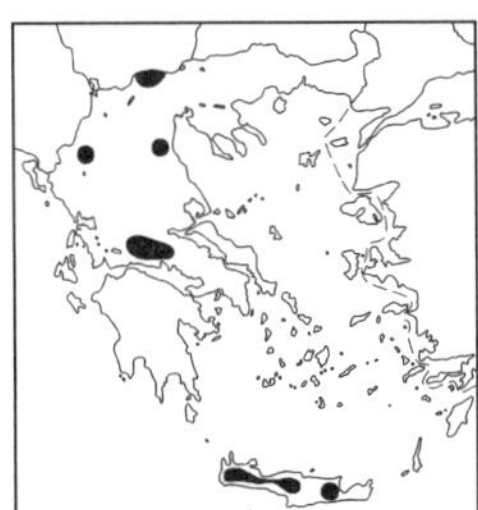

During the 19th and the first decades of this century, Lammergeiers were widespread, and probably fairly common, and recorded from both the mainland (e.g. Attica, Akarnania) as well as from several islands, e.g. the Cyclades and Lefkada (Erhard 1858; Reiser 1905). Much more recently, Lammergeiers were still breeding on the island of Rhodes as late as 1943 (Tortonese & Moltoni 1947), whereas the last record from the Peloponnese is from Mt Chelmos in August 1966 (*CFG*). Today, a few isolated pairs nest on the mainland (NW Macedonia, Ipeiros, Thessaly and Sterea Hellas), and only a single adult survives in Thrace in the Evros district. The main stronghold of the Greek population is Crete, where in the late 1970s, there were at least 23 adults, five immatures and two juvenile birds or an estimated 10–12 pairs (Vagliano 1981). Today, however, the species is reported as having declined even there (C. Vagliano). At present, the total Greek population, previously estimated at 35 pairs (Hallmann 1985a; Handrinos 1985c), is probably not more than 12–18 pairs (Tucker & Heath 1994). Lammergeier is an early breeder and eggs have been collected on 18 December 1846, 9 January 1882 and 15 January 1878 (Reiser 1905), whereas on Crete, a chick was recorded still in the nest on 8 June (*BoC*). On Crete Lammergeiers nest at higher altitudes than most Griffons, their eyries always having a southerly or easterly orientation (Vagliano 1984).

Lammergeier

Egyptian Vulture *Neophron percnopterus*

Fairly widespread and locally fairly common summer visitor and passage migrant

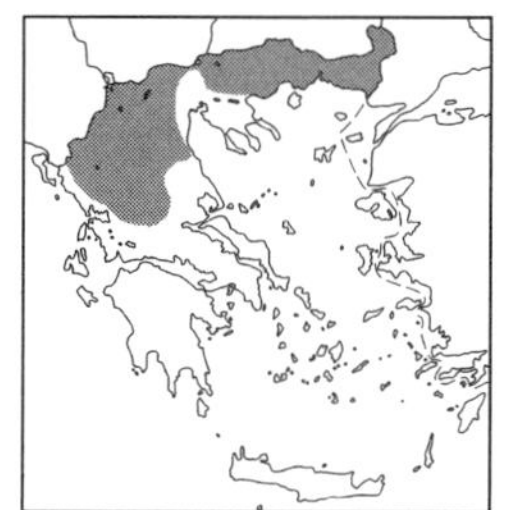

During the 19th century, Egyptian Vultures were reported as very common and it was said that most cliffs in the vicinity of a plain had a pair (Powys 1860; Krüper 1862). At the beginning of this century, though still widespread, they were already decreasing (Reiser 1905). Today, Egyptian Vultures have a patchy breeding distribution in central and northern parts of the mainland, being commoner in the north, with only a few pairs as far south as Sterea Hellas. The total Greek population is estimated at 100–200 pairs, with at least 10 pairs at Meteora (Thessaly). Their movements during migration are little known. It appears that all Greek birds leave Europe via the Bosphorus and only stragglers fly south over the Cyclades and Crete (Magioris 1987a; Handrinos 1985c; Vagliano 1984). They usually arrive from mid March (often earlier) to mid April and adult birds are almost exclusively involved, the immatures largely staying in Africa (*BWP*). Autumn departures take place mainly from early August to mid September, with adults leaving first. Egyptian Vultures usually feed at low altitude, foraging over hills with phrygana, dry plains or other open ground and are frequent at rubbish dumps and near shepherds' huts. Nests are located well below 1000 m and are usually solitary, though at Meteora they form a loose colony (Handrinos 1985b). In the Evros district (but also elsewhere in Greece), tortoises *Testudo* are a major food source. They are normally seen in pairs or small parties but occasionally larger concentrations may form, e.g. 143 were seen near Meteora on 2 August 1979 and about 60 feeding on a carcass near Xanthi on 28 July 1975 (M. Herremans). Such large numbers are becoming increasingly rare in more recent times.

Griffon Vulture *Gyps fulvus*

Fairly common but local resident

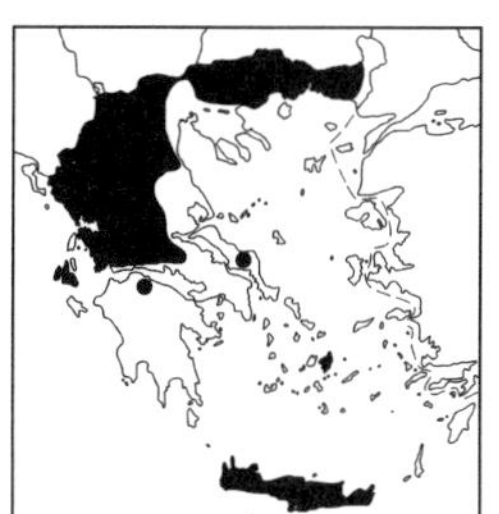

Griffon Vultures were a common sight for many travellers in Greece in the early 19th century and several ornithologists described them as abundant or plentiful up to the turn of the century (Lindermayer 1860; Krüper 1862; Reiser 1905; Powys 1860). After many years of decline due to poisoning, persecution or other causes, particularly after the Second World War, Griffons have been wiped out from nearly all the islands and much of the mainland. They are still found in most regions of the mainland but today colonies are much smaller than in the past, usually numbering only a few pairs, e.g. in the Peloponnese they occur only in Achaia, where in the last ten years the population has dropped from *c.* 27 birds to only five or six in 1994, mainly due to shooting and disturbance (CP). Sterea Hellas and particularly Aitoloakarnania, still remains the stronghold for the species on the mainland. In the Aegean, only the island of Naxos still has a population of 20–30 birds today. In the Ionian a few birds are regularly seen on the island of Kefallinia but nesting there has not yet been confirmed. Nearly half of the Greek population of Griffon Vultures lives on Crete. In the late 1970s the Cretan population was estimated at 500 birds (*c.* 200 active pairs) in nine main and a few smaller colonies (Vagliano 1981). A strong decline was evident by the mid 1980s (C. Vagliano), confirmed by a census in 1990–91 which revealed a total of *c.* 250 birds or 84–92 breeding pairs in 15 colonies (Marinkovic & Orlandic 1994). Others estimate the present Cretan population at 300–400 birds (*BoC*). If the Cretan population has indeed declined, the total Greek population, previously estimated at 400–450 pairs (Hallmann 1985a, Handrinos 1985c), today probably does not exceed 300 pairs.

Griffon Vultures forage over wide ranges, mainly over hills with low vegetation and rocky escarpments, usually at moderate altitudes (200–1500 m) but also over lower areas (e.g. river deltas), provided there are large numbers of grazing animals and cliffs for roosting or nesting. Most colonies are inland, on high cliffs, escarpments and deep gorges, but some are also located on small rocky offshore islands (e.g. Oxeia near the mouth of R. Acheloos) or on high sea cliffs (e.g. on Crete and Naxos). On Crete, the majority of colonies face south–southwest (Vagliano 1981) and are found from 30 m to as high as 800 m, though usually below 600 m (Marinkovic & Orlandic 1994). Five ringing recoveries and/or sightings of marked Griffon Vultures coming from Croatia suggest a movement of birds from the northern Balkans into Greece in the winter.

Black Vulture *Aegypius monachus*

Rare and local resident

Black Vultures were once widespread and probably numerous all over the mainland, as far south as the Peloponnese (Reiser 1905). They have also been collected on some islands, e.g. Kythira and Lefkada (Reiser 1905), and probably used to breed on Rhodes (Salvadori & Festa 1913). Although no nest was ever found, they were still recorded on Crete in the 1940s or perhaps even later. The last though not fully confirmed records on Crete were in mid May 1974, 23 August 1974, 11 August 1975, 7 April 1976 and 2 September 1976 (*BoC*). After a dramatic decline during the post-war decades, Black Vultures are now confined to Dadia Forest, in the Evros district, where in 1994 the population was 80–90 individuals, with at least 20 breeding pairs (Hallmann 1992; Adamakopoulos & Gatzoyiannis 1994). Until 1989, seven more birds, with two pairs nesting successfully in 1987, existed on Mt Olympos but today only two birds survive in this area (Hallmann 1992). Outside the breeding season the species has been seen occasionally in other areas, e.g. at Messolonghi, with up to three birds on six successive winters from 1982–1987 (Joensen & Madsen 1985; F. Pergantis), Delphi, four in June 1980 (V. Sheridan), and Mt Hymmetus, near Athens, where one juvenile was shot on 16 November 1989.

Thanks to conservation measures at Dadia (establishment of the Reserve, operation of a feeding station etc.) the population in that area has almost doubled in the last 10–15 years and shows a promising future. In fact, birds from Dadia have recently recolonised Bulgaria (one pair), where the species had been exterminated long ago. Nevertheless, the Greek population of Black Vultures is the last in the whole of eastern Europe (*BWP*) and therefore remains vulnerable.

Black Vulture

Short-toed Eagle *Circaetus gallicus*

Fairly common and widespread summer visitor

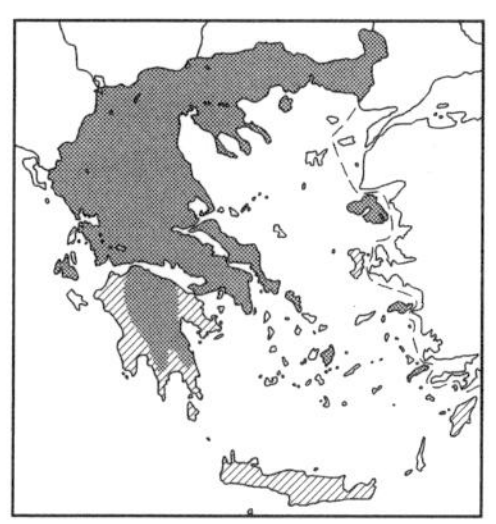

Short-toed Eagles have a wide distribution over the whole mainland and apparently many islands, although breeding has not yet been confirmed on many of them, e.g. a few observations exist from Crete during the breeding season (25 May 1991 and 1 July 1988). They return from Africa mainly from early or mid March to mid April but sometimes much earlier, e.g. one was seen near Xanthi on 18 February 1988. There is little information on the volume of passage through the country, whether of Greek birds or of birds from other parts of SE Europe. In the spring it is not rare to see birds moving west–northwest in Thrace, presumably coming from the Bosphorus and/or Dardanelles, and there is one observation of 44 passing in a generally westerly direction within one hour over L. Ismaris on 22 March 1987 (WIWO 90). Autumn passage is mainly from early September to mid October. However, there are a few records of either late migrants or overwintering birds in November and December. Short-toed Eagles are better able to cross the Mediterranean than Aquila eagles, hence they are regular but scarce over Crete in both spring and autumn (Handrinos 1987b; Vagliano 1984; Handrinos 1987b). The total Greek population has been estimated at 300–500 pairs (Hallmann 1985a). In Dadia Forest Reserve, Short-toed Eagles nest exclusively on black *Pinus nigra* and Calabrian pines *P. brutia* but elsewhere, e.g. Vikos-Aoos National Park, they reach up to 1400 m in mixed forest dominated by beech *Fagus sylvatica*. In Dadia, egg-laying was recorded between 10–20 April, the average incubation period was 47 days and the mean brood size was 0.86 young/nest (Vlachos & Papageorgiou 1994). In the same area the main prey (by frequency of occurrence) were reptiles (87.2%), birds (6.9%) and rodents (5.9%). The commonest reptiles were Montpellier snake *Malpolon monspessulanus* (29.4%), grass snake *Natrix natrix* (20.6%), lizards *Lacerta* spp. (18.7%) and European glass lizard *Ophisaurus apodus* (11.8%) (Vlachos & Papageorgiou 1994). On a nest near Thessaloniki, a leopard snake *Elaphe situla* was recorded (Makatsch 1950).

Marsh Harrier *Circus aeruginosus*

Fairly widespread but scarce resident, common winter visitor and passage migrant

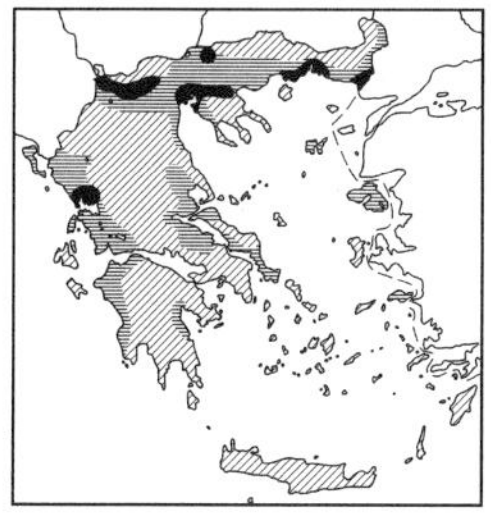

Though historical data are very limited, Marsh Harriers were apparently much more numerous and widely distributed in Greece during the 19th century than today (*RDB*; *CFG*). Following decades of decline due to wetland drainage, they now have a relatively widespread but disjunct distribution only on the mainland, particularly in Macedonia and Thrace. The species does not breed any more in the Peloponnese, though occasionally one pair may still nest in the Kotychi/Kalogria wetlands (CP). In 1988 one pair nested on the island of Limnos (Hölzinger 1991), probably the only island where they may do so at present. The total Greek population is estimated at fewer than 80 pairs (*RDB*).

In winter, Marsh Harriers are locally common, e.g. up to 46 have been counted at L. Vistonis during the IWRB MC. Among birds recorded in January during the midwinter counts, adult males are extremely rare, with female/immatures strongly predominating. They are also common during both migration periods, and since many cross the Mediterranean directly (*BWP*), they are recorded throughout the country and on all islands, often seen soaring over hills or coming in from the sea. The spring migration lasts from early March to mid May, with the main bulk of migrants going through from late March to mid April. Non-breeding birds may stay for long periods at stopover sites, often until June. Autumn migration is less pronounced and occurs mainly from the end of August to mid October. Single birds from Finland, Lithuania, Poland and Slovakia have been recovered in Greece. A bird shot and injured during the winter and released after rehabilitation in the Spercheios Delta in May 1991 was found three years later at L. Ilmen in Russia (58°25'N, 31°07'E).

Hen Harrier *Circus cyaneus*

Widespread and locally fairly common winter visitor and passage migrant

Hen Harriers occur as winter visitors and passage migrants in moderate numbers throughout the country. They are commonest in winter, fairly common on spring passage and rare to scarce on autumn passage. Spring migration and departures of wintering birds take place from early March to early May. The few detailed records available from Crete suggest a peak movement in early–mid April (*BoC*), whereas in the spring of 1987 in Thrace, the main migration period was during March, when a total of 98 passed in westerly directions. In the latter study, the age and sex ratio of 90 birds was 41% adult male and 59% female/immature (WIWO 90). There are very few data from the autumn but on Crete the main movements occur from early September to mid October. During both spring and autumn passage, Hen Harriers can, like other harriers, be seen on both the mainland and the islands and in a wide variety of habitats including high mountains, rocky gorges etc. During winter, Hen Harriers prefer open flat areas, such as farmland and pasture, particularly around wetlands. A single roost in reedbeds at the southwest corner of L. Vistonis held 24 Hen Harriers, 35 Marsh Harriers and two Pallid Harriers on 24 March 1987 (WIWO 90). Hen Harriers are rarely recorded during the summer (mid May to late August) but one interesting record concerns three adult males at Rodia Marshes in the Amvrakikos in late June 1987 (CP).

Pallid Harrier *Circus macrourus*

Widespread but scarce passage migrant

The least common and the least known of all *Circus* spp. occurring in Greece, Pallid Harrier is seen mainly on spring passage, with many fewer records from autumn and even fewer (none recent) from winter. Most records are from late March to mid April and from mid to late September. The majority are of adult males, 'ringtails' being certainly largely overlooked among the more numerous female and immature Montagu's and Hen Harriers. Between 1 March and 21 May 1987, only four birds (all adult males) were seen in NE Greece, though among the ringtails there were probably a few more Pallid Harriers (WIWO 90). In the past, the species was reported as a regular winter visitor to the wetlands of northern Greece (Lambert 1957; Bauer & Müller 1969; *CFG*) but in recent years there have been no winter records and not a single bird has been seen during the IWRB MC (1982–1994). It thus seems that at most only a very few birds may irregularly winter in Greece.

Montagu's Harrier *Circus pygargus*

Rare and local summer visitor, fairly common and widespread passage migrant

Before the 1980s, possible nesting of the Montagu's Harrier in Greece was reported for the Nestos Delta in 1962 and the Turkish part of the Evros Delta in 1968 (Groh 1968; *CFG*). The first nest was found in the early 1980s in a cornfield by L. Cheimaditis and within the next few years a few more pairs were found in the wider district of Florina, always on cultivated land. The species is also reputed to breed in the northern part of the Evros basin. An adult male was seen there (near Kastanies) in suitable breeding habitat on 25 May 1993 (P. Latsoudis). Montagu's Harriers probably also nest on the alpine meadows of Mt Varnous, where they have been seen from May to October (G. Catsadorakis) and on Mt Voras, in similar habitat. The total Greek population has been estimated at 10–20 pairs (Hallmann 1985a).

The species is commoner on migration and it is more often seen in spring than in autumn. In spring the main passage is from early April to mid May with a peak in mid and late April. The age and sex ratio of 29 birds seen in NE Greece in spring 1987 was 28% adult males and 72% females/immatures (WIWO 90). Fewer records exist from the autumn migration period (September), when adult males are very rarely seen. One bird ringed as a chick in Estonia was recovered in the Peloponnese in its first autumn.

Montagu's Harrier

Goshawk *Accipiter gentilis*

Fairly common and widespread resident

Goshawks have a widespread distribution over much of the mainland, particularly in northern and central Greece. They are much less common in the Peloponnese. They nest on the well wooded island of Lesbos, and nesting has been confirmed recently also on the island of Kefallinia (A. Vittery). Nevertheless, it is a secretive and poorly known species, possibly nesting on a few more islands, where woodland habitat exists. The total Greek population is difficult to assess and is estimated at 300–600 pairs but may well exceed 1,000 pairs.

Goshawks occur mainly in coniferous or mixed and less often in deciduous woodland, from *c.* 300 m to the treeline, usually up to 2000 m but even as high as 2500 m (e.g. on Mt Olympos). In winter, the population increases due to immigration from the north. The species also occurs on spring (and autumn?) passage, when it has been recorded from several islands (e.g. Crete) but the pattern of occurrence during these movements is very poorly known. From 1 March to 21 May 1987, only 20 birds were seen migrating over coastal wetlands of NE Greece (WIWO 90). The trends of the Greek population of Goshawks are not known but they are reported as declining in NW Peloponnese both as a breeding and as a wintering species (CP). In Dadia Forest Reserve they feed mainly on birds (particularly pigeons *Columba* and doves *Streptopelia*) but also on green lizards *Lacerta viridis* (Adamakopoulos & Gatzoyiannis 1994).

Sparrowhawk *Accipiter nisus*

Fairly widespread and locally fairly common resident, common and widespread winter visitor

Sparrowhawk is quite widely distributed over much of the mainland but it occurs more regularly in northern and central Greece and less so in the Peloponnese. So far there is no proof of nesting on any of the islands, except Ithaki (CP), Lesbos and perhaps Corfu. Breeding birds are found in various forest habitats, with a preference for conifers at middle to high altitude, and the species seems to largely replace ecologically Levant Sparrowhawk, which is a lowland

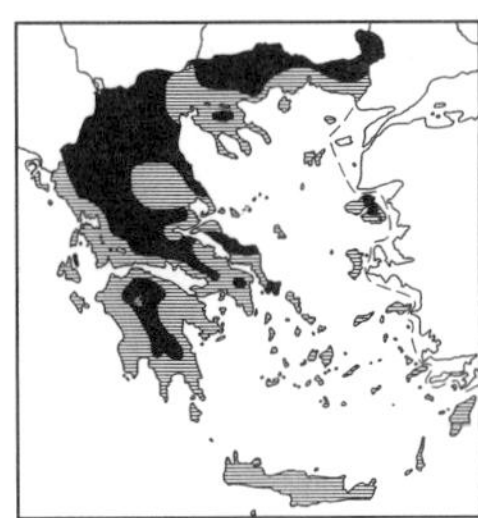

breeder. The total Greek population is tentatively estimated at 1,000–3,000 pairs and is apparently stable.

In winter, Sparrowhawks are very common, with a population that may well exceed 10,000–20,000 birds, and can be seen almost anywhere, including most of the islands. The first arrivals take place in mid October, numbers building up until early November, while in spring most birds have left by mid March, with a few staying until the end of the month. They show no preference for a specific habitat type (provided there are some trees) and occur even in town parks. Sparrowhawks are also passage migrants but their movements are little known, being largely masked by the arrival and departure of the much more numerous wintering birds. They are more commonly seen during autumn than spring migration, particularly in October, e.g. on the islands of Kefallinia and Paxoi (A. Vittery) and Crete (*BoC*). In the spring of 1987, the peak migration period in the coastal plains of Thrace was late March, when a total of 31 birds was seen passing on a broad front (WIWO 90). The age and sex ratio of 20 birds seen during the latter study was 16% adult males and 84% females/immatures. There are five ringing recoveries of Sparrowhawks ringed in Finland and the Baltic States and found in Greece.

Levant Sparrowhawk *Accipiter brevipes*

Fairly widespread and locally fairly common summer visitor and passage migrant

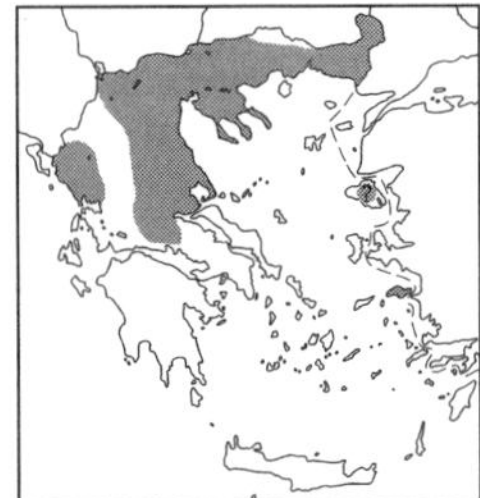

Levant Sparrowhawks have a rather limited distribution in Greece. They are commonest in Macedonia and Thrace and they become progressively rarer in more southern parts of the mainland. Sterea Hellas is their normal southern distribution limit, although in 1994 one pair successfully raised two chicks in Strofylia Forest, NW Peloponnese (J. Millett). Among the islands, breeding has so far been confirmed only on Samos in June 1989 (CP). Levant Sparrowhawks may also nest on Lesbos, where they have been observed on several occasions during the breeding season. Recently they have also been recorded on Kefallinia, with one bird on Mt Ainos on 19 May 1991 (A. Vittery). The total Greek population is estimated at 500–1,500 pairs and is apparently stable. Levant Sparrowhawks are primarily lowland birds, breeding in open woodland, riverine forests, poplar plantations and other similar habitats on coastal plains, river valleys or low hills, very rarely higher than 600 m. Although they often nest near human settlements, they are surprisingly secretive and easily overlooked. Levant Sparrowhawks enter and leave Greece

Levant Sparrowhawk

via the Bosphorus, the main bulk of the population arriving in early May. In the spring of 1987, in the lowlands of Thrace, a total of 244 were seen migrating westwards during the first ten days of May, generally in small groups of fewer than five birds but with a few larger flocks of up to 28 (WIWO 90). A few birds are more or less regularly seen during migration on most of the islands along the Turkish coast, whereas they are rarely recorded on Crete (*BoC*), suggesting that relatively few birds cross the Mediterranean when migrating.

Buzzard *Buteo buteo*

Common and widespread resident and winter visitor

Buzzards are the commonest medium-sized raptors in Greece, with a wide breeding range all over the mainland and on most of the larger islands in both the Aegean and the Ionian Seas. However, they are rather thinly distributed. They nest from sea level to as high as 2200 m but they generally prefer medium altitudes, particularly in hilly country with patches of woodland. The total Greek population is tentatively estimated at about 5,000 pairs and is apparently stable, though reported as declining locally, e.g. in the Peloponnese (CP). In winter, the population of locally breeding Buzzards is greatly augmented by immigrants and the species becomes common, particularly in coastal plains and around large wetlands. In some of these wetlands (e.g. the Evros or Axios Delta) as many as 50 birds can easily be seen in one day. They very often occur on irrigated agricultural land, probably attracted by brown rats *Rattus norvegicus*. This habit, together with the fact that they are rather slow-flying, results in large numbers being shot each year: 300 to 500 injured birds are sent from all parts of the country in each hunting season to the Hellenic Bird Hospital on Aegina.

Although the great majority of Buzzards migrate via the Bosphorus, some of them do fly over peninsular Greece on a rather broad front, both during the spring and the autumn migration. The available data, however, are still too limited to evaluate the extent of these movements. Between 1 March and 21 May 1987, peak migration in the plains of Thrace was noted in mid and late March, when a large proportion of the birds were passing in a west–northwest direction (WIWO 90). Only one of these birds had the characteristics of *B. b. vulpinus* (Steppe Buzzard), which confirms existing knowledge that birds of this race do occur in Greece during migration but are not very common. However, a proportion of both passage migrants and wintering Buzzards, as well as of birds breeding in N or NE Greece (e.g. Dadia Forest Reserve), although not typical 'fox-red' *B. b. vulpinus*, seem to be closer to *vulpinus* than to the nominate race. Of 20 ringed Buzzards recovered in Greece, 14 came from Finland, two each from the Czech Republic and Slovakia and singles from Sweden and the Ukraine.

Long-legged Buzzard *Buteo rufinus*

Fairly widespread and locally fairly common partial migrant

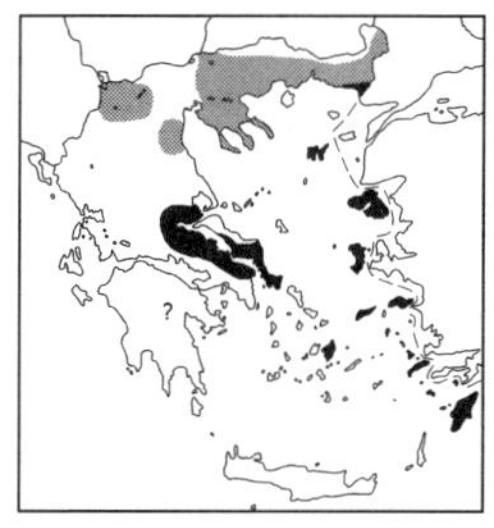

First recorded as breeding in Macedonia in 1930 (*VME*; *BWP*) and for a long time thought as rather rare (*CFG*), Long-legged Buzzards are today known to be quite widespread. They are locally quite common from eastern Sterea Hellas northwards and eastwards to Thrace and scarce in the rest of the mainland. There have been few breeding records from the Peloponnese (*CFG*) and today its breeding status there is unclear, with only two recent records of single pairs nesting near Dimitsana, Arkadia, in 1989 and in Achaia (F. Katsigiannis). Long-legged Buzzards have recently been reported as almost certainly nesting on the island of Kefallinia (A. Vittery) and one pair with juveniles was seen there in July 1994 (J. Millett). They are commoner in the Aegean, breeding on most of the larger islands, with a dense population on the island of Rhodes (Cosson 1985; Scharlau 1989a) and small populations on most other islands of the Dodecanese, a few of the Cyclades, as well as Limnos, Lesbos, Chios and Samos. So far, there are no breeding records from Crete, although they have been recorded there during the breeding season (*BoC*). The total Greek population, previously estimated at 40–60 pairs (Tucker & Heath 1994) probably amounts to more than 150 and perhaps as many as 200–300 pairs. Though typical birds of dry, open areas, Long-legged Buzzards breed in a variety of habitats, both in the lowlands and at moderate altitudes. Locally, they nest in open woodland, though open areas with rocky outcrops are preferred.

Long-legged Buzzards are resident in southern parts of the mainland and on the islands. They are mainly absent from the north during the winter, although a few birds overwinter there too, particularly near the coast. So far, there is only one record of a black-phase bird, seen on Mt Attavyros, Rhodes, on 20 April 1969. In the Evros district, Long-legged Buzzards are known to prey mainly upon European susliks *Spermophilus citellus* (C. Alivizatos) but this prey is absent from most of the rest of their breeding range, where they probably feed mainly on rabbits *Oryctolagus cuniculus* and reptiles.

Long-legged Buzzard

Rough-legged Buzzard *Buteo lagopus*

Fairly widespread but rare winter visitor

Since the mid 19th century, when first collected (Drummond-Hay 1843a), Rough-legged Buzzards have been recorded fewer than 40 times, though they may often be overlooked among the numerous wintering Buzzards. All records are from eastern Greece, with the majority from the coastal plains of Macedonia and Thrace, except for two birds at Kalodiki in Ipeiros in October and November 1994 (P. Harris). There is only one record from the islands, of one shot on Kythira in 1842 (Drummond-Hay 1843a). The majority of the records are from the winter (November–February), particularly February, and there is an unusual record of one in Evvoia in July 1959 (*CFG*). Most records are of single birds but during severe winter weather larger numbers occur, e.g. at least 14 birds were recorded in February 1963 (a severe winter all over Europe). Large numbers apparently also occurred in the severe winter of 1985: in March 1985, 17 birds were seen at a taxidermist's shop in Thessaloniki, who claimed to have handled at least ten more birds, all shot in the Axios basin. Rough-legged Buzzards wintering in Greece apparently belong to the nominate race, *B. l. lagopus*, but one female collected at Thessaloniki in January 1932 was classified as *B. l. menzbieri* (Kattinger 1935; *CFG*). A Rough-legged Buzzard ringed in the Kola Peninsula was recovered in Thessaly in winter.

Lesser Spotted Eagle *Aquila pomarina*

Fairly widespread and locally fairly common summer visitor and passage migrant

Commoner and with a wider distribution in the 19th century and up to the first decades of this century (Reiser 1905; Makatsch 1943b), Lesser Spotted Eagles today are not so widely distributed. The total breeding population is estimated at fewer than 100 pairs, with about 40 pairs in Thrace, 40 in Macedonia, 15 in Thessaly and the rest in Ipeiros and Sterea Hellas, where a single pair still nests as far south as Aitolikon (Hallmann 1989; Pergantis & Handrinos 1992). Lesser Spotted Eagles arrive in Greece in late March to early April and most have departed by the end of September or early October. They often occur in close association with wetlands, where they find the bulk of their food, but they are also found in drier forest habitats. The nests are usually at low (100–300 m) altitudes but in Thessaly they are built at up to 1200 m (Hallmann 1989; Vlachos 1989, 1991). In Dadia Forest Reserve, 18 pairs had territories in an area of 750 ha, with a mean distance of 2600 m between nests (Vlachos 1989, 1991). An analysis of pellets from this area showed that they feed mainly on snakes (frequency of occurrence of 70.6%), followed by birds (57.6%), lizards (52.6%), insects (40.3%) and small rodents (22.0%), though direct observations showed that amphibians (which are not apparent in pellets) constituted 40% of the diet (Vlachos 1989, 1991).

Lesser Spotted Eagles migrate almost exclusively via the Bosphorus but recent evidence suggests that during autumn passage some birds, usually juvenile and perhaps disoriented, move south over the Peloponnese and Crete to Africa (Handrinos 1987b; Ristow *et al.* 1982). There are two recoveries of birds ringed in Slovakia and one in Germany, found in the area of Corinth, on Crete and the island of Zakynthos in their first autumn. Particularly interesting was the satellite tracking of a juvenile from a nest in Germany. This bird moved south to Yugoslavia, into the northern Pindos and then almost directly south to Messinia, where it was either killed or drowned in an attempt to cross the Mediterranean (Meyburg *et al.* 1993). There is also a report of a small flock soaring together over Mallia, Crete, on 7 October 1993 (M. O'Meara). So far, there are only three documented winter records (all single adults), from the Evros Delta (16 December 1989 and 28 November 1990) and L. Kerkini (21 January 1994), as well as a record of perhaps an early migrant from the Evros Delta on 28 February 1980.

Spotted Eagle *Aquila clanga*

Scarce and local winter visitor

Spotted Eagles are winter visitors to Greece, mainly present between mid October and late March. Although they are not numerous, they are the commonest or the only *Aquila* eagle in wetlands in winter. Data from the IWRB MC (1982–1992), which are certainly underestimates, give a national average of 18 birds, a maximum year count of 37 (1989) and a maximum site count of 12 at L. Kerkini (25 January 1988). Young birds of various ages predominate: more than 80% of the total birds counted are juvenile and/or immatures (Handrinos 1987b).

Spotted Eagles wintering in Greece clearly prefer large wetlands, with safe roosting sites nearby, particularly woodland. Birds feeding in the Evros Delta roost in pines *Pinus* in Dadia Forest Reserve, *c.* 40 km away, e.g. a maximum of at least 15 birds was seen there on 28 January 1993 (K. Poirazidis). They are often seen feeding on dead or wounded waterfowl and one has been seen attacking Redshanks *Tringa totanus*. Only stragglers have been recorded further south than the Messolonghi wetlands (Handrinos 1987b).

Steppe Eagle *Aquila nipalensis*

Rare and irregular winter visitor and passage migrant

Steppe Eagle was first recorded in Greece on 22 February 1963, when five birds were seen in the Evros Delta (Bauer & Müller 1969). This is also the largest number ever recorded, followed by four in January and February 1965 and four on 16 February 1968, all from the Evros Delta (Bauer & Müller 1969). Since 1963, there have been at least 18 more records, all of single birds, 14 of them from the R. Evros basin. The remainder of records are from the Paximada islet, off NE Crete (September 1977 and 1979) (D. Ristow & M. Wink), from the Axios Delta in January (*CFG*) and from the island of Ikaria on 23 March 1985 (L. Empeirikos). About half of the records are from winter (November–February) and the rest are from March–April (5), August–September (3) and June (2). The geographical distribution of the records, mainly in NE Greece, suggests birds straying from the main migratory route via the Bosphorus and W Turkey (*BWP*). Since the beginning of the IWRB MC (in 1969), Steppe Eagles have been recorded only once (one in the Evros Delta on 18 January 1972), so wintering in Greece seems to be exceptional. In fact, the possibility that some of the old records of wintering birds actually involved Spotted or Imperial and not Steppe Eagles cannot be ruled out. None of these old records was supported by field notes. Presumably *A. n. orientalis* is the race involved in all cases.

Imperial Eagle *Aquila heliaca*

Rare and local resident and winter visitor

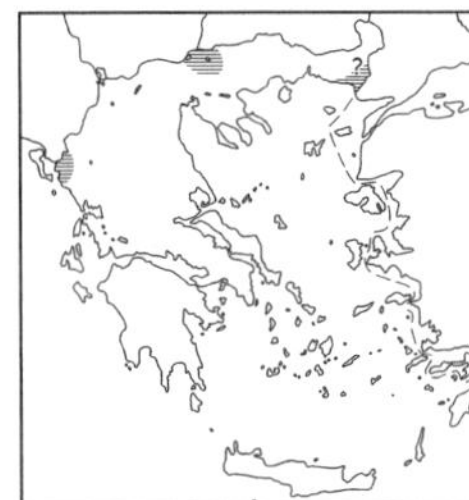

During the 19th century, Imperial Eagles had a much wider distribution than today, breeding as far south as Akarnania, Boeotia and Attica (Reiser 1905) and perhaps even the Peloponnese. In more recent years, they were still common in the plains of central Macedonia, where between 1938 and 1944 at least 25 active pairs were found in the vicinity of Thessaloniki (Makatsch 1950). Following 20–30 years of dramatic decline due to habitat changes, shooting and other causes, Imperial Eagles are now probably extinct as a breeding species in Greece. Up to 1987–88 there were perhaps as many as three pairs in Thrace, one in W Macedonia and one in Thessaly (Hallmann 1989), but since 1992 only one pair may still breed (in Thrace). In

Imperial Eagle

Thrace, nests were built on Calabrian pines *P. brutia* or oaks *Quercus* and the birds preyed upon European susliks *Spermophilus citellus*, tortoises *Testudo*, snakes, birds (including domestic chickens), other small mammals, carrion and insects (Adamakopoulos & Gatzoyiannis 1994).

Outside the breeding season, Imperial Eagles, mainly juvenile, occur in winter in very small numbers and usually in or around a few of the larger wetlands in northern and western Greece, especially the Kalamas Delta (maximum five in January 1990), L. Kerkini and the Evros Delta. During both spring and autumn passage a few Imperial Eagles are occasionally seen but there are too few records to produce a clear pattern. Several (all juvenile) have been seen or shot along the southwest coast of the Peloponnese in the autumn. There are also records from the islands, e.g. three from Crete and singles from Skiathos (17 September 1983) (O. Girard), Mykonos (16 April 1981) (E. Seitz) and Lesbos (17 September 1989) (R. Wake). Five foreign-ringed birds have been recovered in Greece, three from Slovakia and two from Hungary. All had been ringed as pulli and all except one were found (mostly shot) in their first autumn/winter.

Golden Eagle *Aquila chrysaetos*

Widespread and locally fairly common resident

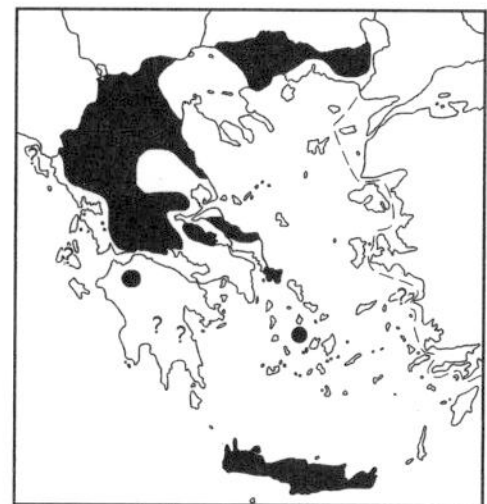

During the 19th century and the first half of this century, Golden Eagles were widespread and even common over the entire mainland and on many islands, both in the Aegean and the Ionian Sea (Powys 1860; Reiser 1905; Harrison & Pateff 1937). In the post-war years, however, they declined significantly. Today no more than one or two pairs may still survive in the Peloponnese (in Achaia) (CP) and the species has been wiped out from most of the islands (e.g. most of the Cyclades, Lesbos and Chios), with odd pairs perhaps still nesting on some (e.g. Corfu and Kefallinia). One island in the Cyclades has been re-colonised since the early 1990s (A. Dimitropoulos). Golden Eagles still occur on Crete, where at least six pairs were estimated in the late 1970s (Vagliano 1981) and eight to ten pairs have been estimated more recently (*BoC*). Their total breeding population has been estimated at 120–200 pairs (Handrinos 1987a; Hallmann 1989).

Golden Eagles occupy a variety of mountain habitats, usually at moderate to high altitudes, but depending on human disturbance and availability of nest sites, they also occur lower down, reaching sea level. On Crete most nests are at around 800 m (Vagliano 1981) but on the mainland they may be as high as 2100 m (e.g. Mt Olympos) (Handrinos 1987a). The preferred nest sites are ledges on cliffs, though in the Evros district nearly 30% of the population nests on trees, mainly pines *Pinus*. Fairly high densities are known from the latter area, with 18–20 pairs in an area of *c.* 180 square km (Hallmann 1979, 1989; Handrinos 1987a). Throughout the country a major constituent of the summer diet of Golden Eagles is tortoises *Testudo* spp., but they have also been recorded feeding on brown hares *Lepus europaeus*, red squirrels *Sciurus vulgaris*, martens *Martes* spp., European susliks *Spermophilus citellus*, red foxes *Vulpes vulpes*, domestic or feral cats, dogs, and in winter, carrion, according to local availability (Handrinos 1987a; Hallmann 1989). On Crete, hares and Chukars are their main diet (Vagliano 1981). According to the older literature, the Greek population of Golden Eagle is divided into two races: *A. c. chrysaetos* on the mainland and *A. c. homeyeri* on Crete and possibly the Peloponnese (*CFG*; *BWP*). However, it has been pointed out that the taxonomic status of the Cretan birds should be further examined (Handrinos 1987a).

Booted Eagle *Hieraaetus pennatus*

Fairly widespread and locally fairly common summer visitor and passage migrant

Although detailed records are lacking, Booted Eagles were apparently not much more numerous in the past (e.g. the 19th century) than today (Reiser 1905; Makatsch 1950). Today they have a patchy distribution on the mainland, being commoner in Thrace and Macedonia and less so in other areas, with only a few scattered pairs as far south as northern Sterea Hellas.

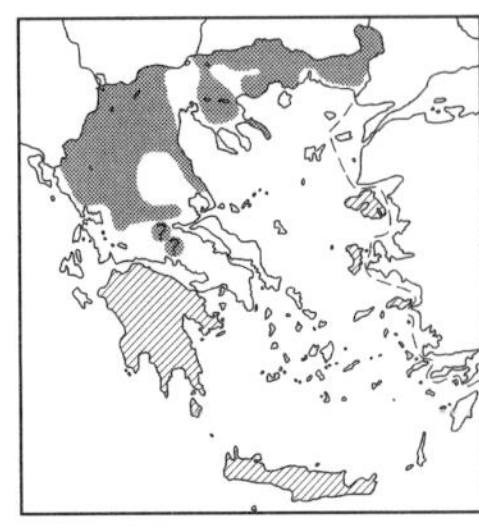

The total Greek population is estimated at 100–150 pairs (Tucker & Heath 1994), with negative trends, having declined during the last 20–30 years. In Greece, Booted Eagles nest at low and middle altitudes, in open coniferous, deciduous or mixed woodland. Although predominantly migrating via the Bosphorus, small numbers of Booted Eagles do cross the Mediterranean during both the spring and autumn migration. Singles appear, more or less regularly, on Crete mainly from mid April to early May and from mid August to mid October (*BoC*). Similar dates (September–October) apply to birds migrating over the NW Peloponnese (CP). There are a few records of wintering birds mainly from the southern mainland and Crete (*CFG*; Londei 1991; CP). There are no detailed data on the plumage-colour ratio of Greek birds but white-phase birds seem to predominate over the dark ones, comprising *c.* 60% of the population. Booted Eagles are one of the least well known Greek birds of prey. In Dadia Forest Reserve they feed mainly on medium and small-sized birds and green lizards *Lacerta viridis* (Adamakopoulos & Gatzoyiannis 1994).

Bonelli's Eagle *Hieraaetus fasciatus*

Scarce and local resident

Bonelli's Eagles were much more widespread in the past (Reiser 1905; Krüper 1860c; Powys 1860) than they are today, one pair even nesting on Mt Penteli, near Athens, as late as the mid 1940s (Steinfatt 1954/55). Their present distribution is still insufficiently known. They are very rare or absent from much of Thrace, Macedonia and Thessaly but they are quite widely though thinly distributed on most of the islands of the Aegean, including Crete. They are rarer in the Ionian islands, probably still nesting on Kefallinia (A. Vittery), Zakynthos, Ithaki and perhaps Corfu. They are very local and scarce in the Peloponnese. In general, their distribution seems to coincide with that of Chukars and, less so, of Rock Partridges, as well as (on some islands) with that of rabbit *Oryctolagus cuniculus* or, to a lesser extent, brown hare *Lepus europaeus*, all these species being their preferred prey. The total Greek population of Bonelli's Eagle is estimated at not more than 50 pairs, and though their exact status is not clear, they are probably still declining, at least on the mainland. The Cretan population has been estimated at *c.* ten pairs (*BoC*). Bonelli's Eagles prefer open, rocky, hilly or mountainous country with phrygana or low, open maquis, with rocky gorges or cliffs for nesting. They are sedentary, not known to undertake any significant movements except perhaps for a seasonal short-distance dispersal.

Bonelli's Eagle

Osprey *Pandion haliaetus*

Widespread but scarce passage migrant

Osprey probably bred, at least irregularly, in Greece in the past. Eggs have been collected from a nest southeast of L. Doirani by Captain A. Sladen, probably in 1917, a piece of information not published by him in his two papers but cited later (Glegg 1924). Another breeding record refers to a nest in the Evros Delta in 1966, which was apparently later destroyed by local fishermen (Bauer & Müller 1969). Today, Ospreys are seen in Greece only on passage, both in spring and in autumn, with only a handful of records from winter. In spring the main passage is from mid March to early May, with a peak in mid April, whereas autumn migration runs mainly from early September to mid October. On passage through Greece Ospreys are almost exclusively seen along the coast or in coastal wetlands and more rarely at inland lakes or along rivers, although they seem to readily cross high mountains (e.g. on Crete). They are usually recorded singly but quite often also in small parties of two or three. There are 33 recoveries of foreign-ringed Ospreys found in Greece. The majority are of birds from Fennoscandia, with 21 from Finland and nine from Sweden, and the rest from Germany and Russia. More than half of them were found on the Ionian coast and Ionian islands, where the species is also commoner than in the rest of the country. On the basis of these recoveries and direct observations of migrating birds it seems that Scandinavian Ospreys migrating south over Greece move mainly along the Ionian coast.

Lesser Kestrel *Falco naumanni*

Fairly widespread and locally fairly common summer visitor and passage migrant

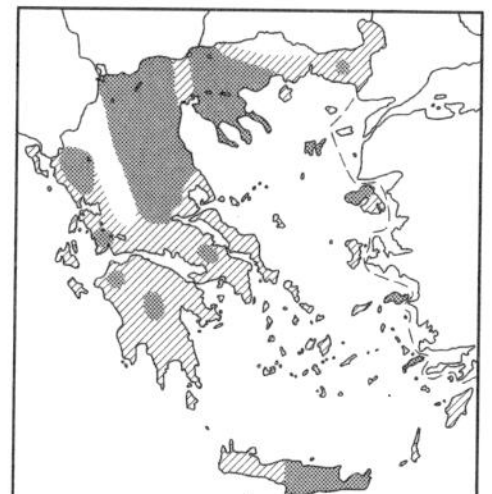

A very common and locally abundant species during the 19th century (Reiser 1905) and even as late as the 1960s (Lambert; *CFG*), Lesser Kestrel has undergone a rapid and dramatic decline almost throughout its range in Greece. Today its main breeding area spans most of Thessaly and parts of SW Macedonia, with a very discontinuous range in the rest of the mainland. There are very few pairs left in the central and NW Peloponnese and the species is almost extinct in Thrace, with perhaps only a few pairs still nesting in the plains of Komotini. During the spring of 1987, only 11 Lesser Kestrels were recorded in the coastal parts of Thrace, with only one breeding pair located in the village of Messi on 7 April (WIWO 90). Among the islands, Limnos and prob-

Lesser Kestrel

ably Kos still hold good breeding populations (although on Limnos too they have declined seriously in recent decades) whereas nesting has also been reported from Lesbos in the past and there may still be one or two pairs there. Lesser Kestrels are scarce as a breeding species on Crete, mainly in the central and eastern part (*BoC*), though they were not recorded in the eastern part of the island by Scharlau (1989b). The vast majority of breeding colonies are in villages and towns, with nests built in old or derelict buildings, and much less often on cliffs or other natural sites. Today the total breeding population is estimated at 1,000–5,000 pairs (Tucker & Heath 1994), the majority in Thessaly.

Lesser Kestrels arrive mainly in late March to early April and passage continues until early to mid May, peaking in mid April, whereas autumn movements occur mainly between late August and mid October. The species is a scarce passage migrant throughout the country, though probably often overlooked. A flock of *c.* 2,000 north of Kilkis in mid August 1981 (Biber 1990) is worth mentioning as it is the largest number recorded in recent years.

Kestrel *Falco tinnunculus*

Common and widespread resident

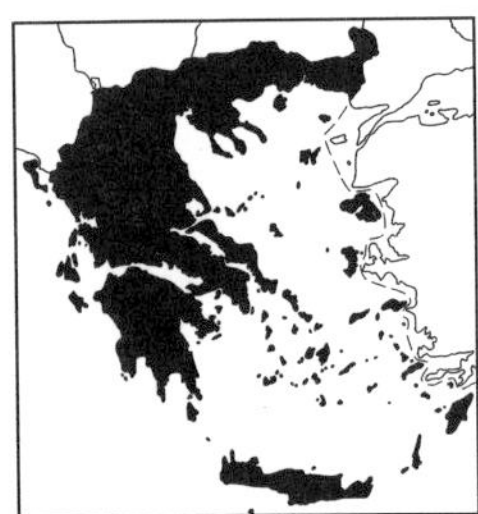

Kestrels are the most numerous species of raptor in Greece and occur widely over the mainland and on most Aegean and Ionian islands. They are seen in a variety of open habitats, from sea level up to the alpine zone on high mountains, and nest on cliffs, rocky gorges, old quarrys, trees, buildings, and other natural or man-made sites. Occasionally they form loose colonies, as in the Selinous gorge, Achaia, with two colonies of up to ten pairs each (CP). The total Greek population is estimated at a minimum of 5,000 pairs and is probably stable. However, local declines have been noted (e.g. in the NW Peloponnese (CP)) and the species is scarce in many areas with perfectly suitable habitat (e.g. Lesbos), possibly due to persecution.

Kestrels are commoner and more widespread in winter, presumably due to immigration from northern countries. The nature of their movements is still not well known but certainly there are some movements, either dispersal of local breeders or true migration. There are only two ringing recoveries of Kestrels, of one bird from Finland and one from Germany, found in Greece in winter.

Red-footed Falcon *Falco vespertinus*

Common and widespread passage migrant

Red-footed Falcons are common and at times very common passage migrants in spring but scarce in autumn. They migrate on a broad front, hence they can be seen anywhere on the mainland and on all islands. The first birds may arrive as early as late March but passage continues until mid or late May, with a peak in late April and the first half of May. Autumn movements occur from early September to early October, with a peak in late September. At peak passage in the spring one is certain to find at least some Red-footed Falcons on any sizable piece of open farmland anywhere in the country. Flocks of up to 100 birds are common at this time of the year and concentrations of several hundred are sometimes recorded in suitable habitat, though flocks of up to 20–30 are more usual. They show a preference for arable or other open cultivated land (e.g. vineyards and alfalfa fields) with a few scattered trees or telegraph wires for perching but they also regularly occur in other types of open habitat, including hill slopes with phrygana and the margins of wetlands. There are no estimates of the numbers migrating over Greece but certainly several tens of thousands are involved. In some years they are more numerous than in others (e.g. in 1992 when large numbers also appeared in W Europe). One bird ringed as a chick in Hungary was recovered in Greece in its first autumn.

Merlin *Falco columbarius*

Widespread but scarce winter visitor

Merlins occur mainly as winter visitors to the country, generally between October and early March but often as late as April or early May. They are most often seen in open lowland areas, such as arable land, *Arhtrocnemum* saltmarshes and low hills with short vegetation, which often hold large numbers of finches, larks, pipits or other ground-feeding passerines. In the spring they also appear on plateaus and open mountain sides at altitudes above 1500 m, as snow melts and small birds begin to move up from the lowlands. Merlins are scarce throughout their period of occurrence in Greece, though probably often overlooked. During the IWRB MC (data from the main wetland sites only) very few are seen, country totals ranging from 2–10 each January. They are generally rare on the islands. So far, there are no records from the Ionian islands and only one unusual record from the Cyclades, of a bird seen on three occasions on the island of Andros, during August 1933 (Bird 1935). Merlins are rare on Crete, with most records (all of single birds) from the spring passage period (*BoC*). One bird ringed as a chick in Finland was recovered in its first winter in Thessaly.

Hobby *Falco subbuteo*

Fairly common and widespread summer visitor and passage migrant

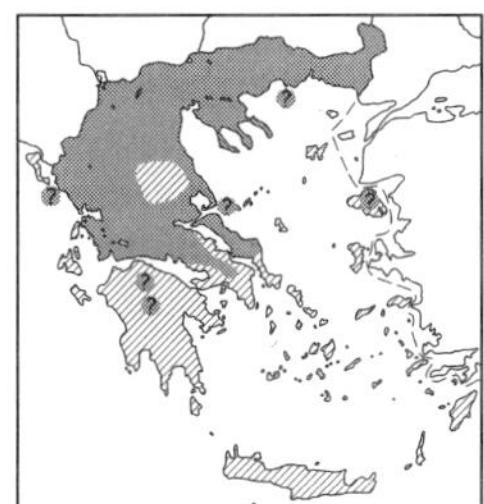

Hobbies are thinly distributed over much of the Greek mainland, being commoner in central and northern parts of the country. Their breeding range in the Peloponnese is still poorly known but apparently they are much less common there than further north. The exact status of Hobbies on the islands is also still not clear. There are no recent documented breeding records from any of the islands, though odd pairs may breed on a few of them, in both the Aegean and the Ionian Seas, e.g. the island of Paxoi (A. Vittery), Skiathos and Lesbos. Hobby is a regular though scarce passage migrant on Crete and some summer records may indicate sporadic breeding (Vagliano 1984; *BoC*). The size of the total Greek population is poorly known but probably lies in the range of 500–1,000 pairs. The first Hobbies arrive from the end of March or early April and passage through the country continues to early or mid May, with peak movements from mid April to early May. The autumn movements are less marked, with fewer birds passing through, mainly in September and October.

Eleonora's Falcon *Falco eleonorae*

Fairly widespread and locally common summer visitor

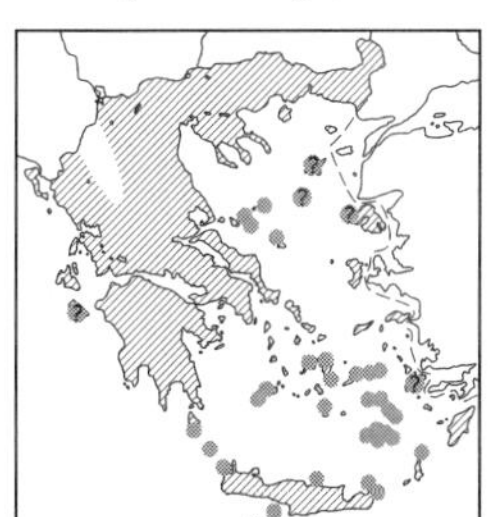

There is no evidence to suggest that the past (e.g. 19th century) distribution of Eleonora's Falcons was different from the present (Reiser 1905; Powys 1860; *CFG*). Eleonora's Falcons breed over much of the Aegean area and existing colonies can be divided into four main geographical units: a) Kythira and Crete, b) the Dodecanese, c) the Cyclades and d) the Northern Sporades. Outside these areas, their breeding distribution is very poorly known: they are listed as breeding on the islands of Psara and Venetiko, off Chios, (Spinthakis *et al.* 1993), with a few (?) pairs possibly on or near Limnos and Kos (Lensch 1979). Their status in the Ionian Sea is also very obscure but even if they nest there, their population is certainly small, with only a few pairs possibly nesting on cliffs in the west of the island of Zakynthos. The most recent and so far the most accurate census of the total Greek population was made in the 1970s by H. Walter, who calculated that in the Aegean sea there are 56 colonies, with an average of 2,873 breeding pairs, representing 65% of the total world population, estimated at 4,400 pairs (Walter 1978a, 1978b, 1979). No census has been made since then and hence their population trends are not known but they seem to be stable and perhaps even slightly increasing.

During the last 20 years the breeding biology and behaviour of Eleonora's Falcons have been extensively studied at an important colony on the islet of Paximada off NE Crete by Dr D. Ristow, Prof. Dr M. Wink and their colleagues. Eleonora's Falcons begin to return to their nesting colonies by mid May. Eggs are laid towards the end of July and most chicks hatch in the end of August. At Paximada the mean clutch size is 2.3 and the mean brood size at fledging is 1.3 young per nest. The fledging period is 35 days (see e.g. Ristow 1975; Ristow & Wink 1985; Ristow *et al.* 1979, 1989; Wink *et al.* 1993).

From the time of their arrival in the spring, sometimes as early as early April but more often towards the end of the month, and up to mid July, Eleonora's Falcons disperse over practically the whole mainland and most islands. During this period, loose flocks of 5–50 birds can be seen in a wide variety of habitats, from coastal wetlands to olive groves, maquis and high-altitude forest. They are regular up to the summits of mountains such as Parnassos and Olympos and they are sometimes recorded at great distances inland, e.g. recorded at Meteora on 14 May 1984 (Noeske 1987) and Grevena on 30 May 1981. By mid July most birds have already established their territories on breeding islands but they still make daily flights to the nearby mainland or large islands to feed on large insects, returning to roost on their nesting islands at night. For example, on Mt Dirfys in Evvoia they usually appear in loose flocks coming in from the coast at about 10:00–11:00 a.m. each morning and stay until about 18:00 p.m.

Most birds depart from their nesting colonies by mid or late October but some birds may linger until a little later. In 1977–78, 200–300 birds were reported as overwintering in the Dodecanese (Cant 1978) and recently a few have been seen on Mt Athos (P. Dragoumis) and on the island of Milos (G. Petrakis), suggesting occasional wintering of some birds in Greece. The bulk of the population, however, migrates to Madagascar and returns to the Aegean from early April to mid May. Eleonora's Falcons ringed at Paximada have been recovered in Madagascar (five in winter), Egypt (two) and Saudi Arabia (one) on migration. Wandering immatures in late summer have been recovered in Spain, Algeria, Corsica, Malta (two), Turkey (six), Cyprus (two) as well as in the Aegean, i.e. on the islands of Chios (five) and Amorgos (Ristow & Wink 1994).

Eleonora's Falcons

Lanner *Falco biarmicus*

Widespread but rare resident

Lanner still remains one of the least known birds of Greece. Apparently commoner during the 19th century and up to 1950s (Reiser 1905; Krüper 1862; Simpson 1860a; *CFG*), today it has a wide but very patchy distribution, on both the mainland and the islands. It appears that the species is mainly distributed in N Greece (Thrace, Macedonia, Ipeiros and northern Thessaly) with odd pairs probably elsewhere on the mainland, e.g. Sterea Hellas and the Peloponnese. Among the islands nesting is almost certain on Corfu, Lesbos and Kos, possibly on Crete (*BoC*) but perhaps not any more on Rhodes (Scharlau 1989a). Observations of adults in suitable habitat during the breeding season (end of May) exist also from Kefallinia (A. Vittery). Lanner is almost certainly a recent colonist to Crete, first observed there in 1973 (*BoC*). There is at least one breeding record from Crete, of a pair at the nest in 1977 (H. Wolf per D. Ristow). The total Greek population of Lanner is tentatively estimated at 20–40 pairs (Tucker & Heath 1994) and is probably stable but certainly vulnerable due to its small size (*RDB*).

Lanners are seen in a variety of habitats, from sea level to as high as 2300 m (e.g. on Mt Kyllini, Niethammer 1943b) but the few nest sites that have been found so far have been at moderate altitudes of about 500–1000 m. On Crete, Lanner is usually seen over rocky slopes between 400 and 1600 m (*BoC*). In 1860, eggs were collected from a nest in Kleisoura, a rocky gorge with sparse bushes and small trees, northeast of Aitolikon (Simpson 1860a). Up to the early 1960s, one pair nested on Profitis Ilias, a low mountain (798 m) covered with pine *Pinus* woodland, on the island of Rhodes (Wettstein 1938; Ralfs 1960), whereas a similar nest site, on a rocky hill with pine forest, is known in Dadia Forest Reserve in Thrace. It is still not known whether Lanners undertake any migratory movements but most probably they simply disperse seasonally. Lanners breeding in Greece belong to race *F. b. feldeggii*.

Lanner (male)

Saker *Falco cherrug*

Widespread but rare winter visitor and passage migrant

Since 1913, when one was collected at Kattavia, on the southern tip of the island of Rhodes on 27 March (Salvadori & Festa 1913), Sakers have been recorded fewer than 50 times in Greece. Most records are from the mainland, particularly Macedonia and Thrace, with only two or three from the Peloponnese. There are few records from the islands, with only one from the Ionian (Corfu, end of September 1984) and the others from Mykonos, 25 September 1933 (Bird 1935), Lesbos, 23 October 1992, Kalymnos, 23 September 1990 (G. Jeff Price), Karpathos, with two birds there from 10 to 23 September 1963 (Kinzelbach & Martens 1965)

and Crete (two records). The species has never been recorded in summer, all records being from either the winter or from the migration periods (March–April and September–October). It is rumoured that one or two pairs of Sakers may nest in N Greece but details have not been publicised.

Sakers are usually seen in open coastal plains and especially in wetlands (several records from the Evros Delta and Messolonghi). On the few occasions when they have been seen hunting they attacked Black-tailed Godwits, Ruff, Black-headed Gulls, and on 30 March 1980 one adult was seen taking a European suslik in the Evros Delta. One bird ringed as a chick in the nest in Hungary was recovered in its first winter in the Peloponnese.

Peregrine *Falco peregrinus*

Widespread but scarce resident and winter visitor

Peregrines have a widespread distribution over mainland Greece. They also occur on most of the islands, in both the Aegean and the Ionian Seas. Despite, however, the availability of optimum nesting habitat over much of the country, they have a rather patchy and thin distribution and they are locally rare, e.g. on Crete (Vagliano 1984). Their population, still difficult to assess due to lack of sufficient data, is estimated at a minimum of 200–300 pairs, with unknown trends. Although locally decreasing, e.g. in the area of L. Prespa (Catsadorakis 1991) and the northern Peloponnese (CP), they do not seem to be threatened.

Peregrines nest from sea level to about 1500 m, on cliffs and rocky gorges, quite often on small rocky islets and coastal cliffs, particularly on the islands. In Greece they are not known to nest on buildings or other man-made structures, though they often use urban areas for hunting. For example, at least two pairs nest on the hills around Athens, feeding mainly on wintering Starlings and pigeons above the city. Outside the breeding season and particularly in winter, Peregrines are less confined to rocky areas and they are often seen hunting over inland or coastal plains, wetlands and other areas rich in suitable prey. Little is known of their migratory movements but presumably local birds are resident or short-distance migrants, depending on local food availability in the winter months. Significant numbers of birds also arrive from the north for the winter. Peregrines breeding in Greece belong to the Mediterranean race, *F. p. brookei.* Birds of the nominate race, *F. p. peregrinus,* occur on passage and in winter, and at least one female of the northern race, *F. p. calidus,* has been collected (*CFG*).

Barbary Falcon *Falco pelegrinoides*

Accidental

One adult bird found exhausted on a ploughed field at Porto Lagos on 28 April 1987 (Potter 1988) is the only record of Barbary Falcon in Greece. The detailed description of the bird suggests it was of the nominate race.

Hazel Grouse *Bonasa bonasia*

Rare and local resident

Hazel Grouse was first recorded in Greece in October 1964, when a female was shot in the Rodopi Mts (Papaioannou 1968; *CFG*). So far, it is known to occur in three well separated areas. The bulk of the Greek population lives in the dense forests of the western and central Rodopi Mts in eastern Macedonia, sharing more or less the same mixed-forest habitat with Capercaillie. On 22 May 1979, a nest was found in this area at 1550 m in an area with silver birch *Betula pendula*, aspen *Populus tremula* and mountain ash *Sorbus aucuparia* (Bauer & Böhr 1987). A much smaller population occurs on Mt Triklarion, near L. Mikri Prespa, also in mixed forest. This locality, at 40°45'N, is the southernmost distribution limit of the species in the Western Palearctic (Catsadorakis 1989; *BWP*). Recently, on 11 November 1990, a small flock of Hazel Grouse was seen in the forest of Lailias, Serres (P. Latsoudis, K. Poirazidis) in an area also known to hold Capercaillies (Poirazidis 1989, 1990). The species has also been reported as possibly occurring on Mt Grammos (Grimmett & Jones 1989) and in the Pindos range (Papaioannou 1968) but its presence there needs confirmation. Hazel Grouse is one of the least known Greek birds and virtually nothing is known about its population size or ecology. The Greek population belongs to race *B. b. rupestris* (*BWP*).

Black Grouse *Tetrao tetrix*

Status unclear. Accidental?

There have been four records of Black Grouse in Greece. The species was first recorded in the Rodopi Mts in 1935 (season unknown): Papaioannou (1968) claims to have seen many individuals in an area dominated by silver birch *Betula pendula* and hazel *Corylus avellana*. The same author gives a record of a male reported as having been shot near Konitsa (Ipeiros) in February 1961, the specimen now kept in the Zoological Museum of the Game Management Department, School of Forestry, University of Thessaloniki. A third record comes from the vicinity of Thessaloniki in February 1956 (*CFG*) and the fourth again from NE Ipeiros, where several birds were reported as having been shot during the winter of 1965/66 (*CFG*). The scattering and the seasonality of these records suggest irruptive or cold-weather winter movements from the north or perhaps dispersal from nearby still undiscovered populations north of the border, rather than the existence of resident birds, which, however, is a possibility that cannot be totally ruled out. The nearest known breeding area of Black Grouse is in central former Yugoslavia (*BWP*).

Capercaillie *Tetrao urogallus*

Rare and local resident

The presence of Capercaillies in Greece was confirmed as late as 1966, when a first-winter male was shot in the Rodopi Mts (Papaioannou 1968). Breeding was confirmed in the Rodopi Mts in 1969, at an altitude of 1400 m (Bauer & Hodge 1970) and more recently a nest with eight eggs was photographed on Mt Chaindou, near Xanthi, on 22 May 1981 (D. Koukouras). Recent surveys have shown that the species occurs in three distinct regions of Macedonia: the western Rodopi Mts, the forest of Lailias near Serres and Mt Athos. The bulk of the Greek population is in the first area, at 1000–1900 m, and is estimated at 330–380 birds (Poirazidis 1989, 1990). In the western Rodopi Mts, Capercaillies prefer dense mixed forests, dominated by Norway spruce *Picea abies*, Scots pine *Pinus sylvestris*, beech *Fagus* and fir *Abies*. In the forest of Lailias, there are an estimated 20–30 birds in mixed forests mainly of beech and fir at 1100–1600 m. Recently a small population was discovered on Mt Athos, between 1140 and 1340 m (Hölzinger & Rözler 1990). This isolated population is 140 km away from the main distribution area of the species in Rodopi. Its presence here may suggest that, in the past, Capercaillies had a wider distribution in Macedonia, although the possibility of these birds having been introduced there by monks (many of them from eastern Europe) of the many monasteries of Athos cannot be ruled out. Whatever their origin, Mt Athos (40°09'N, 24°20'E) is the southernmost distribution limit of Capercaillies in the Western Palearctic. The species may also occur on Mt Grammos (Y. Roussopoulos).

Capercaillie

Chukar *Alectoris chukar*

Fairly widespread and locally common resident

Chukar has a primarily island distribution in Greece: *A. c. cypriotes* occurs on all the Aegean islands (except the Northern Sporades) and Crete. Another race, *A. c. kleini*, is found in Thrace and meets with Rock Partridge near Komotini, in an area with no geographic barriers to partridge movements. Both species have been collected within 40 km of each other but no actual overlap exists (Watson 1962b; 1962c).

Chukars occupy a broad altitudinal zone, from sea level to altitudes of 2000 m (on Mt Idi, Crete) (Watson 1962b; 1962c) but in Thrace they usually occur at 100–650 m. They prefer sunny, dry hill slopes covered with phrygana and maquis but also require the presence of springs, streams or

Chukar

watering places for domestic animals for drinking. Little is known of their population status, breeding and feeding ecology. Population densities have been estimated at 1.2–3.5 pairs/km^2 (Papaevangelou *et al.* in press). The total Greek population has been estimated at 1,000–5,000 pairs (Tucker & Heath 1994), which, however, is probably too low. Papaevangelou *et al.* (in press) estimate a minimum of 11,000–16,000 pairs in the whole country but this includes introduced as well as native populations. A traditional and popular game bird and on many islands the main quarry species, Chukars have locally declined due to intensive shooting and poaching. This is more evident on certain small islands and parts of Crete, whereas no obvious decline has been reported from elsewhere (e.g. Thrace). An average of 60,000–70,000 captive-bred Chukars are released by hunters and hunters' associations every year, with varying success. These are released all over the country, i.e. including the whole mainland, not only within the natural range of Chukars and some of them seem to have established viable populations (e.g. on Corfu, where Rock Partridges have been exterminated). A serious problem with these releases is their mixed origin, resulting in genetic pollution of indigenous populations of Chukars.

Rock Partridge *Alectoris graeca*

Fairly common and widespread resident

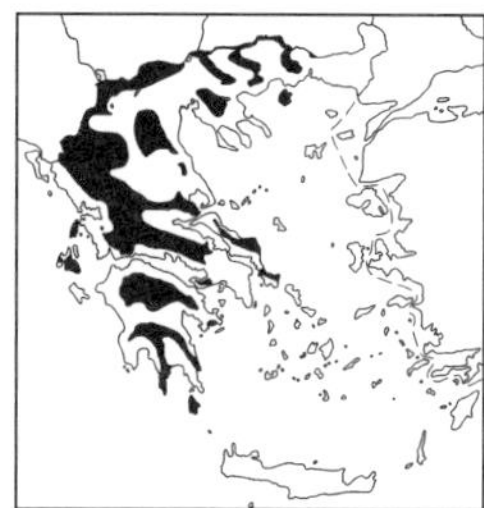

Rock Partridges occur over almost the whole Greek mainland, from eastern Macedonia south to the Peloponnese as well as on the Ionian islands of Kefallinia, Ithaki, Lefkada and Paxoi (A. Vittery). They were exterminated from Zakynthos and Corfu already by the end of the 19th century (*CFG*). They also occur on the island of Kythira (Kominos 1995). Primarily a mountain species involved only in limited altitudinal movements, Rock Partridge is mainly found above 300 m and often up to the summits of the highest of mountains. Locally they may occur down to sea level but in recent years they are most easily seen above the treeline, having become very scarce and restricted to inaccessible areas at lower altitudes. In a study in the region of Serres they were found to occur in habitat dominated by bushy Kermes oak *Quercus coccifera* and junipers *Juniperus communis* and *J. oxycedrus*, but also in very open stands of beech *Fagus*, oak *Quercus* and oriental plane *Platanus orientalis* (Vavalekas *et al.* 1993). In good areas population densities reach 1–1.6 pairs/km^2 (Papaevangelou *et al.* in press). The total Greek population has been estimated at 7,000–13,000 pairs by Papaevangelou *et al.* (in press), who consider the estimate of 2,000–5,000 pairs of Tucker & Heath (1994) much too low, but the true figure is more likely to be in between the two estimates. A traditional and very popular game bird, Rock Partridge has clearly declined seriously over much of its range, particularly in the Peloponnese (Papaevangelou 1980), and has already been exterminated from large areas (e.g. Attica), mainly due to intensive hunting and poaching but also due to habitat changes. Competition with captive-bred Chukars released into Rock Partridge areas should also be considered as a possible reason, though the opposite seems to hold true in the long run (Papaevangelou *et al.* in press).

Red-legged Partridge *Alectoris rufa*

Introduced

Between 1979 and 1981, the Wildlife Department of the Forestry Service experimentally released *c.* 400 captive-bred Red-legged Partridges on the island of Alonnisos. The species seems to have established a viable population there and has withstood controlled hunting since 1983 (E. Papaevangelou). A 19th-century record, with no exact date or location (Mühle 1844), was rejected already by Reiser (1905).

Black Francolin *Francolinus francolinus*

Extinct

Evidence for the former occurrence of Black Francolin in Greece is so scanty and incomplete that it is impossible to define its former status and distribution with certainty. The species was well known to the Ancient Greeks (Pollard 1977) and in later times it was reported as occurring in Greece by at least two travellers: Belon (1555) described a bird from Crete which fits the description of Black Francolin, and Tournefort (1717) said that although uncommon, Black Francolins occurred on the marshy coastal plain of Chora in the south of the island of Samos. In the footnote on page 111 (Vol. II) Tournefort uses the Greek name 'taginari', a word clearly originating from 'attagas' - 'attaginarion', the ancient Greek name for this species. Moreover, an etching of a male Black Francolin facing page 110 (Vol. II) leaves no doubt as to its identity. Black Francolins were reported as having been common on Lesbos, Samos and Rhodes (Bree 1859–63). They possibly also existed on the shores of the Thermaikos Gulf but became extinct there by the middle of the 19th century (Powys 1862). Frivaldzsky (1902) mentioned Black Francolins on Crete between 1843 and 1845 but gave no further details in his work. There have been no records since then and if Frivaldszky's observations are correct, then Black Francolins have been extinct from the whole country for more than 150 years, the last birds probably surviving on Crete or Samos until early in the 19th century.

Grey Partridge *Perdix perdix*

Fairly common but local resident

Grey Partridge was formerly common and locally abundant, with a much wider range than today. During the 19th century it was widely distributed over much of the mainland, though apparently it never occurred in the Peloponnese. In the 20th century and particularly since the 1950s Grey Partridges declined rapidly and they are now confined to northern Greece, mainly from northern Thessaly and SW Macedonia, eastwards to Thrace (*RDB*; Thomaides & Papageorgiou 1992).

There is little information on the ecology of Grey Partridge in Greece. In general, it prefers non-intensively cultivated land, with a mosaic of hedgerows and bushes for nesting and cover. It is a typical bird of the lowlands, not normally found above 600 m. However, in many areas it occurs above 700 m; it has been recorded at up to 1300 m in central Macedonia and there is an extreme case at 2300 m on Mt Grammos (Papaevangelou *et al.* in press). The occurrence of the species at higher altitudes is reported as a recent phenomenon caused by the displacement of birds from lower areas due to pressure from adverse human activities (Papaevangelou *et al.* in press). Over most of the species' range population densities vary between 0.8 and 3.6 pairs/km^2 and in good areas reach up to 12.3 pairs/km^2 (areas of Thessaloniki and Kozani) (Papaevangelou *et al.* in press; Thomaides & Papageorgiou 1992). The total Greek population has been estimated at 2,500–4,000 pairs (Papaevangelou *et al.* in press), which may be too optimistic but the estimate of Tucker & Heath (1994) at 150–300 pairs is certainly far too low. The quick decline of Grey Partridges can be attributed not only to excessive and illegal shooting (now a protected species) but mainly to the use of agrochemicals and modern agricultural methods, as in much of the rest of their palearctic range (*BWP*).

Quail *Coturnix coturnix*

Fairly common and widespread summer visitor and passage migrant, locally resident

Quail has a widespread distribution over much of the mainland and on some of the larger islands but is a very little known species. Its precise breeding range is not known and it is per-

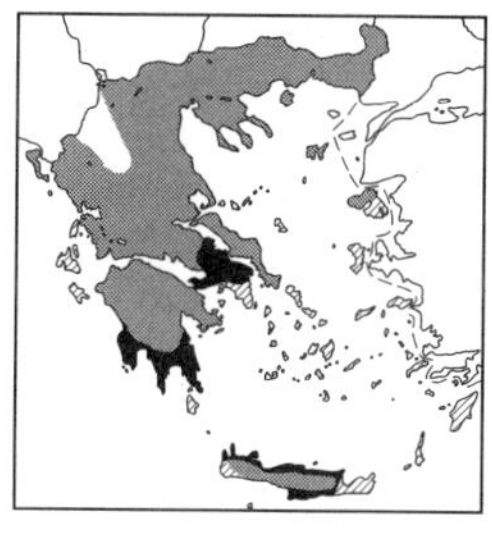

haps more localised than generally thought. It is listed as common on Crete (Vagliano 1984), it nests on Limnos and Lesbos and apparently still does so on Corfu but nesting data from most other islands are very doubtful and it is probably absent from most of them as a breeding bird. Moreover, every year large numbers of captive-bred Quail of mixed origin (including a high proportion of *C. c. japonicus*) are released in many areas for shooting, thus making population estimates and distribution patterns of the wild birds difficult to assess. The total breeding population of wild Quail in Greece is probably well in excess of 5,000 pairs and may be as high as 10,000 pairs. Thus the estimate of Tucker & Heath (1994) at 300–500 pairs is far too low. As in much of Europe, it is a declining species in Greece, mainly due to agricultural intensification and probably overhunting. Hybridisation with released *C. c. japonicus* should also be investigated as a serious threat to local populations (Tucker & Heath 1994).

Quail usually arrive in Greece from early or mid March. Passage of through-migrants may continue to late April or early May, whereas the autumn passage runs mainly from late August to early or mid October, with a peak in the first half of September. On Crete, Quails are probably resident (*BoC*) and irregularly wintering birds are known from other areas as well, e.g. the southern Peloponnese, but their pattern of occurrence in winter is very poorly known.

The species is a popular game bird and in many areas, especially the islands, a major quarry species, subject to heavy hunting pressure. It is much commoner in autumn, particularly in September, than in spring, and although there are marked annual fluctuations in the numbers passing through the country, their overall numbers are now much reduced compared with the past. Up to the 1960s, very large numbers used to be taken with traps, nets and other local devices in Mani Peninsula and on some islands for home consumption. No precise figures are available but whole villages may have depended on salted Quail as the main source of meat during the winter. Very large numbers of Quail were seen on passage in the Cyclades during the autumn of 1933 and on the island of Syros alone, 15,000 birds were estimated to have been killed in one day (Bird 1935). Ringing recoveries of Quail in Greece include four birds ringed in Egypt and one in Italy, all of them apparently ringed on passage.

Pheasant *Phasianus colchicus*

Rare and local resident

Pheasants of the nominate form, *P. c. colchicus*, appear to have been introduced into Greece in prehistoric times, probably from Colchis on the southeast shores of the Black Sea. Ancient Greeks had close links with this area, as the legend of the Argonauts and the Golden Fleece suggests. It is not known precisely when these introduction took place but the species was already well known in classical time (Pollard 1977). During the 19th century, Pheasants were still breeding as far south as Attica, Evvoia and Akarnania (Lindermayer 1860, Powys 1860; Reiser 1905), whereas breeding in several parts of Macedonia was recorded as late as the early 1940s (*CFG*). Today, only one remnant population survives in the riverine forest of the Nestos Delta, partly in a protected, fenced area and partly at a nearby game-rearing station, where an experimental captivc-breeding project is under way. These birds are very different from ordinary stock reared for shooting, being darker and smaller, with no ring on the neck and are much wilder and shier than the latter. The total wild population is not known and estimates vary between *c.* 50 males (Jerrentrup & Resch 1989) to a total of *c.* 800 individuals (Papageorgiou 1992). Outside this area, Pheasants originating from recently released stock occur locally throughout the mainland and on some islands. An average of 100,000 birds are released annually. The results of these re-stocking schemes are questionable but at least in some parts of northern Greece the species seems to have established successfully. Captive-bred birds belong mainly to race *P. c. torquatus*, but their exact origin is not easy to unravel as many races and hybrids are widely used by the game-rearing stations.

Water Rail *Rallus aquaticus*

Common and widespread resident

Water Rail has a wide distribution over much of the mainland as well as on those islands offering suitable habitat (e.g. Corfu, Limnos, Lesbos, Kos and Crete). However, its detailed distribution is not very well known and it may be more localised than thought today, particularly in view of the continuing loss of freshwater wetlands. The total breeding population is probably below 5,000 pairs. It appears that the numbers of Water Rails increase in winter, presumably due to the influx of immigrants from the north. Furthermore, their total numbers and distribution are greatly affected by cold weather and at times of severe cold they may spread to small ditches or temporary pools on flooded fields, often far away from wetlands.

Water Rails also occur as passage migrants but the numbers involved and the patterns of their movements are not well known. They are reputed to be very rare in the Cyclades with only one record (Magioris 1994) and uncommon on Crete from late September to mid April, with some summer records (Vagliano 1984; *BoC*). In a study of bird migration in the wetlands of NE Greece in the spring of 1987, the number of Water Rails increased from early March and peaked in late March, dropping again later (WIWO 90). However, almost all birds were detected by call and, thus, this increase does not necessarily indicate a passage of birds but may be connected with increased territorial activity at that time of the year. Singles ringed in Germany and Austria have been recovered in Greece in the winter.

Spotted Crake *Porzana porzana*

Widespread but scarce passage migrant and winter visitor

There is no proof that Spotted Crakes have ever bred in Greece, although existing evidence suggests that perhaps they did so in the past, e.g. one female was collected at Faliron, Attica, on 2 June 1861 and singles were seen on the island of Skopelos in mid May 1894 (Reiser 1905) and at L. Koronia on 19 May 1943 (Makatsch 1950). The species has also been reported as possibly breeding on Samos and the island of Rhodes (*CFG*). In recent years, one was seen at Aigion Lagoon on 7 July 1987 (CP). On passage, Spotted Crakes occur both on the mainland and on the islands. They are apparently uncommon but like all the three Greek species of crake, they are very elusive and secretive, therefore probably largely overlooked. Spring passage takes place from early April to early May, with a peak in the second half of April. Both on Crete (*BoC*) and on the mainland there appear to be annual variations in the number of spring migrants. There are few records from autumn, mainly in September and October. A few winter records suggest that at least some birds may spend the winter in Greece, e.g. one at Kotychi Lagoon and three in the Amvrakikos in January 1984 (Joensen & Madsen 1985) and one in the Evros Delta on 25 and 26 January 1990.

Little Crake *Porzana parva*

Rare and local summer visitor, fairly common passage migrant

Up to the mid 1960s Little Crakes were reported as probably breeding at L. Kastoria, L. Kerkini, L. Ismaris and the Nestos Delta (Kraus *et al.* 1969; *CFG*) but they were first proved to breed in Greece on 9 May 1968, when a nest was found at L. Koronia (*CFG*). There have been few confirmed breeding records since then but most probably it is still a rare breeding species in Macedonia and Thrace. The total Greek population has been estimated at 10–50 pairs (Tucker & Heath 1994). Little Crake is apparently the commonest crake on passage through Greece, though this may be because it is the least elusive of the three species, often seen swimming on open water near the edge of emergent vegetation. The species is listed as a fairly common spring migrant on Crete (*BoC*), as a migrant in small numbers on Kefallinia

(A. Vittery) and as rare in the Cyclades (Magioris 1994), where suitable habitat is limited. There is also a scattering of records from the rest of the Aegean. Spring migration runs from late March to early May, with a peak in mid April. One male seen on 9 March 1992, near Divari Lagoon, SW Peloponnese, is the earliest record so far (D. Papandropoulos). There are very few observations from the autumn migration period, from mid August to mid October, with one record from the end of October. Small numbers of Little Crakes were found among prey remains of Eleonora's Falcons at a colony off NE Crete (mid August to mid October), compared with very few Spotted Crakes and no Baillon's Crakes (Ristow *et al.* 1986).

Baillon's Crake *Porzana pusilla*

Widespread but scarce passage migrant

The least common of the three crakes occurring in Greece, Baillon's Crake is a regular but scarce or rare migrant. Most records are from the spring passage, from late March to mid May, mainly in the second half of April. Very few records are from the autumn, from the end of August to early October. Baillon's Crakes are scarce on spring passage through Crete (Vagliano 1984; *BoC*). So far there are no known records from the Ionian islands and although listed as a 'common' migrant on the island of Chios (Spinthakis *et al.* 1993), there are very few documented records from the Aegean (other than Crete) e.g. two on the island of Naxos on 29 April 1986 (Broggi & Willi 1986), one at the Alyki Lagoon on Kos on 5 April 1989 (B. de Schutter) and two to three heard also on Kos on 3 April 1992 (J.H. Rahder). Although breeding cannot be discounted and the species appears as a Greek breeding bird in Tucker & Heath (1994), with an estimated population of 10–50 pairs, there are no published breeding records. Baillon's Crakes migrating through Greece belong to the European race, *P. p. intermedia*, but birds of the eastern race, *P. p. pusilla*, possibly also occur (*CFG*; *BWP*).

Corncrake *Crex crex*

Widespread but rare passage migrant

Earlier this century, Corncrakes were reported as breeding in the extreme south of former Yugoslavia, not far from the Greek border (Glegg 1924). They were also recorded at L. Koronia in May (Makatsch 1950) and listed as 'breeding locally in N Greece' (Lambert 1957). Nevertheless, there is no proof that the species has ever nested in Greece. It was apparently much commoner up to 20–30 years ago, being well known and regularly shot by Quail hunters in the autumn. Today, Corncrakes are so rare on passage, that it is even not certain whether they occur regularly every year, though probably they are largely overlooked. After 1970 the species has been recorded fewer than 15 times. There are only three records from Crete, of two found in prey remains of Eleonora's Falcons in autumn 1977 (Ristow *et al.* 1986) and one seen at Mallia in early May 1986 (*BoC*). Corncrakes are listed as rare spring and autumn passage migrants on the island of Chios (Spinthakis *et al.* 1993) but so far they have not been recorded on any of the Ionian islands. Recent records from the mainland include one heard calling at L. Vegoritis on 15 April 1979 (Makatsch 1981), one at L. Ismaris on 2 May 1987 (A. & R. Scott) and another one there on 22 August 1991 (F. Barrault). Most records are from mid April to early May and from mid September to mid October, though one was collected at L. Karla on 27 November 1895 (Reiser 1905).

Moorhen *Gallinula chloropus*

Common and widespread resident

Moorhens breed over much of the mainland and on most of the Aegean and Ionian islands. They are quite ubiquitous, exploiting a wide variety of freshwater habitats from small marshes on the islands to large wetlands. They are frequently found breeding opportunistically even in temporary marshes which are suitable only in certain years or only for the early part of the breeding season. The highest breeding locality known is L. Mikri Prespa at 850 m. The size of their total breeding population is not known but it almost certainly exceeds 20,000 pairs, with a higher density in northern and central Greece and the northern and western part of the Peloponnese. At least 400 pairs nest in the northern Peloponnese alone (CP). In central Greece, nests with eggs have been found as early as the beginning of March and downy chicks as late as mid August.

Although it is certain that Greece is visited by wintering Moorhens from the north (see recoveries below), there is no obvious increase of their numbers in winter. However, during autumn and winter they are often very shy and difficult to detect due to hunting pressure and any change in their numbers would be difficult to observe. They are common on spring passage on Crete and listed as a spring migrant in the Cyclades, where they may also breed (Magioris 1994), but throughout southern Greece and the islands they become more widespread after the middle of winter and in spring, perhaps partly because of cold-weather movements from northern parts of the country or from the northern Balkans and partly because seasonal marshes and pools tend to flood at that time of the year, after autumn rains. Migratory movements of Moorhens are indicated by the finding of some birds among prey remains of Eleonora's Falcons off NE Crete (Ristow *et al.* 1986). Two birds ringed in Germany and singles from Latvia, Poland, the Czech Republic, Slovakia and Bulgaria have been recovered in Greece in winter.

Purple Gallinule *Porphyrio porphyrio*

Former breeding species, now accidental

Purple Gallinules were first recorded in Greece in the 1830s, by members of the *Expédition Scientifique du Morée* who listed the species as 'very rare' (in the Peloponnese), having seen a few individuals at the Divari Lagoon and in the marshes of the Evrotas river mouth (Geoffroy Saint-Hilaire 1832). The species has also been reported from L. Dystos (Evvoia) and L. Kopais (now drained), where it was perhaps a breeding bird (Erhard 1858). There is only one record from the 20th century, of one in the Nestos Delta in April 1965 (*CFG*; *RDB*). These records suggest that, in the 19th century, the species was a resident breeding bird in southern mainland Greece but became extinct by the end of the century, as in much of the rest of the Mediterranean (*BWP*). The Nestos record probably refers to a genuine vagrant, most probably from the Middle East or the Caspian Sea.

Coot *Fulica atra*

Common and widespread resident, very common winter visitor

Coot breed in many wetlands of the mainland, from Thrace and Macedonia south to the northern and western Peloponnese, as well as on a few islands with suitable habitat, e.g. Corfu, Limnos and at least occasionally on Lesbos and Crete (*BoC*). They breed in freshwater or brackish habitats, including lakes, lagoons and canals, from sea level up to 850 m, at L. Mikri Prespa. The total breeding population probably numbers between 3,000 and 5,000 pairs.

The species is much more widespread and numerous in winter, spreading to seasonal pools

or marshes and, occasionally, sheltered marine waters. Greece holds 6% of the Black Sea–Mediterranean population (Rüger *et al.* 1986). Data from the IWRB MC (1982–1992) give a national average of 74,000, against 125,170 for the 1968–1976 period, a maximum year count of 338,920 (1970) and a maximum site count of 130,000 at Ptelea Lagoon on 11 January 1970. In the past, five sites (L. Volvi, Evros Delta, Messolonghi, Amvrakikos and L. Ismaris together with the four Thracian lagoons) used to qualify as wetlands of international importance but today no Greek wetland qualifies as such. Spring and autumn passage appear to be insignificant, but in winter cold-weather movements are frequent and include influxes into Greece from further north as well as the movement of birds from frozen lakes in Macedonia and Thrace to the nearest coast and to milder parts of the country. Wintering birds begin arriving in mid October, numbers building up until mid November, and depart between late February and late March. Nine birds ringed abroad have been recovered in Greece in winter, including four from Lithuania, two from Slovakia and singles from Poland, Latvia and Russia. One ringed at L. Volvi in December was recovered two weeks later in Sicily, and another from the same lake in November 1977 was recovered at L. Lysimachia in December 1978 (P. Belman).

Crane *Grus grus*

Former breeding species, now irregular passage migrant

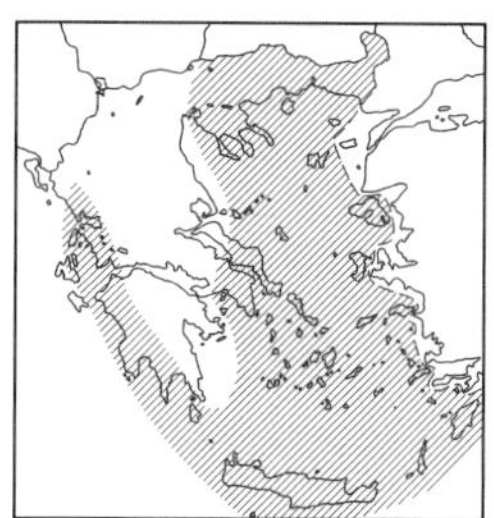

The last but also the only documented breeding record of Cranes in Greece is of one pair nesting in the Evros Delta in 1965 (Bauer & Müller 1969; *CFG*). However, there are indications that the species bred locally in northern Greece before this date, e.g. one pair was seen at Rendina Marshes in early spring 1918 (Harrison 1925) and three were seen in the Evros Delta on 13 May 1935 (Harrison & Pateff 1937). Today, the species is an irregular passage migrant, though possibly overlooked as flocks may overfly parts of the country without stopping. Most recent records of spring migrants are from the 10–25 March period, with a few from late February and early April. There are few records from the autumn passage, mainly from mid September to mid October. Autumn records include a case of flocks flying at high altitude over the mountains of Achaia in September in the early 1980s (CP), a flock of *c.* 150 flying over the west coast of the island of Kythira in late September 1987 (Kominos 1995) and a flock of *c.* 20 at Sami, Kefallinia, flying in south from the island of Ithaki in September 1991 (K.S. Lodge). The majority of migrating Cranes are seen in coastal areas. Most records are from NE Greece, particularly the Evros Delta, Crete and the southern and eastern Aegean islands (e.g. Karpathos, Rhodes, Pserimos, Limnos and Naxos).

The species is usually seen in small flocks of 5–30 birds but in earlier years flocks of 100–300 were not unusual (Powys 1860; Stresemann 1956). On Crete, Cranes are still probably regular on passage, mainly in the spring, with flocks of up to 100 and rarely up to 250, overflying the island at a great height (*BoC*). The largest numbers ever recorded in Greece are both from the Evros Delta, with *c.* 400 on 19 March 1965 (Bauer & Müller 1969) and 610 on 30 March 1973 (W. Suter). On a few occasions small numbers of Cranes have been recorded wintering in Greece, apparently more often in the past than in recent years. In the last 20 years there are only four winter records, of six in November 1986 and 11 on 8 December 1990, both at Messolonghi (Pergantis & Handrinos 1992, P. Latsoudis), and of two on 23 January 1988 and on 22 January 1994, at L. Kerkini.

Demoiselle Crane *Anthropoides virgo*

Accidental

Demoiselle Cranes were first recorded in Evvoia (Lindermayer 1859) and in the Cyclades, where they were also believed to breed (Erhard 1858). However, subsequent authors have

rejected both records (*CFG*). The first confirmed record was on 5 April 1859, when one was shot in Attica and kept in the collection of the Zoological Museum of Athens University (Reiser 1905). The only other known record is of one between Serres and Drama on 2 May 1956 (Kumerloeve 1957).

Little Bustard *Tetrax tetrax*

Former breeding species, now rare and irregular winter visitor and passage migrant

During the 19th century Little Bustards bred in Boeotia (Makatsch 1950) and in Macedonia (Glegg 1924; Elwes & Buckley 1870) and the last known breeding case in Greece was of two nests found in the Kilkis area on 18 and 19 May 1917 (Clarke 1917). Since then there have been fewer than 20 records, six of them from the Axios basin, where the last nests were found. In this area, near Polykastro, H. Percy, a British Army officer, claims to have seen 'many thousand' Little Bustards during the cold February of 1946. Another record from the same areas is of a flock of *c.* 250 flying over Kymina (Axios Delta) on 14 February 1940 (Makatsch 1950). There are also five records from the Evros Delta, with a maximum of 22–23 birds in December 1966 (Bauer & Müller 1969), and others of singles or small parties from various parts of the mainland, e.g. Messolonghi (September 1960), Marathon (March 1964), the Nestos Delta (10 January 1972) and Kanallaki, near Preveza (1985). The only recent island records are from Limnos in 1942 (Kummer 1981) and Kythira (one shot) in December 1987 (Kominos 1995). The most recent record is of one female shot in the Evros Delta on 18 October 1993.

Houbara Bustard *Chlamydotis undulata*

Accidental

The only record of Houbara Bustard is of one bird flushed by the dog of a German soldier in the Spercheios Delta in June 1841 (Mühle 1844; Reiser 1905).

Great Bustard *Otis tarda*

Former breeding species, now accidental

During the 19th century, several authors have commented on the status of Great Bustards in Greece describing them as plentiful in Akarnania (Sperling 1864), very common in Macedonia, or feeding in immense flocks in the plains of Thessaly near Meteora (Drummond-Hay 1846). In the winter of 1855 they were also recorded in the Cyclades (Erhard 1858). They were reported breeding in Thessaly, Evvoia, Fthiotis, Attica, Boeotia and Arkadia and were possibly breeding at Cherson in the Kilkis region as late as 1918 (Sladen 1918). Since then, there have been fewer than 20 records, all from winter (December–March), with one to

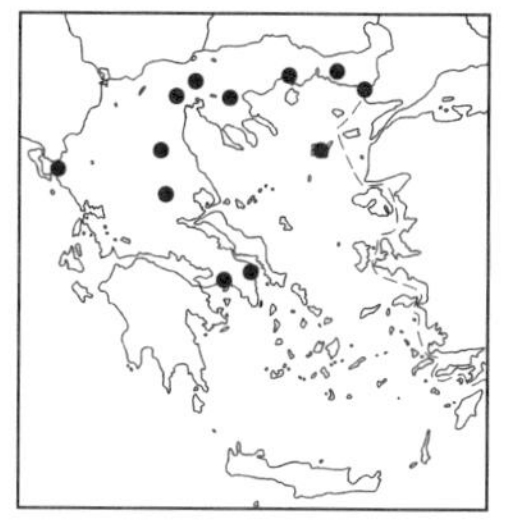

three birds in all cases. Most recent records are from Macedonia and Thrace, e.g. three (one shot) near Kavala in December 1920, one at Sarigiol Marshes, near Ptoelemais, in January–February 1946, one female (shot) at Skydra on 18 March 1954, one male (shot) at Nea Apollonia on 12 January 1963 and 'several' near Komotini in March 1935. There are three records from the Evros Delta: one pair in March 1954, three in winter 1962/63, two in January 1968 (Bauer & Müller 1969), as well as one shot at Dikella in the Evros basin in March 1968. Additional recent records from other areas have been from Farsala (Thessaly) in December 1922, Skaramagkas (Attica) on 23 December 1931, one (shot) in the Kalamas Delta on 6 January 1934, three (one male shot) on the island of Limnos in December 1953, one at Marathon in February 1957 (*CFG*) and four to five at Elasson in the winter of 1962/63 (G. Goumbouros). During the last 20 years there have been a few more unsubstantiated reports, especially during severe winters, e.g. from the island of Kefallinia, Thessaly and the Evros Delta. The last confirmed record remains that of the bird shot at Dikella in 1968.

Oystercatcher *Haematopus ostralegus*

Scarce and local resident, fairly common winter visitor

Oystercatchers breed in most of the major coastal wetlands of Macedonia and Thrace, with isolated populations at Messolonghi (*c.* 25 pairs in 1990) (Roussopoulos 1990) and the Amvrakikos. In the past, they probably bred further south (e.g. Attica) (Reiser 1905) than they do today but like today they were a rather scarce species. However, during the last 20–30 years their population has undergone dramatic declines at certain main sites (e.g. the Evros Delta). Their total Greek population is now estimated at perhaps not more than 50–60 pairs.

Oystercatchers are more widespread outside the breeding season but they are still not numerous and restricted mainly to central and northern parts of the mainland. In the Peloponnese they occur only as scarce passage migrants. Data from the IWRB MC (1982–1992) give a national average of 57 birds, a maximum of 213 (1971) and a maximum site count of 98, at Lafri Lagoon on 17 January 1988. A few more birds are probably present outside areas covered by the MC. There is little information on either spring or autumn passage but it is clear that only a few birds cross the Aegean or the Ionian Seas. During the 20th century there have been no records from the Cyclades (Magioris 1994), only three records from Crete (*BoC*), a few from the eastern Aegean islands, e.g. Rhodes (*CFG*) and Lesbos, and two from Kefallinia (A. Vittery). However, a small but regular passage exists on the mainland between mid March and mid April. Increased numbers where observed in the Porto Lagos area in mid March in the period from 1 March to 21 May 1987 (WIWO 90), suggesting a small passage. In the same study it was estimated that 500–1,000 Oystercatchers used the wetlands of this area during the entire spring migration period. According to the literature (*VME*; *BWP*) and biometric data of ringed birds (WIWO 90), it is not clear which race of Oystercatcher occurs in Greece but birds of the eastern race, *H. o. longipes,* (breeding from the Black Sea eastwards) seem to occur, at least on migration.

Black-winged Stilt *Himantopus himantopus*

Fairly widespread and locally common summer visitor, common and widespread passage migrant

Apparently more widespread and numerous in the past, Black-winged Stilts today have a patchy distribution on the mainland. They also breed regularly on two of the larger islands, Limnos and Lesbos, and occasionally also on Corfu, Naxos and Kos. On the mainland, Black-winged Stilts breed in most of the major coastal and a few of the inland wetlands, from the western Peloponnese northwards. Within their breeding range and particularly during the last

20–30 years, they locally declined or even became extinct as in the Evros Delta, where there were 165–180 pairs in 1967 (Bauer & Müller 1969) but no regular breeding since 1989. However, even today Black-winged Stilts frequently form large temporary breeding concentrations, wherever suitable habitat becomes available. This most often involves unusual flooding of normally summer-dry marshes after heavy rainfall. For example at least 300 pairs were counted in the Agios Mamas Lagoon in 1988 (Joensen & Jerrentrup 1988) and 29 pairs on the island of Limnos also in 1988 (Hölzinger 1991). Another recently discovered and perhaps recently formed population is at Kalogria Lagoon, with 350 pairs in 1993, 270 pairs in 1994 and 300 in 1995 (CP). The total Greek population probably exceeds 1,000 pairs. Breeding Black-winged Stilts prefer fresh or brackish marshes with little submerged vegetation and scattered clumps of emergent reeds *Phragmites* or rushes *Juncus*. Such habitat is frequently seasonal and may be maintained by regular grazing and/or drying up in the summer. Furthermore, its suitability may vary from year to year, when nests are built at the edge of large areas of shallow water parents and their broods may have to follow the receding water as its level drops during the summer. Occasional pairs may nest in rice fields, especially neglected patches with sparse rice plants.

During passage, particularly in spring, Black-winged Stilts can be seen practically all over the mainland and on most of the islands, wherever there is suitable habitat. The first birds usually arrive between 15 and 20 March, though they may be up to a week earlier in the southern Peloponnese (CP). Peak passage is from mid April to early May, numbers declining thereafter. Occasional non-breeders may linger until much later, depending on water levels whilst later in the summer (mid July onwards) many birds disperse from breeding sites due to progressive drying-up. The autumn passage is much less marked, as most patches of habitat which were suitable in the spring are dry in the autumn. Departures take place mainly from early August to the end of September and the last birds are usually seen in early October.

Avocet *Recurvirostra avosetta*

Fairly widespread and locally fairly common resident and winter visitor

More widespread up to 1960s, today Avocets have a very limited and disjunct breeding distribution: they breed only at Messolonghi, in the coastal wetlands of the Thermaikos Gulf (e.g. the Alyki Kitrous Lagoon and the Axios Delta) and in the wetlands of the Porto Lagos complex, with a few odd pairs elsewhere, e.g. the Amvrakikos and the Keramoti Lagoons. Small colonies also exist at Kalloni Saltpans (Lesbos) and on Limnos. In the last 20–30 years their population has decreased significantly and they have even become locally extinct, e.g. they became practically extinct in the Evros Delta after 1987 (Goutner & Kazantzidis 1992), where there were 200–220 pairs in 1967 (Bauer & Müller 1969) and up to 120 pairs in 1982 (Goutner & Jerrentrup 1987). Today the Greek breeding population is estimated at 500–700 pairs, with a trend of further decline.

Outside the breeding season and particularly in winter, Avocets occur more widely and are more numerous, though again the bulk of the population is concentrated at a few coastal sites. Data from the IWRB MC (1982–1992) give an average of 2,840 birds, a maximum year count of 8,506 (1989) and a maximum site count of 3,500 in the Spercheios Delta on 21 January 1989. Although existing data are still limited, it seems that insignificant numbers pass through the Ionian and Aegean islands, including Crete, during migration. Most wintering birds depart from early March and a small passage is evident in late March and early April. A total of 3,000 birds in the Axios Delta on 5 March 1967 (Eber 1967) is one of the largest numbers recorded outside the main winter season.

Egg-laying of local birds begins soon after peak spring passage, with most eggs laid from mid April to mid May. Breeding colonies of Avocets are found almost exclusively in saline and hypersaline lagoons and saltpans, with the nests on small islets or inaccessible dikes. In winter they remain in more or less the same types of habitat, though a few are also seen at inland freshwater sites and in the Spercheios and Aliakmon deltas they occur on tidal mudflats. There are ten recoveries of ringed Avocets found in Greece: five from Austria, four from the Ukraine and one from Bulgaria.

Avocets

Stone Curlew *Burhinus oedicnemus*

Fairly widespread and locally fairly common summer visitor and passage migrant

Stone Curlews breed in most of the major coastal wetlands, mainly in W Greece, Macedonia and Thrace, with a few pairs in the NW Peloponnese, Thessaly and Sterea Hellas (including N Evvoia). Among the islands, nesting has so far been confirmed only on Limnos, Lesbos and Crete. During the 19th century and early this century, they were much more widespread (Reiser 1905; Krüper & Hartlaub 1875; Drummond-Hay 1843a) than today. The total breeding population is not known and is especially difficult to assess due to the poor quality of available data but it is estimated at a few hundred pairs, probably under 500. A survey on the island of Limnos in 1988 has revealed a total of 45–50 pairs, a remarkable density compared with breeding sites on the mainland (Hölzinger 1991).

Stone Curlew

Stone Curlews nest mainly in sparse halophytic vegetation on the margins of coastal wetlands or on extensive sandy beaches and dunes. The high population on Limnos was found in similar habitat but also on dry hills with phrygana and dry grass. This habitat common over much of the country is apparently perfectly suitable for Stone Curlews but, although occasionally used by passage migrants, it is not commonly used for breeding elsewhere in the country.

On both spring and autumn passage the species is more widespread. The main passage appears to be from early April to early May and from late August to early October. According to some authorities (e.g. *BWP*; *CFG*) Stone Curlews winter in parts of southern Greece such as the Peloponnese. However, there are very few documented records and the only known cases of wintering in recent decades are of one near Ierapetra on 24 December 1978 (*BoC*) and one on the island of Kythira in January 1991 (Kominos 1995). Both the nominate race, *B. o. oedicnemus*, and *B. o. saharae* are known to occur in Greece, with breeding birds belonging to the latter race (*CFG*; *BWP*).

Cream-coloured Courser *Cursorius cursor*

Accidental

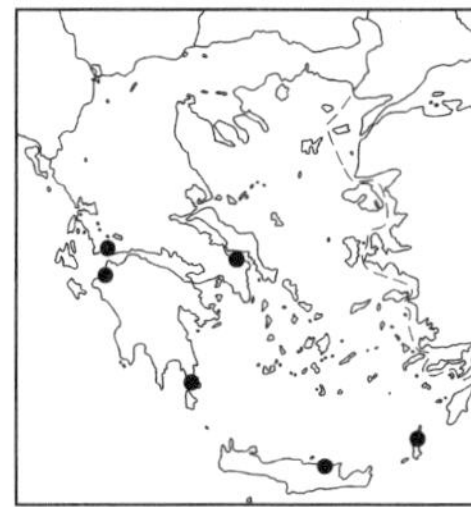

There are six records of the Cream-coloured Courser, all in April: one pair near Kastelli on the island of Karpathos on 3 April 1963 (Kinzelbach & Martens 1965), one at Oropos Lagoon on 6 April 1977 (H. Harrop), one at Viglafia Lagoon, Lakonia, on 23 April 1990 (M. Gaetlich), one at Messolonghi also on 23 April 1990 (WIWO 95), one at Aposelemis river mouth, N Crete, between 31 March and 4 April 1993 (J. Metcalf) and one at Kalogria Lagoon on 21 and 22 April 1995 (D. Papandropoulos & L. Logothetis). Most of the records are from the southern part of the mainland or the southern Aegean region, as expected from the nearest breeding areas of the species in N Africa.

Collared Pratincole *Glareola pratincola*

Fairly common but local summer visitor, widespread passage migrant

Existing information suggests that the breeding range of Collared Pratincole in Greece has not changed much since the mid 19th century. The breeding population of the species, however, has declined dramatically during the last 20–30 years and within their present range many local populations have become extinct, e.g. in the Kalamas Delta where there were 10–20 pairs in 1989, only one or two remained in 1994 (F. Pergantis). Today, Collared Pratincoles nest at a few coastal sites from Messolonghi north–northwest to the Kalamas Delta and from the Alyki Kitrous Lagoon eastwards to the Evros Delta. Colonies exist also at L. Ismaris, L. Kerkini and the Spercheios Delta. Occasionally, a few pairs nest at L. Petron in western Macedonia and in the NW Peloponnese (e.g. Kotychi Lagoon). No recent survey has been made but in the late 1980s the population was estimated at 1,000–1,500 pairs. As elsewhere in the Western Palearctic, Collared Pratincoles usually nest on dry coastal saltmarshes, dry meadows or other similar sparsely vegetated areas near water. They mostly feed over adjacent shallow water, wet marshes or flat dry land, and are often numerous over rice fields.

Collared Pratincoles are more widespread on passage, especially in spring, from early April to mid May, with a peak in late April. A total of *c.* 800 birds seen in the Axios Delta on 5 September 1963 (Bezzel & Müller 1964) is the largest number ever recorded in Greece, whilst *c.* 500 at Messolonghi on 3 August 1980 (Pergantis & Handrinos 1992) is also a remarkable concentration at the end of the breeding season.

Collared Pratincoles

Black-winged Pratincole *Glareola nordmanni*

Rare and irregular passage migrant

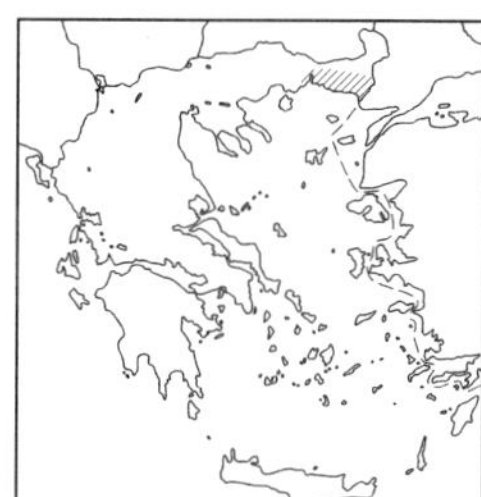

Since the first record of Black-winged Pratincole in 1843/45, when one was collected on Crete (Frivaldszky 1906), the species has been recorded in Greece fewer than 20 times. Undoubtedly some Black-winged Pratincoles are taken for Collared Pratincoles and conversely not all existing records (particularly those in the past) are beyond doubt of confusion with the latter. All records are from spring and late summer to early autumn, with the majority from April–May and August. Usually singles or up to three are seen, with a maximum of *c.* ten in the Evros Delta in May 1955 (Flach 1955a) and seven on the island of Rhodes on 17 April 1960 (Ralfs 1960). Most of the records are from Macedonia and Thrace, particularly Porto Lagos and the Evros Delta. Five records are from the Aegean islands (Paros, Rhodes, Crete, two from Lesbos) and one from Corfu.

Little Ringed Plover *Charadrius dubius*

Fairly common and widespread summer visitor and passage migrant

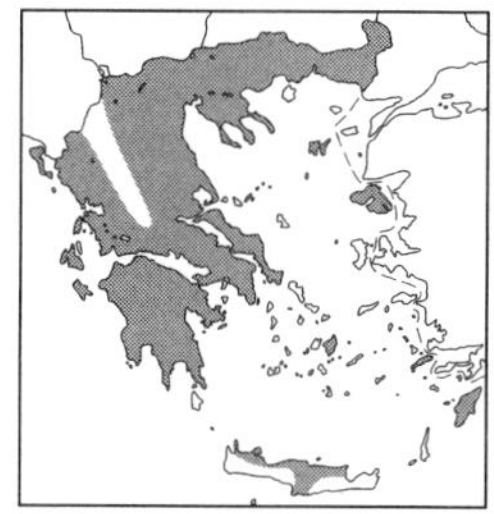

Little Ringed Plovers have a widespread breeding distribution over much of the Greek mainland, including most of the Peloponnese. They also nest on several of the larger islands, e.g. Corfu, Limnos, Lesbos, Rhodes (Scharlau 1989a) and Crete. Little Ringed Plovers nest from coastal wetlands to mountain river valleys and the highest known site is at 550 m on the R. Voidomatis (Schmid & Reichenecker 1988). They show a clear preference for areas of gravel or flat expanses of dry mud or compacted sand with stones and pebbles near water. This habitat is most frequent in seasonal river beds but the species also regularly occurs in such habitat on lake shores and on the coast. Little Ringed Plovers are locally fairly common and generally present wherever suitable habitat exists. In a sample census along the R. Kompsatos in Thrace, at least 30 pairs were found in *c.* 10 km of river course (WIWO 90). There are no estimates of their numbers but the total breeding population probably amounts to 3,000–10,000 pairs. Some through-passage probably takes place but it is masked by the arrival and departure movements of local breeding birds. The species is present in Greece from early March to early October, with a few late birds up to early November. One bird ringed in Germany and another one from the Czech Republic have been recovered in Greece.

Ringed Plover *Charadrius hiaticula*

Fairly common and widespread passage migrant, rare winter visitor

There is no concrete evidence that Ringed Plovers have ever nested in Greece. Sladen (1917) reported a nest with one egg at L. Pikrolimni, Kilkis, on 8 June 1917 but later authors have pointed out that this was most probably the nest of a Little Ringed Plover (*CFG*). On at least two more occasions pairs have been seen in suitable habitat during the breeding season but nesting has not been confirmed: in the Axios Delta on 7 June 1942 and at Kotychi Lagoon (two pairs) on 18 May 1979 (Makatsch 1950, 1981). Ringed Plovers occur mainly as passage migrants, both in the spring and in the autumn, when they may be seen at coastal sites throughout the country. Overall, they are the least common of the three widespread Greek *Charadrius*, most often seen singly and rarely in parties of more that 10–20 birds. Passage runs from early March to early May and from early August to the end of October. Autumn passage is on a larger scale than in spring. Ringed Plovers also occur irregularly and in very small numbers in winter. According to the literature (*CFG*), all Ringed Plovers seen in Greece belong to the north Russian race *C. h. tundrae*.

Kentish Plover *Charadrius alexandrinus*

Common and widespread resident

Kentish Plover is one of the commonest small waders in Greece and breeds in almost all the major coastal wetlands of the mainland, as far south as the S Peloponnese. They also nest on some of the larger islands in both the Aegean and the Ionian Seas, e.g. Lesbos, Limnos, Zakynthos and Corfu. There is no complete census of the breeding population, which, however, certainly numbers many hundreds of pairs, perhaps more than 2,000. Kentish Plovers nest exclusively in coastal wetlands with a preference for dry mudflats, saltpans, and saltmarshes with sparse halophytic vegetation and large bare patches of mud. In the Evros Delta, egg-laying starts in mid April with a peak in early May, whereas post-fledging dispersion starts already in the end of June (Goutner 1983b).

Kentish Plovers are present all year round and it is difficult, if not impossible, to separate the movements and the timing of arrival and departure of local breeders, passage migrants and winter visitors. In addition, they tend to be spread out over large areas of suitable habitat, not concentrating in large flocks as most other waders do, which makes them difficult to count. Over the whole country, they tend to be most numerous on passage, from early March to early May and from late August to mid October. In winter they are numerous in western and southern Greece but not in Macedonia and Thrace, where rather few, probably locally breeding birds, remain. Maximum site counts include 577 at Messolonghi in March 1990 (WIWO 95) and 1,675 also at Messolonghi on 16 January 1993.

Greater Sand Plover *Charadrius leschenaultii*

Rare and irregular winter visitor and passage migrant

There are 11 records of Greater Sand Plover so far. The species is probably overlooked due both to its similarity to commoner plovers and to the often difficult conditions of observation in its preferred habitat (inaccessibility, heat haze). Most records are concentrated at a few sites only, particularly the NW Peloponnese, Messolonghi and Zakynthos, with five of them from the Aigion Lagoon (CP), where observations are regular and meticulous. The species has been recorded mainly in August and September with one record in December, one in April and one in July. In most cases single birds have been seen but a flock of six was seen in the Spercheios Delta on 16 September 1954 (Watson 1961a). At least four of the birds seen at Aigion Lagoon appeared to belong to the west Asian race, *C. l. columbinus* (CP).

Caspian Plover *Charadrius asiaticus*

Accidental

There are two records of Caspian Plover, both fully substantiated by photographs: an adult female in the Evros Delta on 23 July 1986 (Cook 1988) and a single at Mallia, Crete, on 23 and 24 April 1990 (G. Potter & R.D. Oades).

Dotterel *Charadrius morinellus*

Widespread but rare passage migrant

Since October 1836, when six juveniles were seen for sale in the Athens market (Mühle 1844), Dotterels have been recorded fewer than 25 times in Greece. Most records are from migration periods, both spring (mid March to late April) and autumn (late August to late October), with a few from winter (November to January). Only three records are from western Greece: one juvenile at Aigion Lagoon on 13 November 1988 (CP), two juveniles shot at Messolonghi on 28 August 1990 and one on Kefallinia on 25 March 1994 (A. Vittery). All other records are in the eastern part of the country, from Crete and the island of Kythira in the south to the Evros Delta in the north. In most cases single birds or twos have been seen but there is one record of four birds in the Evros Delta on 28 March 1965 (Knotzsch 1965) and of a small group at above 2000 m on Mt Idi on 4 October 1980 (H. Märki).

Between 17 and 21 June 1956, Peus (1957) saw at least two adults on a high plateau of Mt Olympos at 2200–2300 m. Considering the time of year, the suitability of the habitat and the general behaviour of the birds, he thought they might be nesting in this area. More recently, one adult male with two juveniles was seen on Mt Taygetos on 26 August 1990 (Warncke 1995). Although the birds behaved as if they were at a breeding site, the late date is more indicative of, or at least cannot rule out, birds on passage.

Pacific Golden Plover *Pluvialis fulva*

Accidental

On 15 February 1963 Dr I.C.T. Nisbet and J.J. Swift saw two birds at close range among 65 Golden Plovers at Oropos Lagoon in Attica. In their report they listed them as 'Asiatic Golden Plovers *Pluvialis dominica*' but in view of the taxonomic changes that have been made since then, with the two races of the former Lesser Golden Plover now treated as distinct species, it is uncertain what name should be assigned to these two birds. Most probably they were Pacific Golden Plovers *Pluvialis fulva*, a species slightly more likely to occur in Greece than American Golden Plover *P. dominica*. Pacific Golden Plovers have also been recorded and positively identified on two occasions on Crete: one at Rethymnon on 12 April 1985 and another at Damnoni beach in April 1989 (*BoC*).

Golden Plover *Pluvialis apricaria*

Fairly widespread and common winter visitor

The overall numbers of Golden Plovers wintering in Greece are difficult to estimate because the birds are spread out over large areas of farmland, meadows and marshes. Data from the IWRB MC (1982–1992) give an average of 488 birds, a maximum year count of 1,764 (1988) and a maximum site count of 1,750 at Messolonghi on 26 January 1988, but all these counts are to a greater or lesser extent underestimates. On the basis of winter counts, Golden Plovers are much more numerous in W Greece, particularly Messolonghi, than Macedonia and Thrace. They are apparently rare on the islands of both the Aegean and the Ionian Seas. There have been no records from the Cyclades since 1950 (Magioris 1987a) and very few from Crete (*BoC*), Chios (Spinthakis *et al.* 1993) and Corfu. Golden Plovers appear to be rare in the Peloponnese too, with only a couple of records in recent years. However, it is almost certain that they occur more widely than records suggest, being easily overlooked. The first birds usually arrive towards the end of October. At this time of the year they frequently occur on stubble or recently ploughed fields but as the new vegetation grows and becomes denser and taller, they often have to shift to short-grazed grassland, meadows or the edges of saltmarshes from about December onwards. As elsewhere in their wintering range, they are frequently found in mixed flocks with Lapwings.

Winter visitors start leaving towards the end of February but some birds can be seen until much later in spring, when a small passage seems to occur from late March to late April. Occasionally they are also recorded on autumn passage, e.g. one near Kalloni, Lesbos, on 13 September 1995 (J.D. Wilson & D.E. Balmer). On the basis of former taxonomy, Golden Plovers occurring in Greece belonged to race *P. a. altifrons* (*CFG*; Vaurie 1965), but the species is now treated as monotypic (*BWP*).

Grey Plover *Pluvialis squatarola*

Fairly widespread and locally common winter visitor and passage migrant

Although Grey Plovers can occasionally be seen in the summer, they are mainly winter visitors and passage migrants. They occur in most of the major coastal wetlands of the mainland but are much less common on the islands, presumably due to lack of suitable habitat, e.g. there is only one record from the Cyclades, of one at Naxos on 9 August 1980 (R.E. Batty), one from Chios (Spinthakis *et al.* 1993) and only a few from Crete (*BoC*), Lesbos, Kefallinia and Corfu. Data from the IWRB MC (1982–1992) give an average of 381 birds and a maximum year count of 855 (1993) but the species is usually underestimated and probably present in significant numbers outside the main areas covered by the counts. In the Evros Delta, between 1979 and 1982, peak numbers occurred between mid March to late April, with a maximum count of 3,000 on 11 March 1981 (Goutner 1983b), which is the largest number ever recorded in Greece. Other records of large numbers on passage include 259 at Porto Lagos on 30 March 1987 (WIWO 90) and 112 at Messolonghi in March 1990 (WIWO 95). In winter, Grey Plovers are found almost exclusively on the coast, on tidal mudflats, sandbanks or other shallow sandy and muddy coastline. Sizable flocks can be seen, especially in the tidal areas of the Thermaikos Gulf and the Spercheios Delta. On both spring and autumn migration Grey Plovers are sometimes recorded inland, e.g. at L. Mikri Prespa (Catsadorakis 1986) and L. Ismaris (Jerrentrup 1986). Biometric data from 15 birds ringed at Porto Lagos in the spring of 1987 show that they were, on average, larger than birds breeding in W Siberia, indicating that birds migrating over Greece probably breed farther east, between the Yamal and Taimyr peninsulas (WIWO 90).

Spur-winged Plover *Hoplopterus spinosus*

Rare and local summer visitor

Before the early 1960s, Spur-winged Plovers were recorded as accidental visitors to Greece, with seven or eight records from various southern areas, e.g. Evvoia (Lindermayer 1860), Crete (Kelham 1922) and the island of Milos and Attica (Reiser 1905) and with a further six records from Thrace (Makatsch 1950; Flach 1955a, 1956; Watson 1961a). The first nest was discovered at Porto Lagos on 28 June 1959 (Vader 1965) and within the next few years more pairs were recorded breeding: four pairs in the Nestos Delta (1960), eight pairs and three nests at Porto Lagos, five pairs in the Evros Delta (1961) and one or two pairs in the Axios–Aliakmon Delta (*CFG*; Bauer 1969). One pair possibly nested on the island of Kos in 1968 (*CFG*; Bauer 1969). In 1965 there were at least 40 pairs between the Nestos and Evros Deltas (Kraus & Conradty 1965) but others estimated the population of the Evros Delta alone at 40–50 pairs (Bauer & Müller 1969). In 1979 there were 50–70 pairs in the Nestos Delta (*BWP*) but the population of the Evros Delta had declined to ten pairs in 1979 and further declined to six pairs in 1982 (Goutner 1983b). In 1993 the total Greek population was estimated at 32–45 pairs (Tucker & Heath 1994) with the majority in the Nestos Delta and the rest at Porto Lagos, L. Ismaris and the Evros Delta, where not more than one or two pairs still survive.

Spur-winged Plovers start to arrive from mid or late March. In the Evros Delta, egg-laying was recorded between 8 and 15 May (with re-laying in the case of failed clutches up to early June), the first chicks hatched in early June, fledged in 25–30 days and the last birds left the area in mid August (Goutner 1983b). In 1984, at Porto Lagos, one pair with five chicks, about a week old, were seen on 28 August (Hallmann 1986). Spur-winged Plovers breed in areas of dry mudflats or sandy coastal zones and nests are usually placed on bare ground or among sparse halophytic vegetation. The decline of the population, particularly that of the Evros Delta, is clearly attributed to excessive numbers of free-grazing cattle, which trample the nests or disturb the birds during the nesting period. Recent records of Spur-winged Plover on passage are more or less confined to Crete and the Dodecanese, e.g. Rhodes (Watson 1961a), Kos (*CFG*) and Karpathos (Broggi 1993). So far, there are only three known records away from these areas: one in the Amvrakikos in August 1968 (*CFG*), one caught and ringed at Messolonghi on 20 April 1986 (Pergantis & Handrinos 1992) and one near Chalkis on 12–14 April 1995 (V. Kotriklas).

Spur-winged Plovers

Sociable Plover *Chettusia gregaria*

Accidental

Sociable Plovers have been recorded three times: one juvenile and one adult female were shot near Athens on 3 January 1868 and preserved in the collection of the Zoological Museum, Athens University (Reiser 1905), an immature was seen and photographed at Gouves Lagoon, Crete, on 29 April 1986 (*BoC*) and one was recorded on Lesbos on 14 May 1994 (Brooks 1995).

White-tailed Plover *Chettusia leucura*

Accidental

There are four records of White-tailed Plover: two on the island of Rhodes on 14 April 1958 (Ralfs 1960), one in the Nestos Delta in August 1966 (*CFG*), one at Mallia, Crete, on 24 April 1986 and one at Elounda, Crete, on 6 April 1994 (*BoC*).

Lapwing *Vanellus vanellus*

Scarce and local resident, common and widespread winter visitor

Lapwings have a restricted and localised breeding distribution in Greece: they nest only in some of the larger wetlands of Thrace and Macedonia, from L. Ismaris (Jerrentrup 1986) westwards to L. Kerkini and to the coastal wetlands of the Thermaikos Gulf. Very few pairs may still occasionally nest at higher altitude, in the larger lake basins of W Macedonia, e.g. around L. Petron and L. Mikri Prespa. They used to be more numerous and during the last 15–20 years the total breeding population has declined to under an estimated 100 pairs. Between 1979–82 in the Evros Delta alone there were *c.* 35 pairs (Goutner 1983b) but after 1990 not a single pair has been recorded.

Outside the breeding season and particularly during winter Lapwings are much more widespread, with small numbers reaching as far south as the southern Peloponnese. They are scarce winter visitors to Crete (*BoC*) and to most of the other islands. Their winter abundance and distribution depend very much on the weather and during cold spells their numbers increase significantly and they spread more widely. Winter visitors are usually present in good numbers from the middle of November to late February. The IWRB MC (1982–92) give an average of 4,532 birds, a maximum year count of 9,870 (1988) and a maximum site count of 4,675 at Messolonghi on 20 January 1987 (Joensen *et al.* 1987). However, the species is present in numbers outside areas covered by the MC and the actual wintering population is probably at least double and probably many times more than the above totals. For example, on 28 February 1980, 3,000 birds were counted in the Spercheios Delta, when a passing Peregrine flushed large flocks from fields not normally covered by the counts. Locally, Lapwing is a popular game bird, though no bag statistics exist to evaluate the impact of hunting on the wintering population. The passage of migrants through the country is on an insignificant scale.

Breeding Lapwings occur in habitats similar to those in the rest of their breeding range in

Europe, i.e. wet pasture by freshwater lakes, poorly drained farmland and the muddy shores of brackish coastal lagoons, avoiding the more saline areas preferred by Spur-winged Plovers. In the Evros Delta egg-laying has been recorded as early as the beginning of March and most birds leave the area immediately after fledging (Goutner 1983b). In summer, Lapwings are more often seen on river banks, lake shores and mud banks in lakes or rivers than at other times of the year, presumably because their breeding grounds tend to dry up. In winter they occur in a wider variety of habitats, often on ploughed or fallow fields and on rice stubble. Single Lapwings ringed in Belgium, Germany, Finland and the Ukraine have been recovered in Greece in winter.

Knot *Calidris canutus*

Scarce and local passage migrant and winter visitor

Since March 1939, when first recorded at L. Karla (Dathe 1950), Knot have been seen in Greece fewer than 40 times but they are possibly overlooked and their occurrence might actually be more regular. Records exist from almost all months of the year, including July and August but most are from mid March to mid May, with a peak in early May, and from mid August to early October. The majority of records are from the coastal wetlands of Thrace, particularly tidal mudflats and sandy beaches at Porto Lagos and the Evros Delta. The species has also been recorded more than five times at Messolonghi, where more than 100 were seen on 1 September 1980, the largest number ever recorded in Greece (J. Walmsley). It is very rare on the islands, with only two records from Crete (*BoC*) and one from Kefallinia (Vittery 1994). Knot are usually seen singly or in groups of up to 6–10 birds, occasionally up to 30. Other large counts include 72 at Porto Lagos on 18 March 1987 (WIWO 90), 65 at Lafri Lagoon on 18 January 1993 and 40 at Porto Lagos on 16 January 1969 (M. Hodge & A. Johnson). On geographic grounds, Knots wintering or on passage in Greece must belong to the nominate race, *C. c. canutus,* breeding in Siberia (*CFG*; WIWO 90).

Sanderling *Calidris alba*

Fairly common and widespread passage migrant, scarce winter visitor

On passage, Sanderlings are widely distributed on sandy beaches and coastal wetlands both on the mainland and on some of the larger islands. They are, however, not very numerous and only in NE Greece (e.g. Porto Lagos and the Evros Delta) and western Greece (e.g. Messolonghi) are larger concentrations observed. On passage they are mainly recorded from mid March to late May or even early June, with the largest numbers usually in mid May, and from mid August to the end of September. They usually occur in parties of up to ten and less often up to 50 birds, although in the Evros Delta flocks of up to 250 are regular (Goutner 1983b; Goutner & Kazantzidis 1992). A record count of birds on passage is of 2,000 in the Evros Delta on 24 April 1981 (Goutner 1983b). Sanderlings were found to be 'quite numerous' at the Lefkimmi saltpans on Corfu in May 1988 (K.S. Bovey & M. Mitchell) whereas at least 170 were seen on 16 May 1984 at Tigkaki Lagoon, Kos (S.B. Edwards). In general, Sanderlings occur in small numbers on sandy beaches and there they are probably frequently overlooked. Few birds stay to spend the winter in Greece, probably totalling well under 500.

Little Stint *Calidris minuta*

Very common and widespread passage migrant, locally common winter visitor

The most numerous *Calidris* sandpiper in Greece, at least on passage, Little Stints are widely distributed in suitable habitat throughout the country, including the islands. They are most often seen in areas of shallow brackish or saline water with sparse vegetation, such as the shores of coastal lagoons, saltpans, shallow sea coasts and tidal mudflats. Sometimes, and especially on passage, they also occur by fresh water, such as in rice fields, muddy pools and on lake shores.

In winter, Little Stints are more numerous in the milder parts of the country, in western and southern Greece, where they frequently outnumber Dunlins, whereas in the rest of the country the reverse is true. Spring passage is on a larger scale than in autumn and lasts mainly from early April to late May, with a peak in the first half of May. A few birds are still on passage in early June and some, presumably mainly non-breeding individuals, are recorded later in June and in July. A study of wader migration in the wetlands of NE Greece in the spring of 1987 showed that Little Stint flocks have a rapid turnover and it was estimated that the total number using the Porto Lagos area alone during spring migration may range between 15,000–25,000 birds (WIWO 90). Autumn passage is mainly from late July to mid October, with a peak in late August and early September. Two Little Stints ringed in Bulgaria have been recovered in Greece.

Temminck's Stint *Calidris temminckii*

Fairly common and widespread passage migrant

Temminck's Stints are seen mainly during spring migration, from mid April to late May, with a peak from late April to early May. They are less common on autumn passage, between mid August and mid September. The species has been listed as a winter visitor too (*CFG*). However, in recent years there have been only two winter records, both from Messolonghi, with four on 21 January 1970 and eight on 9 January 1973 (Pergantis & Handrinos 1992) and the only other published winter record is of one at Velestino in Thessaly on 30 December 1895 (Reiser 1905). On migration, Temminck's Stints occur throughout the mainland and the islands. They usually occur singly or in small parties and, as is typical of the species, they often spend much of their time at the edge of vegetation by small pools or larger areas of open water and thus may easily be overlooked. They are equally frequent inland and on the coast but they prefer fresh and brackish to saline water. The largest numbers recorded so far include 30–40 at Messolonghi on 24 April 1958, 30 in the Amvrakikos on 29 May 1980 and (on rare occasions) up to 40 on Crete (*BoC*). There is one ringing recovery in Greece in September of a bird ringed in Swedish Lappland (*BWP*).

Long-toed Stint *Calidris subminuta*

Accidental

There is only one recent record of Long-toed Stint, a bird in winter plumage, seen and photographed at Vai, E Crete, on 28 March 1991 (A.G. Gosler, C.M. Jackson-Houlston & P. Grundy).

Baird's Sandpiper *Calidris bairdii*

Accidental

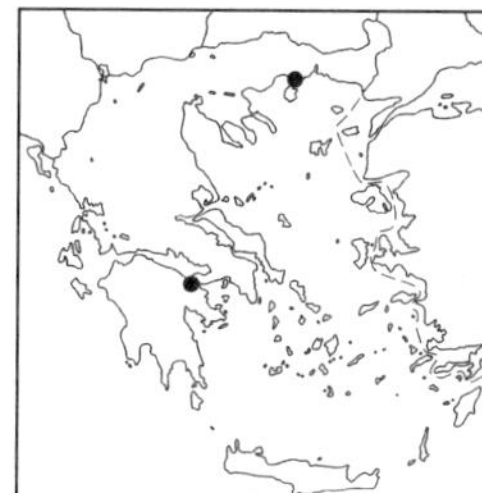

The species has been recorded twice in Greece: an adult at a small lagoon near Corinth on 21 April 1986 (Fossey 1988) and one in summer plumage at Keramoti on 24 April 1995 (E. Schwarze).

Curlew Sandpiper *Calidris ferruginea*

Widespread and locally common passage migrant

Curlew Sandpipers appear in larger numbers and are more widespread on spring than on autumn passage, a pattern which agrees with the loop migration known for this species (*BWP*). They occur throughout the mainland and the islands but they tend to be found in a few large concentrations at a limited number of sites, rather than being spread out uniformly as happens with Little Stint for example. They prefer saline or hypersaline water with very sparse halophytic vegetation and are more or less restricted to coastal sites, with only small numbers occurring inland. Very often large numbers turn up in saltpans, where they tend to be the most numerous wader at times of peak passage, feeding on *Artemia* shrimps. Their other main habitats are the shores of coastal lagoons and *Arthrocnemum*-dominated saltmarshes. Large numbers are regularly recorded, especially in the Axios Delta, Porto Lagos, Evros Delta, Messolonghi and the Amvrakikos.

Spring passage is mainly from mid April (exceptionally earlier) to early June, with a peak from the end of April to mid May. A few birds are seen all through the summer. Autumn passage is mainly from late July to the end of September, with rare sightings to the end of October or early November. In autumn, the largest numbers are seen from early August to mid September. Record counts include 3,045 on 10 May 1987 and 1,795 on 18 May 1987, at Porto Lagos (WIWO 90), *c.* 2,000 at the Alyki Kitrous Lagoon on 27 April 1987 and 2,095 at Messolonghi on 14 May 1990 (WIWO 95). However, they may also occur in large numbers at other less well known sites, e.g. several hundred may be seen at the Kalloni Saltpans on Lesbos in early May. It has been estimated that the total number of Curlew Sandpipers using the Porto Lagos area during spring migration may well exceed 10,000 birds (WIWO 90). Single Curlew Sandpipers ringed in Sweden and the Ukraine have been recovered in Greece.

Purple Sandpiper *Calidris maritima*

Accidental

During the 19th century, Purple Sandpipers were recorded on the mainland by various authors (Mühle 1844; Lindermayer 1860) and reported as winter visitors to the Cyclades (Erhard 1858) but all these records were later rejected (Reiser 1905; *CFG*). There are only two recent records: one at L. Vistonis in 1966 (*CFG*) and three at the Alyki Kitrous Lagoon on 13 May 1980 (Hallmann 1980).

Dunlin *Calidris alpina*

Common and widespread winter visitor and passage migrant

Dunlin are one of the commonest species of wader in Greece. In suitable habitat they occur on the coast of the whole mainland and of most of the larger islands both in winter and on passage. They are almost exclusively coastal, the largest numbers being on tidal mudflats and in shallow lagoons and saltpans. The timing of passage is difficult to define because it merges into the arrival and departure movements of wintering birds. In spring, the largest numbers occur in late March to mid April, and the last birds are usually seen towards the middle of May, although a few individuals are regularly recorded during the whole summer. In autumn, passage of through-migrants is even less marked than in spring. The first arrivals are usually recorded from early or mid August but numbers build up very gradually until mid October to early November. Maximum counts on passage include *c.* 7,000 in the Evros Delta on 24 April 1981 (Goutner 1983b) and 2,370 at Porto Lagos on 26 March 1987 (WIWO 90). Data from the IWRB MC (1982–1992) give a national average of 6,900 birds, with a maximum of 18,600 in 1989 and a maximum site count of 10,600 at Messolonghi on 18 January 1986 (Joensen *et al.* 1987). Messolonghi seems to be the most important site for the species, with further wintering maxima of 9,200 on 27 November 1986 (Joensen *et al.* 1987) and 6,650 on 30 January 1989.

Two Dunlins ringed at Porto Lagos on 1 April 1987 have been recovered abroad: one at Etang de Thau in southern France on 3 August 1987 and one near Gdansk in Poland on 18 July 1988 (WIWO 90). A further 11 ringed birds from abroad have been recovered in Greece, with five from Sweden, four from Poland and one each from Denmark and the Ukraine. Biometric data from 47 Dunlins ringed at Porto Lagos show that the majority were birds of the nominate race *C. a. alpina*, with very few probably belonging to *C. a. sakhalina* or to an intermediate form between these two races. The occurrence of *C. a. schinzii* was not confirmed (WIWO 90), though this form has been listed as probably occurring in Greece (*CFG*).

Broad-billed Sandpiper *Limicola falcinellus*

Widespread but scarce passage migrant

Broad-billed Sandpipers are regular passage migrants in both seasons. They are most often recorded in the coastal wetlands of Macedonia and Thrace, especially the Porto Lagos wetland complex. There are still no records from any of the major wetlands of western Greece (e.g. Messolonghi and the Amvrakikos) and only three records from the islands: two at Kalloni Saltpans on Lesbos between 2 and 12 August 1989 (M. & J. Lewis), one adult on Naxos on 23 August 1993 (R. Allen) and one on Crete on 18 August 1990 (*BoC*). Broad-billed Sandpipers are also rare inland, with very few sightings from freshwater sites such as L. Mikri Prespa (Catsadorakis 1986), L. Ismaris (Jerrentrup 1986) and L. Koronia. The rarity of the species on islands and inland is justifiable on the grounds of shortage or unsuitability of habitat respectively but elsewhere it is almost certainly overlooked. Thus although rare on the western coast, regular coverage of Aigion Lagoon, NW Peloponnese, produced 12 records between 1988 and 1993 (CP).

Passage seems to take place mainly between late April and late May and between early August and late September. Autumn passage is on a larger scale than in spring, with the majority of records in mid and late August. The latest autumn record in recent times is of five birds at Aigion Lagoon on 21 November 1987 (CP). In older literature (Lambert 1957; Raines 1962), Broad-billed Sandpipers were listed as winter visitors to Greece but there have been no sufficiently documented records from the strict winter period (December–February). Even at peak passage in August, Broad-billed Sandpipers are seen in small numbers, usually singly or in small parties, although at Porto Lagos flocks of 15–20 are not rare. The only ringing recovery of the species in Greece is of a bird ringed in Poland in August 1986 and found a month later on Corfu.

Broad-billed Sandpiper

Ruff *Philomachus pugnax*

Very common and widespread passage migrant, scarce winter visitor

Ruffs are among the commonest waders during migration, particularly in spring, both on the mainland and on the islands. They occur in a diverse variety of habitats, ranging from freshwater to hypersaline. These include shallow lagoons, marshes, flooded fields, wet meadows, rice fields and saltpans. Both in autumn and in spring they are attracted to high densities of the brine shrimp *Artemia* in saltpans, and in spring they often concentrate where there is an abundance of Chironomid midges, in both saltmarshes (WIWO 90) and saltpans.

In spring, males begin to arrive in late February or early March, with the largest numbers usually recorded in late March. Males with some breeding plumage feathers are frequent but it is rare to see birds with a fully developed ruff. Females begin arriving just after the middle of March but their numbers peak much later, around mid April. The passage of females seems to be on a significantly larger scale than that of males, presumably because the latter stay for shorter periods and quickly continue onwards to their mating grounds. Relatively few birds remain after the end of April and the latest birds are usually seen around 20 May. Occasionally Ruffs are recorded in late May and exceptionally in June and July. These latter are presumably non-breeding birds spending summer away from the breeding grounds. Ruff are less numerous in autumn, not unexpectedly so, since most of their habitat has dried up by then. Autumn passage is from mid August to early October, mainly in the first half of September. Maximum numbers recorded on passage include 5,000–6,000 at Messolonghi in the spring of 1981 (Szijj 1983; Pergantis & Handrinos 1992) and *c.* 4,500 in the Evros Delta in mid April 1988 (Goutner & Kazantzidis 1992).

A few Ruff winter in Greece, especially in western areas. The national average (1982–1992) from the IWRB MC is of 44 birds, with a maximum of 363 (1983). There are 12 recoveries of birds ringed abroad and found in Greece: one had been ringed in the Netherlands, two in Norway, four in Sweden and five in Finland.

Jack Snipe *Lymnocryptes minimus*

Widespread but scarce winter visitor and passage migrant

One of the least known Greek birds due to their very secretive habits, Jack Snipe are more often seen bagged by hunters than alive. Their overall status is very difficult to define but they seem to occur as both winter visitors and spring migrants in small numbers throughout the country. Therefore, the recent estimate of the average population wintering in Greece at 0–100 birds (Tucker & Heath 1994) is probably far too low. As elsewhere in their wintering range, Jack Snipe occur in a variety of marshland habitats, usually fresh or brackish, with tall grass, sedges, or clumps of rush *Juncus*. Winter visitors arrive from late October and usually

leave from late February to mid March. There also appears to be a spring passage since many birds are seen as late as the end of April and early May. Single Jack Snipe ringed in Germany, Sweden and Finland have been recovered in Greece.

Snipe *Gallinago gallinago*

Common and widespread winter visitor and passage migrant

Snipe are quite numerous and widespread winter visitors on the mainland and most of the larger islands. They may regularly be found in wet meadows and marshes, flooded fields and wet pastures, and sometimes very high densities may be observed in partly flooded cotton and rice fields. Snipe are normally restricted to freshwater and brackish habitats but they do also occur in saltmarshes. Under average weather conditions, several hundred are often present in individual large wetlands but their numbers are strongly affected by the incidence of cold weather. At such times they become very numerous and widespread in milder parts of the country and in extreme cases every wet low-lying area will hold at least some birds. It is under such conditions that they may be seen in flocks of up to 50 or more birds whereas normally they are spread out singly or in small loose parties. Their numbers are not assessed efficiently by the IWRB MC which are primarily oriented towards waterfowl and waterfowl habitats. Indicatively, the maximum site count is of 1,000 birds at Messolonghi on 30 January 1989. They are a popular game bird in many parts of the country and probably many thousands are shot each year.

There is a small autumn passage of Snipe from mid August to early October, merging towards the end of the period with the arrival of much larger numbers of winter visitors. Spring passage is more pronounced and takes place from mid March to early May, with peak numbers from late March to early or mid April. At this time of the year suitable habitat is plentiful, the opposite of the situation in autumn, which, as in many other marsh birds, may explain the difference in numbers between the two seasons. Five ringed birds, two from the Czech Republic and one each from Belgium, Sweden and Finland have been recovered in Greece.

Great Snipe *Gallinago media*

Widespread but scarce passage migrant

Great Snipe are one of the least common wader species in Greece, yet they are regular passage migrants, more numerous in spring than in autumn. Although certainly not common, they are probably often overlooked, perhaps even more so than common Snipe as they tend to fly less on their own initiative and are usually detected only when flushed.

Great Snipe have been recorded from many parts of the mainland and some of the larger islands. Spring passage is from mid March to early May, with a peak in mid April or slightly earlier, and autumn passage mainly from late August to early October. There has been a small number of winter records but, in view of the possibility of confusion with Snipe, only two recent ones are acceptable, both of single birds at Messolonghi, on 21 January 1982 and on 18 January 1984. One further record from Crete on 4 November 1976 (*BoC*) may refer to a winter visitor or a late autumn migrant. There is only one recovery of Great Snipe in Greece, of a bird ringed in Norway and found on the island of Chios.

Long-billed Dowitcher *Limnodromus scolopaceus*

Accidental

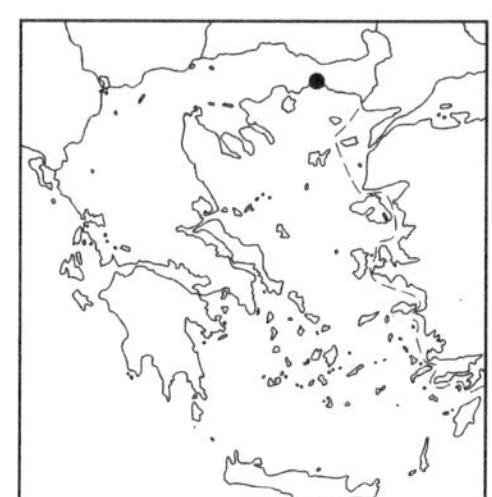

One adult in full summer plumage seen at Porto Lagos on 7 May 1962 (Raines 1962) is the only Greek record of Long-billed Dowitcher.

Woodcock *Scolopax rusticola*

Rare and local resident, fairly common and widespread winter visitor

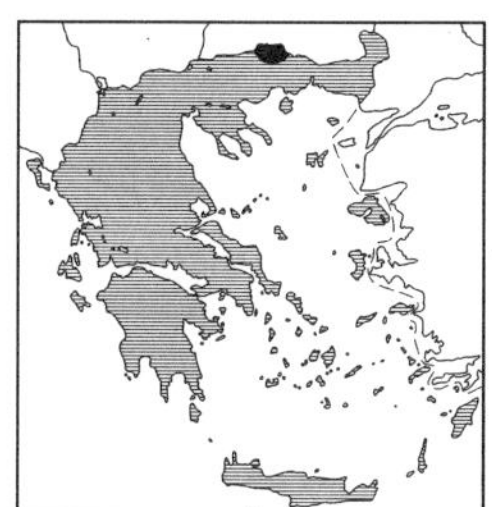

Probable nesting of Woodcock in Greece was first suspected in 1993 when between 14 and 20 May two birds were seen 'roding' at 1500 m in the dense forests of the Rodopi Mts, north–northwest of Paranesti. Further breeding season records of roding males from the same area were obtained in 1975 and 1979 (Bauer & Böhr 1987). Interestingly, one male was shot south of Kallipefki, on Mt Kato Olympos, on 27 May 1936 and considered by local forest workers as belonging to a nesting pair (E. Euthymiadis).

However, Woodcock is mainly a winter visitor to Greece, and is fairly common and widespread. It is one of the most popular game birds, much sought after, and well over ten birds can be shot in one day by a single hunter in appropriate weather conditions. Most birds arrive from early November onwards and most have departed by the end of February, though a few may appear as early as mid October and a few may occasionally be seen up to mid March. They spread over practically the whole mainland and all the larger islands as well as many smaller ones in both the Aegean and the Ionian Seas. Although they occur in a wide variety of habitats, from sea level to medium altitudes, and at times can be seen in orchards and rural gardens, they show a preference for hilly country with mixed evergreen or deciduous scrub and maquis, especially near streams and wet valleys. The number of wintering birds fluctuates widely from year to year and large influxes occur during severe weather. The total wintering population has been estimated at 1,000–10,000 birds (Tucker & Heath 1994) but this seems too low and in average winter conditions it is more likely to be in the order of 10,000–50,000 birds. Of 13 ringed Woodcock recovered in Greece so far, ten had been ringed in Finland, two in the Ukraine and one in Bulgaria.

Black-tailed Godwit *Limosa limosa*

Widespread and locally common passage migrant, scarce winter visitor

Black-tailed Godwits are widespread during both migration periods and are particularly numerous in the spring. However, they tend to occur in large numbers at a few favoured sites and to be rather uncommon elsewhere. They are most numerous in the large wetlands of Thrace, Macedonia and western Greece. Their habitat is quite varied and includes both freshwater and saline marshes, lagoons, coastal mudflats (especially near river mouths) and saltpans. In early spring large flocks are often seen in rice fields, which are in the form of partly flooded stubble at that time of the year.

Spring migration may start already from late February and usually peaks towards the end of March or early April. Maximum numbers recorded on spring passage include 4,000 in the Axios Delta on 5 March 1967 (Eber 1967) and 934 at L. Vistonis on 25 March 1987 (WIWO 90). The last spring migrants are usually seen in early to mid May. In autumn many of the spring staging areas are dry and Black-tailed Godwits occur in smaller numbers and at fewer sites than in spring, mainly in large wetlands, where some suitable habitat exists even after severe drought. Passage movements usually occur from early August, with a peak in late August and early September. However, locally concentrations of presumably non-breeding birds may start building up much earlier. In the Evros Delta numbers increased from mid June onwards (Goutner & Kazantzidis 1992). A remarkable count, of 4,100 in the Evros Delta in mid July 1968 (Bauer & Müller 1969), comes from this period.

In winter the species is much less numerous and found most regularly and in larger numbers in southern and western Greece. Data from the IWRB MC (1982–1992) give a national average of 355 birds, a maximum January count of 8,050 (1971) and a maximum site count of 8,000 at L. Kerkini on 15 January 1971 (H. Hafner & J. Walmsley). So far there is only one recovery in Greece, in January, of a bird ringed in Estonia.

Bar-tailed Godwit *Limosa lapponica*

Rare and local passage migrant and winter visitor

Bar-tailed Godwits are among the least common Greek waders and with a rather localised distribution. They occur most regularly at coastal sites in Macedonia and Thrace, with the majority of records from Porto Lagos. In most cases, singles or small parties of up to five birds are seen. Maximum numbers recorded include 20 at Porto Lagos between 15 and 20 May 1961 (Raines 1962) and 20 also at Porto Lagos on 11 January 1971 (Hafner & Walmsley 1971). They are most frequent in winter, from November onwards, and on spring passage, until late May. Peak spring passage seems to occur in early or mid May. Between 1 March and 21 May 1987, only 11 observations involving a total of 32 birds were made in the wetlands of NE Greece, all at Porto Lagos and in the Evros Delta, with a maximum of seven at Porto Lagos on 14 May (WIWO 90). Bar-tailed Godwits are rare in the autumn, with most records in the first half of August and single records in late July and mid October. There are few records from areas other than Macedonia and Thrace, e.g. three records from Messolonghi, two of which in the 19th century (Reiser 1905) and one on 31 May 1990, 'a small flock ' on the island of Naxos in December 1933 (Bird 1935), two in the Kalamas Delta on 5 January 1973 (Johnson & Carp 1973) and single birds at Aigion Lagoon on 16 May 1990 and 11 August 1993 (CP). Bar-tailed Godwits are almost always recorded in areas of tidal mud- and sandflats, their preferred habitat outside the breeding season.

Whimbrel *Numenius phaeopus*

Widespread but scarce passage migrant

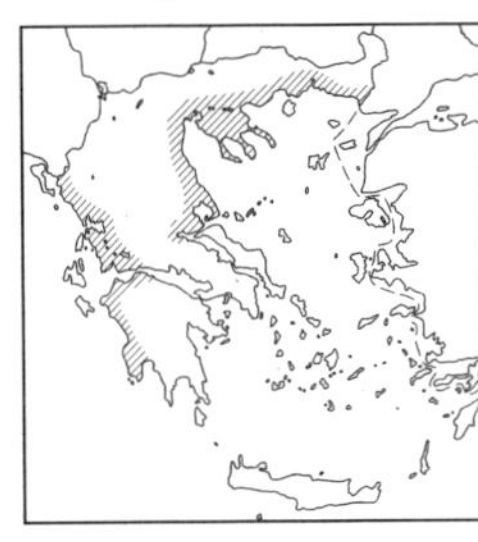

Whimbrels are usually seen in Greece only on spring and autumn passage, and although records are widespread over the whole country, including some of the islands, they are not numerous. The first birds normally appear in mid March, numbers peak in mid April and the last birds are seen in mid May. Autumn passage is mainly from mid July to early September. They are usually seen singly or in small groups but there are also several records of 20–45. Existing data indicate that only small numbers migrate through Greece, though to a certain extent they may be overlooked. The maximum number ever recorded is of three flocks totalling 91 birds at Messolonghi on 28 March 1990 (WIWO 95).

There are a few cases of Whimbrel reputedly having been seen in winter, with one from the 19th century and two or three recent ones, but none is sufficiently documented. Most migrant Whimbrels are seen in coastal wetlands, with only a few records from inland freshwater habitats.

Slender-billed Curlew *Numenius tenuirostris*

Rare and local passage migrant and winter visitor

Since September 1857, when Slender-billed Curlews were recorded for the first time in Greece (Powys 1860), there has been a total of 87 records of the species (Goutner & Handrinos 1990; Gretton 1991; Handrinos 1994b). There are records in all months of the year except November and December. The seasonal pattern of combined records and numbers (bird-days) gives three distinct peaks, the main one during the whole of April and in early May and two minor ones in late September and early to mid January (Goutner & Handrinos 1990). Two of the largest flocks ever recorded in the world have been seen in Greece, both in the Evros Delta: 150 (20 October 1978) and 250 (4 April 1981). However, though possibly genuine, the latter record has recently been rejected (Gretton 1991). In two cases flocks of 14 have been seen (Porto Lagos, 28 September 1984 and Evros Delta, April 1995). Groups of two or three have been seen on 16 occasions and single birds were involved in all remaining cases.

Thrace is an area of great importance for the species: 53 records come from this region, with 34 from the Evros Delta and 19 from the Porto Lagos complex. Other sites where the species has been recorded include the Axios Delta (6 records), the Faliron Delta, near Athens (now drained) (5 records), the Amvrakikos (4 records), the island of Corfu (3 records), Alyki Lagoon on the island of Kos (3 records), Messolonghi (2 records), L. Koronia (2 records) and Angelochori Lagoon, near Thessaloniki (2 records). There are also single records from the Spercheios Delta, L. Trichonis, Marathon marshes, Agios Mamas Lagoon, Mouria Lagoon, Tuzla Lagoon and Lixouri on the island of Kefallinia. In Greece, Slender-billed Curlews clearly prefer coastal wetlands with a complex mosaic of habitats: saltmarsh, halophytic grassland, brackish lagoons and sandy or muddy coasts. These habitats are much more often used than others such as freshwater marshland and wet meadows (Handrinos 1994b). Otherwise, almost nothing is known of their ecology in Greece. The only prey that has been recorded so far is *Theba pisana*, a common small land snail found in the stomach of one male shot at Lixouri on 23 March 1897 (Reiser 1905).

Slender-billed Curlew

Curlew *Numenius arquata*

Common and widespread winter visitor and passage migrant

In suitable habitat, Curlews are quite numerous and widespread in winter and during spring and autumn passage. They occur widely in both coastal and inland wetlands of the mainland and on some of the larger islands but the larger concentrations are found along the coasts of Thrace, Macedonia, western Greece and in the Spercheios Delta. The species shows a clear preference for coastal habitats with shallow lagoons, tidal mudflats, sandbanks and saltmarshes and only small numbers use freshwater marshes, wet freshwater meadows and lake shores. Spring passage takes place from about mid March to late April or early May. Early in the season the departure of wintering birds merges with the movements of passage migrants. A few non-breeding birds spend the whole summer in the larger wetlands. In autumn, movements are noticeable from mid July to late October, peaking in early to mid September. Data from the IWRB MC (1982–1992) give a national average of 1,222 wintering birds, a maximum January count of 2,215 (1989) and a maximum site count of 890 in the Axios Delta on 16 January 1971. Maximum numbers outside winter come mainly from the Evros Delta, e.g. *c.* 1,000 on 13 July 1981 (Goutner 1983b) and 1,130 in September 1994 (D. Vangeluwe). There are still no ringing recoveries of Curlews in Greece but apparently birds of both the nominate race, *N. a. arquata,* and *N. a. orientalis* occur, as well as intermediates between the two (*CFG*).

Spotted Redshank *Tringa erythropus*

Fairly common and widespread passage migrant, scarce winter visitor

Spotted Redshanks are widespread and, in suitable habitat, fairly common passage migrants. They occur in most of the coastal wetlands of the mainland but they are most numerous in N and W Greece, where more habitat is available, and they are more localised in other parts of the country. They are listed as fairly common on spring passage on Crete (*BoC*) and they are fairly common on some the other islands with sizable wetlands (e.g. Corfu, Lesbos, Limnos and Kos).

Very small numbers of Spotted Redshank winter in Greece. Data from the IWRB MC (1982–1992) give a national average of only 12 birds, with a maximum count of 170 in 1971. There is an interesting sighting of 165 at Kalogria Lagoon on 20 December 1994 but these were not seen later in January when the MC took place (CP). Spring passage lasts from mid March to mid May, reaching a peak around mid April. A few non-breeding birds, usually in first summer plumage (i.e. non-breeders), seem to stay in Greece all through the summer. In autumn, the first increase in the numbers of summering birds is apparent already from early July. These early arriving birds may be non-breeders that have spent the summer in neighbouring countries, south of their breeding range. The main passage takes place during September and significant numbers are still present in Greece up to mid October. The maximum number ever recorded in Greece is *c.* 4,500 in the Evros Delta in mid July 1968 (Bauer & Müller 1969), whereas 1,372 were seen also in the Evros Delta in late April 1988 (Goutner & Kazantzidis 1992). Throughout the year, Spotted Redshanks are found singly or in small loose flocks, rarely exceeding 50–100 birds. They seem to prefer brackish or saline coastal habitats such as saltmarshes, shallow lagoons, mudflats and saltpans but they are not uncommon inland or in freshwater habitats on the coast (e.g. rice fields). There is one ringing recovery of a bird ringed on spring passage in Sweden and found in Greece the following autumn.

Redshank *Tringa totanus*

Widespread and locally common resident

Redshank is the only species of *Tringa* breeding in Greece. Isolated breeding populations exist in suitable habitat over much of the coastal mainland, from Messolonghi and the Spercheios Delta in the south, north to the Kalamas and Evros Deltas. Among the islands, nesting has been confirmed only on the island of Limnos, with nine pairs in 1988 (Hölzinger 1991). A few pairs may also possibly breed at Kalogria Lagoon, NW Peloponnese (CP) and on Lesbos. Throughout their breeding range, Redshanks are not very numerous and the total Greek population has been estimated at 400–800 pairs (Tucker & Heath 1994).

Spring passage of Redshanks is evident from early or mid March to mid May with a peak in late March and early April, whereas in autumn, movements span the mid August to late October period, with a peak in late September and early October. However, large numbers may occur much earlier: the maximum number ever recorded in Greece outside winter is of 3,800 in the Evros Delta in mid July 1968 (Bauer & Müller 1969). Such midsummer concentrations may result when birds breeding in parts of SE Europe or western Asia Minor are forced to leave many of their breeding sites due to drying up (as many Greek breeders seem to do). Additional large counts of Redshank during autumn migration have also been observed in the Evros Delta and include 1,405 on 24 September1994 (D. Vangeluwe) and *c.* 1,400 in early October 1988 (Goutner & Kazantzidis 1992).

Data from the IWRB MC (1982–1992) give a national average of 1,942, a maximum January count of 4,816 (1989) and a maximum site count of 1,600 in the Amvrakikos on 28 January 1989. However, the total wintering population may be double this figure because many birds are present in areas or types of habitat not covered well by the MC. At all seasons, Redshanks frequent mainly coastal wetlands with shallow lagoons, saltmarshes, tidal mudflats, sandbanks and rice fields. Nests are usually placed on sandy or muddy islets with halophytic vegetation. Outside the breeding season Redshanks may also be found at inland freshwater sites, such as lake shores, marshland and flooded meadows, as well as in saltpans. There are six ringing recoveries of Redshank ringed abroad and found in Greece, with one each from Denmark, Poland, Estonia, Hungary, the Ukraine and Bulgaria.

Marsh Sandpiper *Tringa stagnatilis*

Fairly common and widespread passage migrant

Marsh Sandpipers are reasonably common passage migrants, though they are never very numerous. Like most other members of the genus *Tringa*, they tend to occur in loose concentrations, spread over suitable feeding habitat. They are usually seen in small groups of 5–20 birds but records of 40 or more are not rare. Maximum numbers recorded include 380 in the Evros Delta in mid April 1988 (Goutner & Kazantzidis 1992) at least 250 at Kalogria Lagoon on 19 April 1994 (CP) and 210 in the Evros Delta in mid July 1968 (Bauer & Müller 1969). Marsh Sandpipers prefer coastal habitats, such as saltwater and brackish marshes, shallow lagoons and tidal mudflats. They are not so numerous at freshwater sites and also seem to avoid the highly saline environment of saltpans. The main passage periods are from mid March to mid May in spring and from mid July to mid October in autumn, with peaks in early to mid April and from late August to mid September. A few birds are often seen all through summer in large wetlands.

Marsh Sandpiper

Greenshank *Tringa nebularia*

Fairly common and widespread passage migrant, scarce winter visitor

In suitable habitat, Greenshanks occur throughout the country, mainly as passage migrants but also as winter visitors and rare non-breeding summer visitors. They are usually seen singly or in small parties of two to four birds but larger concentrations may form in the larger wetlands of Thrace, Macedonia and western Greece. Spring migration takes place from mid March to mid May, with largest numbers in the second half of April. They are generally less numerous and widespread in autumn, from mid July to late October, mostly in early and mid September. Small numbers of birds can be seen all through summer. Record counts of Greenshanks include 350 at Messolonghi in spring 1981 (Chwallek *et al.* 1981; Pergantis & Handrinos 1992) and 110 also at Messolonghi on 3 August 1980 (Pergantis & Handrinos 1992). Data from the IWRB MC (1982–1992) give a national average of only 17 birds, a maximum January count of 87 (1987) and a maximum site count of 82 in the Evros Delta on 5 January 1987. The actual wintering population is, however, probably two or three times larger than these averages suggest. At all times of the year Greenshanks can be found in both coastal and inland sites with saline, brackish or freshwater habitats.

Lesser Yellowlegs *Tringa flavipes*

Accidental

On 9 August 1986 one immature Lesser Yellowlegs was seen and photographed in the Evros Delta (Millon *et al.* 1988).

Green Sandpiper *Tringa ochropus*

Fairly common and widespread winter visitor and passage migrant

Green Sandpipers occur as passage migrants and winters visitors throughout the country. They are among the earliest autumn migrants and the first birds may arrive already from the end of June. Although other waders begin to form large concentrations at a few favourable sites in early to mid July, Green Sandpipers become not only more numerous but also very widespread as early as the second half of July. They are fairly common and widespread during the whole winter season. As elsewhere in their range, they occur in a variety of freshwater and brackish habitats but they have a liking for small patches of open water flanked by tall vegetation and are most often flushed from the banks of ditches rather than observed in wide open spaces. The main spring passage is between late March and mid April but birds may still be seen is small numbers up to late May and rarely through June, when the first autumn migrants begin to arrive. The species is thus effectively present almost all year round. Green Sanpipers are usually seen singly but parties of up to ten or more birds may form at times of peak passage.

Wood Sandpiper *Tringa glareola*

Common and widespread passage migrant

The commonest medium-sized waders in Greece, Wood Sandpipers occur as passage migrants throughout the country. They are most numerous on spring passage, when they are locally very common. The first spring migrants usually appear in late March. Passage peaks in late April and most birds have left by mid May. Southward movements usually start from early July onwards. However, the main autumn passage is much later, from late August to early October, with a peak in the first half of September. Wood Sandpipers prefer well vegetated fresh or brackish marshland. They very often share the same habitat with Ruff, either when feeding during the day or when roosting, though the two species never form mixed flocks. Being so common, their calls are one of the commonest of the waders one can hear overhead at night during migration periods. Their numbers are difficult to estimate and existing counts in large wetlands clearly represent a small fraction of the total numbers present in the whole country. Daily maxima of 500 or 1,000 are not uncommon at many sites. In the wetlands of NE Greece, in spring 1987, Wood Sandpiper movements suggested a rapid turnover and it was thus estimated that many thousands use these areas during each spring passage (WIWO 90). There is only one winter record of one bird in the Axios Delta in January 1966 (*CFG*). One bird ringed near Chalkis on 2 May 1990 was recovered in northern Nigeria in January 1994. Further Wood Sandpipers ringed in Sweden (2), Denmark (1) and the Czech Republic (1) have been recovered in Greece.

Terek Sandpiper *Xenus cinereus*

Rare and irregular passage migrant

Terek Sandpipers were first recorded in Greece in relatively recent times, when one was seen at Lechaion Lagoon, near Corinth, on 5 April 1954 (Flach 1956). Since then, there have been more than 20 records, almost exclusively of single birds, with the exception of four in the Evros Delta on 20 May 1961 (Raines 1962). All records are of birds on passage with half of them in the spring (April–May) and the others from the end of July to early October. May is the month with the largest proportion of records. With the exception of two records from western Greece (the Amvrakikos and Messolonghi) and the one from Lechaion Lagoon, all others are from the Aegean area, particularly the coastal wetlands around the Thermaikos Gulf and in Thrace. Other records exist from the Aegean islands, e.g. two from Lesbos (Brooks 1995), one from Kos on 6 September 1975 (Kumerloeve 1977) and one from Agia Triada, Crete, on 27 April 1983 (J. Thorogood). The appearance of Terek Sandpipers in Greece after the 1950s has coincided with the westwards expansion of the breeding range of this species in recent decades (*BWP*).

Common Sandpiper *Actitis hypoleucos*

Rare and local summer visitor, fairly common and widespread passage migrant

The first confirmation of Common Sandpipers breeding in Greece was obtained on 3 June 1971, when a pair with chicks were found on Mt Dokimi, near Trikala, at 800 m. (Bauer *et al.* 1973). In subsequent years breeding was recorded near Smixi in the district of Grevena on 30 May 1981 and on the R. Voidomatis in Ipeiros (Schmid & Reichenecker 1988). Although the species is probably more widespread than the few records suggest, its exact breeding distribution is still very poorly known. The information available so far suggests that in Greece, as in the rest of their range, Common Sandpipers nest in the middle or upper reaches of small undisturbed river valleys, with clear running water and gently sloping banks, with boulders or shingle.

Common Sandpipers are widespread on passage. They occur on lake shores and river banks as well as on the shores of coastal lagoons and on rocky coasts of the mainland and the islands. A careful observer will often notice their presence in small or large harbours of seaside towns and villages. They are usually seen as isolated individuals or as parties of fewer than ten birds, though larger flocks of 50 or even more have been recorded. They appear to be slightly more numerous in spring than in autumn. Spring passage is from late March to mid May, with a peak in the second half of April. Autumn passage is more protracted, mainly from late July to late September, but some birds arrive already from the end of June. On rare occasions Common Sandpipers have been recorded in winter (*CFG*; *BoC*).

Spotted Sandpiper *Actitis macularia*

Accidental

One adult Spotted Sandpiper seen at close range on Spinalonga, E Crete, on 11 May 1992 (B. Lee) is the only record of this nearctic species in Greece.

Turnstone *Arenaria interpres*

Fairly common and widespread passage migrant

Turnstones are widespread passage migrants along the coasts of both the mainland and of some islands in the Aegean and Ionian Seas. They are, nevertheless, most regular and numerous in the large coastal wetlands of Thrace, Macedonia and western Greece. The main migration periods are from mid March to late May, peaking around mid May, and from early August to mid October. Turnstones occur almost exclusively on the coast, on sand or shingle beaches or in tidal areas. Occasionally they may appear inland and they have been recorded for example at L. Ismaris (Jerrentrup 1986) and L. Mikri Prespa (Catsadorakis 1986). They are usually seen in small numbers but flocks of 20–40 are not uncommon. The maximum

number recorded during the migration period of spring 1987 at Porto Lagos was 103 on 10 May 1987 (WIWO 90). They are rare and irregular in winter and, since 1965, when the first wintering birds were recorded in the Axios Delta, there have been only five further winter records. One Turnstone ringed in Britain in August has been recovered in Greece in October.

Red-necked Phalarope *Phalaropus lobatus*

Rare and local passage migrant

The first Red-necked Phalarope was recorded in Greece on 25 May 1955, at the mouth of R. Strymon (Flach 1956). Since then, Red-necked Phalaropes have been recorded almost annually. All records are from early May to late September, with the majority in August, particularly in the second half of the month. With the exception of one pair at Messolonghi on 21 August 1983 (Tsounis 1984) and a single bird on Crete in autumn 1979 (*BoC*), all records are from Macedonia and Thrace, in particular from the area of the Alyki Kitrous Lagoon eastwards to L. Ismaris. The geographical position of Greek records fits well with the southeast direction of autumn movements of the Scandinavian population across Europe (*BWP*). Usually single birds are seen, both adult and juvenile, with maxima of six at Porto Lagos on 27 August 1983 (D. Fisher) and five at the same site on 21 August 1981. Most records are from coastal sites (lagoons, river deltas etc.) but also from inland freshwater lakes, such as L. Kerkini, L. Koronia and L. Ismaris.

Grey Phalarope *Phalaropus fulicarius*

Accidental

Grey Phalarope has been recorded three times in Greece. One was seen in the Evros Delta in December 1963 (*CFG*) and another, in winter plumage, was seen and photographed at the Alyki Kitrous Lagoon on 3 August 1982 (Siblet 1986). Between 1 and 20 August 1980 up to 20 were seen in the Evros Delta (Goutner 1983b), a remarkably large number away from the main migration route of the species.

Pomarine Skua *Stercorarius pomarinus*

Accidental

There are only six records of Pomarine Skua in Greece, though it is possible that they are often overlooked. The species was first recorded off the island of Zakynthos in the late 19th century (no date given) (Reiser 1905). The remaining records are of a single off Kyrinthos, NE Evvoia, in September 1959 (*CFG*), an adult off the eastern coast of the island of Karpathos on 25 April 1965 (Kinzelbach & Martens 1965), one off the island of Rhodes in May 1967 (*CFG*), a light-phase adult in summer plumage at Messolonghi Saltpans on 2 August 1989 (M. Versluys) and a light-phase adult at sea *c.* 10 km south of Nafplion on 16 August 1990 (M. Versluys).

Arctic Skua *Stercorarius parasiticus*

Widespread but scarce passage migrant

The commonest species of skua in Greece, Arctic Skuas are regularly seen in almost all months of the year, except for the December to February period. Existing information suggests that they are scarce but it is very likely that they are often overlooked. They are mainly seen from early April to early June (spring passage) and from mid July to mid October (autumn passage), with a large proportion of records in early to mid May and from mid August to mid September. There are only two winter records, of an immature in the Nestos Delta on 20 November 1976 (P. Doherty) and of one found freshly dead at Megalo Livari Lagoon, N Evvoia, on 22 January 1989 (P. Dragoumis).

The species is most often recorded on the coasts of Macedonia and Thrace, from the Thermaikos Gulf eastwards to the Evros Delta. In recent years there have been at least seven records from the Patraikos and western Korinthiakos Gulfs (CP), suggesting that the concentration of records in Macedonia and Thrace may to a certain extent be due to the high observer activity in these areas. There are only two records from the islands, of singles off Gavdos on 20 April 1928 (*BoC*) and off Corfu on 15 October 1991. There is also only one inland record of one at L. Mikri Prespa in July 1984 (G. Catsadorakis). Most of the records refer to singles but small groups are not rare and the maximum single count is of six birds, off Aigion Lagoon on 2 September 1993 (CP). Birds are most often noticed when chasing small gulls and terns and are thus more often recorded near wetlands or harbours, where there are large concentrations of such seabirds. There is one recovery of a bird ringed on the island of Charlov, Murmansk, on 16 July 1939 and found off the western coast of the Peloponnese on 1 March 1940 (Grempe 1981).

Great Skua *Stercorarius skua*

Accidental

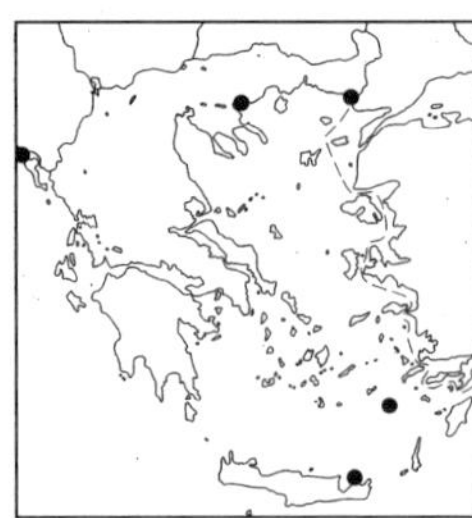

Great Skuas have been recorded five times, in all cases as single birds: at sea, near the Karavonisia islands (36°00'N, 26°30'E) on 18 March 1958 (Mörzer-Bruyns & Voous 1965), in the Evros Delta (harassing a Yellow-legged Gull) on 15 September 1977 (Magerl & Francis 1979), at Asprovalta on 9 September 1987 (L. Maumary), at sea *c.* 50 km northwest of Igoumenitsa on 14 August 1991 (F. Barrault) and off Siteia (Crete) on 19 October 1993 (Grimmond 1993).

White-eyed Gull *Larus leucophthalmus*

Accidental

The only record of White-eyed Gull is of an adult male collected by Lindermayer in the spring of 1860 (Lindermayer 1860) and now in the Smithsonian Museum. Lindermayer claims that the bird was shot off Piraeus, Attica, but later examination of the label on the specimen suggested that it was in fact collected in the Cyclades (Watson 1968).

Great Black-headed Gull *Larus ichthyaetus*

Rare and irregular non-breeding visitor

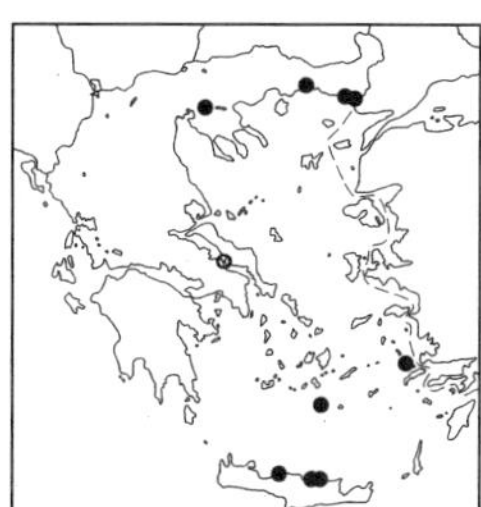

Great Black-headed Gulls have been recorded 16 times in Greece, mostly in recent decades. The first record was of one at Chalkis in 1835 (Reiser 1905). All cases involve single birds, mainly juveniles or immatures, with only two in full adult plumage. There are four winter records: Irakleio, 27 February to 7 March 1990 and 2 January to 19 March 1993 (M. Dretakis), Porto Lagos, January 1992, and Evros Delta, 20 January 1995 (IWRB MC). All other records are from the March to early October period, particularly from June to September. Great Black-headed Gulls have been seen in the Aegean area, with six records from the coastal wetlands of Thrace (Porto Lagos and the Evros Delta) and another seven from the islands of the southern Aegean. A recent observation of an adult bird at L. Koronia on 15 July 1994 (J.T. Wakenshaw) is the only record from an inland site.

Mediterranean Gull *Larus melanocephalus*

Widespread and locally common resident

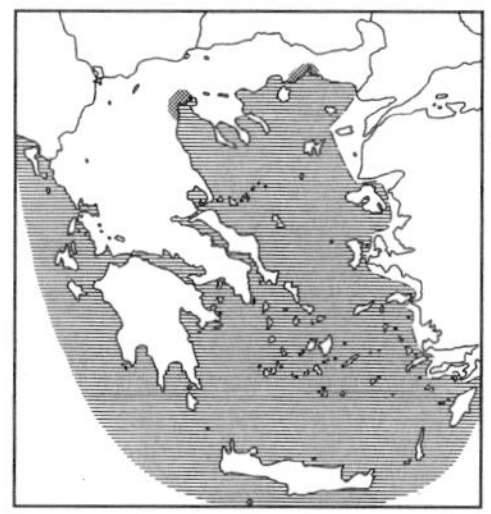

Although the first colony of Mediterranean Gulls in Greece was discovered in 1903 at L. Karla (Reiser 1905), nesting of the species in Greece was not recorded again until 1961 (Makatsch 1963). Mor colonies were discovered in 1966, when *c.* 500 pairs were found three or four colonies in Macedonia (Conradty & Hohlt 196 Makatsch 1968a). These colonies existed up to the early 1980s wit fluctuating numbers and a maximum of 4,000 pairs in the Axi Delta in 1973 (Goutner 1980). Following human interventions (mainly drainage and disturbance) the birds shifted to two new sites: the Alyki Kitrous Lagoon (since 1975 but mainly in 1980) and the Evros Delta (since 1981). The colony of the Evros Delta increased to 1,000 pairs in 1985 but rapidly declined to 85 pairs in 1988 and then was completely abandoned, whereas the colony at the Alyki Kitrous Lagoon increased dramatically to a maximum of 7,300 pairs in 1988 (Goutner 1986; Goutner & Isenmann 1993) but after that year it also collapsed. Between 1989 and 1993 a few scattered small colonies existed, mainly in the Alyki Kitrous Lagoon, the Axios Delta and Porto Lagos and in 1994 the birds established one large colony in the Axios Delta, with *c.* 2,000 pairs (S. Kazantzidis).

Mediterranean Gulls have always bred within large coastal wetlands and the colonies have been on small undisturbed islets in brackish lagoons or on offshore sandy islets with short halophytic or ammophilous vegetation. The birds fly out from the colony to feed over farmland, marshes and pasture. The laying period is generally in May (occasionally eggs are laid from late April) whilst the chicks fledge by the end of July. The chicks' diet consists mainly of

Mediterranean Gulls

large insects (especially Orthoptera) but also fish (Goutner 1986; 1994).

Outside the breeding season, Mediterranean Gulls are widespread and more numerous. Small numbers begin to spread over the country from early July, although the main passage is later, from mid August to early October. Large flocks are rare in autumn and the passage is protracted, being difficult to distinguish from the wandering summer movements of immatures or failed breeders on the one hand and from the arrival of winter visitors on the other. In winter, Mediterranean Gulls are common on the coast, especially in and around harbours, often following trawlers to feed on discarded fish. Wintering birds tend to be entirely marine and are rare in wetland habitats, especially those far from the coast. In milder parts of the country they often feed on flying ants (*Messor*) on warm sunny days in autumn and early winter, together with Black-headed Gulls. The winged ants appear in very large numbers for a few hours around midday and are caught by the gulls in a slow, gliding and flapping flight at a height of 20–100 m above the ground. Densities of 50–200 mixed Mediterranean and Black-headed Gulls per square kilometre can be seen on such occasions, spread over large areas of cultivated land, maquis or woodland near the coast.

The first spring migrants can be seen from mid or late February but fairly large flocks are still on the move until early May. Full adults appear first (February to mid April), followed by immatures (first and second year) later in the season. At this time of the year they form large dense flocks of several hundred birds or more when resting during the day. It appears that colonies may be started from such flocks if they find favourable feeding and nesting conditions. A total of 52 ringed Mediterranean Gulls, all from the Ukraine and almost all from the Chernomorski Reserve on the northwest coast of the Black Sea, have been recovered in Greece on passage or in winter.

Laughing Gull *Larus atricilla*

Accidental

One adult Laughing Gull in summer plumage was seen and photographed in the harbour of Alexandroupolis on 15 August 1984 (Hart 1986). The bird stayed in the area for several days and was seen by many other observers.

Little Gull *Larus minutus*

Widespread and locally common passage migrant, scarce winter visitor

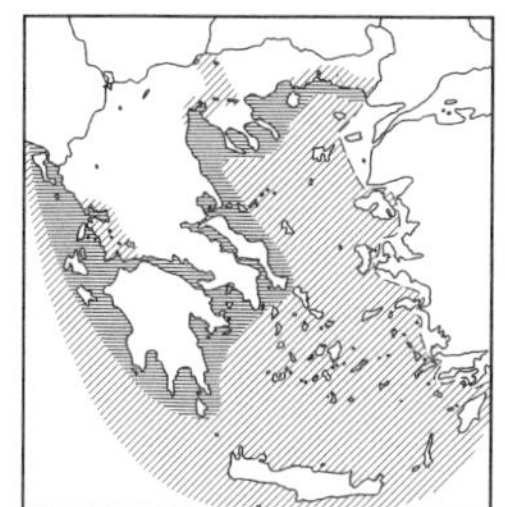

Little Gulls are fairly widespread both as wintering and as passage birds, although the overall pattern of their movements is still imperfectly known and data on their numbers are still limited. In winter small numbers are regular in coastal wetlands and inland lakes, as well as in and around harbours. Usually small groups of up to 5–10 birds are seen, indicating a total wintering population of 2,000–5,000 birds. However, their occurrence is rather unpredictable and flocks of 50–100 birds may suddenly appear throughout winter. Large numbers have been reported passing through the Dardanelles in August and September (Ballance & Lee 1961) but these apparently move on very quickly as comparable numbers have never been detected in the Aegean. The passage of Little Gulls starts around mid August and is often prolonged into late November–early December, e.g. a few thousand were recorded in the western part of Korinthiakos Gulf in early December 1988 (CP). In general it appears that both in winter and on migration Little Gulls favour offshore waters and that the relatively few birds recorded along sea coasts and in coastal wetlands may be a small fraction of much larger numbers offshore. This is supported by the recent discovery (1990) of large numbers wintering in the Nile Delta; these had previously gone undetected and may originate from a population wintering somewhere offshore in the eastern Mediterranean (Meininger & Sørensen 1993).

In spring, migrating flocks appear from early March to mid May, with a peak in late March and early April. This is the only time of the year when they are noticeably attracted to coastal lagoons and lakes. Large flocks of several hundred or thousand birds may appear but they stay for only one or two days. For example, well over 2,000 birds were seen at L. Vistonis on 8 April 1980 but only about 500 remained in the evening of the following day. Indicative of the erratic nature of their movements is also a record of at least 5,000 birds in the Evros Delta in May 1968 (Bauer & Müller 1969), much later than the main passage period. Isolated individuals or small parties may be seen through summer months.

Black-headed Gull *Larus ridibundus*

Rare and local resident, very common and widespread winter visitor

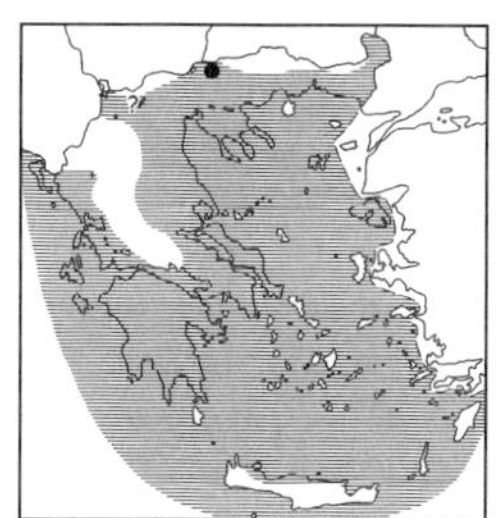

Nesting of Black-headed Gull in Greece was first confirmed in 1987, when two nests were found at L. Kerkini on 2 June (Jerrentrup 1988). Nesting also took place in 1988 (R. Hume) and probably every year since then, with about five pairs in 1994 (N. Petrou). A 'colony' was also reported at L. Petron on 8 July 1982 (B. Pambour) but no further details are known. Although the species is present in small numbers at all lakes in the north of the country during the summer, there has been no other case of breeding and the great majority of these oversummering birds are non-breeding immatures.

Black-headed Gulls are commonest during winter. At this time of the year they are the most numerous gull throughout the mainland and the islands, greatly outnumbering Yellow-legged Gulls. Apart from inshore waters, large numbers also occur in wetlands, both coastal and inland, and on cultivated land. Concentrations of 5,000–10,000 birds occur on many lakes, large river deltas and in the vicinity of large fishing ports. In the last 20 years they seem to have increased and spread to urban areas near the coast, picking up scraps of food from wide streets, schoolyards and town squares, a habit which was unknown up until the late 1970s. At about the same time the habit of following the plough also began to spread. Wintering birds frequently visit rubbish dumps, sewage outfalls, and follow trawlers. In the south they also feed on flying ants, as Mediterranean Gulls do (see above). The total wintering population is probably well in excess of 500,000 birds.

Significant numbers of Black-headed Gulls probably pass through the country on migration but the volume and timing of this passage is difficult to estimate as it is swamped by the arrival and departure movements of wintering birds. The first immatures begin to arrive towards the end of June or early July and the first adults from early August onwards. Numbers increase gradually through the late summer and early autumn. The majority of the wintering birds have arrived by mid September and the rest have arrived by the middle of October. Further influxes may be observed at times of unusually cold weather in winter. Departures of adult birds begin in late February and from late March onwards the population consists mainly of immatures in partial summer plumage. At this time of the year there is a significant shift from sea water to fresh and brackish water wetlands. Some immatures are still present up to mid May and a small number of them may stay for the whole summer. There are 36 recoveries of foreign-ringed Black-headed Gulls in Greece, with 11 from Russia, eight from Hungary and smaller numbers from Finland, the Baltic States, Poland, Germany, the Czech Republic and the Ukraine.

Slender-billed Gull *Larus genei*

Rare and local resident, locally common winter visitor and passage migrant

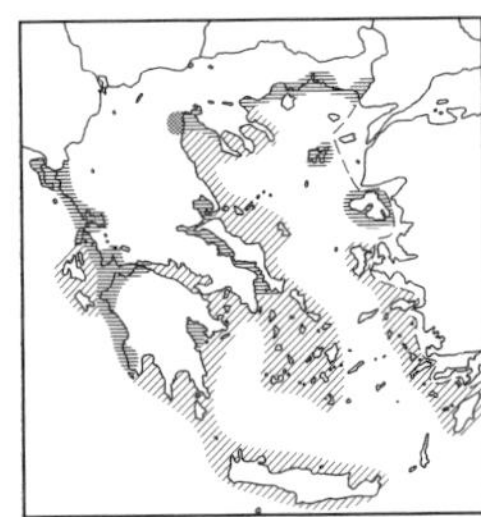

The first record of Slender-billed Gulls breeding in Greece was in 1966, when two pairs were found at Porto Lagos (Conradty & Hohlt 1967). In 1967 a few pairs were found nesting in the Axios Delta (Kraus *et al.* 1969). This colony reached *c.* 100 pairs in 1972 (Isenmann 1975) but in 1974 the birds moved to the Alyki Kitrous Lagoon, where 10–20 pairs nested. At this latter site there were 40 pairs in 1980, 23 in 1985, none in 1987 and 1988 (Isenmann & Goutner 1993) and 45 in 1992. Apparently the Alyki Kitrous Lagoon still remains the only breeding site for the species in Greece.

Much more numerous outside the breeding season, Slender-billed Gulls are recorded in largest numbers during spring migration. Peak passage takes place from mid March to mid April. At such times large flocks may occur in large coastal wetlands, e.g. 2,266 were counted at Porto Lagos on 26 March 1987 (WIWO 90) and 812 in the Amvrakikos on 22 March 1990 (WIWO 95). At all times Slender-billed Gulls prefer shallow brackish, saline or hypersaline coastal lagoons (including saltpans), or shallow coastlines. They also occur in small numbers in harbours but they are very rare inland. Autumn passage generally runs from late July to October, with a peak in the first half of September. Fairly large numbers remain in winter, especially in western Greece. Data from the IWRB MC (1982–1992) give an average of 640 birds for the whole country, a maximum count of 2,490 in 1988 and a maximum site count of 1,600 at Messolonghi on 23 January 1995. However, many more birds are probably present in areas not covered by the counts and a certain number may go undetected among the much more numerous Black-headed Gulls. Seventeen ringed Slender-billed Gulls have been recovered in Greece, all ringed as chicks at the Chernomorski Reserve on the northwest coast of the Black Sea.

Slender-billed Gulls

Audouin's Gull *Larus audouinii*

Scarce and local resident

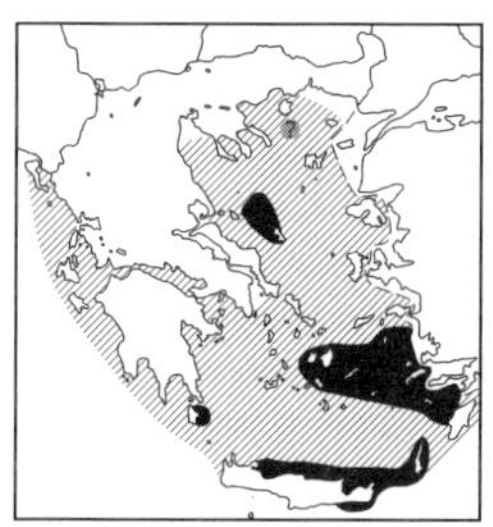

Audouin's Gulls are scarce and local and seem to have always been so. Breeding was first recorded in the Northern Sporades in 1894 (Reiser 1905), though later authors doubted the validity of this record (Makatsch 1968b). The species remains very poorly known. Its breeding distribution is not precisely known and its current numbers and status are difficult to assess. The main strongholds of Audouin's Gull are the archipelago of the Northern Sporades, with one known colony, and the southeastern Aegean, including Crete, with breeding at a few known and probably several more undiscovered colonies. The Northern Sporades colony numbered 15–20 pairs in 1961, 20 pairs in 1966, 22–25 pairs in 1973 and 60–66 adults in 1980 (*VME*), whereas in 1966, the population in the southeastern Aegean was estimated at 52 pairs (De Juana & Varela 1993). Breeding is also reported on the eastern coast of the island of Kythira (Kominos 1995). The total Greek population was estimated at over 40 pairs in 19 colonies in 1979 (*BWP*) and more recently at 70–100 pairs (Tucker & Heath 1994). However, a thorough survey in 1995 revealed at least 110 breeding pairs in the northern Dodecanese alone (Papaconstantinou *et al.* 1995) and it now seems that the total population of the species may be nearer 200 pairs.

Audouin's Gulls nest on small uninhabited islets, generally rather flat and with little vegetation, mainly of grasses, *Eryngium maritimum* and patches of low lentisc *Pistacia lentiscus* bushes. Colonies are monospecific and their establishment is usually dictated by the pressure or not of Yellow-legged Gull colonies (Makatsch 1968b, 1969a, 1969b). The movements of the species outside the breeding season are inadequately known but existing data suggest that Greek birds do not wander far from their colonies. They have been recorded along most of the coasts of the Aegean and Ionian Seas, usually as single birds. Since 1989, they have become commoner in the NW Peloponnese, particularly in autumn (July to September) and have started to occur in the winter too. For example, more than 30 were present at Aigion Lagoon on 8 February 1994. This increase probably reflects a range expansion and/or increase in numbers, perhaps paralleling the recent population increase in the western Mediterranean (CP).

Audouin's Gull

Common Gull *Larus canus*

Fairly common but local winter visitor

Common Gulls are regular winter visitors in small numbers from early November to late March. Although they are often encountered on the coast, they seem to prefer inland freshwater lakes. They are present most regularly and in larger numbers in Macedonia and Thrace and become progressively less common towards the south and west. They are rare in western Greece or the Peloponnese and extremely rare on most islands (e.g. the Cyclades or the Ionian), from which very few records exist (Magioris 1987a; Joensen & Madsen 1985). Data from the IWRB MC (1982–1992) show an average wintering population of 45 birds, a maximum count of 543 (1993) and a maximum site count of 1,055 in the Evros Delta on 20 January 1995. However, the actual average wintering population is probably much higher as Common Gulls often occur in areas not visited by counters and many are missed among large flocks of other gulls. The wintering population may expand further during cold spells with influxes of birds coming from the north. Common Gulls occurring in Greece seem to belong mainly to the eastern race, *L. c. heini* (WIWO 90; CP), though birds of the nominate race may also occur.

Lesser Black-backed Gull *Larus fuscus*

Widespread and locally fairly common passage migrant and winter visitor

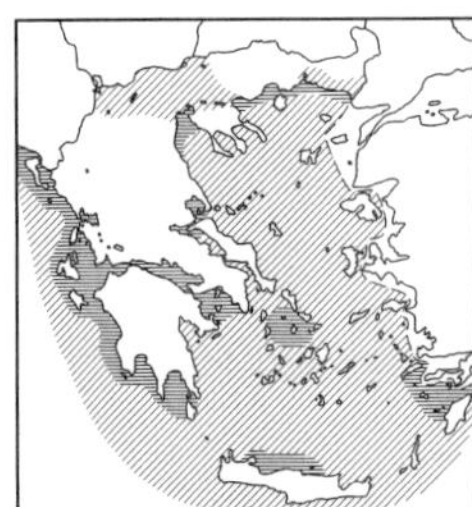

Lesser Black-backed Gulls are widespread as passage migrants and winter visitors on the coasts and islands of both the Aegean and the Ionian Seas. In the majority of cases, single birds are seen but groups of up to ten are not rare. Small numbers winter in Greece and up to 15–20 occur regularly in the Patras area every winter (CP). Spring passage is usually from early March to mid May, with a peak in late April to early May, whereas in the autumn, movements are obvious from late August until late October. A few birds may spend the whole summer in Greece. It is certain that throughout the year Lesser Black-backs, particularly immatures, are often overlooked among the much more numerous Yellow-legged Gulls.

The species is seen mainly in harbours, coastal wetlands and rubbish dumps during the winter. Passage migrants also frequently turn up on inland lakes. Most passage migrants and perhaps some winter visitors belong to the highly migratory nominate race *L. f. fuscus*. However, the majority of those wintering clearly show characteristics of *L. f. intermedius*. There are also two records of the north Russian race, *L. f. heuglini*, both of single birds in immature to sub-adult plumage, at Patras harbour on 26 September 1990 and 22 January 1993 (CP).

Herring Gull *Larus argentatus*

Widespread but rare winter visitor

Partly due to the difficulty of distinguishing between immature Herring and Yellow-legged Gulls and partly because the two forms were until very recently treated as one species, existing information on the occurrence of Herring Gulls in Greece is very scanty and disputable. The only early record is Harrison's (1925) report of comparatively small numbers of 'the Atlantic race of the Herring Gull' in the northern Aegean Sea during the winters of 1917 and 1918. In more recent years there have been fewer than 10–15 sufficiently documented records, almost exclusively in winter. Most records refer to single adult birds and thus it seems that many immatures are overlooked. Observers should be aware of the frequent occurrence of sub-adult Yellow-legged Gulls with pink legs and streaky head, as well as of immatures with a rather pale grey-brown plumage due to bleaching. There are two ringing recoveries of *L. argentatus* found in Greece. One was ringed in Finland, within the breeding range of *L. a. omissus* (though one must bear in mind the possibility of a misidentifed nominate Lesser Black-back *Larus fuscus fuscus*); the other was ringed in Poland and recovered in its first winter at Patras, on 22 January 1994. This bird showed characters of the nominate *L. a. argentatus* (CP).

Yellow-legged Gull *Larus cachinnans*

Very common and widespread resident

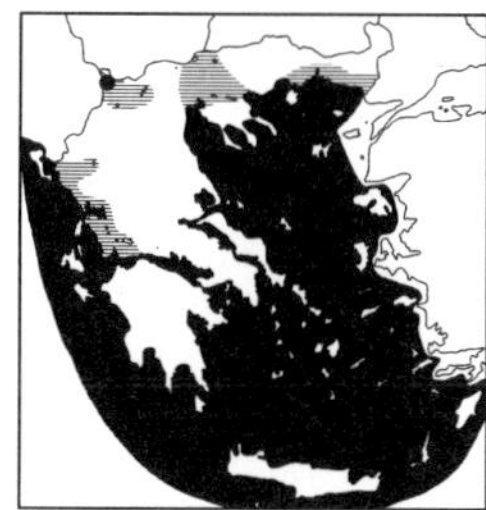

Although they are the commonest of the resident gulls in Greece, Yellow-legged Gulls still remain relatively little known. They are widely distributed on all coasts and the highest densities occur near large fishing ports and large towns, largely depending on discarded fish and refuse for their food supply. Most of the larger breeding colonies are on small uninhabited inshore islets but significant numbers also nest on low islets or enbankments within large lagoons, extensive saltmarshes and saltpans. They are scarce inland and usually restricted to the vicinity of large lakes and large rivers, though since 1991 they have nested at L. Mikri Prespa (15 pairs in 1994) (G. Catsadorakis), where they had been non-breeding visitors for a number of years. Many colonies of more than 100 pairs are known, and although no complete census of the total breeding population has ever been made, it probably amounts to well over 15,000 pairs. Breeding birds belong to race *L. c. michahellis*, which is also the commonest race in all seasons. In winter the population is probably augmented by immigrants from the Black Sea or eastern Europe and western Asia. It is very likely that relatively large numbers of *L. c. cachinnans* are present in winter but they have not yet been identified with certainty. However, there are two recoveries of birds ringed as pulli on the northern coast of the Black Sea (within the range of *L. c. cachinnans*) and found in winter in Greece. Furthermore, adult birds with a dark mantle, small body and comparatively small head, small 'mirrors' on the primaries and a short bill with traces of a dark subterminal band, closely resembling Armenian Gulls *L. armenicus*, have been seen on several occasions in the NW Peloponnese (CP). Further ringing recoveries and close study of wintering and passage birds are obviously needed before the subspecific status of the *L. cachinnans/argentatus* group is clarified.

Iceland Gull *Larus glaucoides*

Accidental

A second-winter Iceland Gull was seen in the harbour of Chalkis on 19 December 1980 (Handrinos 1985a).

Great Black-backed Gull *Larus marinus*

Rare and irregular winter visitor and passage migrant

Great Black-backed Gull was first recorded in the mid 19th century in the Cyclades (Erhard 1858) and since then there have been fewer than 20 additional records, almost exclusively of single birds. Almost half of the records are from the winter, with nine in January. There are six records from the March–May period and four from the August–September period. The

species has been seen on the coast of the mainland and on islands of the Aegean Sea. Nine records are from the Evros Delta but seven of these apparently involve the same individual, an adult bird recorded in January 1982, 1985, 1989, 1990, 1991, 1992 and 1994. There are several reports of the species from Crete, but none of them is currently accepted due to lack of supporting details (*BoC*).

Kittiwake *Rissa tridactyla*

Widespread but rare winter visitor

The status of Kittiwakes in Greece is still unclear. The species was first recorded in January 1895 (Reiser 1905). Systematic observations of gulls in the harbour of Chalkis since 1977 showed Kittiwakes regular in small numbers between late October and late March. Up to four birds are present there, often following trawlers or roosting on piers and buildings amidst other gulls. Most birds are immatures but adults have also been recorded, with up to two seen together. Records of the species from other parts of the country are scanty. All are of single birds, mainly immatures, with the exception of Harrison's (1918) report of 'fair numbers' in the NE Aegean Sea in the winter of 1917/18. There is a concentration of records from the coast of Macedonia and Thrace, with few elsewhere and only five from the islands: two from the Ionian Sea, two from Crete (*BoC*; M. Dretakis) and one from the island of Tilos (S. Keen). Kittiwakes have been recorded as late as April and May but the majority of records are from winter. Interestingly, several records have been from coastal lagoons and river deltas, an atypical habitat for this open-sea species. This may be partly attributed to high observer activity in such habitats and indicates that Kittiwakes are probably much more regular and widely distributed than existing records suggest.

Gull-billed Tern *Gelochelidon nilotica*

Scarce and local summer visitor and passage migrant

Gull-billed Terns apparently had a wider distribution in the 19th century than at present (Reiser 1905). Major colonies were discovered at Messolonghi (300 pairs) in 1963 (Wolff 1966) and then in the Nestos Delta (300–400 pairs in 1966) (Conradty & Hohlt 1967), the Evros Delta (30–40 pairs in 1967) (Bauer & Müller 1969) and the Axios Delta (400 pairs in 1967) (Kraus *et al.* 1969). Following many years of wetland drainage and habitat degradation, the breeding population declined dramatically to 180–200 pairs in 1989, with no further decrease since then. The majority of the population is concentrated at Messolonghi, with 138 pairs in 1994 (Y. Roussopoulos). Smaller colonies exist in the Amvrakikos, at the Alyki Kitrous Lagoon and at Araxos Lagoon. Gull-billed Terns often forage over agricultural land, as well as over marshes, lagoons and other shallow coastal waters. An analysis of pellets from three colonies (Evros Delta, Alyki Kitrous Lagoon and Messolonghi) showed that insects (mainly Coleoptera and Orthoptera) were important prey items at the first two but crabs *Carcinus* spp. were important at Messolonghi (Goutner 1991). The dependence of Gull-billed Terns on insect prey may be the cause of their decline, particularly since the 1970s, when the use of pesticides began to spread and agricultural methods began to intensify in general.

Gull-billed Terns begin to arrive in late March but peak numbers are not usually observed until late April. At Messolonghi most clutches are started in mid and late May. After fledging,

Gull-billed Terns

adults and juveniles leave the breeding colonies and disperse locally. Juveniles are often observed being fed by parents until early August. Departures probably begin around this period, with the majority leaving in late August and early September. The last birds are usually seen in late September. Small numbers of Gull-billed Terns can be seen over much of the country on spring and autumn passage. Two birds, one ringed in the Camargue (France) and one at Crimaea (both ringed as chicks), have been recovered in Greece whilst one chick ringed at the Alyki Kitrous Lagoon was recovered in Italy in its first autumn.

Caspian Tern *Sterna caspia*

Fairly widespread but scarce non-breeding visitor

Caspian Terns may be seen in Greece all year round, being commonest on passage, particularly in autumn. They occur fairly widely along the coasts of mainland Greece and occasionally of the islands but they are never very numerous. They are usually limited to large coastal wetlands (lagoons, river mouths etc.) and inland freshwater lakes, especially in eastern Macedonia, Thrace and the area of Messolonghi.

In spring the first migrants appear in late March or early April and movements are detectable until late May. Autumn passage is more important and runs from early August to mid October, with a peak in mid September. The largest number ever recorded in Greece is of 300 at L. Kerkini on 10 September 1980 (J. Walmsley) whilst 85 were seen also at L. Kerkini on 2 October 1994. Caspian Terns are scarce in winter and data from the IWRB MC (1982–1992) give an average of only six birds in the whole country, probably a slight underestimate of the true numbers present. Messolonghi seems to be the most important site for wintering birds with maxima of 60 on 21 January 1970 (A. Johnson & H. Hafner) and 26 on 18 January 1984 (Joensen & Madsen 1985).

A few Caspian Terns can be seen in June and July but these seem to be mainly non-breeding birds and no nest has ever been found in Greece. However, there are a few records of single pairs seen during the breeding season in suitable habitat, displaying or otherwise showing signs of possible breeding, e.g. at Messolonghi on 24 May 1990 (F. Pergantis), Porto Lagos on 19 June 1967 (Kraus *et al.* 1969) and a pair feeding a fledged young at Porto Lagos in late August 1960 (Raines 1962). Therefore, occasional nesting of single pairs cannot be ruled out. So far, there are 60 recoveries of foreign-ringed Caspian Terns found in Greece, with 37 from Finland, 20 from Sweden and three from Estonia. Many more birds, presumably from the same populations of the Baltic, have been seen carrying rings.

Lesser Crested Tern *Sterna bengalensis*

Accidental

There are three records of Lesser Crested Tern, all in recent years. The first record was of an adult in the Evros Delta between 11 and 13 June 1987. It was seen in a colony of Sandwich Terns and its behaviour indicated pairing with a bird of the latter species (Goutner 1988). The second record is of an adult at Aigion Lagoon on 4 July 1990, roosting amidst a flock of eight Sandwich Terns (Papaconstantinou 1991). The third is of an immature bird photographed at sea off the Akarnanian coast in late July 1993 (P.A. Casales).

Sandwich Tern *Sterna sandvicensis*

Rare and local resident, common and widespread winter visitor and passage migrant

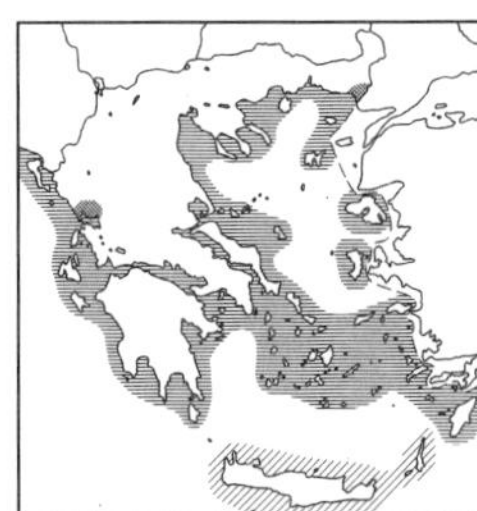

Sandwich Terns were first discovered nesting in Greece on 10 June 1979, when *c.* 70 birds were seen on a sandy islet in the Evros Delta, many of them feeding young. A further small colony has existed since at least the early 1980s in the Amvrakikos. There is also a report of nesting in the Loudias Delta in 1980 (*BWP*) but no further details of this record are known. In 1988–89 the total breeding population comprised *c.* 30 pairs in two colonies (Amvrakikos and Evros Delta). The Evros Delta colony showed signs of decline in the early 1990s, coinciding with almost complete breeding failure of Little and Common Terns at nearbly colonies, but about 300 birds were observed again in late summer of 1995 (D. Vangeluwe).

Sandwich Terns are fairly common and widespread in the winter, with small numbers present along most coasts. In the spring numbers gradually increase from late February to a peak in early April and then slowly decline, with a few birds still on passage up to about mid May. At this time of the year they very often form relatively large flocks when roosting, whereas on autumn passage and in winter they are more often seen in small loose groups of up to 10–15 birds. The autumn movements are more protracted and some birds appear already from mid July, though the majority pass through from mid August to mid October. The largest numbers recorded include counts of 575 at Porto Lagos on 7 April 1987, 269 in the Nestos Delta on 8 April 1987 (WIWO 90) and 206 at Messolonghi on 21 January 1990. On passage and in winter Sandwich Terns are usually seen fishing over shallow coastal waters and they regularly occur in and around harbours. They are very rare inland. There are five ringing recoveries of Sandwich Terns in Greece, all of birds ringed in the large colonies of the northern Black Sea coast.

Common Tern *Sterna hirundo*

Widespread and locally common summer visitor and passage migrant

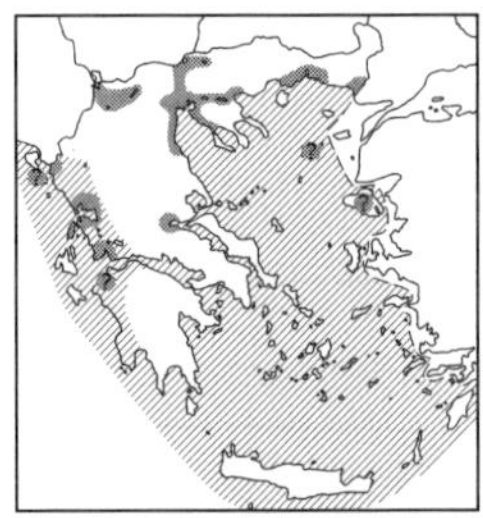

Common Terns have a widespread breeding distribution on the mainland, with colonies in most of the major coastal and inland wetlands, from Messolonghi and the Spercheios Delta in the south to the Kalamas Delta, L. Mikri Prespa and the Evros Delta in the north. A few pairs may also occasionally breed elsewhere on the mainland or on some islands (e.g. Lesbos and Limnos). The total breeding population numbered a minimum of 1,300 pairs in 1988–90, with major colonies in the Amvrakikos (500–600 pairs in 1989) (Pergantis & Akriotis 1994), Messolonghi (220 pairs in 1990) (Roussopoulos 1990), Porto Lagos and the Evros Delta. Most of the colonies are on sandy or muddy islets, devoid of vegetation or with sparse low halophytic shrubs, and located within coastal lagoons, river deltas or saltpans. Smaller colonies also exist at inland freshwater lakes (e.g. L. Mikri Prespa and L. Kerkini) or along large rivers.

Common Terns usually first appear in late March and numbers increase up to the end of April or early May. Significant numbers of passage migrants are probably included among the birds present in April and early May. Migratory movements have been observed at Porto Lagos, mainly in an easterly direction along the coast (WIWO 90). In autumn, birds begin to disperse from breeding colonies in early July and departures of adults probably start in mid to late July. The bulk of the population has left by the end of August and the last birds are usually seen in late September or early October. Exceptionally the species has been recorded in winter in southern Greece, both in the 19th century and in recent years (Reiser 1905, CP). There is only one ringing recovery of the species in Greece, of a bird ringed as a chick at Tendrovskii Bay on the northwest coast of the Black Sea and recovered at L. Trichonis on passage.

Arctic Tern *Sterna paradisaea*

Accidental

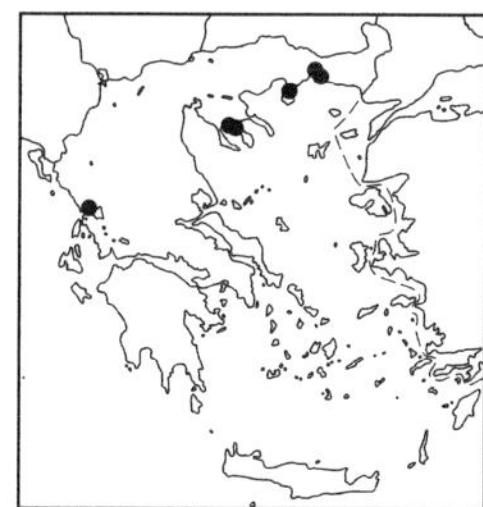

So far, Arctic Terns have been recorded eight times but it is very likely that they occur more frequently than existing records suggest. The first two records are both from the Amvrakikos, with two birds on 25 April 1958 and four on 7 May 1959 (Flach 1960). All other records are from the north Aegean coast. Three records are from Porto Lagos and L. Vistonis (single birds in each case), in May 1961, April 1966 (*CFG*) and on 17 April 1985 (J. Wittbrodt & D. Förnzlar). Two records are from Polychrono and Pefkochori in Chalkidiki, on 22 and 25 May 1975 (Lensch 1979) and another from the island of Thasos on 29 July 1978 (Ritzel 1980). There is also an unconfirmed record from Ierapetra (Crete) on 10 April 1979 (*BoC*).

Bridled Tern *Sterna anaethetus*

Accidental

An adult Bridled Tern was seen at Tsoukalio Lagoon in the Amvrakikos on 6 June 1987 (M. Ganoti & P. Dragoumis). This is the only confirmed record of the species in Greece. Interestingly, a few days earlier, on 16 May 1987, another possible Bridled Tern was recorded at sea between Sithonia and Mt Athos (B. J. Summerfield).

Little Tern *Sterna albifrons*

Widespread and locally common summer visitor and passage migrant

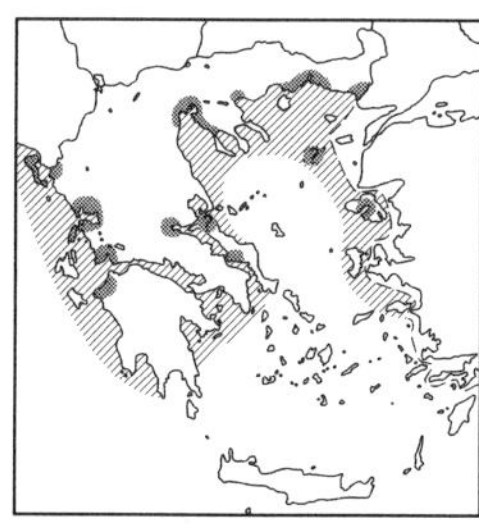

The breeding range of Little Tern more or less coincides with that of Common Tern. However, Little Terns do not occur inland and they are slightly more widespread on the coast, e.g. a few pairs nest at the saltpans of Lechaina in the W Peloponnese (CP), the saltpans of Lefkimmi on Corfu (J. van der Linden), the coast of central Evvoia, and Lesbos. In 1989–90 the total breeding population was 1,500–2,000 pairs, with large populations at Messolonghi (500 pairs in 1990) (Roussopoulos 1990) and the Amvrakikos (at least 1,350 pairs in 1986) (Fasola *et al.* 1991). Population size seems to fluctuate significantly, at least on a local scale, with colonies often not lasting long and sometimes shifting location. Little Terns are seen fishing mainly over lagoons and shallow sea coasts. Colonies are formed either on natural islets, sandspits and (rarely) sandy shores, or at similar sites created by man. For nest-building, they seem to have a strong preference for unvegetated ground and probably for this reason they are particularly attracted to low enbankments of gravel or dry mud within saltpans, which are often devoid of vegetation due to the high salt concentration. Because they often nest only a few centimetres above water level, it is not rare for whole colonies to be destroyed by waves during late spring and early summer thunderstorms. Although, like other species of tern nesting in saltpans, they obtain most of their food in adjoining lagoons and shallow sea water, Little Terns are the only ones to feed on the sole species of fish present there, Mediterranean toothcarp *Aphanius fasciatus*. This small fish is often abundant in saltpans but it is reputed to be toxic or distasteful and is taken by few other species of fish-eating bird (e.g. Little Egret) and only in small quantities.

Spring arrivals of Little Terns usually start in mid April (rarely early April) and peak numbers are reached by late April or early May. Departures probably begin as soon as the breeding season comes to a close, in mid to late July. Most birds have left by late August and a few isolated individuals may stay until September or early October. The largest post-breeding concentrations of Little Terns recorded include 3,000–5,000 birds at Messolonghi on 14 July 1973 (P. Barthel & N. Kroftt) and 5,000 at Porto Lagos on 14 August 1987 (J. Drachman). A small flock seen flying northeast at great height over Porto Lagos on 3 May 1987 suggests some overland passage (WIWO 90). Away from breeding areas, Little Terns are scarce. For example, they are listed as very scarce and irregular passage migrants on Crete (*BoC*). The only ringing recovery of Little Tern is of a bird ringed as a chick at Messolonghi Saltpans on 11 June 1989 and recovered in Morocco on 10 September of the same year.

Whiskered Tern *Chlidonias hybridus*

Rare and local summer visitor, common passage migrant

The first colony of Whiskered Terns in Greece was discovered at L. Ismaris in 1965 (Kraus & Conradty 1965). In 1967 two more colonies were found in the Turkish part of the Evros Delta (Bauer & Müller 1969) and at L. Kerkini (Kraus *et al.* 1969). At that time the total breeding population was 200–230 pairs. Today it is estimated at *c.* 300 pairs in three main colonies: L. Kerkini, L. Ismaris and L. Cheimaditis. Since 1984 a few pairs have bred occasionally at L. Mikri Prespa too. Colonies of Whiskered Terns are always located in the shallow parts of freshwater lakes particularly on dense carpets of floating vegetation, mainly of white water lily *Nymphaea alba* and water chestnut *Trapa natans*.

Whiskered Terns pass through the country in fairly large numbers in the spring, though they are much less numerous than White-winged Black Terns. The first birds usually make their appearance in the last few days of March but numbers do not build up significantly until after the middle of April. Peak passage occurs in early May and smaller numbers of migrants can still be seen in early June. On spring migration Whiskered Terns occur both on the coast and inland, on freshwater lakes, brackish or saline lagoons, marshes, rice fields, flooded meadows and other similar habitats. Although they are most often seen in small parties of up to five or ten birds, up to 200–300 birds may be seen together in large wetlands in early May, usually in mixed flocks with White-winged Black or Black Terns. Such flocks frequently make brief forays to feed over nearby cornfields, low hills with phrygana or maquis and other dry habitats. During summer a few non-breeding birds are regularly present in suitable habitat away from breeding sites. In autumn, Whiskered Terns are less numerous and, since many of the smaller wetlands are dry, they are much less widespread too. Autumn passage and departure of local birds takes place mainly from late August to mid September.

Whiskered Terns

Black Tern *Chlidonias niger*

Rare and local summer visitor, common passage migrant

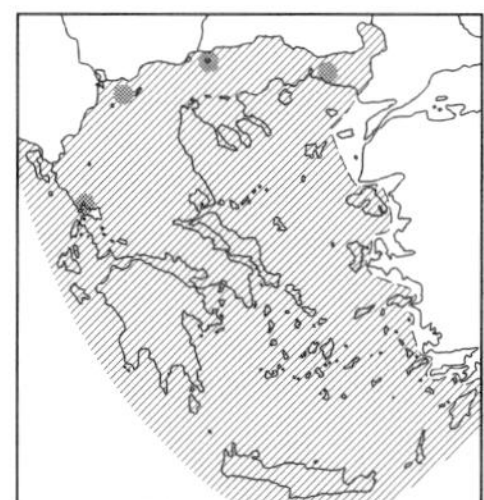

The first breeding of Black Terns in Greece was at L. Artzan in 1917 (Chasen 1921). Breeding was confirmed again in 1965 at L. Agras (*CFG*) and was recorded as probable at L. Karla in 1963 and 1964 (*CFG*). In 1967 another colony of 40 pairs was found at L. Kerkini (Kraus *et al.* 1969) and a smaller one (10–15 pairs) in the Turkish part of the Evros Delta (Bauer & Müller 1969). Small colonies were also reported in the Kalamas Delta (six nests in 1970) (Bauer *et al.* 1973), the Louros Delta and perhaps at L. Mikri Prespa (*CFG*). Today the population is estimated at fewer than 200, and perhaps as few as 50 pairs, in a few small colonies at L. Ismaris, L. Kerkini, L. Cheimaditis and the Louros Delta, with occasional nesting at L. Agras. Breeding Black Terns share more or less the same nesting habitat, and often the same breeding site, with Whiskered Terns.

In spring, Black Terns migrate on average a little earlier than the other two marsh terns, with a peak in the second half of April or early May. However, their arrival is often sudden, in early April, without the early vanguards (in March) of Whiskered Tern. They may be seen in flocks of several tens or hundreds. The maximum number ever recorded in Greece is 6,000 birds, counted in one day in May (1968?), in the Evros Delta (Bauer & Müller 1969). Autumn passage is from late July to early October, with a peak in the first half of September. In autumn, Black Terns occur not only in wetlands but also at sea, either in small numbers on the coast or, more often, offshore in flocks of up to several hundreds. In the NW Peloponnese up to *c.* 1,000 birds per day have been recorded passing through at peak passage (CP). There is one winter record of a bird in full summer plumage at Messolonghi on 23 January 1995.

White-winged Black Tern *Chlidonias leucopterus*

Common and widespread passage migrant

White-winged Black Terns are common and widespread passage migrants in the spring. Passage takes place from early April to late May, with largest numbers in early May. On autumn passage they are much less numerous, from mid July to early October and mainly from early August to mid September. They are highly gregarious and almost invariably occur in flocks, usually of 10–50 birds, but in spring it is quite common to see up to a few hundred together. The maximum number ever recorded is of at least 1,500 moving rapidly north along the river in the Evros Delta on 30 April 1980. In spring, flocks generally stay for only brief periods at stopover sites and quickly move on, but are continually replaced by fresh arrivals. White-winged Black Terns occur in all kinds of freshwater or brackish lakes, lagoons, marshes and flooded fields. They often venture into nearby dry habitats, as described for Whiskered Tern.

Pin-tailed Sandgrouse *Pterocles alchata*

Accidental

One bird shot on the island of Kos on May 1953 is the only record of Pin-tailed Sandgrouse in Greece. The specimen was sent to and identified by Prof. H. Hatzissarantos of the Zoology Department, Athens University (Hatzissarantos 1953; Handrinos 1994a).

Pallas's Sandgrouse *Syrrhaptes paradoxus*

Accidental

Pallas's Sandgrouse has been recorded only once, in the spring of 1888, at Kalamata (Reiser 1905). This record coincides with one of the most spectacular irruptions of the species from the steppes of Asia into Europe (*BWP*).

Rock Dove *Columba livia*

Fairly common and widespread resident

Although Rock Dove is the most widespread of the three Greek species of *Columba*, its precise distribution is still not well known, partly due to the difficulty of separation from feral pigeons and partly due to the remote location of its breeding sites. The species is locally common on most of the Aegean islands, including Crete (Vagliano 1984), but apparently less common on the Ionian islands. It is also rare in Thrace and Macedonia, whereas in the rest of the mainland it is more or less confined to inaccessible, rocky areas. The population size of Rock Doves is impossible to estimate accurately but it is reported as declining in the Peloponnese (CP). The species is extensively hunted on most of the islands. In most of the Aegean, Rock Doves are restricted to the vicinity of sheer coastal cliffs and caves, whereas on the mainland and inland on Crete they are mainly seen in sparsely vegetated, rocky habitats, with gorges and cliffs, as high as 2300 m (e.g. on Mt Parnassos and Samaria Gorge). In some regions records exist of feral/domestic pigeons among flocks of wild birds, even in remote areas. Birds on Crete and in the Dodecanese have been classified as race *C. l. gaddi*, whereas those of the mainland and the Ionian islands belong to the nominate race (*CFG*). The taxonomic status of populations in the eastern and central Aegean has not yet been determined with certainty.

Stock Dove *Columba oenas*

Rare and local resident, scarce winter visitor

As has already been pointed out (*RDB*), Stock Dove is still one of the least known Greek birds. It has a very restricted breeding distribution, mainly from NW Macedonia to Thrace, on mountains along the northern border. The southernmost locality where breeding is certain is the Vikos–Aoos National Park (Schmid & Reichenecker 1988). A few breeding season records also exist from other areas (e.g. Mt Athos and Mt Parnassos) (*CFG*; Bauer & Hodge 1970; Bauer *et al.* 1973; Peterson *et al.* 1981; Bauer & Böhr 1987) but with no proof of breeding yet. From what is known so far, the most typical breeding habitat of Stock Doves is mature beech *Fagus* forest at moderate altitude but they have also been found in other deciduous and mixed forest, from 500 to 1500 m and locally a little higher, e.g. at up to 1700 m on the Rodopi Mts (Bauer & Böhr 1987). In the latter area, one pair was found nesting in an abandoned Black Woodpecker nest-hole in May 1971 (Bauer *et al.* 1973). The total breeding population of Stock Dove is not known but it certainly is very small (*RDB*) and probably under 1,000 pairs. The species may be locally declining. For example, there have been no records from Mt Triklarion, a former breeding site, since 1988 (Catsadorakis 1991).

Outside the breeding season Stock Doves are more widely distributed and more easily seen. They occur mainly as winter visitors to the lowlands of northern Greece. A few also spread further south but even in the north they are local and not common. They are generally seen in small to medium-sized flocks of up to 50–100 birds and are often found in riparian woodland or poplar plantations adjoining farmland or meadows, such as found in and around large wetlands (e.g. L. Kerkini and the Nestos Delta). Stock Doves are also known as passage migrants (*CFG*) but the pattern of their movements and the numbers involved are very poorly known. In the spring of 1987 only 48 birds were seen in coastal NE Greece, all between 4 and 24 March (WIWO 90). In the northern Peloponnese they have been seen a few times in the autumn and once in the spring (CP). There are only two records from the Cyclades, from Naxos and Milos (Magioris 1994), one from the Ionian islands (four birds on Paxoi, 8–10 October 1979) (A. Vittery) and 12 from Crete (*BoC*). A large proportion of records from the southern mainland, Crete and other islands are from September, October, April and May, suggesting some passage through the country. However, the species winters mainly north of the Mediterranean (*BWP*) and it remains a puzzle where such apparent migrants spend the winter. Two ringed birds recovered in Greece came from Russia and the Ukraine.

Woodpigeon *Columba palumbus*

Fairly common and widespread resident

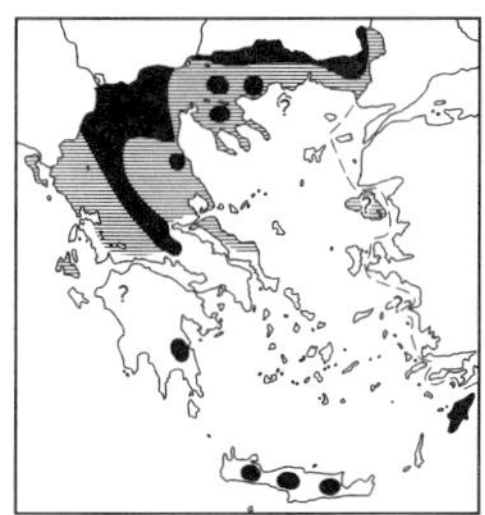

Woodpigeons have a widespread but rather patchy distribution in Greece. They breed on the mountains along the Greece/Bulgaria border, on most of the mountains of mainland Greece along the Pindos range, as far south as Mt Parnassos, and in scattered localities elsewhere on the mainland. They also breed in very small numbers on Crete, Rhodes (Scharlau 1989a) and Lesbos, and possibly Thasos and Samos. They usually nest at moderate altitudes, as high as about 1500 m (Bauer & Hodge 1970; Bauer *et al.* 1973). On Rhodes they nest in pine *Pinus brutia* woodland, in eastern Crete in all types of natural woodland (Scharlau 1989a, 1989b) and in the Peloponnese locally in holm oak *Quercus ilex* (CP). However, in most other areas and for most of the year they are closely associated with deciduous oaks *Quercus*, as is the rule for the rest of their Western Palearctic range.

Outside the breeding season, Woodpigeons are more numerous and widespread, though they tend to form large flocks in favoured areas and to be rare or absent elsewhere. Large numbers appear in oakwoods in October, to feed on acorns. They are also numerous in maize fields in the early autumn, just after the harvest, and flocks of several thousand are occasionally recorded in fertile farmland from Thessaly northwards during the winter. Overall, they are commonest in northern and central parts of the mainland. In Sterea Hellas and the Peloponnese they are local and not very numerous whilst on the islands they are very scarce. There are no records of Woodpigeons from the Cyclades during this century (Magioris 1994) and there are few records from the other Aegean islands (excluding those on which they breed). On Lesbos, Woodpigeons are said to have been very numerous winter visitors and an important quarry species up to the 1950s or 1960s, whereas now they are scarce.

Collared Dove *Streptopelia decaocto*

Common and widespread resident

At the beginning of the 20th century, Collared Doves had a restricted range, in Thrace, Macedonia and some of the eastern Aegean islands such as Rhodes and Lesbos. Reiser (1905) has suggested that in the past they also existed in the rest of the country but were largely exterminated soon after the end of Ottoman rule (1821 onwards). There is, however, no other evidence to support this hypothesis and it is more probable that the lack of records from central and southern Greece at the turn of this century was due to a truly more limited distribution of the species up to that time. Whatever the situation in the distant past, Collared Doves were still confined to northern and eastern Greece until *c.* 1930 and then started to spread (*VME*; *BWP*). In the late 1960s and early 1970s they had already expanded to much of the mainland, as far south as the Peloponnese, and most of the islands in both the Aegean and the Ionian Seas. In the late 1960s they were still rare in the central and southern mainland and since then they have become common and widespread. On Crete there were only three records up to 1986 (*BoC*), with no indication of breeding. Since then, they have rapidly spread over the island but mainly along the northern coast, where they now breed regularly (D. Townsend). It has been suggested that this recent expansion of Collared Doves on Crete could be attributed to the growth of tourism, providing more food, but it could also indicate a natural trend for a gradual expansion of their present range to the southeast (D. Townsend). Collared Doves are still uncommon on Kefallinia, where they became established in the town of Argostoli in the mid to late 1980s (A. Vittery). Nowadays, they are common and widespread in the rest of the country, though they are confined to towns, villages and isolated farm buildings, being extremely rare in true 'wild' situations.

Turtle Dove *Streptopelia turtur*

Common and widespread summer visitor and passage migrant

Turtle Doves breed over much of the Greek mainland. They are widespread and common in Macedonia and Thrace but they are more thinly distributed farther south and rather uncommon in much of the Peloponnese. Small numbers also breed on several of the larger Aegean islands, such as Crete, Lesbos, Chios and Rhodes. Their breeding status in the Ionian is uncertain but they probably breed on Corfu, and they have been seen during the breeding season on Kefallinia, Ithaki and Paxoi (CP; A. Vittery). Their total breeding population in Greece has been estimated at 10,000–30,000 pairs (Tucker & Heath 1994) and although their numbers seem to fluctuate, there have probably been some local decreases due to excessive hunting (*BWP*).

Turtle Doves are much commoner on passage, particularly in the spring. Their movements are on a broad front but large numbers concentrate along the coasts, particularly in western Greece. In spring very large numbers pass over Zakynthos, Kefallinia and the Strofades, a group of small islets 44 nautical miles south–southeast of Zakynthos. On these islets birds arrive in flocks from the southwest and make their first landing after crossing the Mediterranean. The maximum number of birds recorded on Strofades during spring of 1995 was on 25 April, when 5,000 birds were estimated to be present on the main island and an additional 5,000 birds passed without stopping (I. Schogolev & M. Dimaki). Spring passage is from early April to mid May, with peak numbers in late April. The return passage is on a smaller scale and takes place from mid August to early October, with a peak in early September.

Turtle Dove is a very popular quarry species and large numbers are shot each year. In some areas (especially on Zakynthos), the shooting of Turtle Doves is almost part of the local tradition. Today, shooting is permitted only in autumn but up to the early 1980s there was a special open season in spring (15 April–15 May), specifically for shooting Turtle Doves. Very large numbers were killed then, as well as large numbers of birds of prey, herons and other protected and often rare or endangered species. This spring shooting has now been banned. There are 38 ringing recoveries of Turtle Dove found in Greece. These include birds ringed mainly in the Czech Republic (12) and Hungary (12), with smaller numbers from Italy (4), Poland (3), Slovakia (2) and singles from Austria, Slovenia, the Ukraine, Cyprus and Chad.

Rufous Turtle Dove *Streptopelia orientalis*

Accidental

Rufous Turtle Dove has been recorded five times. One was shot on the island of Spetses on 18 September 1948 and another near Kiato (area of Corinth) on 22 April 1963 (J. Koutsis). Two were seen and photographed in the Evros Delta on 21 August 1965 (Loterijman 1968) and singles were seen in the Strymon Delta on September 1966 (*CFG*) and near the monastery of Agia Triada (Crete) on 27 April 1986 (A. Vittery). In view of the similarity of this species with Turtle Dove, it may be assumed that it occurs more frequently but is overlooked.

Laughing Dove *Streptopelia senegalensis*

Accidental

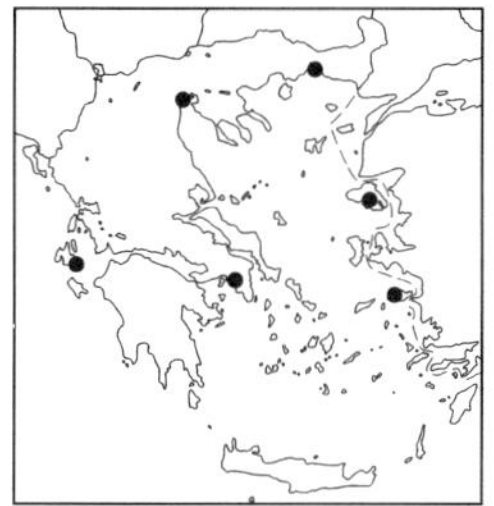

There are six records of Laughing Dove, all of singles and the majority from eastern parts of the country: Aliakmon Delta, May 1962 (*CFG*), Porto Lagos, 27 September 1977 (Magerl & Francis 1979), Samos, 26 April 1992 (Y. Roussopoulos), Kefallinia, 20 October 1992 (J. Grearson), Athens, 11 May 1993 (L. Rose) and Achladeri (Lesbos), 24 May 1994 (P.D. Hanson).

Great Spotted Cuckoo *Clamator glandarius*

Rare and local summer visitor and passage migrant

Although nesting of Great Spotted Cuckoo in Greece was suspected since the 19th century, e.g. in the Axios floodplain (Sladen 1917) or Attica (17 June 1871) (Reiser 1905), it was not proven until much later: first at Peristeronas, near L. Volvi, on 6 May 1978 (Conradty 1979) and a few days later (26 May 1978) at Asvestochori, near Thessaloniki (Limbrunner 1979). A third breeding case was recorded in the Evros Delta on 7 May 1981 (V. Goutner). In all three cases nestlings were found in nests of Magpie. Great Spotted Cuckoos have also been seen regularly during the breeding season in other areas, such as the Nestos Delta, the plains of Komotini (Jerrentrup 1986) and the island of Kos (Bauer *et al.* 1969b). They occur in various lowland habitats with a park-like character, including agricultural land with scattered

trees, olive groves, open oak *Quercus* woodland, open scrub and the margins of wetlands with patches of tamarisk *Tamarix*. The nest at Asvestochori was in white oak *Quercus pubescens* scrub infested with gypsy moth *Lymantria dispar* caterpillars, a favourite prey of Great Spotted Cuckoos (Limbrunner 1979). The breeding of Great Spotted Cuckoos may be restricted to areas with a high Magpie population and this may be the reason why they seem not to breed in many areas where they occur on spring passage. This applies especially to the islands, most of which (e.g. Crete, Lesbos and Samos) lack Magpies.

Great Spotted Cuckoos arrive in Greece as early as mid March and the great majority of records are from the spring migration period (late March to early May). At this time of the year they have been recorded from many parts of the mainland and some Aegean islands but they are rare and irregular outside the above mentioned known or suspected breeding areas. Autumn records are very few and mainly from Crete and the Dodecanese. In autumn, remains of Great Spotted Cuckoos have been identified in nests of Eleonora's Falcons *Falco eleonorae* off NE Crete (Walter 1979; Ristow *et al.* 1986).

Great Spotted Cuckoos

Cuckoo *Cuculus canorus*

Fairly widespread but scarce summer visitor, widespread and fairly common passage migrant

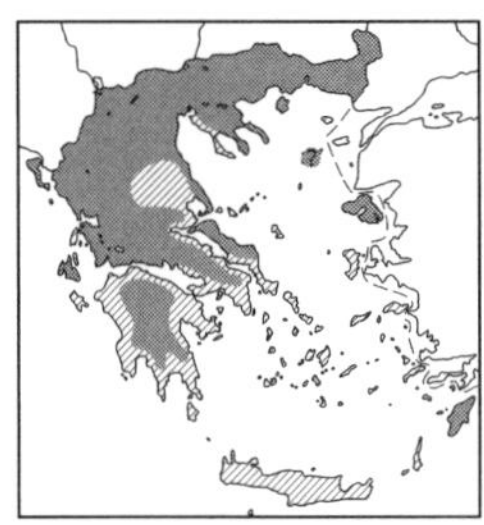

Cuckoos have a wide breeding distribution over the mainland but they are generally scarce, except in certain central and northern parts. They are generally absent from low altitudes in southern parts of the country with a pure Mediterranean climate and vegetation. They are also absent from most of the islands except for some of the larger ones and especially the more well vegetated ones, such as Rhodes (Scharlau 1989a), Kefallinia (A. Vittery) and Lesbos. They are more widespread on migration and occur throughout the country in small numbers. The spring passage is mainly from early April (occasionally from mid March in the south) to mid May and the autumn passage from late August to mid October and, on Crete, to early November (*BoC*).

Very little is known about the ecology of Cuckoos in Greece. During the breeding season they occur mainly at low and medium altitudes in Macedonia and Thrace but in other parts of the country they are rare below about 500 m. Their overall geographical and altitudinal distribution may be a reflection of the density of their potential hosts. So far, the species has been found to parasitise Black-eared Wheatears, Stonechats, Orphean Warblers and Sardinian Warblers but the main hosts are probably other species (e.g. Robin or other *Sylvia* warblers), which are commoner than the above in the sub-Mediterranean habitat types preferred by Cuckoos. At least in southern and central Greece, the species has never been found parasitising Reed or Great Reed Warblers, both of which are common hosts elsewhere in Europe (*BWP*). On passage, Cuckoos are widespread and at times fairly common. In spring they are fairly common in Aleppo pine *Pinus halepensis* woodland, probably attracted by the huge numbers of hairy caterpillars of the pine processionary moth *Thaumetopoea pityocampa* that are present on the trees at that time of the year. However, this habitat is rarely used for breeding. Eight Cuckoos ringed abroad have been recovered in Greece: two had been ringed in Finland, two in Poland and singles in Britain, Germany, Sweden and Latvia.

Barn Owl *Tyto alba*

Fairly common and widespread resident

Although it has been described as scarce (Lambert 1957) or rare (*BWP*; Mikkola 1983) in the past, Barn Owl is a fairly common resident species, widespread all over the mainland, including the Peloponnese. It also occurs on many islands in the Aegean (Crete, Lesbos, Chios, Karpathos, Rhodes, Samos etc.) but in the Ionian its status is still unclear: it certainly breeds on Corfu (Böhr 1962; *CFG*) and probably on Lefkada but apparently not on Kefallinia (A. Vittery). The Greek population of Barn Owls does not appear to face any serious conservation problems and appears to be relatively stable. It probably numbers between 3,000 and 6,000 pairs.

Barn Owls are mainly lowland birds, most frequent on farmland, pastures, phrygana and open olive groves. Where they occur in high density, they sometimes nest and forage in towns and villages. They are most numerous in areas of sparse human habitation, such as farmland with isolated farm buildings, where they find suitable nest sites and a good food supply. Apart from buildings, they have been found nesting in hollows in large oak *Quercus* or plane *Platanus* trees, caves, disused quarries and rock faces. The few published data available so far (Böhr 1962; Cheylan 1976; Pieper 1977; Tsounis & Dimitropoulos 1992a) and unpublished data suggest that small rodents of the family Muridae are their commonest prey in Greece. These are represented predominantly by house mice *Mus domesticus* and young brown rats *Rattus norvegicus* near human settlements but in wilder areas species such as wood and rock mouse *Apodemus sylvaticus* and *A. mystacinus* are much more important.

The local population of Barn Owls appears to be resident but a few birds may disperse to Greece from central or eastern Europe during eruptive movements, as they do for example in Spain (*BWP*). There is one recovery of a bird ringed in Germany and found in Greece in January. Both *T. a. guttata* and *T. a. alba* breed in Greece. According to the older literature (*CFG*; *BWP*), the former is found in eastern Macedonia and Thrace and the latter in remaining areas. However, the situation appears to be more complicated than this and it has still not been clarified. Many birds show a high variation in the degree of 'paleness' of the underparts whilst, for example, pairs of pure *T. a. guttata* have been found breeding in central Evvoia, amongst a chiefly *T. a. alba* population. *T. a. erlangeri*, similar to *T. a. alba*, breeds on Crete (*BWP*).

Scops Owl *Otus scops*

Common and widespread partial migrant

Scops Owls have a very widespread distribution all over the Greek mainland and on almost all of the islands in both the Aegean and the Ionian Seas. They occur in a variety of habitats, both natural and man-made, and their distinctive call is one of the most familiar night sounds in villages and small towns in spring and early summer. They are numerous in open woodland, olive groves, orchards, gardens and town parks from sea level to middle altitudes, up to about 1200–1300 m. Their total breeding population probably exceeds 5,000 pairs and may be as high as 20,000 pairs. Nests are usually located in holes in trees (e.g. olive *Olea*, mulberry *Morus* and plane *Platanus*) but occasionally also under the eaves of buildings, in ruins or at rock sites.

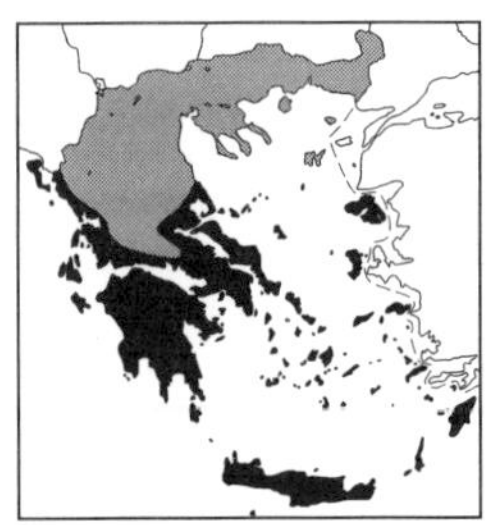

There are two races of Scops Owl in Greece. *O. s. scops* is found on most of the mainland and on the Ionian islands whilst *O. s. cycladum* is found on Crete, the Cyclades and probably the Peloponnese and the eastern Aegean (*CFG*). Many birds are regularly present in winter north at least to Sterea Hellas. In general the population of O. *s. scops* seems to be partly migratory, whereas that of O. *s. cycladum* is mainly or exclusively resident (*CFG*; Vagliano 1984; Magioris 1987a). However, the exact winter range of the species, the proportion of birds migrating and the distances travelled are still largely unknown. Furthermore, virtually nothing is known on the volume and timing of the passage of birds from northern populations through the country. The few data available suggest that spring passage is from early March to early May and autumn passage from early September to mid October. One spring migrant ringed at Cap Bon, Tunisia, has been recovered in Greece (*BWP*).

Eagle Owl *Bubo bubo*

Widespread but scarce resident

Eagle Owl has a widespread breeding distribution all over the Greek mainland as far south as Mt Taygetos or perhaps the Mani peninsula (Grimmett & Jones 1989). It seems, however, to be missing from all the islands except Lesbos and Kalamos, a small island off the Akarnanian coast (D. Papandropoulos). Within their range, Eagle Owls have a rather patchy distribution but locally (e.g. Dadia Forest Reserve and Evvoia) they are not uncommon. In fact, the species has probably been under-recorded and the total population, estimated at 200 (*BWP*) or 200–500 pairs (Tucker & Heath 1994), may well exceed 500 pairs. Despite severe human persecution, especially in the past, and hence local declines and extinctions (e.g. in parts of Attica), the overall range of the species does not appear to have changed much during the last 100 years (Reiser 1905).

Eagle Owls occur in a wide variety of habitats, from sea level to high altitudes. They prefer open treeless areas or light woodland, with gorges, cliffs or other broken terrain and most nest sites known so far have been in hollows in rocks, rather than trees. Because of their nocturnal habits, they may occur very near villages and isolated human settlements in the countryside, much more so than similar-sized diurnal birds of prey. Pellets from Lesbos contained 12 mammal species, including lesser mole rats *Nanospalax leucodon*, young dogs and cats

Eagle Owl

(Pieper 1981), whilst prey remains from a nest near Chalkis were composed almost exclusively of large adult brown rats *Rattus norvegicus*, with small numbers of eastern hedgehogs *Erinaceus concolor*, brown hares *Lepus europaeus* and medium-sized birds (probably corvids). Their breeding season does not appear to be particularly early and at a closely watched nest at low altitude in Evvoia the young fledge usually in late June or early July.

Eagle Owls are not known to undertake any significant movements within the country. In the past they have been listed, presumably erroneously, as a migrant in the Cyclades (Erhard 1858). However, dispersive movements may bring them to islands on which they are not known to breed, such as Chios, where they have been recorded in September and October (Spinthakis *et al.* 1993).

Pygmy Owl *Glaucidium passerinum*

Rare and local resident

Pygmy Owls have been recorded only in the dense mature forests of the Rodopi Mts, north of Paranesti, along the Greece–Bulgaria border. In this area, Pygmy Owls calls were heard in the twilight on two occasions (15 May 1973 and 10 June 1975) and on 15 May 1984, at 1350 m, a similar call was heard in daylight, causing a strong alarm reaction to singing passerines (Bauer & Böhr 1987). So far, breeding has not been confirmed in this area, though the dates of the records and the fact the Pygmy Owls are principally a non-migratory species strongly indicate a small resident population. The presence of this species here is apparently connected with the presence of Norway spruce *Picea abies*. For both species the Rodopi Mts are the southernmost distribution limit in Europe (Bauer & Böhr 1987).

Little Owl *Athene noctua*

Fairly common and widespread resident

Little Owls have been familiar birds in Greece for at least 2,500 years. They appear in ancient greek art and in classical times were associated with goddess Athena. They still breed locally within Athens and other urban centres, though they are more typically found in rural areas. They occur widely over the whole mainland and on most islands, in a wide variety of open habitats, including farmland, phrygana and the surroundings of villages and shepherds' huts. Pellet analysis shows that they seem to be attracted to the latter by the plentiful dor and dung beetles (Geotrupidae and Scarabaeidae) near flocks of grazing animals as well as of grasshoppers and bush crickets (Orthoptera) on grazing land.

Little Owls have been recorded as high as 1650 m on Mt Oiti (Peus 1957) and occur at relatively high altitudes in many other areas, provided suitable open habitat is available. It appears that Little Owls have declined since *c.* 1970 (*BWP*). This is more evident in agricultural areas, where increased use of insecticides has probably reduced their food supply, and in some coastal areas, where urbanisation has resulted in loss of habitat, increased disturbance and disappearance of derelict buildings. Furthermore, although they have been a protected species for many decades, they are disliked and persecuted in many rural areas due to a superstitious belief that their call is a bad omen. However, there are no censuses or other data to show the extent of this decline and they still remain quite numerous and widely distributed. Their total population probably lies between 5,000 and 15,000 pairs. The entire Greek population of Little Owls has been classified as race *A. n. indigena* (*CFG*; *BWP*), though a few birds from Rhodes show some tendency towards the paler eastern race, *A. n. lilith* (*CFG*).

Tawny Owl *Strix aluco*

Fairly common and widespread resident

Not so well known as some other species of owl, Tawny Owl is widely distributed and locally quite common on the mainland. Its breeding range on the islands is still not well known. It is absent from most of them, e.g. Crete (Vagliano 1984; *BoC*) and the Cyclades (Magioris 1994), but it is present on Corfu and Kefallinia (J. Millett, A. Vittery) in the Ionian Sea and on Thasos, Samos, Lesbos and possibly Rhodes in the Aegean. Tawny Owls occur in a wide variety of wooded habitats, whether coniferous, deciduous or mixed, from Aleppo pine *Pinus halepensis* woodland and groves of oriental plane *Platanus orientalis* at sea level, to old fir *Abies* forest at the treeline. However, they do not normally occur in woodland of poor growth on dry, stony soils at low altitude, nor olive groves, preferring taller trees and more congenial conditions. Thus, in southern parts of the country they tend to occur near stream beds or at moderate to high altitude. The total Greek population probably amounts to 5,000–20,000 pairs.

Long-eared Owl *Asio otus*

Fairly common and widespread resident and winter visitor

Although Long-eared Owls seem to occur widely and in fairly good numbers, their breeding distribution is still relatively little known. Breeding has been confirmed in only a few cases on the mainland but breeding season records exist from many other parts of the mainland and many of the larger islands. At least one pair apparently nested on the island of Naxos in the 1980s (Magioris 1989) and the species is probably a scarce resident on Crete (*BoC*). Their population size is very difficult to estimate but it probably lies between 2,000 and 10,000 pairs.

Long-eared Owls occur in park-like habitats, in phrygana, pasture or farmland with scattered trees and thickets or at the edges of woodland, avoiding the central parts of dense and extensive forest, as well as open treeless areas. They seem to be commonest at low altitude and it is not known if they regularly occur at higher elevations, e.g. as high as Tawny Owls do. In most cases, nests or breeding pairs have been found in pine trees *Pinus*, and these are also widely used for roosting at all times of the year. Birds have also been seen in dense olive groves and poplar plantations. Long-eared Owls are slightly more numerous (or easily seen) in winter, when the local population is probably augmented by immigrants. The relative proportion of winter visitors to resident birds is not known but in some areas winter roosts of five to ten birds are not uncommon. A few Long-eared Owls have been recorded on autumn passage (or post-breeding dispersal) on Chios (Spinthakis *et al.* 1993) and Crete (*BoC*).

Short-eared Owl *Asio flammeus*

Widespread but scarce winter visitor and passage migrant

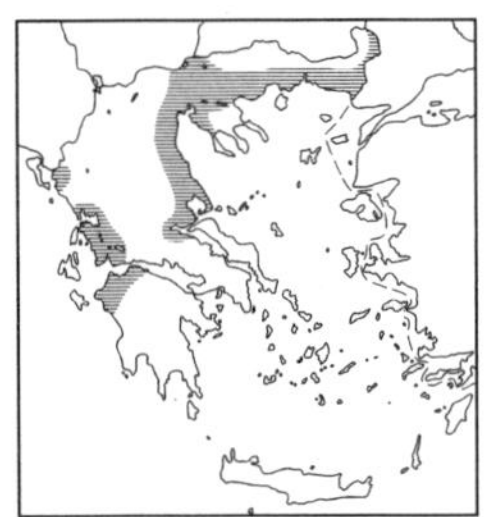

The only probable breeding case of Short-eared Owls in Greece is of a pair showing definite signs of nesting in the Evros Delta between 17 and 19 May 1971 (Bauer *et al.* 1973). Two more breeding season records from the 1960s possibly also refer to breeding: one bird seen at L. Karla on 12 May 1962 (Groh 1968) and another at L. Ismaris in May 1962 (*CFG*). There have been no more recent indications of breeding.

The species is more regularly seen in the winter half of the year, especially from December to February. The majority of records are from the large coastal wetlands of Thrace and Macedonia, with a scattering further south on the mainland (Messolonghi, Spercheios Delta, NW Peloponnese etc.). Short-eared Owls may be under-recorded but even so they are certainly not common and despite their partly diurnal habits (at least in other parts of their range) they are much more rarely seen than e.g. Barn or Long-eared Owls. In most cases singles or small groups of two to three birds are seen and the maximum number ever recorded in Greece is of 38–40 birds, in the Axios Delta on 4 January 1989 (S. Kazantzidis). At the same site, 12 were seen roosting communally within a few square metres of saltmarsh on 30 January 1983. There are few confirmed records of Short-eared Owls from the islands, mainly in the north (e.g. Corfu and Lesbos). There are only six records from Crete since 1925 (October, January, April) (*BoC*) and only one from Naxos, where one female was collected on 21 December 1933 (Bird 1935). The passage through the country is on a very small scale in both seasons and seems to take place mainly in October and March–April. In the spring of 1987 only four birds were seen in the wetlands of NE Greece, between 22 and 30 March (WIWO 90).

Tengmalm's Owl *Aegolius funereus*

Rare and local resident

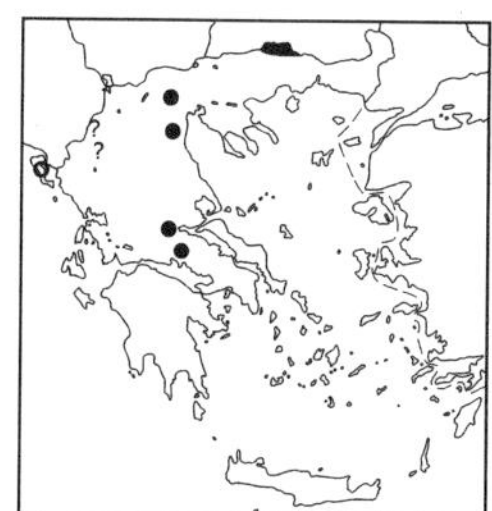

The first indication of the presence of Tengmalm's Owls in Greece was in 1857–58, when a mounted bird was found in a taxidermist's shop in the town of Corfu. The bird was claimed to have been shot on the island (Powys 1860). However, in view of the lack of suitable habitat on the island, it is very doubtful that this was true and it seems much more likely that the bird had been imported from the mainland or from abroad. In more recent times, Tengmalm's Owls have been reported from seven different areas of the mainland. These include Mt Parnassos (*CFG*), Mt Oiti (Peus 1954) and Mt Olympos (Eggers 1964) but the main stronghold of the species seems to be in the Rodopi Mts, along the Greece–Bulgaria border (Bauer & Böhr 1987). Mounted specimens have also been seen in a small taxidermist's collection at Edessa (Flach 1960) and presumably these had been collected somewhere in western Macedonia. A recent report refers to the occurrence of the species in the Vikos–Aoos National Park (Schmid & Reichenecker 1988) but since no details are given, this needs confirmation. Finally Tengmalm's Owls may occur on Mt Grammos (Grimmett & Jones 1989). In the Rodopi Mts Tengmalm's Owls have been seen in mature coniferous and mixed forests, as high as 1600 m (Bauer & Böhr 1987), whereas on Parnassos, Oiti and Olympos they have been recorded from high-altitude fir *Abies* or pine *Pinus* forest.

Nightjar *Caprimulgus europaeus*

Common and widespread summer visitor

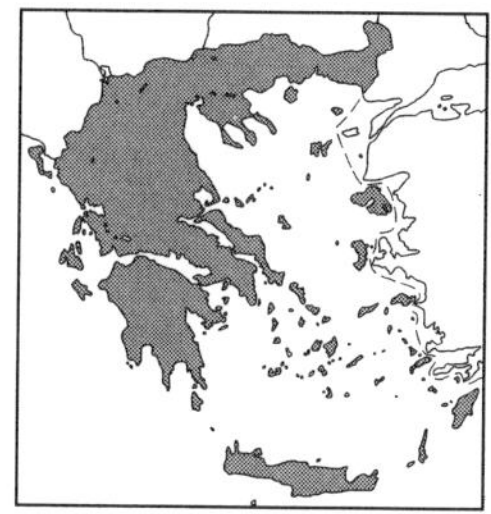

Nightjars have a widespread distribution all over the mainland and on most of the islands of the Aegean and Ionian Seas. They occur in a wide variety of open habitats, from sand dunes and the margins of marshy areas on the coast to high-altitude stony pasture, e.g. at up to 1500–1700 m on Mt Parnassos or up to 1800 m on Mt Olympos (Peus 1957). However, they appear to be commonest on dry, stony hills with phrygana and scattered trees at low altitude. At night they often sit on unmetalled roads with little traffic. They seem to be so attracted to such roads that one is almost guaranteed to see at least one and probably several birds in car headlights when driving through suitable habitat one or two hours after sunset. At dusk and dawn, one also regularly sees Nightjars hawking over marshy habitats, including reedbeds. It is not easy to arrive at a reliable estimation of the total breeding population of the species but it almost certainly exceeds 10,000 pairs and may well be as high as 30,000 pairs.

The first birds arrive in early April but larger numbers are not observed until early May. The singing period is mainly from mid April to early August. In autumn, departures seem to take place mainly in late August and the first half of September. Birds are more elusive at this time of the year than in spring and these dates will need confirmation in the future. Occasional late birds have been seen up to the end of October. There is probably a significant passage through the country but this is not separable from the arrival and departure movements of locally breeding birds. Nightjars breeding in Greece belong to race *C. e. meridionalis*, whereas passage migrants include *C. e. europaeus* (*CFG*). There is one recovery of a Nightjar ringed in the St Petersburg district in Russia in summer and recovered on Kefallinia in early May.

Swift *Apus apus*

Very common summer visitor and passage migrant

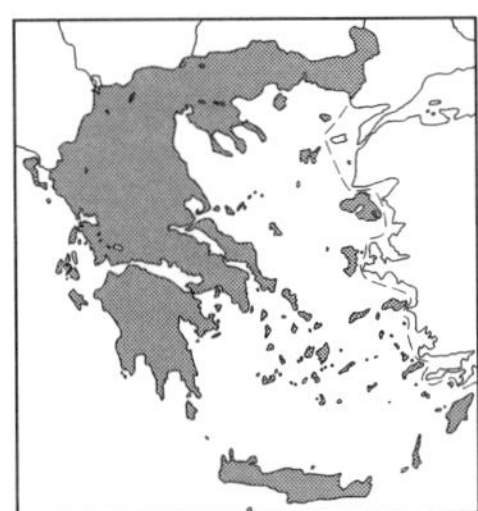

One of the commonest summer birds, Swifts have a widespread distribution all over the mainland and on most of the islands of the Aegean. Their exact breeding range on the Ionian islands is less well known. They are common breeding birds on Corfu, but while they are common passage migrants on Kefallinia, their nesting there has not yet been confirmed (A. Vittery). On Ithaki it appears the species is absent, whereas Pallid Swifts occur in small numbers (CP). Unlike the situation in central and northern Europe, Swifts are early migrants in the spring, arriving on average only about ten days after Swallows. They are first seen usually in mid March though the majority arrive from early April onwards. In early spring they very often feed over wetlands together with hirundines. Freshwater lakes and canals are frequently visited throughout summer for bathing or drinking.

Swifts nest mainly in towns and large villages, with nests often placed under broken clay roof tiles on old buildings. Modern methods of roofing may pause a threat to Swifts (and Pallid Swifts) in the future. Suitable sites outside urban areas (e.g. cliffs, old quarries and rocky islets) are also freely used. Breeding Swifts are regularly found in mountain villages up to at least 1000 m. Most birds leave between mid August and mid September but flocks of up to 100 birds occur irregulary up to the middle of October and these may be migrants passing through the country after the local breeders have left. Smaller numbers have been recorded up to the first days of November, though some of these very late records may in fact involve Pallid Swifts. Both in spring and in autumn the movements of Swifts are strongly influenced by influxes of warm or cold air and the first and last dates of arrival or departure are quite variable. Swifts breeding in Greece belong to the nominate race but, as in Cyprus (Flint & Stewart 1992), most birds are duller and paler than those of western Europe, tending towards *A. a. pekinensis*.

Pallid Swift *Apus pallidus*

Common and widespread summer visitor

The breeding range of Pallid Swifts spans most of the mainland and many of the islands but they are much more localised and overall are less numerous than Swifts. They are often confused with the latter so that neither their breeding range nor the timing of their occurrence are very clear yet. They are generally confined to coastal areas and low altitudes, nesting at similar sites to Swifts, in both man-made and natural situations. Locally they breed at least as high as 1200 m (e.g. on Mt Parnassos, see also Kroymann & Kroymann 1992a). Pallid Swifts are now known to breed on Crete in small numbers (*BoC*) but their status on most other islands is still uncertain, with contradictory data from different sources.

The species is certainly present in Greece from late March to late October (mainly early April to mid October) but some of the Swifts observed outside the limits of this period may include Pallid Swifts. Contrary to Swifts, they are present in good numbers until much later in the autumn. Furthermore, fledglings have been found as late as early October and recently fledged young up to mid October. Both their late departure and their late breeding are in accordance with the long breeding season of the species in various parts of the Mediterranean (*BWP*). Pallid Swifts breeding in Greece are darker than west Mediterranean birds, intermediate between *A. p. illyricus* and *A. p. brehmorum* (*BWP*). They have been variously included in the former (*CFG*; Vaurie 1965) or the latter (*BWP*).

Alpine Swift *Apus melba*

Common and widespread summer visitor and passage migrant

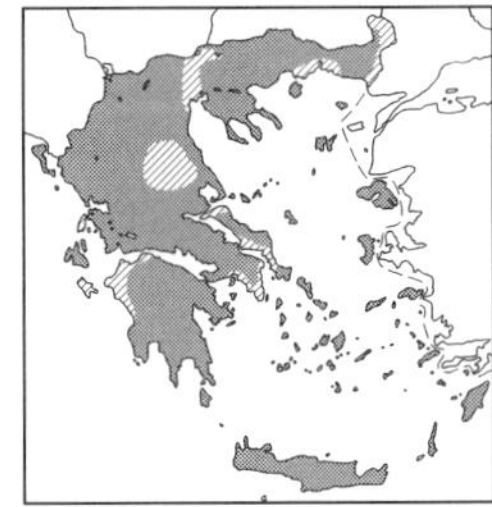

Alpine Swifts breed all over the mainland and on most of the larger islands in both the Aegean and Ionian Seas. They nest in a variety of rocky habitats, from small rocky islets up to 2400 m (Schmid & Reichenecker 1988). In some parts of the country they nest in towns, with the most notable example being the town of Corfu, which probably holds several hundred pairs. During the breeding season they forage over very large areas and can thus turn up very far from breeding sites. They often form larger flocks than Swifts or Pallid Swifts, commonly exceeding 500 birds, e.g. up to 4,000 were seen feeding together in the southeast part of Mt Chelmos on 20 August 1987 (CP).

Alpine Swifts first arrive just after the middle of March and numbers slowly build up until late April. In addition to the arrival of locally breeding birds, a spring passage is also evident, with large numbers passing through, especially in the second half of April. There is no evidence for a corresponding passage in autumn. Departures take place mainly between early September and early October. Sightings in the second half of October are rare but there is a record of a flock of *c.* 200 above L. Kournas, Crete, on 2 November 1993 (A. & J. Hakala). Race *A. m. tuneti* breeds on Rhodes and probably Karpathos and Kos whilst the nominate race breeds in the rest of the country (*CFG*). On Crete the population is either intermediate or mixed (*BoC*; *BWP*).

Alpine Swifts

Little Swift *Apus affinis*

Accidental

The only confirmed record of the Little Swift is of a bird at Skala, on the island of Kefallinia, on 27 May 1988 (S.B. Edwards). Another record of a small flock of *c.* ten birds near Veroia on 29 June 1992 (C.L. Gibson) cannot be accepted due to lack of substantiating details.

White-breasted Kingfisher *Halcyon smyrnensis*

Accidental

There are four records of White-breasted Kingfisher, all from eastern parts of the country. The first record is of four birds at the marshes of Filippoi, Kavala, on 30 April 1941 (Kummer 1964). Between 1960 and 1965 one was shot near Komi, on the island of Chios (Spinthakis *et al.* 1993). One was seen at Psili Ammos, on the island of Samos, on 11 August 1988 (J. Poulopoulos) and one at Agia Reservoir, near Chania, on 9 August 1989 (N. Curry).

Kingfisher *Alcedo atthis*

Scarce and local resident, common and widespread winter visitor

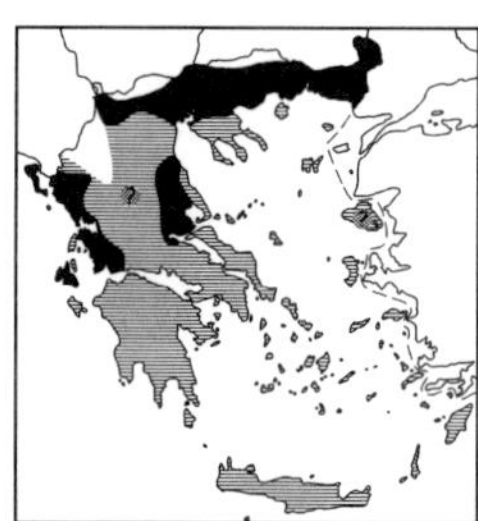

The breeding range of Kingfisher is limited to central and northern parts of the country. Some pairs may nest as far south as the Peloponnese but there are no definite nesting records from this area. The only islands on which they breed regularly are Corfu (*CFG*) and Kefallinia (A. Vittery). They may also have nested on Lesbos (Sonnenschein 1980; Tsounis & Dimitropoulos 1992b), though there have been no recent breeding records. On Crete they were recorded twice in summer in the 1940s but not since then. There is no reliable estimate of the Greek population, which probably does not exceed 1,000 pairs. Existing data may suggest a wider distribution in the past and it is quite likely that the species has suffered from large scale extraction of water from rivers and lakes in recent decades. Breeding birds occur in a variety of freshwater and brackish habitats, from coastal lagoons and river deltas up to 853 m at L. Prespa (Catsadorakis 1986).

Kingfishers are much more widespread and numerous in winter and on passage. Autumn passage is on a large scale and takes place mainly from late July to about early October, with a peak from mid August to mid September. A few birds may arrive already from the middle of July. Some of these early migrants may sometimes have been mistaken for breeding birds and given rise to reports of probable breeding on islands or parts of the mainland where the species is now known to be absent during the breeding season. In late summer and autumn, when the largest numbers occur, Kingfishers may be seen in a wide variety of habitats. In addition to rivers, lakes and lagoons, they are common on sea coasts and regularly occur in harbours. They also visit even small pools, small ditches, open water tanks in suburban areas and saltpans. High densities may occur at this time of the year, e.g. *c.* 60 were recorded at Divari Lagoon on 9 October 1993 (A. Bonetti). In small reservoirs or artificial pools their most important prey is the introduced mosquito fish *Gambusia affinis*, which may be the only fish present there, whereas on the coast they seem to feed predominantly on small grey mullet *Mugil* and sand smelt *Atherina*. Winter visitors leave between late February and the end of April. In many areas a decline is obvious already from December but it is not known whether this is due to emigration or winter mortality. Spring passage is comparatively insignificant and merges with the departure of the last wintering birds. Kingfishers breeding in Greece belong to race *A. a. atthis*, but winter visitors also include *A. a. ispida* (*CFG*).

Pied Kingfisher *Ceryle rudis*

Accidental

There are five records of Pied Kingfisher in Greece, with four of them from the 19th century. The species was recorded in the Cyclades (no further details given) (Erhard 1858) and on the islands of Mykonos and Kythnos, probably around 1850 (Lindermayer 1860; Reiser 1905). One was shot on the island of Zakynthos on 14 February 1882 (Reiser 1905). The only recent record is of one near the town of Kos on 3 April 1992 (J.H. Rahder). There is an additional unconfirmed record of one near Plakias, Crete, in late April 1984 (*BoC*).

Blue-cheeked Bee-eater *Merops superciliosus*

Rare and irregular passage migrant

Blue-cheeked Bee-eater has been recorded as an irregular visitor to Greece since the 19th century. At least four 19th- or early 20th-century records are from Attica: a small flock on 19 April 1874, and further records in 1880, 1890 and 1901 (Mühle 1844; Lindermayer 1860; Reiser 1905). The species was listed as a summer visitor, perhaps even breeding, in the Cyclades (Erhard 1858). There have been ten records since the middle of the 20th century, the majority from the southeast Aegean (Crete and the Dodecanese) and in April. The Crete records are all of single birds: one near Chersonisos on 6 April 1987 (*BoC*), one near Chora Sfakion on 27 April 1988 (*BoC*), one (photographed) at Tympaki on 6 April 1990 (Juilliard *et al.* 1990), one on Elafonisos on 21 April 1991 (P. Henderson), one near Plakias in early April 1991 (*BoC*), one at Georgioupolis on 12 April 1992 (M. Dretakis) and one, possibly the same as the previous bird, near Xerocampos on 18 April 1992 (M. Leuenberger). Records from the Dodecanese areas: one on Karpathos on 22 April 1965 (Kinzelbach & Martens 1965), one on Rhodes in 1966 (*CFG*), two at Marmari, Kos, on 29 March 1989 (B. de Schutter) and three on Karpathos from 30 April to 3 May 1993 (Berg 1993). One adult seen at Kleisova Lagoon on 20 April 1992 (H. Vonk) is the only late 20th-century record from the mainland. The geographical distribution of records strongly suggests that birds seen in Greece belong to race *M. s. persicus*, which breeds in the Nile Delta and migrates through the Middle East and Egypt (*BWP*).

Bee-eater *Merops apiaster*

Widespread and locally common summer visitor and passage migrant

Bee-eaters are common breeding birds in parts of the mainland, particularly in Macedonia and Thrace, becoming less common further south. They are scarce and local in Sterea Hellas and rare in the Peloponnese. They are also absent from most of the islands, yet they are fairly common on some (Samos, Lesbos, Limnos etc.). One or two small colonies may also exist on Crete (*BoC*). The total Greek population of Bee-eaters has been estimated at 2,000–3,000 pairs (Tucker & Heath 1994). The species is apparently declining, as it was formerly much more

widespread and colony sizes were generally larger than today.

Bee-eaters are common passage migrants in the spring and, although widespread, their appearance is irregular, as they tend to migrate in flocks of 10–100 birds which quickly move on. Flocks of migrating birds can often be heard flying over at such a height that they are almost impossible to see. They do this especially in the middle part of the day, when they seem to use thermals to rise to great heights. Local breeders and passage migrants arrive mainly from late April onwards and migration continues to late May, with a peak in the end of April and early May. Most departures take place from mid September to early October and the last birds have usually left by the middle of October. In the past, Bee-eaters were classed as pests and were heavily shot, particularly in autumn. Their present numbers and distribution may partly be due to past persecution and they may be expected to increase and spread now that they are protected. So far, there are five recoveries of Bee-eaters, of birds ringed in Slovakia, Hungary and Israel, all found in Greece in September.

Roller *Coracias garrulus*

Scarce and local summer visitor and passage migrant

Rollers had a much wider distribution in the past, nesting as far south as the southern Peloponnese (Reiser 1905) and most probably on Crete (Stresemann 1956). They were probably still quite common until the 1950s or early 1960s and the main decline probably took place in the late 1960s and 1970s. Today they are more or less confined to parts of Thessaly, Macedonia and Thrace. Even in these areas they are generally thinly distributed as isolated pairs, except for parts of central Macedonia. The species also breeds on the islands of Samos, Kos (a dense population), and probably Lesbos but not on any of the other islands. In the early 1990s the total Greek population was estimated at fewer than 200 pairs (Tucker & Heath 1994), but is more likely to be higher, at up to 400 pairs.

A small passage is obvious in both spring and autumn, apparently at the same time as the arrival and departure of locally breeding birds, from early April to mid May and from mid August to late September, with peaks in late April and early September respectively. Migrants occur singly or in twos, rarely in larger numbers. There are eight ringing recoveries of Rollers in Greece, of birds originating from Germany (1), Poland (1), Latvia (3), Lithuania (2) and Bulgaria (1).

Roller

Hoopoe *Upupa epops*

Fairly common and widespread summer visitor and passage migrant

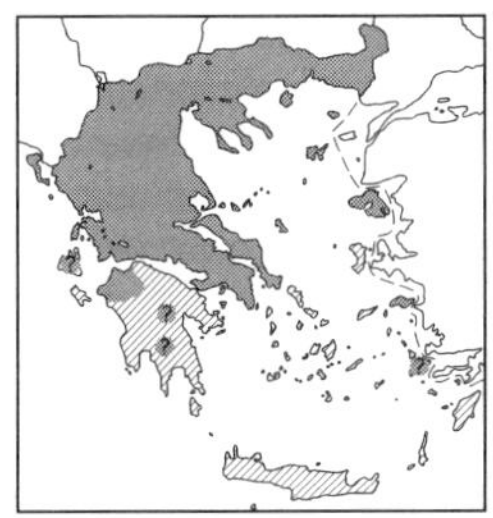

Hoopoes breed over most of the mainland, from the northern Peloponnese northwards, as well as on some of the islands, such as Lesbos, Limnos, the Northern Sporades, Corfu and possibly Kefallinia (A. Vittery). Hoopoes have also bred on Chios (1989) (Spinthakis *et al.* 1993) and on Aigina (P. Dragoumis). There is no published estimate of the total breeding population, which probably amounts to 5,000–20,000 pairs. A decrease in the number of Hoopoes passing through the island of Chios has been reported since the 1960s (Spinthakis *et al.* 1993) but this is not evident in other areas. Despite protection, the species was quite heavily persecuted in the past, when it was shot either for taxidermy or simply because it provided an easy target. As with many other protected species, this illegal shooting has been on the decline in recent years.

Breeding Hoopoes occur at low and medium altitudes in open habitats with scattered trees and bushes, in natural habitats, agricultural land (e.g. olive groves and orchards) and locally even in suburban areas. Nests are located in holes in trees, rock faces, old quarries, ruins and abandoned buildings. A through-passage occurs in both spring and autumn. The first birds usually arrive just before the middle of March but exceptionally as early as February, e.g. one was seen in the Evros Delta on 5 February 1965 (*CFG*). Peak spring passage is in early April. Autumn passage is from mid August to early or mid October, with a peak in early September. Hoopoes ringed in Germany (1), Poland (3), the Czech Republic (1), Austria (1), Croatia (1), Hungary (3) and Rumania (1) have been recovered in Greece, mainly on autumn passage.

Wryneck *Jynx torquilla*

Scarce and local resident, fairly common and widespread passage migrant

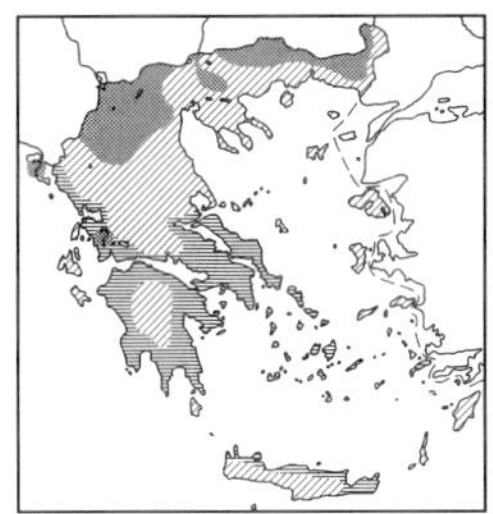

Owing to their secretive nature, the status of Wrynecks in Greece is still relatively little known. Breeding has been recorded locally in Thrace, Macedonia, NE Ipeiros and NW Thessaly, south to about 40°N, with perhaps a few pairs on Corfu (CP) and in western Sterea Hellas. They nest from sea level up to *c.* 1500 m (mean 494 m), occupying mainly oak *Quercus* woodland and scrub but also a variety of other habitats, such as riverside vegetation and olive groves (Hölzinger 1992a). The total Greek breeding population probably numbers fewer than 200 pairs. Wrynecks winter in very small numbers and perhaps irregularly in central and northern Greece but in much of southern Greece (including Crete and many other Aegean and probably Ionian islands) they are regular winter visitors in small numbers. In winter they are perhaps even more difficult to detect than at other times of the year, calling very rarely. Many of the winter records are of birds caught in mist-nets.

The species is commonest and most widespread on passage. In autumn, passage takes place from late August to mid October, with a peak in the second half of September. Spring passage is from about mid March to late April, with a peak in early April. The species is generally more numerous in autumn than in spring, though on Crete the reverse seems to be the case (*BoC*). Six Wrynecks have been recovered in Greece. These had been ringed in Finland (4), Hungary (1) and Malta (1, ringed on spring passage) and found in Greece in September, October and April. No Greek breeding birds seem to have ever been examined in the hand and existing information on their subspecific status is contradictory (*BWP*; *CFG*). In a sample of about 20 wintering birds handled for ringing, all were either definite or probable race *J. t. tschusii* (which breeds in the central Mediterranean) whereas four autumn and spring migrants apparently included both *J. t. tschusii* and *J. t. torquilla*. These observations are in agreement with the recoveries of foreign-ringed birds and the suggestion in *BWP* that birds wintering in Greece probably originate from Dalmatian or northern Greek populations of *J. t. tschusii*, with the nominate race occurring mainly as a passage migrant.

Grey-headed Woodpecker *Picus canus*

Scarce and local resident

A poorly known species, Grey-headed Woodpecker has been recorded at a small number of sites in central and northern parts of the mainland. Its main range is in the hills and mountains of Macedonia, Thrace and Thessaly, as far south as Mt Olympos and the central Pindos Mts (*CFG*; *BWP*). From the little knowledge available so far, it seems that the species occurs mostly as isolated sub-populations, with little communication between them. The southernmost and most isolated population is on Mt Oiti (Grimmett & Jones 1989), which is also the southern distribution limit of the species in the Western Palearctic. The total Greek population has been estimated at 50–200 pairs (Tucker & Heath 1994). On Mt Oiti, Grey-headed Woodpeckers occur in old open coniferous forest, mainly of Greek fir *Abies cephalonica*, between 500 and 2000 m, but in northern Greece they are mainly found in mixed or pure beech *Fagus* forest.

Grey-headed Woodpecker

Green Woodpecker *Picus viridis*

Widespread and locally fairly common resident

Green Woodpecker is one of the more widespread species of woodpecker in Greece. It is commonest in Macedonia, Thrace and parts of Ipeiros and Thessaly, becoming increasingly scarce and local farther south, as far as the central Peloponnese. On a few occasions Green Woodpeckers have been reported from various Aegean and Ionian islands but none of these records is confirmed, with the exception of one from Crete, of a male seen and heard near Kritsa on 1 April 1978 (*BoC*). It appears that many sightings outside the normal range of the species between mid April and September actually refer to female or immature male Golden Orioles, seen briefly in flight.

Green Woodpeckers are mainly found at medium altitudes, rarely reaching as high as 1800–2000 m. In northern parts of the country, they locally occur down almost to sea level but from Thessaly and Ipeiros southwards they are absent from the lowlands, i.e. from pure Mediterranean-type habitats. They occur in a variety of open woodland habitats, both coniferous and deciduous, as well as orchards, hill farmland and pastures with hedges, scattered trees and patches of woodland. The species is nowhere very common and the total Greek population probably lies in the range of 5,000–10,000 pairs.

Black Woodpecker *Dryocopus martius*

Fairly widespread but scarce resident

Black Woodpeckers are widely distributed on mountains of the mainland, from the northern borders of the country south to Mt Parnassos. Although generally present at low densities, within their range they seem to occupy evenly and consistently all suitable habitat. The only island on which they occur is Kefallinia, which is also the only Mediterranean island on which the species is found (*BWP*). Already in the 19th century, Powys (1860) reported two Black Woodpeckers shot on Kefallinia but the presence of a permanent population on the island was not verified until much more recently: first a female was seen on Mt Ainos, at 1200 m, on 6 May 1988 with further sightings there in 1989, 1991 and 1993 (Vittery 1994). In southern parts of their range (e.g. Mt Parnassos, Mt Oiti and Mt Ainos) Black Woodpeckers are restricted to mature forests of Greek fir *Abies cephalonica*, whereas in northern Greece they may also be found in mixed coniferous/deciduous forest. They usually occur from about 800 m upwards, reaching up to the limit of tree growth, in areas of scattered stunted trees. It is in such sparsely wooded areas, often with snow-damaged trees, that they can be seen most easily, especially in spring when the ground is still covered by snow. Elsewhere they can be quite elusive and difficult to detect, even though their presence may be revealed by numerous holes and excavations on old tree trunks.

Great Spotted Woodpecker *Dendrocopos major*

Scarce and local resident

Great Spotted Woodpeckers are one of the least well known and apparently least common species of woodpecker in Greece. They are found over a wide area of the mainland, including the Peloponnese, but they seem to be local and generally rare, although probably under-recorded. So far, they are known to occur only at relatively high altitudes, between about 700 m and 1900 m. They occur in both coniferous and deciduous woodland, including oaks *Quercus* in the Rodopi Mts (Bauer & Böhr 1987), pines *Pinus* (e.g. Mt Vermion and Mt Olympos), beech *Fagus* on other mountains of Macedonia and open stands of Greek fir *Abies cephalonica* on Mt Mainalon, in the Peloponnese. Many records exist from lowland areas but the vast majority are unconfirmed and probably refer to misidentified Syrian Woodpeckers. Greek populations of Great Spotted Woodpecker were formerly classified as race *D. m. pinetorum* (*CFG*) but more recently have been treated as *D. m. candidus* (*BWP*).

Syrian Woodpecker *Dendrocopos syriacus*

Fairly common and widespread resident

The range of Syrian Woodpeckers in Greece covers the whole of Thrace, Macedonia and eastern Thessaly, as far south as *c.* 39°N. There is a published record from Delphi (*CFG*) but the species has never been seen there since then and it is quite likely that the record refers to another resident black-and-white woodpecker of Mt Parnassos, such as White-backed or Middle Spotted. The species has also been recorded from the islands of Samothraki (Harrison & Pateff 1937) and Thasos (*CFG*) and altough their presence there is much more likely, confirmation is needed for both areas. There are further unpublished records from west of the Pindos range, in Ipeiros and Sterea Hellas, as well as from the Peloponnese and the island of Lesbos, all unconfirmed. Syrian Woodpeckers are typically lowland birds, occurring from sea level to medium altitudes.

The highest site recorded is at 1100 m, on Mt Varnous (V. Hatzirvassanis). They are relatively catholic in their habitat choice, which includes open deciduous and coniferous woodland, riverside trees, poplar plantations, agricultural land with scattered trees, orchards and suburban areas. They are by far the commonest woodpecker species in and around villages and on roadside trees, in winter often feeding on almonds and walnuts from trees in gardens and small parks. The total breeding population of Syrian Woodpeckers has been estimated at 5,000–10,000 pairs (Tucker & Heath 1994). This is probably an underestimate, and the true figure seems more likely to lie in the 10,000–25,000 pairs range.

Middle Spotted Woodpecker *Dendrocopos medius*

Fairly common and widespread resident

Middle Spotted Woodpeckers have a widespread distribution on the mainland, from the central Peloponnese northwards. They also occur on the island of Lesbos, the only island on which they are found. On the mainland, they are mainly found at moderate altitudes, in deciduous woodland dominated by oak *Quercus*, but locally they range from sea level (e.g. in the riverine forest of Fraxos near Messolonghi) to as high as 1500–2000 m. However, they are totally absent from dry Mediterranean-type vegetation and they occur at low altitude only in riverine woodland or in deciduous oaks (e.g Valonia and white oak *Quercus macrolepis* and *Q. pubescens*) in the moister northern and western parts of the country. In some areas (e.g. the Peloponnese) they have also been seen in high-altitude coniferous forest of black pine *Pinus nigra* or Greek fir *Abies cephalonica*. Middle Spotted Woodpeckers are unusually widespread and numerous on Lesbos and here they not only occur in oaks or sweet chestnut *Castanea sativa* but they are also common in the olive groves which cover a large part of the island. They are very rare in this habitat elsewhere in the country. Their total breeding population is estimated at 10,000–30,000 pairs. The nominate race occurs on the mainland but it is more likely that the Lesbos population belongs to race *D. m. anatoliae.*

White-backed Woodpecker *Dendrocopos leucotos*

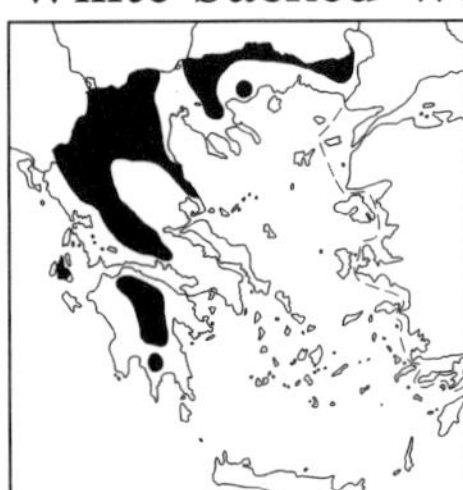

Widespread but rare resident

White-backed Woodpeckers are very thinly distributed over much of the mainland, from the southern Peloponnese northwards. They are absent from the islands except for Kefallinia, where they were recently discovered on Mt Ainos (Vittery 1994). They reach as far south as Mt Taygetos in the Peloponnese (Hölzinger 1990b), which is probably the southernmost distribution limit of the species in the Western Palearctic (*BWP*). White-backed Woodpeckers are montane birds. In the Peloponnese they occur at altitudes of 800–1800 m (i.e. up to the treeline), with a mean at *c.* 1370 m (Hölzinger 1990b). In this region, as well as on the mountains of Sterea Hellas and on Kefallinia, they are found in mature Greek fir *Abies cephalonica* forest. Further north, where pure fir forest is less common, they use other types of forest. For example, on Mt Ossa they occur in mixed fir and beech *Fagus* forest and on Mt Olympos in black pines *Pinus nigra*, up to 1600 m. White-backed Woodpeckers are a little known species. They are apparently rare (*CFG*; *RDB*) but there is no indication that they have declined in recent times, as they have in parts of N Europe (*BWP*). The total Greek population probably numbers between 500 and 2,000 pairs and belongs to race *D. l. lilfordi*

White-backed Woodpecker

Lesser Spotted Woodpecker *Dendrocopos minor*

Fairly widespread but scarce resident

The status of Lesser Spotted Woodpeckers in Greece is not well known. They seem to be thinly distributed from Sterea Hellas northwards and are commonest in northern parts of the country. There are no recent definite records from the Peloponnese, where they were reported as a very rare resident species in the past (*BWP*; Reiser 1905). The species has been recorded from a variety of woodland habitats, deciduous, coniferous and mixed. In northern Greece they often occur in areas of riparian woodland (e.g. in the Nestos Delta or around L. Cheimaditis) or along streams with willows *Salix*, alders *Alnus*, poplars *Populus* or ash *Fraxinus*. On Mt Olympos they have been seen in black pine *Pinus nigra* forest between 800 and 1600 m, though they are rare above about 1000 m (Malakou 1985). In Ipeiros, Thessaly and Sterea Hellas they are generally absent from the lowlands. Lesser Spotted Woodpeckers breeding in most of the country belong to the Greek and Turkish race, *D. m. danfordi*, but the southern European *D. m. buturlini* probably occurs in northern Greece (*BWP*).

Three-toed Woodpecker *Picoides tridactylus*

Rare and local resident

Three-toed Woodpeckers are known to occur in only two areas in Greece. They were first recorded on 5 and 7 July 1942, in a forest of Scots pines *Pinus sylvestris* at *c.* 1200 m on Mt Olympos (Makatsch 1950, Peus 1954). The existence of this population was re-affirmed in the early 1980s (Malakou 1985). More recently, the presence of Three-toed Woodpeckers was confirmed also in the Rodopi Mts, in an area dominated by old Norway spruce *Picea abies* forest at 1650–1950 m (Bauer & Böhr 1987). In both areas populations are small and whereas that of the Rodopi Mts is connected with populations in Bulgaria, that of Mt Olympos is very isolated. Three-toed Woodpeckers have also been reported from Pindos National Park (Tsounis 1987a; Grimmett & Jones 1989) but their presence in this area has not yet been confirmed. Three-toed Woodpeckers breeding in Greece belong to race *P. t. alpinus* (*CFG*; *BWP*).

Dupont's Lark *Chersophilus duponti*

Accidental

One juvenile seen at Damnoni, S Crete, on 16 April 1988 (*BoC*) is the only Greek record of this lark. The bird was on the beach feeding with a small party of Short-toed Larks.

Calandra Lark *Melanocorypha calandra*

Widespread and locally common resident

Calandra Larks breed in most plains of Thrace, Macedonia, Thessaly and Sterea Hellas and more locally in coastal areas of the western mainland. In the Peloponnese, breeding is likely, though not confirmed, only in NW Achaia (Peterson *et al.* 1981; CP). There are no recent confirmed records from the Ionian islands, whereas in the Aegean the species breeds only on Limnos and Kos. During the breeding season Calandra Larks occur in dry, stony pasture, non-intensive arable land, sand dunes, the borders of saltmarshes and similar habitats with a low and sparse ground cover. They find their preferred habitat chiefly near sea level but locally they may reach up to 1200 m (Watson 1964). The total Greek population probably amounts to 3,000–5,000 pairs. Outside the breeding season Calandra Larks spread into adjacent areas but their is no marked migratory movement and no obvious change in population size due to departure of local breeders or arrival of winter visitors. However, the species is a scarce and irregular passage migrant, mostly in spring, on Crete (*BoC*) and isolated individuals were observed on small islets in the Dodecanese in May 1995 (Papaconstantinou *et al.* 1995), indicating a small passage across the southeast Aegean. In the past, Calandra Larks were a familiar and popular cage bird. Some local declines have been noted since the 1960s (e.g. in the plains of Thiva and Thessaloniki), probably caused by the intensification of agriculture and the conversion of pasture into arable land.

Calandra Lark

Bimaculated Lark *Melanocorypha bimaculata*

Accidental

There is only one record of Bimaculated Lark, of a single at Skala on the island of Kefallinia on 1 May 1988. The bird appeared during a period of westerly displacement of many migrants due to unsettled weather (Vittery 1994).

White-winged Lark *Melanocorypha leucoptera*

Accidental

There are three records of White-winged Lark, all from N Greece: eight near Nea Zichni, Serres, on 4 May 1959 (Flach 1960), one in the Axios Delta on 24 February 1963 (I.C.T. Nisbet & J.J. Swift) and one on the island of Corfu in June 1966 (Hellebrekers *et al.* 1969).

Black Lark *Melanocorypha yeltoniensis*

Accidental

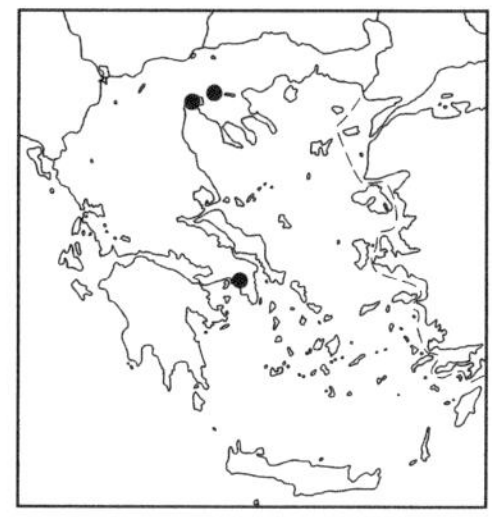

Black Larks have been recorded four times in Greece. The first and second records are both from the Athens area: a single collected in the spring of 1930 (*CFG*) and a male seen on 20 April 1958 (Flach 1960). Eight birds were seen at L. Koronia on 20 February 1963 (I.C.T. Nisbet & J.J. Swift) and two in the Axios Delta on 8 February 1964 (Hoffmann *et al.* 1964).

Short-toed Lark *Calandrella brachydactyla*

Common and widespread summer visitor and passage migrant

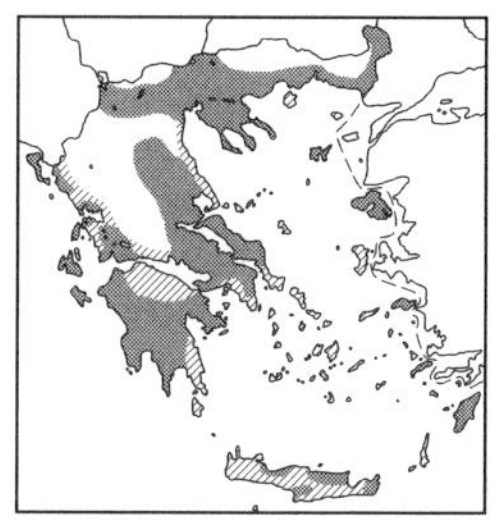

Short-toed Larks breed throughout the mainland, including the Peloponnese, where, however, they are rather local. In the Ionian islands they breed on Corfu and probably on Kefallinia and Zakynthos, whereas in the Aegean breeding has been confirmed on Limnos, Lesbos, Samos, Kos, Crete and Rhodes but not on the Cyclades (Magioris 1994). Short-toed Larks breed in open, flat sandy or stony terrain, arid steppe-like areas with very sparse low vegetation, dry saltmarshes, heavily grazed pasture, vineyards and non-intensive arable land. Most numerous in the coastal lowlands, they locally breed at up to 1500 m on the mainland and on Crete (Watson

Short-toed Lark

1964; *BoC*). The total breeding population is probably in the order of 20,000–50,000 pairs.

There is a significant passage of through-migrants, both in spring and in autumn. During passage periods flocks may often be seen flying overhead at a relatively low height by day, especially early in the morning and at dusk. Short-toed Larks begin to arrive in mid March in the south to late March in the north but they are present in good numbers from early April onwards, with some movements noticeable until the end of the month. In autumn, departures start around mid August, with the main passage period in late August, and only a few late birds remaining after mid September.

Crested Lark *Galerida cristata*

Common and widespread resident

One of the most familiar passerines in rural landscapes throughout Greece, Crested Larks have a wide distribution all over the mainland and the majority of the islands. They breed almost anywhere where there is some open, flat land with low and sparse ground cover, such as arable land, vineyards, dry, stony pasture, saltmarshes and dry mud within wetlands, sandy areas, beaches and by dust roads. In altitude they range from sea level up to about 1200 m and at times even higher (Watson 1964). Their wide distribution should not be taken to mean that they are ubiquitous and very numerous. On the contrary, they are generally lacking from various important habitat types, such as maquis, woodlands and scrub of all kinds and are scarce in phrygana, olive groves and orchards. Their total breeding population almost certainly exceeds 50,000 pairs and may be as high as 200,000 pairs.

The Greek population of Crested Larks is sedentary. There is no indication of passage but possibly small numbers of birds from northern countries may irregularly move south to Greece to winter. Three races have been identified in Greece: *G. c. meridionalis* on the mainland, Ionian islands, Cyclades and Crete, *G. c. cypriaca* in the Dodecanese and *G. c. caucasia* on the islands of the northeastern Aegean south to Samos (Watson 1962a; *BWP*).

Woodlark *Lullula arborea*

Fairly common and widespread resident

Woodlarks are widely distributed throughout the mainland, though they are not very common in the Peloponnese. In the Ionian Sea possible breeding has been recorded only for Corfu (Böhr 1962) whereas in the Aegean they breed on Limnos, Lesbos, Kea, Karpathos, Rhodes, Crete (Watson 1964; Scharlau 1989a, 1989b; Magioris 1994) and probably on Samos (D. Papandropoulos & F. Katsigiannis). There is no breeding record from Chios (Spinthakis *et al.* 1993), though it is probable that they breed there. Breeding birds usually occur in hilly country, in open rocky or stony areas, partly wooded or with scattered trees and bushes, including open olive groves, open maquis and thorny meadows with scattered bushes above the treeline. They are most numerous around

200–1200 m but can be found breeding from sea level upwards to beyond the treeline, e.g. up to 1800 m on Crete (*BoC*), 1600 m on Mt Chelmos (CP) and 2100 m on Mt Parnasos. The total breeding population probably lies in the range 5,000–20,000 pairs.

The Greek population is chiefly sedentary, though birds breeding at higher altitudes descend to the lowlands in winter. Woodlarks are more widespread and conspicuous in winter, when the local population is augmented by birds from northern countries. Winter visitors arrive rather late, beginning in mid October and becoming common only towards the end of the month or early in November. They depart from mid February to the end of March. Through the winter they stay in small groups, not mixing with other seed-eating birds. In mild parts of the country they often have to shift habitat as the season progresses and the new ground vegetation develops, e.g. from olive groves to phrygana (where grazing keeps the grass short). No obvious migratory movements can be seen but it has been claimed that some regular migration involving small numbers does occur (*CFG*). Woodlarks breeding in Greece have been identified as race *L. a. pallida* but birds of the nominate race *L. a. arborea* occur in the winter and possibly also on passage (Watson 1964; *BWP*).

Skylark *Alauda arvensis*

Fairly common but local resident, very common and widespread winter visitor

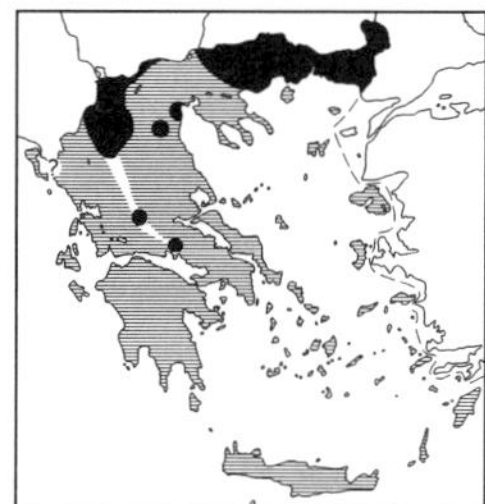

Breeding Skylarks have a localised breeding distribution in Greece. Their range spans the whole of eastern Macedonia and Thrace, from the R. Strymon eastwards to the Evros, the northern part of the Pindos range and the northwest Macedonian plateaus. Breeding has also been reported from Mt Tymfristos (Bauer *et al.* 1973) and Mt Olympos (Peterson *et al.* 1981). On Mt Olympos birds were heard singing at *c.* 1500 m on 15 April 1980 but they were not found later (Malakou 1985, Hölzinger 1933c). Skylarks also nest at the Alyki Kitrous Lagoon, have nested at least once near Messolonghi (F. Pergantis) and may also nest in the Kalamas Delta and on Mt Parnasos. In the past they have been reported as breeding on the islands of Corfu and Thasos and probably erroneously on Rhodes, where they were not found later by Scharlau (1989a). Within this range they have a rather patchy distribution and highly differentiated breeding habitat, on the coastal plains of the northeast Aegean coast, on plateau farmland and pasture and in the alpine zone of high mountains. In W. Macedonia and Ipeiros they nest locally from 800 m upwards, reaching up to the highest altitudes, e.g. to 2500 m at the peak of Mt Voras (Bauer *et al.* 1973). The total Greek population probably amounts to 2,000–5,000 pairs.

In winter, Skylarks are much more widespread and common, locally even abundant. Birds of the local population breeding on higher ground vacate their breeding areas in winter and probably join the much larger number of immigrants from the north at lower altitudes. Wintering birds form large flocks on farmland, pasture or other open, flat land, inland or on the coast. They are present from mid October to late March, mainly from the end of October to early March. They are most numerous in the larger plains of the mainland and are thus much less common on most islands where suitable habitat is in short supply. Cold-weather movements are marked during spells of particularly severe winter weather. Skylarks breeding in Greece belong to the Mediterranean race *A. a. cantarella,* but winter visitors also include birds of the nominate race *A. a. arvensis* (*CFG*; *BWP*).

Shore Lark *Eremophila alpestris*

Fairly widespread but scarce resident

Shore Larks breed only on the major mountain massifs of the mainland, from Mt Taygetos in the Peloponnese northwards along the Pindos range to W Macedonia, and on the high mountains of Thessaly and of central and eastern Macedonia to Mt Falakron. They frequent the alpine zones of the higher mountains particularly those with barren limestone slopes, rocky plateaus with short

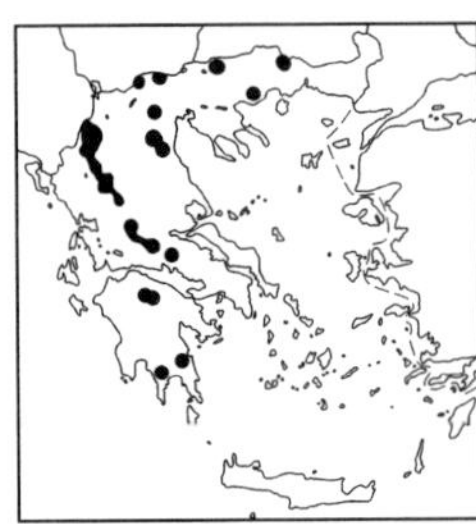

grass or low thorny bushes, usually above 2000 m. Their total breeding population is probably between 500 and 2,000 pairs.

Shore Larks are vertical migrants, often descending only as low as necessary to avoid deep and permanent snow cover. In recent years there exist only a handful of records away from their breeding areas, of which only two are sufficiently substantiated: three birds in the Aliakmon Delta on 21 January 1973 and eight in the Evros Delta on 29 December 1983 (Alkemeier & Hennig 1988). The scarcity of records away from the vicinity of known breeding sites suggests that they do not normally migrate far. Greek Shore Larks belong to the southern race *E. a. balcanica.*

Sand Martin *Riparia riparia*

Widespread and locally common summer visitor, very common passage migrant

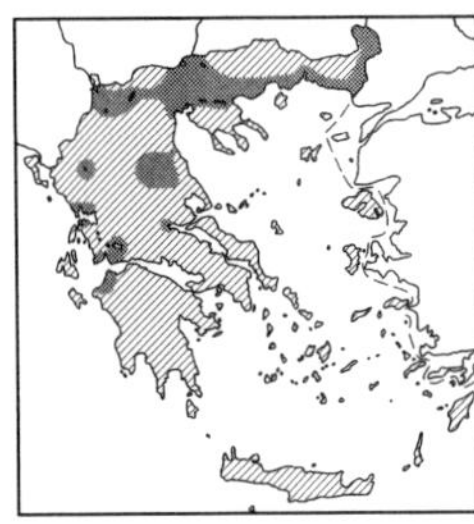

Sand Martins are widely distributed throughout the mainland and the Peloponnese though within this range colonies are localised due to their special nesting requirements. There are no definite breeding records from any of the Greek islands but they may breed on Corfu and perhaps on Lesbos. Breeding colonies have been found by moderate or large-sized freshwater or brackish wetlands, from sea level upwards and the highest known population is at 850 m at L. Mikri Prespa. Very often a site is a good feeding place but no suitable sand or earth banks are available for nesting. In such cases they have benefited from excavations, road-building or other similar human activities, spreading to areas where they had never bred before (e.g. large part of the Messolonghi area). An incomplete census in coastal NE Greece, in spring 1987, revealed at least ten colonies with a minimum of 2,860 occupied nests, colony sizes ranging from eight to 950 nests (WIWO 90). The total Greek population probably exceeds 20,000 pairs.

Sand Martins are migratory, arriving in Greece in mid to late March, rarely from early March. Passage continues until mid or late May, peaking from about the middle of April to early May. Southward passage is usually from late August to early October but occasionally a few are recorded until mid November. The species is very common and locally abundant during both spring and autumn passage, at night roosting in reedbeds together with Swallows. Very large numbers are recorded in spring, especially in and around wetland areas, e.g. tens of thousands were present at Kalogria Lagoon, NW Peloponnese, in mid April (CP) and *c.* 10,000 at Georgioupolis, Crete, on 3 May 1989 (M. Cocker).

Crag Martin *Ptyonoprogne rupestris*

Fairly common and widespread partial migrant

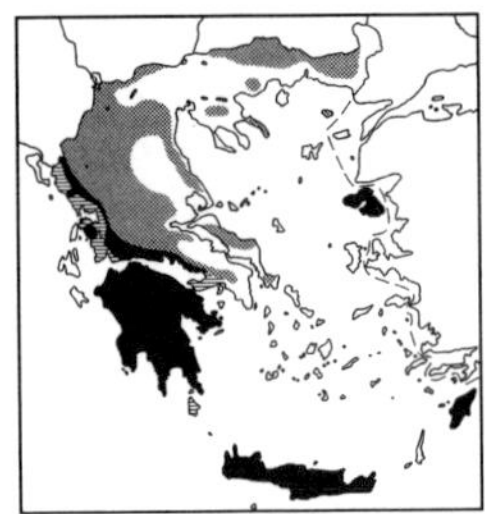

A widespread species breeding commonly over much of the mainland, the Peloponnese and on some of the islands of the Aegean Sea, though much less common on the Ionian islands. Crag Martins breed in rocky areas, usually inland but also coastal, in gorges, rocky outcrops and cliff faces, mainly from about 200 m up to 2500 m. A remarkable nesting site is Rhodes Castle, within the town of Rhodes. Nests are built singly or in loose and usually small colonies. The total breeding population probably amounts to 5,000–20,000 pairs. The species appears to be less common in NW Peloponnese now than it was in the 1980s, both as a breeding and as a wintering bird, indicating possible local declines (CP).

The population of the eastern and northern mainland is migratory but many winter in southern and western areas such as the Peloponnese and Akarnania and on some of the islands, including Crete, Rhodes and Lesbos, and populations of these areas are probably mostly sedentary or short-distance migrants. In winter, Crag Martins occur in habitats similar to those used for breeding but they also feed over wetlands, almost invariably in small or moderate-sized flocks of up to 150–200 together and exceptionally even more, e.g. up to 1,000 were present at Divari Lagoon,

S Peloponnese, in January 1995 (CP). It is possible that these wintering flocks contain visitors from outside Greece but this would require ringing recoveries to prove. Crag Martins are winter visitors to the island of Kythira in quite large numbers (Kominos 1995). Birds that leave their breeding grounds in winter return mainly in late March or early April, those at high altitudes still later, and stay until the end of September or early October.

Swallow *Hirundo rustica*

Very common and widespread summer visitor and passage migrant

Swallows breed widely throughout the mainland and on most of the main islands in both the Ionian and the Aegean Seas, as well as on some smaller islands with human settlements such as Gavdos and Gioura. They breed in any open habitat from sea level up to an altitude of about 1000 m. The total Greek population has been estimated at 20,000–50,000 pairs (Tucker & Heath 1994). Although, admittedly, breeding Swallows are not always found in high densities, they are so widely distributed that we believe this is an underestimate and a more realistic estimate would be 50,000–200,000 pairs.

The first Swallows usually arrive in central Greece around 10 March, though the exact date depends on the weather, the first birds making their appearance with the first warm weather, after about 5 March. Passage continues to late May, peaking from mid April to mid May. In autumn, passage usually starts in mid August and may continue until mid October but the main body of migrants goes through from late August to late September. A few have been recorded in November and up to early December and there also exist a few winter records (late December), e.g. from NW Peloponnese, Attica and Crete. During both spring and autumn passage Swallows are very common and locally abundant. After breeding, local birds, later joined by migrants, congregate in large flocks to roost in reedbeds and huge roosts may form there both in spring and in autumn. Swallows breeding in Greece belong to the nominate race *H. r. rustica*. A few records of *H. r. savignii* have been reported in the literature (Reiser 1905; *CFG*) but these have not been confirmed and they may simply involve dark variants of the nominate race.

Red-rumped Swallow *Hirundo daurica*

Widespread and locally common summer visitor

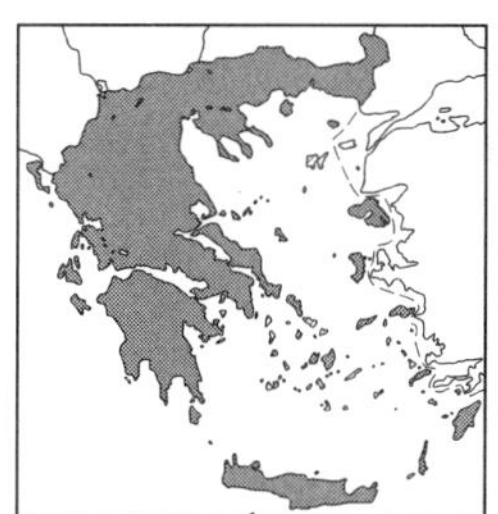

Although much less numerous than Swallow, Red-rumped Swallow breeds commonly over much of the mainland, including the Peloponnese, and on most of the main islands in both the Ionian and Aegean Seas, though in the latter it is more local and scarce than on the mainland. The species is a recent colonist on Crete and was first recorded breeding there in 1978 (Géroudet 1979). It is now regular but scarce (*BoC*). Red-rumped Swallows occur in the same altitudinal range as Swallows but they tend to be slightly more montane, being rather uncommon at sea level and more numerous in higher areas, e.g. above 400 m in the Peloponnese (CP) and above 100 m further north. They avoid open farmland and flat areas and seem to prefer hill slopes covered with maquis or open woodland, interspersed with pasture. They are thus less associated with human activities than Swallows, though they regularly build their nests under bridges or on other isolated human structures. Their total breeding population probably lies in the range 10,000–50,000 pairs.

Red-rumped Swallows arrive in numbers in late March but the first birds often appear just before the middle of the month. Departures probably begin in August but an obvious decline in numbers is not observed until early September. A few late birds can be seen up to early or mid October. Red-rumped Swallows breeding in Greece, belong to the Mediterranean race *H. d. rufula*.

Red-rumped Swallow

House Martin *Delichon urbica*

Common and widespread summer visitor

House Martins are a widespread species throughout the mainland and the islands in both the Ionian and the Aegean Seas, though generally less numerous there than on the mainland. They nest in a wide variety of habitats from sea level up to at least 1600 m on Crete (Watson 1964). They are much more numerous than Swallows in large towns and cities but colonies also occur in natural situations, on remote cliffs, caves and gorges. One of the largest colonies in Greece exists at Thessaloniki 'Makedonia' Airport, numbering several hundred pairs. The total breeding population of House Martins probably exceeds 50,000 pairs and may be as high as 200,000 pairs or more.

The majority of House Martins arrive in Greece from mid March onwards, with numbers peaking in early to mid April, though the exact dates vary according to the weather. In most years, the first birds are recorded in late February, so that they are one of the first passerine migrants to be seen in spring. Birds have been seen from as early as mid February in the Peloponnese and many tens were seen on the island of Samos on 20 February 1989 (CP). The southward movement is usually from mid August to late September, with some birds still around up until the middle of October. Although it is certain that many House Martins migrate through Greece from eastern Europe to Africa and back again, it is difficult to separate these from local breeders (unlike for example Swallows and Sand Martins which on passage roost in reedbeds) so it is not easy to assess the magnitude of this passage.

Richard's Pipit *Anthus novaeseelandiae*

Rare and irregular passage migrant

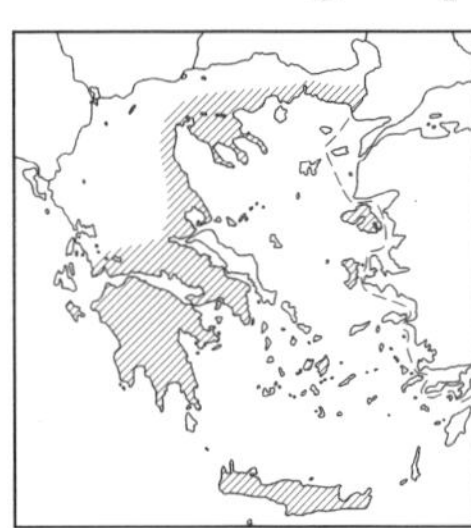

With around 30 properly documented records, Richard's Pipit may be classed as a rare passage migrant, although it is possibly overlooked and may in fact be more regular. All records are from the eastern part of the country (east of 22°E), except for one at Kotychi Lagoon on 22 January 1991 (Y. Roussopoulos) and two at Keri Lagoon on the island of Zakynthos, on 7 May 1993 (P.F. Whitehead). Seven records are from Crete (*BoC*). The majority of records are from April and May (which may be due to observer bias towards these months), the rest from August, October and November, in addition to one bird collected on the island of Naxos on 22 January 1959 (Watson 1961a). In all but one case single birds were seen.

Tawny Pipit *Anthus campestris*

Widespread but scarce summer visitor

The only species of pipit commonly breeding in Greece, Tawny Pipits have a widespread distribution over the mainland south to the Peloponnese. They also breed on several of the larger islands in both the Ionian and the Aegean Seas. However, they are quite thinly distributed, never occurring in high density. They are quite unobtrusive and the best way to locate them during the breeding season is by listening for their distinctive song, given from a low perch or during the song flight. Tawny Pipits breed in all types of open, flat, dry areas either sandy or rocky, bare or with sparse vegetation such as phrygana, *Arthrocnemum* saltmarshes, sand dunes and montane dry, stony pastures. In altitude they range from sea level up to the alpine zone, above 2000 m. They seem to be commonest at the extremes of their altitudinal range and less common at intermediate altitudes, probably a reflection of the distribution of their preferred habitat. Their total breeding population is difficult to estimate but is probably of the order of 5,000 to 20,000 pairs.

The species is a summer visitor, usually first arriving after the middle of March and mainly from early April onwards. In autumn, birds start leaving from late August and most are gone by the end of September, though a few individuals can still be seen up to the middle of October.

Tree Pipit *Anthus trivialis*

Scarce and local summer visitor, common and widespread passage migrant

As a breeding species, Tree Pipits have a wide but patchy distribution in montane parts of the mainland, mainly from the eastern Rodopi Mts in the north, south to Mt Kithairon in Attica (Bauer *et al.* 1973). Recently a few pairs have been found breeding on Mt Parnon and Mt Taygetos (Hölzinger 1992d), this being the southernmost limit of the species in the Western Palearctic. Tree Pipits usually frequent the upper montane zone, up to 2340 m, but in northern Macedonia and Thrace they nest down to 300 m, with a mean altitude of 1515 m (Hölzinger 1992d). The total Greek population probably numbers 400–800 pairs.

Tree Pipits migrate in large numbers through Greece in spring. They begin arriving from late March (rarely a little earlier) and passage continues until early May, peaking in early to mid April. They are usually observed singly or in small groups but sometimes they form flocks of 30–50 and rarely up to 200–300 birds. Though less numerous in autumn they are not uncommon, usually from the last days of August to the middle of October, with the main passage in

Tree Pipit

mid September. It is the commonest pipit identified in prey remains of Eleonora's Falcons, off NE Crete in autumn (Ristow *et al.* 1986). Data from adjacent countries suggest that large numbers overfly the Mediterranean during the southward passage (*BWP*). A few winter records exist, mainly from Crete and the Cyclades, but most (if not all) are not sufficiently documented and are probably erroneous.

Meadow Pipit *Anthus pratensis*

Common and widespread winter visitor

Meadow Pipits are by far the commonest species of pipit wintering in Greece and they are spread all over the mainland and on practically all of the islands. They arrive from mid October and they become common and widespread by late October and early November, departing mainly from early to late March. In spring there is a small through-passage, obvious by the fact that while their numbers are declining after mid March, short-staying flocks of birds may appear until the end of the month and into April. A very few birds can still be seen up to late April.

During winter, Meadow Pipits occur in all kinds of open habitat with short or sparse ground vegetation, including open farmland, pastures, phrygana, open maquis, open olive groves and orchards and freshwater or saltmarshes. They extend up the mountains to the edge of snow cover, i.e. usually about 1200–1500 m in southern and western Greece, lower further north. There is one unusual breeding record of a pair with a just fledged young near Ag. Nikolaos on Crete on 4 April 1972 (*BoC*).

Red-throated Pipit *Anthus cervinus*

Fairly common and widespread passage migrant, scarce winter visitor

Formerly listed as an uncommon migrant (Lambert 1957, Raines 1962), it has recently turned out that Red-throated Pipit is a fairly common passage migrant, especially in spring, as well as a local winter visitor in southern parts of the country. It is markedly more secretive than other Greek species of pipit and most often seen when flushed from *Arthrocnemum* saltmarshes or, less commonly, freshwater marshes, rising to the air without calling much, flying for quite a long distance and then diving down and settling among the dense vegetation again. Thus, the species is probably often overlooked. In spring, Red-throated Pipits migrate from early April to early May, mostly in mid and late April. The autumn passage is much less conspicuous and takes place from early September to early or mid October but the number of records available is so small that these dates will probably need reconsideration in the future, when more data become available. Wintering birds have been found regularly in recent years in Sterea Hellas and the Peloponnese. At all times of the year they tend to occur in small flocks but aggregations of 60–80 birds are not uncommon in spring.

Water Pipit *Anthus spinoletta*

Scarce and local resident, common and widespread winter visitor

Water Pipits have a restricted breeding range north of 39°N on the major massifs of Thessaly, Ipeiros and Macedonia, as far east as Mt Pangaion (Peterson *et al.* 1981), but even within this limited range they have a patchy distribution. They occur in the subalpine and alpine zone, in marshy patches with springs and brooks within meadows and dolines, often with scattered rock outcrops and small trees (e.g. white bark pine *Pinus heldreichii*). They range from an altitude of about 1600 m to 2300–2500 m (Bauer *et al.* 1973; Malakou 1985; Hölzinger 1993c). The total Greek population is tentatively estimated at 200–500 pairs.

The species is much more widespread and numerous in winter, usually from late October

or early November to mid or late April. Numbers begin declining from mid March onwards, indicating that the small flocks of birds seen later into April may be migrants passing through. During winter, Water Pipits are found in wet meadows, freshwater marshes, saltmarshes, flooded fields and lake shores, singly or in loose flocks. In April they are quite often seen in wet habitats at high altitude in much of the country, not only near breeding areas.

Water Pipit is a polytypic and taxonomically puzzling species classified in two distinct groups: *A. s. petrosus* (= Rock Pipit) and *A. s. spinoletta* (= Water Pipit) (*BWP*), sometimes considered separate species. The Greek breeding population belongs to the nominate race, *A. s. spinoletta*, but populations wintering in Greece most probably include birds of the northern race, *A. s. littoralis* (*CFG*). There is one unconfirmed record of two *A. s. petrosus* on the island of Karpathos on 14 April 1964 (Kinzelbach & Martens 1965).

Yellow Wagtail *Motacilla flava*

Common and widespread summer visitor and passage migrant

The Black-headed race, *M. f. feldegg*, is common and widespread as a breeding species throughout the mainland and on several of the islands of the Aegean and Ionian Seas. It is a typical species of coastal saltmarshes, dominated by *Arthrocnemum* or *Juncus*, sometimes dotted with clumps of tamarisk *Tamarix*. On the coast breeding is also frequent in rice fields whilst inland breeding pairs are found in wet meadows and marshes with low vegetation. The earliest males arrive in mid March (the first usually around the 10th) and most birds are on their breeding territories by early April. Passage of *M. f. feldegg* breeding further north in the Balkans peaks in the last days of March and is detectable up to about the middle of April. Other races, mainly *M. f. flava* and *M. f. thunbergi* migrate later, from late March to early May, with peak numbers in mid April.

It is not easy to identify all birds seen as to race but there is a distinct difference in the flight call of *M. f. feldegg* on the one hand and *M. f. flava* and *M. f. thunbergi* ('northern' races) on the other, with the former having a harsh 'tsree' and the latter a clearer whistling 'psii', not unlike that of the British race (*M. f. flavissima*). This difference in call is especially useful in autumn when even adult male birds may be hard to distinguish and the majority of birds are juvenile anyway. Autumn departure of local breeding birds merges into the migratory period of *M. f. feldegg* passing through, from (mid–) late August to late September. Northern races come about a week later, from early September to early October, with occasional ones even in

'Black-headed Wagtail' (race feldegg *of Yellow Wagtail)*

late October. Autumn passage is heavier than in spring and the species is a common prey of Eleonora's Falcons at colonies off NE Crete and in the Northern Sporades (Ristow *et al.* 1986, Warncke & Wittenberg 1961). In spring, migrant flocks can be seen in all kinds of wet places, including the breeding habitat of local birds, but also seasonally flooded fields, winter-harvested or burnt reedbeds and other similar habitats available only in early spring. In autumn there is a marked difference, in that they are very often seen in flocks on hills and mountains, following sheep, goats or cattle or on freshly ploughed fields and stony pastures grazed short.

Flocks of migrant Yellow Wagtails in both spring and autumn are generally composed of birds of different races and intergrades. So far, the following races have been identified on passage: *M. f. feldegg* and *M. f. flava* are by far the most numerous. A large proportion of adult male *M. f. feldegg* on spring passage show a tremendous variation in head colour, with e.g. black or grey nape and/or cheeks, short or long white or yellow supercilium and yellow or white throat, presumably belonging to the hybrid populations between the above two races (possibly *M. f. cinereocapilla* too) in the area of the lower Danube basin and southern Ukraine (*BWP*). *M. f. thunbergi* is scarce and *M. f. cinereocapilla* more or less regular but rare. *M. f. lutea* and *M. f. beema* have also been reported on a few occasions (*CFG*; *BoC*), whereas *M. f. flavissima* and *M. f. leucocephala* have been recorded only two or three times (*CFG*), and though possibly genuine. It is not unlikely that some of these are unusual variants of commoner races. So far, 22 Yellow Wagtails ringed abroad have been recovered in Greece, nine from Nigeria, nine from Finland and the rest from Latvia, Poland, Czechoslovakia and Croatia. This agrees well with the known breeding distribution of the two commonest migrant races, *flava* and *thunbergi*.

Citrine Wagtail *Motacilla citreola*

Widespread but rare passage migrant

Citrine Wagtails were regarded as accidental visitors to Greece up to recently. With at least 14 records, they now qualify as rare passage migrants. They are probably often overlooked among large flocks of Yellow Wagtails and in recent years they have been recorded almost annually. In fact the species was not recorded until 1978 (an adult male at Keramoti, 29 April, Inskipp 1979).

There is only one autumn record, of a first-year bird at L. Ismaris on 22 August 1991 (F. Barrault). All other records are from spring, with the earliest record being of an adult male at Lafri Lagoon on 15 April 1987 (Meininger 1988) and the latest of a female at Eressos (Lesbos) on 21 May 1986 (K. Bannister). All records refer to single birds, with the exception of a pair in mid May 1995 (Brooks 1995).

Grey Wagtail *Motacilla cinerea*

Fairly common and widespread resident and winter visitor

Grey Wagtails breed throughout the mainland and the Peloponnese but are very local and scarce on the islands in both the Ionian and the Aegean Seas: there are no definite breeding records from the Ionian, except Corfu (K.S. Bovey, M. Mitchell), whereas in the Aegean, they breed very locally on Crete (Stresemann 1943; *BoC*), Samothraki (Watson 1964) and Lesbos. Breeding birds are confined to the hills and mountains, usually from about 200 m to 2200 m, in fast-running streams and rivers with rocks and boulders. The Greek population probably totals 5,000–10,000 pairs.

It is likely that the majority of Greek birds are only altitudinal migrants but many birds probably move only as low as necessary to avoid deep snow and ice, as even in midwinter they are often found at relatively high altitudes. Grey Wagtails are widespread and fairly numerous throughout the lowlands in winter, suggesting immigration of birds from further north. Winter visitors begin to arrive in the lowlands at the end of September and become numerous and widespread by the middle of October. They leave from late February to late March. During winter, Grey Wagtails occur in a variety of habitats, including those similar to the breeding habitat but they are also common on rocky coasts and perhaps most conspicuous in built-up areas, even the centres of large towns and cities. They are not infrequent around derelict buildings, industrial plants and on high flat-topped buildings, especially near pools of rainwater.

White Wagtail *Motacilla alba*

Fairly widespread but scarce resident, common and widespread winter visitor

White Wagtails breed throughout the mainland, including parts of the Peloponnese. They also breed on many of the Aegean islands but are very scarce in the Ionian Sea, so far known to breed only on Corfu (Böhr 1962). Though widespread, they are very thinly distributed and with a discontinuous range. They occur from sea level up to 1600 m, breeding on rocky coasts and offshore rocky islets, coastal and inland wetlands, wet meadows, the wide stony beds of partly dried up streams and in suitable man-made habitats with wide open unvegetated expanses near water, such as harbours and airports. Their total breeding population probably lies in the range 5,000–10,000 pairs.

The Greek population of White Wagtails is presumed to be chiefly sedentary but birds from higher elevations probably move down to sea level in the winter where they are joined by very much larger numbers of immigrants from northern countries. The species is very widespread in winter and large roosts form in reedbeds or in town parks, sometimes numbering up to 10,000 birds (e.g. in Athens). Wintering birds begin to arrive in the last few days of September and their numbers peak at the end of October. Departures seem to occur during the first half of March but they merge into a passage late in the month and up to mid April, with a significant influx of birds in flocks especially at the end of March (for NE Greece see WIWO 90), frequently in loose association with migrant Yellow Wagtails. Autumn passage, if it exists, seems to be on a non-detectable scale and the species is rare as a prey of Eleonora's Falcons off NE Crete (Ristow *et al.* 1986). There exist 11 ringing recoveries of White Wagtails ringed abroad and recovered in Greece, all ringed in north–northeast Europe, from Poland in the south to Norway and Russia in the north and east.

Waxwing *Bombycilla garrulus*

Accidental

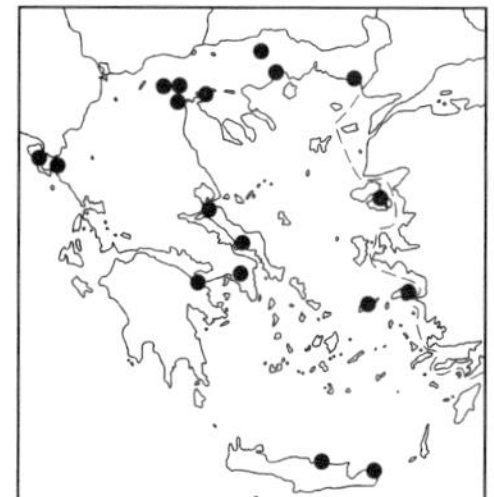

Waxwings were first recorded in Greece in 1962, when a bird ringed in Hungary the previous winter was shot near Igoumenitsa on 22 November. All other Greek documented records are from the large invasion in the winter of 1965–66 and from a second smaller one in the winter of 1973. In the first case flocks of up to *c.* 500 birds were seen in December 1965, mainly in E Macedonia and Thrace (e.g. Kavala, Drama and Alexandroupolis), whereas from December 1965 to March 1966 invading birds reached as far south as Crete (e.g. 'many' were seen near Irakleion in March 1966) as well as the islands of Lesbos and Samos. During this invasion recoveries of birds ringed in Sweden (1), Finland (2), the Czech Republic (1) and Hungary (3) were obtained from Corfu, Istiaia (N Evvoia), Attica, Thessaloniki and the island of Ikaria. In January 1973, there was another invasion but it was much smaller, with records only from the Axios basin and the area of Thessaloniki, e.g. *c.* 2,000–3,000 at Aiginion, near Katerini, on 20 January 1973, *c.* 1,500 at Giannitsa on 24 January 1973 and smaller numbers, *c.* 500–1,000 each at Skydra, Alexandria and Platy, also in late January 1973. There have been no reliable records since then, though there have been several reports of birds shot in N Greece. During both invasions, most birds were seen in town parks and gardens and, at least in January 1973, feeding almost exclusively on *Pyracantha coccinea* berries.

Dipper *Cinclus cinclus*

Widespread but scarce resident

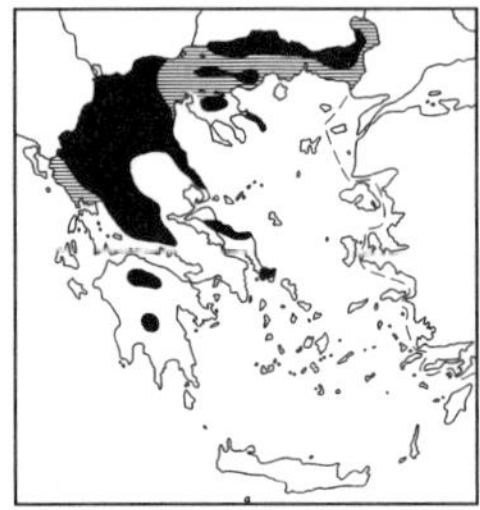

Dippers breed over much the mainland but within this range they are quite thinly and patchily distributed. They are commoner in Ipeiros, Macedonia and Thrace, where there is more suitable habitat, and become gradually more localised and scarce towards the south. In the Peloponnese they breed in the northern and central massifs but they are scarce throughout the region (CP). Dipper is a poorly known species but apparently it is more numerous than originally thought, nesting usually at middle to high altitudes in clear, fast-flowing streams and small rivers with a stony and rocky bed. With a conservative estimate, the total breeding population may be put at 500–2,000 pairs. The species is chiefly sedentary, with very few records far outside the breeding range, suggesting very limited movements, perhaps mainly an altitudinal shift to lower levels in the winter. There is one (unconfirmed) 19th-century winter record from the Cyclades (Erhard 1858), one from Crete in April 1966 (*CFG*), one from Corfu in February 1937 (*CFG*), two (unconfirmed) from Rhodes in May 1966 and 1967 (*CFG*) and one from Samos in December 1994 (I. Schogolev & M. Dimaki). Dippers breeding in Greece belong to race *C. c. aquaticus*.

Dipper

Wren *Troglodytes troglodytes*

Fairly common and widespread resident

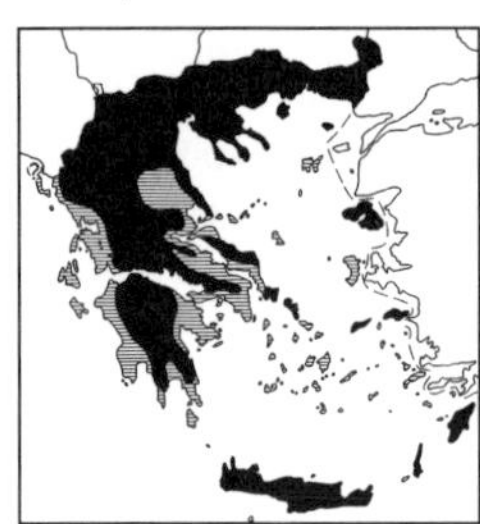

Widespread and generally fairly common, Wrens breed over much of the mainland but their island distribution is very localised. There are still no confirmed breeding records from the Ionian Sea, except Corfu, where they probably breed (Böhr 1962), whereas in the Aegean they breed on Thasos, Samothraki, Lesbos, Ikaria, Samos, Rhodes, Karpathos, Crete and Andros. Probably they also breed very locally in the rest of the Cyclades (Magioris 1994). Over most of the country Wrens breed in a variety of hilly and montane habitats, usually from 500–600 m upwards and in many cases up to above the treeline. They occur in dense undergrowth vegetation in all kinds of woodland and forest, in scrub, maquis (particularly where it grows taller and denser in deep valleys and ravines beside streams), as well as in hedgerows in farmland, parks and large gardens in the uplands. On Mt Idi (Crete) they occur above the treeline, at an altitude of 1800–2200 m, among junipers *Juniperus* and barberries *Berberis cretica* (*BoC*). The total breeding population of Wrens probably lies in the range 30,000–100,000 pairs.

The Greek population of Wrens, particularly that of the islands, is probably entirely sedentary whereas birds nesting on high mountains of the mainland apparently move to lower altitudes in winter. The species is much more widespread and conspicuous in winter, when local populations seem to be augmented by immigrants from the north. There is no indication of a passage through Greece. In the lowland wintering grounds immigrants begin to appear from the middle of October, with larger numbers from early November onwards. They begin to depart from mid or late February and the last birds leave by the end of March. Wrens breeding in Greece have been assigned to two races: the nominate form *T. t. troglodytes* breeding on the mainland and wintering throughout Greece and *T. t. cypriotes* breeding on Crete and Rhodes. Populations of Lesbos, Ikaria and probably Samos also belong to the nominate form grading, however, into *cypriotes* (Watson 1964; *BWP*).

Dunnock *Prunella modularis*

Scarce and local resident, common and widespread winter visitor

Dunnocks have a very restricted breeding range in Greece, and their southern limits are still not well known. They definitely breed along the northern borders of the country, on the main mountain massifs of Macedonia and Thrace, from Mt Grammos eastwards to the Rodopi Mts (Peterson *et al.* 1981), as well as on Mt Olympos (Peus 1957; *CFG*). Breeding has also been reported as probable, from the Chasia Mts, Mt Parnassos and Mt Kyllini (Bauer & Hodge 1970; Bauer *et al.* 1973; Peterson *et al.* 1981) and more recently from Mt Oiti (Hallmann 1985b). In these areas Dunnocks occur in montane forests, usually of fir *Abies*, black *Pinus nigra* or Scots pine *P. sylvestris* mixed with beech *Fagus*, or on open slopes with scattered bushes from 1400 to 1950 m, and on Mt Olympos in the subalpine zone up to 2100–2150 m (Bauer & Hodge 1970; Bauer *et al.* 1973; Bauer & Böhr 1987; Peus 1957). Their total breeding population is probably in the order of 1,000–5,000 pairs.

Dunnock is much more widespread and fairly common in winter, from sea level upwards in all types of dense vegetation, maquis, streamsides with dense bushes, open woodland, olive groves or orchards with undergrowth and hedges and the margins of wetlands. Winter visitors appear from late October (rarely before 20 October) to the end of March. In most years there is also a significant increase in numbers in the lowlands from mid December to early February which indicates that further movements occur with cold weather in midwinter, either of birds wintering at higher altitudes or further north in the Balkans. The Greek breeding population was formerly regarded as belonging to race *P. m. modularis* (*CFG*) but possibly they belong to the Mediterranean race *P. m. mabbotti* (*BWP*). Winter visitors belong to the nominate race.

Alpine Accentor *Prunella collaris*

Fairly widespread but scarce resident

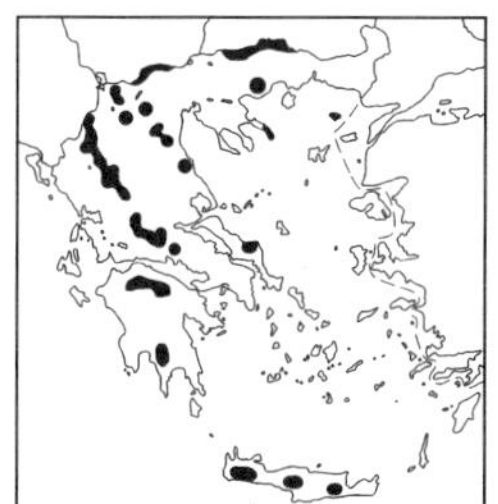

Alpine Accentors breed in the alpine zone of the mountains of mainland Greece from Mt Taygetos in the Peloponnese, northwards along the Pindos range, as well as on the major massifs of Macedonia, such as Mts Olympos, Voras, Tzena and Athos. Among the islands they occur only on Crete and Samothraki (*CFG*). On the mainland, Alpine Accentors breed mainly from 1800 to 2700 m (Hölzinger 1994) and on Crete from the limit of oaks *Quercus* to the summits (1400–2400 m) (*BoC*). In all areas they usually occur on rocky slopes and plateaus with very sparse low shrubs or grass, often with scattered stunted trees. The total Greek population probably numbers between 2,000 and 5,000 pairs. Alpine Accentors are almost sedentary, descending to lower areas in winter depending on snow cover. On Crete the species is gregarious, even during the nesting period, and large numbers often congregate in caves to roost (Watson 1964; *BoC*).

Rufous Bush Robin *Cercotrichas galactotes*

Widespread but scarce summer visitor

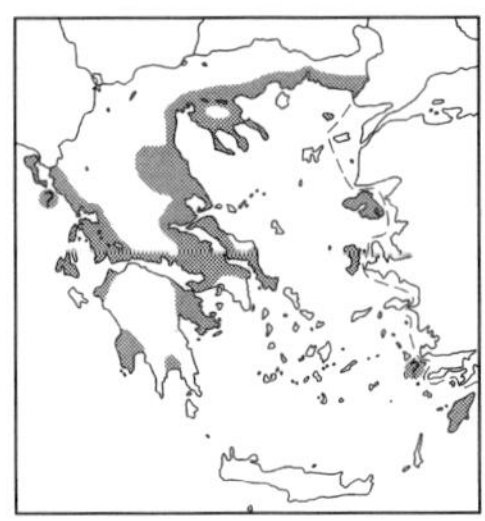

Despite availability of much suitable habitat, Rufous Bush Robins are not common and have a widespread but patchy and discontinuous range. They breed locally on the mainland and also on a few of the islands in both the Ionian and the Aegean Seas, i.e. Kefallinia (A. Vittery), Corfu (Böhr 1962), Lesbos, Rhodes, Samothraki, Chios (Spinthakis *et al.* 1993) and possibly Paxoi (P. Barry) and Kos (Haensel 1992). They breed in a variety of lowland habitats offering bare ground interspersed with bushes. In particular, they are most regularly seen in dried up river beds or in dried up areas at the edges of lowland wetlands with scattered tamarisks *Tamarix* or chaste trees *Vitex agnus–castus*. Sometimes they also occur in open maquis, especially near seasonal streams, and less often in olive groves, vineyards and patches of *Agave* or prickly pear *Opuntia*. The total Greek population is difficult to assess but probably amounts to 1,000-3,000 pairs. The species is a late migrant, arriving from late April and mainly in early May and departing again in mid to late August. It has been reported as rare on passage in the Peloponnese (CP) and as an accidental on Crete (*BoC*), which suggests that there is no significant passage through the mainland or the Aegean, as expected from their restricted distribution in SE Europe (*BWP*).

Rufous Bush Robin

Robin *Erithacus rubecula*

Fairly common and widespread resident, very common winter visitor

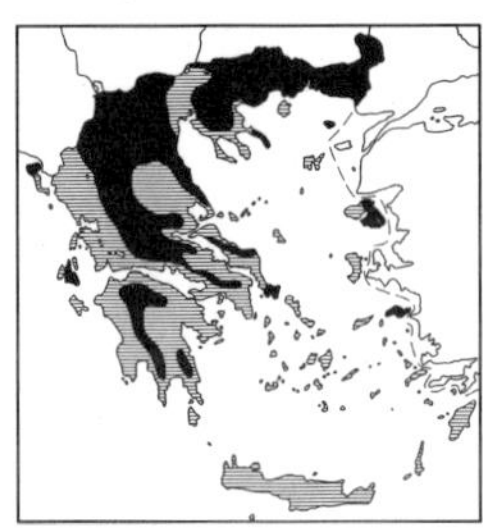

Robins breed throughout the mainland including the Peloponnese but on only a few of the islands. In the Ionian Sea they breed on Mt Ainos (Kefallinia), and on Corfu whereas in the Aegean they breed on Lesbos and perhaps Samothraki, whilst recently breeding has been confirmed on Samos (G. Jeff Price). In southern parts of Greece and on the islands, Robins are mainly a scarce breeding species of montane fir *Abies* but also deciduous or mixed forest, usually above 600 m and up to 2000 m. In NW Peloponnese, Lesbos and perhaps elsewhere too, they rarely breed down almost to sea level, in olive groves or rich maquis. In northern Greece they are much more widely spread, in all types of woodland and scrub and at lower altitudes. Their total breeding population may exceed 30,000 pairs.

The Greek population of Robins is probably mainly sedentary, with birds from higher elevations making altitudinal movements. In winter very large numbers of immigrants, far outnumbering the local breeding population, arrive and the species becomes locally abundant. Winter visitors first appear in early October and numbers quickly build up, the species becoming very common by the end of the month. High densities are recorded in mid to late autumn, when in optimal habitats (especially olive groves) they are often the commonest bird species. For example, 7.4 birds/ha were estimated in Chalkidiki in late October (Da Prato & Da Prato 1983) but even higher densities apparently occur elsewhere, e.g. on the island of Paxoi (A. Vittery) and on Lesbos. In many areas, a large proportion of their winter diet is olives, mainly small pieces pecked from the fruit after they have fallen to the ground. Wintering Robins are also common in all types of wooded or bushy areas including low-altitude pine *Pinus* woodland, maquis, town parks, orchards and gardens. Most of the wintering birds have departed by mid to late March. There are 48 recoveries of foreign-ringed Robins in Greece. Most of these are from Finland (16) and Sweden (11), with smaller numbers from Denmark, Poland, Latvia, Lithuania, Hungary, Croatia, Bulgaria, Russia, the Ukraine, and Malta.

Thrush Nightingale *Luscinia luscinia*

Widespread but scarce passage migrant

Thrush Nightingales occur only as passage migrants and though existing data show they are uncommon or scarce, it is likely that often they are either overlooked or confused with Nightingales. Generally speaking, they are more numerous in autumn than in spring. Migrant Thrush Nightingales can be seen throughout the country but they appear to be much commoner in eastern parts, i.e. Thrace and the eastern Aegean. They are less common than Nightingales in prey remains of Eleonora's Falcons off NE Crete in autumn (Ristow *et al.* 1986) and among birds mist-netted for ringing on Crete (*BoC*) and on the mainland. In spring, passage takes place from mid March to mid May and in autumn from mid or late August to late October. Thrush Nightingales are most often seen in damp habitats near the coast, such as densely vegetated valleys, riparian woodland and the edges of marshes.

Nightingale *Luscinia megarhynchos*

Common and widespread summer visitor

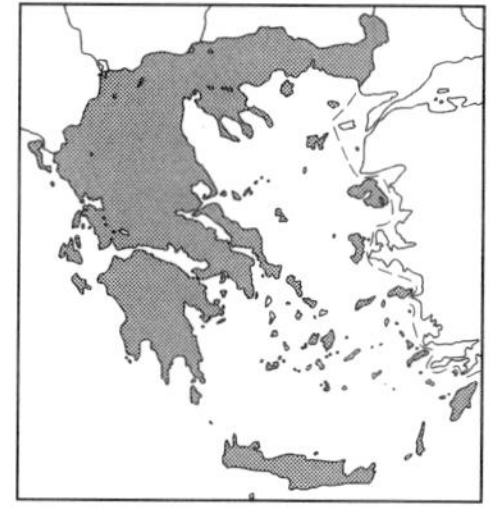

Nightingales breed commonly throughout the mainland and on most of the islands in both the Aegean and the Ionian Seas. They frequent all kinds of habitat with dense bushy vegetation, usually in damp areas, from sea level up to about 800 m but sometimes up to about 1200 m. They reach particularly high densites along streams and rivers and in deep valleys with luxuriant vegetation, where it is not unusual to have 20–50 birds within hearing range. Besides natural habitats they also regularly occur in large gardens and parks within towns and villages. Their total breeding population almost certainly exceeds 100,000 pairs and may well be even higher than 200,000 pairs.

In central Greece, the first singing Nightingales can usually be heard from the last few days of March, with further arrivals and through-passage until early May. There seems to be some differentiation of arrival dates within Greece: on Crete the first birds arrive from mid March (*BoC*) whilst in Thrace, in spring of 1987, the first bird was recorded on 2 April (WIWO 90). Autumn passage takes place from mid August to mid October but only isolated individuals remain after mid September. At least some local breeders appear to leave earlier than these dates and perhaps it is mainly migrants from further north that are recorded towards the end of the autumn migratory season. There is one recovery of a Nightingale ringed in Hungary and recovered in the Peloponnese but the find date (18 February 1965) of this bird is almost certainly erroneous. Nightingales breeding in Greece belong to the nominate race *L. m. megarhynchos* but they show some similarities to *L. m. africana,* which breeds from eastern Turkey and the Caucasus to central Asia (Watson 1964; *BWP*).

Bluethroat *Luscinia svecica*

Rare and irregular winter visitor and passage migrant

Bluethroats occur both as passage migrants and winter visitors. Although they are probably overlooked, they are certainly not common. There are fewer than 30 records from various areas, mainly from Crete and the east or northeast of the country. Most of the records are from March–April and September–October, clearly suggesting birds on passage. The remaining few records are from November–February, indicating a small number of wintering birds. The species was also recorded as a prey item of Eleonora's Falcons off NE Crete in autumn of 1977 (Ristow *et al.* 1986). Bluethroats are usually seen in coastal or low-lying areas, particularly in and around wetland habitats, including reedbeds. Both *L. s. svecica* and *L. s. cyanecula* have been recorded (*CFG*; *BoC*; Stresemann 1956).

White-throated Robin *Irania gutturalis*

Accidental

Although White-throated Robins have a fairly widespread breeding distribution in southern and eastern Turkey, they have been recorded in Greece only four times. One was seen at Sappes, near Komotini, in May 1966 (*CFG*) and a female was seen in the southeast of the island of Zakynthos on 29 May 1991 (P.F. Whitehead). The latest two records, both from the island of Lesbos, are of particular interest because they may indicate breeding: a singing male on 16 May 1994 (Brooks 1995) and a pair, with the male carrying either food or nest material, on 28 May 1995 (D.V. McMillan).

Black Redstart *Phoenicurus ochruros*

Fairly widespread and locally common resident, common and widespread winter visitor

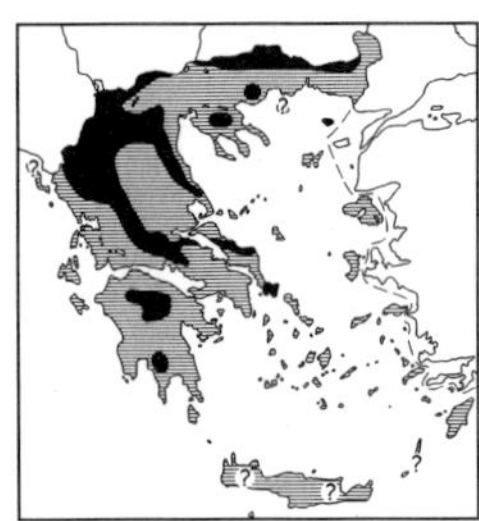

As a breeding species Black Redstart occurs over much of the mainland, including the Peloponnese. It is scarce on the islands, breeding only on Samothraki and possibly Thasos, Corfu and Karpathos (Watson 1964; *CFG*; Kinzelbach & Martens 1965). There are two May records in suitable breeding habitat from Crete but there is no other evidence of breeding there yet (*BoC*). Black Redstarts breed on high mountains, above 1000 m and mainly above the treeline, up to 2100–2600 m. Their breeding habitat includes rocky areas with scattered bushes or stunted trees, screes, boulder slopes and the vicinity of ski installations, shepherds' huts or other mountain buildings. At their lower altitudinal limit they often breed on rock outcrops or in rocky clearings within montane forest. The total breeding population probably amounts to 10,000–30,000 pairs.

In winter, Black Redstarts are common throughout the country, including the islands. The first winter visitors appear in the lowlands usually around 25 October and they become widespread from early November onwards, departing again from late February to late March. All breeding grounds are vacated in winter and in the absence of ringing recoveries we can only presume that birds simply move to lower altitudes, joined there by immigrants from the north. At this time of the year Black Redstarts prefer rocky habitats similar to those used for breeding though they are less demanding and a small isolated building, a dry-stone wall or a heap of rubble may suffice within orchards or maquis. They are also common in urban and suburban areas. At night they often roost under the eaves of houses. There is an indication of a small through-passage during both migration seasons. However, even the very first birds to appear in the lowlands in autumn engage in territorial disputes, suggesting that the majority intend to stay for the whole of winter. Populations breeding and wintering in Greece belong to race *P. o. gibraltariensis*. There are 38 ringing recoveries of Black Redstart in Greece. These had been ringed in the Czech Republic (14), Germany (11), Poland (7), Austria (5) and Hungary (1).

Redstart *Phoenicurus phoenicurus*

Scarce and local summer visitor, fairly common passage migrant

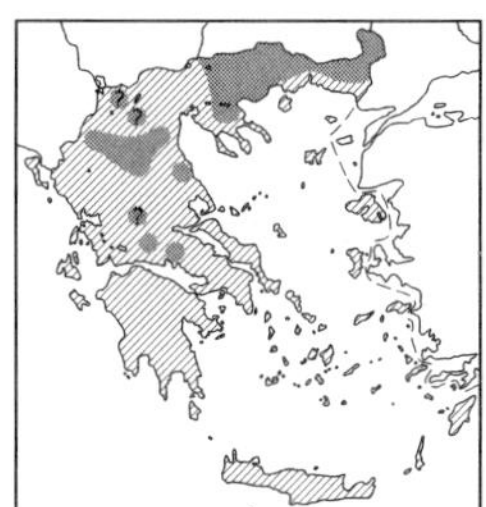

Much less numerous than Black Redstarts, Redstarts have a restricted and disjunct breeding range on the mainland, mainly north of 39°N. The southernmost known breeding site is Mt Parnassos. Redstarts breed in open woodland, mainly deciduous (especially oak *Quercus* and beech *Fagus*) but also coniferous (e.g. in *Abies* on Mt Parnassos). The total breeding population is probably between 2,000 and 5,000 pairs.

The species is a fairly common and widespread passage migrant. In most of the country it is much more numerous in autumn than in spring, although on Crete it is reported as commoner in the latter season (*BoC*). Spring passage is from mid March to late April and occasionally up to early May. In autumn some birds are on passage already from mid August but the largest numbers occur throughout October, with diminishing numbers until mid November. Redstarts are rather uncommon as prey of Eleonora's Falcons off NE Crete (Ristow *et al.* 1986) but their peak passage is at the end of the breeding season of the falcons. The Greek breeding population belongs to both *P. p. phoenicurus* and *P. p. samamisicus*, the latter mainly in northeastern Greece and the former further west. However, the exact boundaries are difficult to establish and in fact there is a wide intergradation zone between the two in the Balkans (*CFG*; *BWP*). Both races occur on passage, though *samamisicus* is rare. Two Redstarts ringed in Poland have been recovered in Greece.

Moussier's Redstart *Phoenicurus moussieri*

Accidental

Moussier's Redstarts have been recorded twice, both records of adult males: one at Methoni, Messinia, on 30 March 1988 (Iles 1988) and another near Sykia, Chalkidiki, on 18 September 1994 (K.S. Lodge).

Whinchat *Saxicola rubetra*

Scarce and local summer visitor, common passage migrant

The first proof of breeding of Whinchat in Greece came comparatively late, in 1969 (Bauer & Hodge 1970). It is now known that Whinchats breed regularly in small numbers, mainly in two areas along the northern borders of the country, from Mt Varnous eastwards to Mt Tzena and in eastern Macedonia. Small isolated populations nest elsewhere in the northern half of the country, such as the northern part of the Pindos range and Mt Olympos. Their breeding habitat is clearings within montane beech *Fagus* or coniferous forest and alpine meadows near the treeline, usually from 850 to 1900 m. Rather surprisingly, there are three breeding records from low-altitude areas in the Aegean, two from Crete (1968 and 1976) (*BoC*) and one from

the island of Kythnos (1990) (Hölzinger 1990e). The Greek population is tentatively estimated at 300–1,000 pairs.

Outside the breeding season Whinchats are common passage migrants throughout the country. They are generally more numerous in spring than in autumn but in both seasons they may be very common on days of peak passage, and on such days 50 or more birds may be seen within an hour's walking. Spring passage is from early April to mid May, with a peak in the second half of April, and autumn passage from mid August to mid October, with a peak in early to mid September. On Crete, Whinchats may arrive from late March whilst in autumn they have occasionally been seen as late as mid November (*BoC*). Whinchats are one of the commonest prey species of Eleonora's Falcons off NE Crete in autumn (Ristow *et al.* 1986).

Stonechat *Saxicola torquata*

Common and widespread resident

Stonechats are widespread and common throughout the country, including most of the islands in both the Aegean and Ionian Seas. They occur in a variety of open habitats, especially low or sparse maquis, phrygana, farmland with hedges or scattered low bushes and the edges of wetlands, from sea level to 1600–1800 m. Their total breeding population lies probably within the 50,000–100,000 range.

Stonechats breeding at low and medium altitudes seem to be largely sedentary, with pairs remaining on or near their territories all year round. Birds from higher altitudes vacate their territories in winter, presumably moving to the lowlands but perhaps also making short-distance movements to milder parts of the country or to N Africa. The species becomes slightly more numerous and widespread in the lowlands in winter. This increase in numbers may be noticed on low-lying farmland and the edges of wetlands, where the population density during the breeding season is generally low. However, it is not known to what extent these wintering birds are altitudinal migrants or migrants of northern origin. Most populations of Stonechat breeding in central and eastern Europe are migratory (*BWP*), therefore, winter visitors and passage migrants from these parts of Europe would be expected in Greece. There is only one ringing recovery of Stonechat in Greece, of a bird ringed as a chick in Hungary and found in the Peloponnese in winter. On Crete, winter visitors which are distinct from local breeding birds on account of body measurements (see below) are common from mid October to February or March (*BoC*). Very few Stonechats have been identified as prey of Eleonora's Falcons off NE Crete in autumn (Ristow *et al.* 1986), suggesting that any migration taking place before mid October (the end of the breeding season of the falcons) is on a very small scale. Greek Stonechats are on average shorter-winged and longer-billed than those of central Europe but these differences are clinal and the Greek population is now treated as race *S. t. rubicola* (*BWP*; *BoC*). On 6 November 1986, a male bird of the eastern race *S. t. variegata* was seen at Keri Lagoon, on the island of Zakynthos (Hoffmann 1993). Further records of Eastern Stonechat may exist but have not been reported as they involve a species which is otherwise common.

Isabelline Wheatear *Oenanthe isabellina*

Rare and local summer visitor

Isabelline Wheatears were first discovered breeding in Greece in the Evros Delta on 4 May 1960, though the species had been recorded as probably breeding in this area since 1954 (Watson 1961a). Between 1960 and 1965 Isabelline Wheatears were found breeding as far west as the Strymon Delta (possibly also in the Axios Delta and in the vicinity of Thessaloniki), in Attica (1965 only), on the island of Kos and possibly on Rhodes (Watson 1964; *CFG*). Today the main range of the species is in NE Greece and the islands of Kos and

Lesbos. Odd pairs have nested or still nest elsewhere in Greece: there are two confirmed breeding records from Crete, in 1964 and 1973, as well a more recent probable ones (*BoC*; M. Dretakis) and probable records from Meteora in 1981 and Dimitsana in the Peloponnese in 1989 (D. Papandropoulos). Even within their main breeding range Isabelline Wheatears are not common and in most cases occur as isolated pairs. The total Greek population is estimated at 50–200 pairs. Isabelline Wheatears breed in dry river beds, bare or eroded low hills, fallow farmland, the dried up margins of wetlands and other similar sparsely vegetated habitats, almost exclusively near sea level. Nests have been reported in abandoned burrows of European susliks *Spermophilus citellus* (in Thrace) or of black rat *Rattus rattus* (on Kos) but they also excavate their own burrow or enlarge existing ones in sandy soil or earth banks.

Isabelline Wheatears are infrequent passage migrants in the rest of the country, being most regular on the eastern mainland, Crete and the southeast Aegean, though it is likely that they are often overlooked. Birds arrive from mid or late March to mid May, mostly in early to mid April. The timing of autumn passage is still poorly known but movements probably start already from late July or early August.

Isabelline Wheatear

Wheatear *Oenanthe oenanthe*

Common and widespread summer visitor and passage migrant

Wheatears have a widespread distribution, breeding over much of the mainland, including the Peloponnese, and on many islands. In most of the country they breed at medium and high altitudes, being commonest above the treeline and reaching up to the mountain summits wherever suitable habitat exists. Thus they largely replace Black-eared Wheatears on higher ground. The two species overlap in a broad zone between about 500 and 1000 m but they are also spacially separated by their different habitat preferences. This altitudinal separation does not apply to parts of Thrace and the eastern Aegean islands (perhaps also some of the Cyclades), where the species breeds commonly down to sea level. On the island of Limnos (where Black-eared Wheatears are rare) they reach a remarkably high density: they are very common on sandy coastal areas and on the low hills that cover most of the island but also breed within villages and the small town of Myrina, nesting in stone walls and perching on buildings in a manner reminiscent of wintering Black Redstarts. Throughout the country Wheatears prefer fairly level, barren, stony habitats with sparse low vegetation, e.g. phrygana and pseudosteppe at low altitude and stony grassland or screes at high altitude. Their total Greek population may be as high as 100,000 pairs, with a minimum estimate of 30,000 pairs.

Wheatears are common passage migrants throughout the country. They are one of the earliest migrants in spring and are sometimes seen before 10 March but more usually spring passage is from mid March to late April and peak numbers occur in early April. Autumn passage runs from mid August to late October, occasionally later, with a peak in mid September. Wheatear is a common prey of Eleonora's Falcons off NE Crete in autumn (Ristow *et al.* 1986). The only ringing recovery of the species in Greece is of a Swedish-ringed bird found in the Ionian on autumn passage. All Wheatears breeding in Greece are now treated as race *O. o. libanotica* (*BWP*). This race differs in several details from *O. o. oenanthe*, with the most striking difference in the field being the plumage of adult females, which resembles that of adult males, with grey (rather than brown) upperparts. Formerly populations of the mainland and the Ionian islands were assigned to *O. o. oenanthe* and those of the Aegean region to *O. o. virago* (*CFG*; Watson 1964). *O. o. oenanthe* (in the modern sense) is the common form of Wheatear on passage. One *O. o. leucorhoa* has been reported from Crete on 8 April 1978 (*BoC*).

Pied Wheatear *Oenanthe pleschanka*

Rare and irregular summer visitor, widespread but rare passage migrant

Owing to difficulties in identification, the status of Pied Wheatears in Greece still remains unclear. Both in the past and at present great confusion has been created by the misidentification of very pure black-and-white male Black-eared Wheatears, whilst females and immatures are difficult or impossible to separate from female Black-eared Wheatears of the eastern Mediterranean race, even in the hand (*BWP*). Records of Pied Wheatears go back to the 19th century but none of these early observations was accepted by later authors (Reiser 1905; *CFG*). More reliable records exist since 1950. Almost all refer to migrating birds, seen mainly in spring (April–May), with a few in autumn (August–September). The majority are from eastern parts of the country, i.e. central and eastern Macedonia, Thrace, Sterea Hellas and the eastern Aegean islands (Rhodes, Lesbos and Patmos). The species has been recorded only twice further west, at L. Mikri Prespa on 11 April 1981 (Berlic 1983) and 24 km west of Ioannina on 15 August 1991 (F. Barrault). There are no sufficiently documented records from Crete (*BoC*).

In very recent years Pied Wheatears have been found nesting in Greece. The first breeding case was near Akrasi, on the island of Lesbos, in 1988 (Tsounis 1990a, 1992) and the second near Sarti, on the Sithonia Peninsula (Chalkidiki), on 12 June 1989 (Hölzinger 1989b). Possibly one pair also nested on Mt Symvolon, near Kavala, in 1985 (Hölzinger 1989b). Since the breeding range of Pied Wheatears extends to Bulgaria and Rumania, it is not unlikely that more pairs may nest occasionally in northern Greece. However, it seems that all nesting so far has been irregular and there is no case of a permanent population, however small. Furthermore, the possibility of mixed pairs with Black-eared Wheatears or of hybrids that are frequent where the two species overlap (*BWP*) cannot be ruled out.

Black-eared Wheatear *Oenanthe hispanica*

Common and widespread summer visitor

In general, Black-eared Wheatears appear to be slightly more numerous than Wheatears, with a more widespread breeding range. They largely replace Wheatears below about 500 m but locally they may reach higher up, up to about 1000 m on the mainland and to 1500 m on Crete (*BoC*). They are common in open areas with rock outcrops, rocky gullies, scattered boulders, dry-stone walls or in old quarries. They prefer more broken terrain than Wheatears and may occur in more vegetated habitats (e.g. vineyards, rather dense maquis, open woodland) than the latter species. The total Greek population has been estimated at 30,000–60,000 pairs (Tucker & Heath 1994) but this is probably an underestimate and a more realistic minimum would be 50,000 pairs, with 150,000 pairs not an unlikely upper limit.

Black-eared Wheatears begin to arrive in late March and most birds are on their territories by mid–late April. Some post-breeding dispersal is evident from mid July onwards, with many birds (mainly immature) leaving their breeding sites and moving to cultivated land, especially freshly ploughed fields. Departures begin in mid August (possibly even earlier for adults) and may continue to early October but relatively few remain after early September. Not surprisingly, in view of their early departure and relatively small total European population, Black-eared Wheatears are much less common than Wheatears in prey remains of Eleonora's Falcons off NE Crete in autumn (Ristow *et al.* 1986). Black-eared Wheatears breeding in Greece belong to the eastern race, *O. h. melanoleuca*. As in the nominate race, male *O. h. melanoleuca* may have either a black or white throat. Black-throated birds slightly predominate in Greece and elsewhere in SE Europe (Watson 1964).

Male eastern race Black-eared Wheatear in spring plumage

Desert Wheatear *Oenanthe deserti*

Accidental

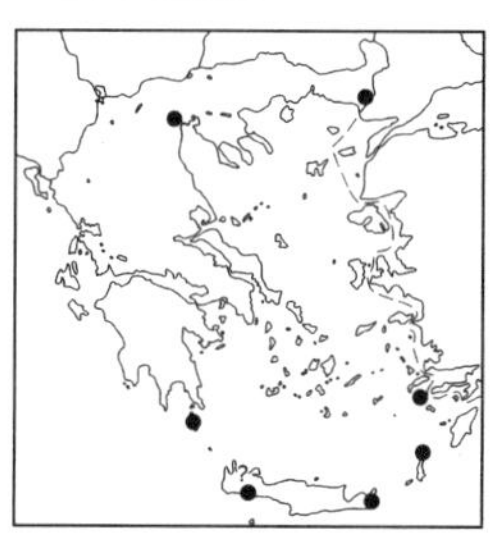

There are about seven records of Desert Wheatear in Greece. The first record is of a female on the island of Saria, near Karpathos, on 14 March 1964 (Kinzelbach & Martens 1965). Singles were seen near Ferres, Evros, in May 1966 (*CFG*) and at Alexandria, near Thessaloniki, in 1970 (Raines 1971) whilst a male was seen on the island of Nisyros on 18 March 1970 (*VME*). The species has been recorded two or three times on Crete, with four females/immatures near Agia Roumeli on 15 August 1974, one at Kato Zakros on 14 April 1989 and one 'probable' at Palio Gerani on 22 April 1987 (*BoC*). A single was seen on the island of Kythira on 22 August 1993 (Kominos 1995).

Finsch's Wheatear *Oenanthe finschii*

Accidental

One adult male Finsch's Wheatear was seen and filmed at Megalochori, near Agiasos (Lesbos), on 10 June 1993 (S.C. Norman). One more undocumented record of the species, with no further details is mentioned in Peterson *et al.* (1981).

White-crowned Black Wheatear *Oenanthe leucopyga*

Accidental

The only confirmed record of White-crowned Black Wheatear is of a male seen and photographed between Laki and Omalos (Crete) on 15 April 1993 (J. Potts).

Black Wheatear *Oenanthe leucura*

Accidental

There is one record of a pair of Black Wheatears seen and photographed at Plaka, near Trypiti on the island of Milos on 7 and 8 June 1989 (Handrinos 1994a). Two earlier records exist from Crete: one near Siteia on 24 March 1958 (Altner & Reger 1959) and a male, identified as a probable Black Wheatear, near Spili on 6 August 1964 (*BoC*). Both records are more likely to refer to White-crowned Black Wheatear (*BoC*; *CFG*).

Rock Thrush *Monticola saxatilis*

Fairly common and widespread summer visitor and passage migrant

Rock Thrushes are relatively widespread on mountains of the mainland, including the Peloponnese. They breed on the larger Ionian islands but are generally absent from those of the Aegean, except for the islands of Thasos (Peterson *et al.* 1981), Samothraki and Samos (Watson 1964). Their breeding habitat is alpine and subalpine, almost exclusively above 1000 m and occasionally up to the summits of the higher mountains, i.e. up to 2300–2500 m. They prefer rocky plateaus, screes, boulder fields, cliffs and other rocky habitats, often with scattered trees. Breeding pairs are thinly distributed and the estimate of 10,000–20,000 pairs for the total breeding population (Tucker & Heath 1994) is probably too high.

Outside the breeding season Rock Thrushes occur at lower altitudes as scarce passage migrants, mainly in spring. Migrants appear in non-breeding lowland areas from late March

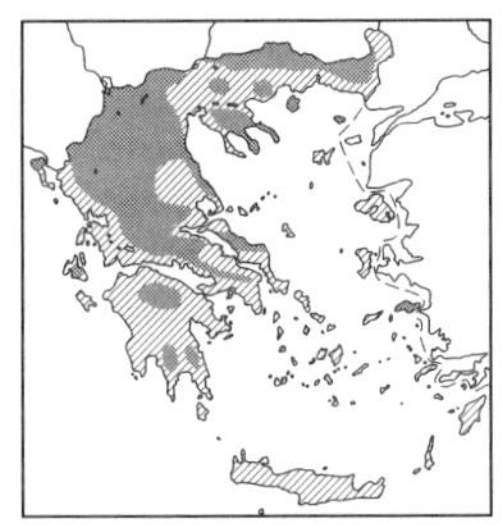

to late April. They are usually seen as single birds but it is not uncommon to see two or three together. Autumn passage is insignificant, with very few records, mostly in September. Only one Rock Thrush was identified in prey remains of Eleonora's Falcons off NE Crete in autumn of 1977 (Ristow *et al.* 1986).

Rock Thrush

Blue Rock Thrush *Monticola solitarius*

Fairly common and widespread resident

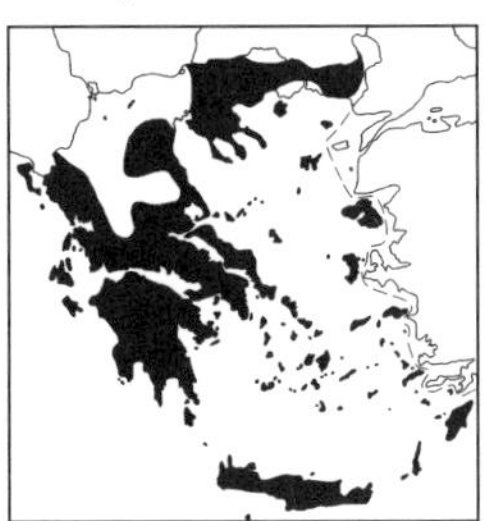

Although thinly distributed and nowhere very numerous, Blue Rock Thrushes are spread over the greater part of the mainland and also occur on most islands, even small ones, in both the Ionian and the Aegean Seas. They are more or less restricted to rocky habitats, more so than Rock Thrushes, including coastal and inland cliffs, small rocky islets, gorges and quite often ruins, from sea level up to about 1500 m and, on Crete, as high as 2200 m (*BoC*). However, they are generally rare above 1000 m, where they are replaced by Rock Thrushes. Wandering or foraging individuals often perch on buildings, telegraph poles or aerial cables at the edges of towns and villages and in some areas odd pairs even nest within old towns. The total Greek population probably exceeds 10,000 pairs and may be as high as 30,000 pairs.

Blue Rock Thrushes are chiefly sedentary, with some birds from higher elevations probably descending to lower areas during the coldest winter months. On the basis of biometric data, it has been suggested that birds from northern Greece may migrate south to Africa in winter (Watson 1964). Moreover a few individuals with a longer wing than local breeders have been trapped on Dragonada, off NE Crete, in late September and early October, indicating some passage across the Aegean (*BoC*).

White's Thrush *Zoothera dauma*

Accidental

White's Thrushes have been recorded twice: one was seen on the island of Chios in the autumn of 1954 (Spinthakis *et al.* 1993) and another in the Evros Delta on 3 February 1965 (Bauer & Müller 1969).

Ring Ouzel *Turdus torquatus*

Rare and local resident, widespread but rare passage migrant and winter visitor

Ring Ouzels were first discovered nesting in Greece on 22 and 25 May 1979 in open Norway spruce *Picea abies* forest on the Rodopi Mts, at 1850 m (Bauer & Böhr 1987). A few more breeding pairs have been discovered since then: on 28 June 1987, among white bark pines *Pinus heldreichii* on Mt Orvilos at 1580 m, and on 23 May 1988, near the peak of Megalo Livadi, in eastern Rodopi at 1267 m (Hölzinger 1988a). On 16 May 1980 one female was seen carrying nest material near Milia (area of Metsovo) and in May 1981 a male was seen twice among sparse *P. heldreichii* and beech *Fagus sylvatica* near Vrysochori (Mt Timfi), at 1600 m. Thus breeding is also likely on mountains of Ipeiros and western Macedonia but even if this is true the total population probably does not exceed 50–100 pairs. Outside the breeding season Ring Ouzels are recorded more often and in various parts of the country but still irregularly and in very small numbers. Most winter records come from the 19th century and from central Greece (e.g. Attica and the Peloponnese), whereas in recent years the species has been seen mainly on passage in October, November, March and April. Ring Ouzels breeding in Greece belong to race *T. t. alpestris* but birds of the nominate race, *T. t. torquatus,* have also been seen or collected in winter (*CFG*). There is one recovery of a bird ringed as a chick at Piatra, NE Rumania (within the breeding range of *T. t. alpestris*), on 1 June 1969 and recovered on the island of Chios on 29 September 1974.

Blackbird *Turdus merula*

Common and widespread resident

Although not so numerous as in many parts of central and northern Europe, Blackbirds are among the most widespread birds on both the mainland and the larger islands. They are common in woodland and scrub habitats, mainly on hills and mountains, and they reach up to the treeline. They are less common at lower altitude (e.g. in maquis and olive groves) or on agricultural land and in such areas they tend to be restricted to valleys with dense bushes or other well vegetated and often damp places. Nevertheless, they are not rare in dry Aleppo pine *Pinus halepensis* woodland and, locally, in parks and gardens. Their total breeding population probably exceeds 300,000 pairs and may be as high as 2,000,000 pairs.

Greek Blackbirds seem to be mainly sedentary but significant numbers of immigrants augment the local population in winter. From about mid October to early March the species becomes slightly more widespread and numerous, with highest densities in lowland and coastal areas. At times of heavy snowfall large numbers of birds from higher ground descend to the lowlands and move into villages and towns but otherwise their movements are not very obvious (compared with other thrushes) and are rather little known. Blackbird is a popular game bird. Significant numbers are shot each year and local declines have been reported in many parts of the country, particularly the south and west. So far, all of the recoveries of Blackbirds in Greece are of birds ringed in the eastern half of Europe: there are two recoveries from Finland, two from Poland, three from Russia, three from Rumania, one from the Ukraine and two from Bulgaria. Blackbirds nesting on Crete and Rhodes were formerly classified as race *T. m. insularum*, being consistently smaller than the mainland form, *T. m. aterrimus* (Watson 1964). The latter is now recognised as the only race nesting throughout Greece (*BWP*). In winter, birds of the nominate race, *T. m. merula,* also occur.

Black-throated Thrush *Turdus ruficollis*

Accidental

One bird of the black-throated race, *T. r. atrogularis,* seen near Naousa on 4 March 1956 (Flach 1956; Lambert 1957) is the only Greek record of this Siberian species.

Fieldfare *Turdus pilaris*

Fairly common and widespread winter visitor

Fieldfares are widespread though not very numerous winter visitors to much of the mainland. They are commonest in the north, uncommon in the southern mainland and scarce to rare on most of the islands. In general their numbers and distribution tend to fluctuate annually and seem to be strongly influenced by the severity of the winter further north. Fieldfares occur in a variety of habitats, especially arable land, orchards and open woodland, from sea level up to 1000–1500 m, depending on snow cover at higher altitudes. Wintering birds are present mainly from late October to mid March but the species is occasionally recorded up to late April and from mid September onwards. Largest numbers are usually recorded in the December to mid February period. There are 33 ringing recoveries of Fieldfares in Greece, ringed in 14 European countries, from Britain and France in the west to Scandinavia and northern Russia in the north, to the Ural Mts in the east and to Hungary and Rumania in the south.

Fieldfares were found nesting in Greece on three occasions in recent years: in fir *Abies* forest, at 1230 m on Mt Krikellon, Sterea Hellas (38°48'N, 21°50'E) in 1981, in beech *Fagus* forest, at 1030 m on Mt Voras in NW Macedonia (40°57'N, 21°55'E) in 1986 (Hölzinger 1986b) and on Mt Vardousia, 30 km east of the first breeding record, in 1992 (Schmid 1992). These are the southernmost breeding records of the species in the Western Palearctic so far, 800–1000 km south of the nearest regular breeding grounds in Rumania, and may possibly be connected with the range expansion observed in other parts of Europe in recent decades (*BWP*).

Song Thrush *Turdus philomelos*

Scarce and local resident, very common and widespread winter visitor

As a breeding species Song Thrush has a restricted range, breeding only on the major mountain ranges along the northern border of the country (Mts Rodopi, Voras, Tzena etc.), in the northern part of Pindos range and on a few isolated mountains further south (e.g. Mt Olympos). The southernmost breeding limit of the species is still poorly known but breeding has been reported as far south as the Katara Pass (Bauer *et al.* 1973). Song Thrushes nest at middle to high altitudes (approximately 700–1800 m), in both coniferous and deciduous forests but most often in beech *Fagus*. Their total breeding population probably lies in the 1,000–3,000 pairs range.

In winter, Song Thrushes are widespread in all kinds of habitat with at least some bushes or trees. Although locally outnumbered by Blackbirds, overall they are easily the most numerous thrush species throughout the country. They are especially numerous in olive groves, being one of the main olive-eating bird species. They are also common in maquis, where they feed on a variety of wild berries, such as those of *Pistacia lentiscus* and *Juniperus phoenicea* (as well as wild olives). The first birds begin to arrive in early October and numbers build up until early November. The calls of migrating Song Thrushes can be heard regularly over any part of Greece on clear nights in October and November, with a peak in late October and the first few days of November. Their calls are the most numerous of any night migrant and occasionally can be heard with such high frequency (e.g. an average of one call every 3–4 seconds for hours on end) that indicates a huge passage overhead. In midwinter further influxes from the north or movements within the country may occur during periods of cold weather. These movements take place partly during the day, often in association with flocks of Redwings, Fieldfares or other ground-feeding birds, such as Skylarks and Chaffinches. For a large proportion of hunters, Song Thrushes are the major game species and very large numbers are shot each winter. Departures of winter visitors begin in late February or early March and most birds have left by late March. Some late stragglers and probably through-migrants are regularly observed until mid April and occasional birds may be seen until mid May. Of 41 ringing recoveries of Song Thrushes in Greece so far, 11 are of birds ringed in the Ukraine, and the rest of birds ringed practically throughout the wider European region, from Italy, Malta and Cyprus in the south to Sweden, Finland and Russia in the north.

Redwing *Turdus iliacus*

Fairly common and widespread winter visitor

A wintering species in variable numbers, Redwings are locally not uncommon in northern and central parts of the country but much less numerous and irregular in the south, including most of the islands. They are most often seen in open woodland, maquis, olive groves, orchards and farmland with patches of bushes and trees. They seem to feed freely on olives when these are available though, unlike Song Thrush, they cannot be classed as one of the main olive-eating bird species, being much less numerous than the latter. Indicatively, Song Thrushes are usually five to ten times more numerous than Redwings. Redwings arrive later and depart earlier than wintering Song Thrushes. The first birds are usually seen in late October and peak numbers are not reached until late November or even early December. Their calls are regularly heard on clear nights from late October to early December and especially in mid and late November, i.e. as the calls of Song Thrushes begin to become less frequent. Cold-weather movements of Redwings are also evident in midwinter and large numbers of birds arrive when severe conditions prevail further north. They seem to be the most mobile of Greek thrush species: small flocks are often observed flying high overhead in both northerly and southerly directions throughout the winter. Departures of winter visitors probably begin in early or mid February and the last birds are normally seen in early March, rarely to the end of March. It may be said that Redwings are regarded as a variant of Song Thrush by hunters and, keeping to the proportions of their relative abundance, they are as heavily shot as the commoner species. There are 45 ringing recoveries of Redwings found in Greece. Eighteen of these are of birds that had been ringed in Finland, 11 of birds ringed in Britain and the rest of birds ringed in Belgium, the Netherlands, Estonia, Poland and Hungary.

Mistle Thrush *Turdus viscivorus*

Fairly common and widespread resident

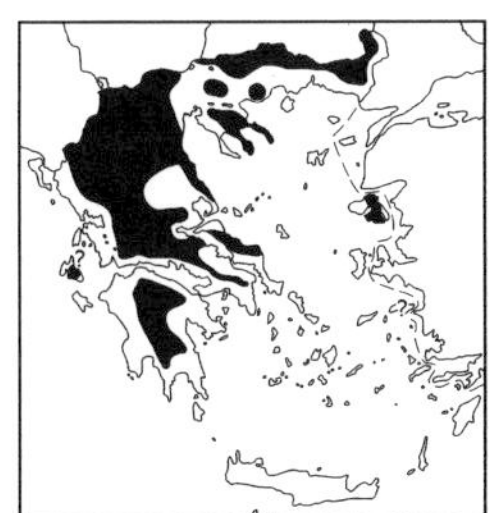

Mistle Thrushes are much more widespread and numerous than Song Thrushes, nesting on higher ground over much of the mainland, from the southern Peloponnese northwards. They are much more scarce on the islands, probably in part because of the shortage of suitable habitat. Nesting has been confirmed on Lesbos and Kefallinia (A. Vittery). The species has probably bred on Ikaria (Watson 1964) and possibly on Samos. Typically, Mistle Thrushes occur in upland coniferous forests, especially fir *Abies*, where they may be quite common. They also occur in pine *Pinus* and deciduous (oak *Quercus*, beech *Fagus*) forest. It is probably relevant that in Greece firs are the main host of mistletoe *Viscum album*, with old trees often bearing dozens of mistletoe plants. Mistletoes are much less often seen on deciduous trees, though the latter often host another plant of the mistletoe family, the yellow-berried *Loranthus europaeus*. Mistle Thrushes usually breed from about 500 m upwards to the treeline, though locally they may be found down to almost sea level. On Lesbos, where they are scarce, they occur in low-altitude Calabrian pines *Pinus brutia* and Valonia oak *Quercus macrolepis*, as well as in higher altitude Calabrian pines and sweet chestnuts *Castanea sativa*. Their total breeding population is probably in the order of 30,000–100,000 pairs.

Greek Mistle Thrushes appear to be largely sedentary, with some altitudinal movements in winter. The local population is augmented by immigrants at this time of the year. The number of wintering birds shows strong annual fluctuations, apparently not linked with hard winters, with large numbers appearing already from October and November in good years. In most years the species is only a scarce winter visitor to lowland habitats, far less numerous than Song Thrushes or Redwings. It is an accidental visitor to Crete (*BoC*). There are five recoveries of Mistle Thrushes ringed abroad and found in Greece, three from Finland, one from Poland and one from Bulgaria.

Cetti's Warbler *Cettia cetti*

Common and widespread resident

A reasonably common and widespread species, Cetti's Warblers breed over much of the mainland and many of the islands. They breed on most of the Ionian islands but they are more restricted in the Aegean, breeding on Lesbos, Kythira (Watson 1964), Crete, Samos, locally on Rhodes (Scharlau 1989a) and most probably on Kos (D. Gaunt, J.H. Rahder). Cetti's Warblers are primarily lowland birds and reach their highest density in lowland marshy habitats with dense old reedbeds or thick woody vegetation. They also regularly occur in dense thickets in damp valleys, riparian woodland with plenty of bushes, wet saline coastal areas with tamarisks *Tamarix*, cane *Arundo* hedges and other densely vegetated and usually damp habitats. Locally they reach to about 1000 m, either along streams (e.g. on Mt Parnassos) or on plateau wetlands (e.g. L. Prespa). In years of high population levels isolated singing males may be heard in drier habitats, such as large gardens or bushes in farmland, but they seldom persist there for long. The total breeding population of the species probably amounts to 50,000–200,000 pairs or territorial males.

The Greek population of Cetti's Warbler is sedentary but some movements seem to occur through the Aegean, since small numbers have been identified as prey of Eleonora's Falcons off NE Crete in autumn (Ristow *et al.* 1986).

Fan-tailed Warbler *Cisticola juncidis*

Fairly common and widespread resident

Fan-tailed Warblers are restricted to the coastal belt of the mainland and some of the islands. In the Ionian Sea, they breed on the four larger islands and perhaps Ithaki. Their distribution in the Aegean is not precisely known but they certainly breed on Limnos, Lesbos, Samos, Kos (*CFG*) and probably on Naxos (Broggi & Willi 1986). The species is a recent colonist on Crete, where it was first recorded in 1967 and is now well established in many areas (Parrot 1977; *BoC*). Although almost exclusively lowland birds, Fan-tailed Warblers have been recorded at up to 500 m on Crete (*BoC*). Their main habitat is seasonally wet marshes with tall grass and rushes *Juncus*, usually coastal but also inland, at a short distance from the coast. Less often they may be found breeding in short halophytic vegetation (such as *Arthrocnemum*), in areas with sparse, low, bushy tamarisks *Tamarix* and in cornfields. The species is polygamous and the total Greek population probably numbers around 5,000 territorial males in average years. In eastern and northern parts of the mainland the population of Fan-tailed Warblers shows strong annual fluctutations in size and range: locally the species may be totally exterminated when deep snow covers coastal areas for more than one or two days and it takes a few years before all breeding sites are recolonised and numbers return to their maximum level. Their main habitat is being seriously depleted in many areas due to housing development. As a result the species has become locally extinct in parts of the Peloponnese (CP). Fan-tailed Warblers are sedentary. However, they make considerable dispersive movements, as evidenced by the colonisation of Crete and occasional sightings in atypical habitats (e.g. olive groves and maquis) during the post-breeding period.

Fan-tailed Warbler

Grasshopper Warbler *Locustella naevia*

Widespread but rare passage migrant

Existing records of this secretive and inconspicuous species indicate it is a rare passage migrant throughout the country. The remains of several birds have been recorded among prey remains of Eleonora's Falcons off NE Crete in autumn (Ristow *et al.* 1986), suggesting that it may in fact be commoner. On the other hand, Grasshopper Warblers have never been captured in the course of ringing operations, neither have they ever been caught (or at least positively identified) on lime on the island of Chios (Spinthakis *et al.* 1993). Thus it is not unlikely that small numbers regularly overfly Greek territory without landing. As a prey of Eleonora's Falcons the species is far less numerous in the Aegean than in the western Mediterranean and NW Africa (Walter 1979).

The majority of records are from mid April to mid May and from mid August to early October. There is one late autumn record of one at Marathon in November 1965 (*CFG*). There are also a few records of singing birds in suitable habitat in spring but these probably refer to migrants and there is no other evidence of nesting in Greece.

River Warbler *Locustella fluviatilis*

Widespread but rare passage migrant

As in the case of the Grasshopper Warbler, River Warbler records are very few but the species may be similarly overlooked. The majority of records are from mid to late May, with a few from April and August. Only very few River Warblers have been recorded as prey of Eleonora's Falcons off NE Crete in autumn but even these may in fact have been misidentified Savi's Warblers (*BoC*). One was captured on a ship in the Cretan Sea on 12 May 1963 (Casement 1966). One pair, with the male in full song, seen in suitable habitat at L. Kerkini on 30 May 1980 (J. Peters), may indicate occasional breeding in the north of the country but there is still no confirmation of nesting in Greece.

Savi's Warbler *Locustella luscinioides*

Scarce and local summer visitor, fairly common and widespread passage migrant

Savi's Warblers breed in most of the major wetlands of Macedonia and Thrace, from L. Kastoria and L. Mikri Prespa eastwards to the Evros Delta. Breeding has also been recorded in the Louros Delta and possibly on Corfu (*CFG*). The total breeding population is difficult to estimate but probably is in the order of 500–2,000 pairs.

The species is a regular and widespread though not numerous passage migrant in both seasons. Passage is from late March to early May, with a peak in mid April, and then from early August to early October, with a peak in late August and early September. Spring migrants can often be heard singing and this should be taken into account when considering possible breeding sites. Both during the breeding season and on passage, Savi's Warblers occur mainly in reedbeds, pure or mixed with tall weedy growth and in climbers such as greater bindweed *Calystegia sepium*. They particularly favour dense tangled beds of *Phragmites* with a mixture of fresh and old stems. There is one recovery of a bird ringed in East Germany and found at Athens on 8 November 1962 (*BWP*), a very late date which may have been erroneously reported.

Moustached Warbler *Acrocephalus melanopogon*

Scarce and local resident, fairly common winter visitor

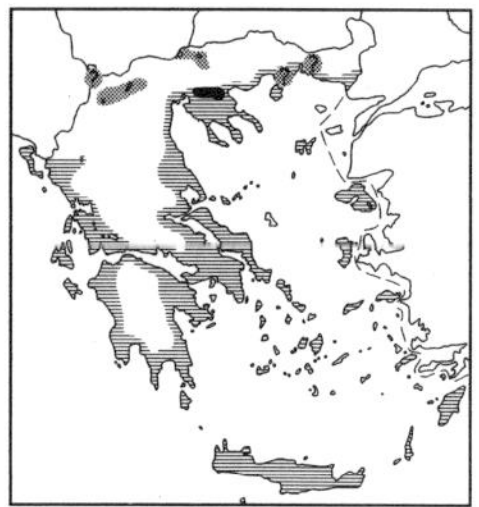

The breeding range of Moustached Warbler is still poorly known. It appears to be a scarce (or rare) breeding species, nesting in only a few major wetlands of northern Greece, and it may be less common than previously thought: there are no confirmed recent nesting records from L. Mikri Prespa (G. Catsadorakis) or the Nestos Delta (Jerrentrup 1986). Therefore, the total breeding population, previously estimated at 100–1,000 pairs (*BWP*), may be closer to or even below the lower figure.

Moustached Warblers are the only *Acrocephalus* species wintering in Greece. Winter visitors are present from early October to mid April but in larger numbers from late October to late March. They are fairly common throughout the country, especially along the coast and in the milder central and southern areas and on the islands, in reedbeds, lake shores, canals and ditches. Moustached Warblers are most easily detected by listening for their 'tuck' call, unlike the call of any other bird likely to be heard in reedbeds in winter. Typically they are seen at the margin of reeds with open water, hopping from one reed stem to another and pecking at the water surface for small insects. It is very rare to see them away from patches of open water or perching near the top of reeds.

Moustached Warbler

Aquatic Warbler *Acrocephalus paludicola*

Accidental

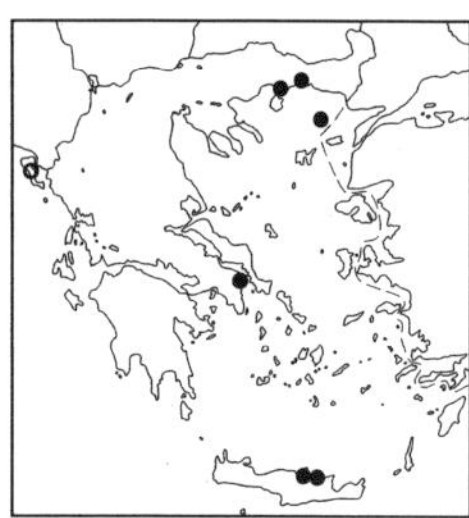

Since the first record of Aquatic Warbler on the island of Corfu in 1858 (Powys 1860), the species has been recorded fewer than ten times. Even accounting for its secretive nature and the fact that Greece must lie on or close to the migratory route between its European breeding quarters and its wintering quarters in Africa, it cannot be expected to be anything more than a rare visitor, and at present it seems most appropriate to treat it as an accidental. Further confusion arises from the not infrequent misidentification of Sedge Warblers (especially juveniles in the autumn) with Aquatic Warblers. The 1858 record itself must be treated as suspect as it is the only winter record of the species, a very unlikely time of the year for Aquatic Warblers in Europe. Other records have been in April, May and August, all of single birds: Nestos Delta, late April–early May 1962 (Raines 1962), L. Karla, April 1964 (*CFG*), L. Kastoria, August 1964 (*CFG*), the island of Samothraki, 26 April 1987 (Broggi & Willi 1988), Porto Lagos, 23 April 1969 and Marathon, 30 April 1969 (M. Hodge), and two probable records from Crete, one on 16 April 1990 and one on 1 May 1991 (M. Dretakis). A further record is of at least two among prey remains of Eleonora's Falcons at a colony off NE Crete between 17 and 23 September 1965 (Walter 1968) but these too may have been misidentified Sedge Warblers (*BoC*).

Sedge Warbler *Acrocephalus schoenobaenus*

Scarce and local summer visitor, common passage migrant

The breeding distribution of Sedge Warblers is not yet fully known and breeding season records are confused by the regular singing of birds on passage. Nesting has been confirmed or recorded as probable at only a handful of sites: the vicinity of Thessaloniki (Makatsch 1950), L. Mikri Prespa (G. Catsadorakis) and L. Kerkini (P. Atkinson). Thus, the recent estimate of the total Greek population at 500–1,000 pairs (Tucker & Heath 1994) may be too high.

Sedge Warblers are more numerous and widespread on passage, from mid March to late May, with a peak from late March to mid April, and from mid August to late October, with a peak from late August to mid September. In spring they can be very common in all types of marshy habitat and often outnumber Reed Warblers up to the middle of April. Autumn passage is on a smaller scale and then they are much less numerous than Reed Warblers. However, Sedge Warbler was the commonest *Acrocephalus* among prey remains at a colony of Eleonora's Falcons off NE Crete in autumn 1977 (Ristow *et al.* 1986), the relative abundance of Sedge to Reed and Marsh Warblers combined being 18:8. In autumn Sedge Warblers are strongly attracted to high densities of the reed-plum aphid *Hyalopterus pruni* throughout Europe and often fatten up much more than other *Acrocephalus* warblers in an apparent preparation for long non-stop flights (*BWP*). In Greece, peak numbers of *Hyalopterus* occur far too early for the migratory period of the species (in the first half of June in central parts of the country) and it seems likely that many birds fatten up north of Greece and overfly the country without landing or landing for only short periods. The difference in the abundance of the species between those taken by Eleonora's Falcons and those seen on the ground is in agreement with this hypothesis. Six foreign-ringed Sedge Warblers have been recovered in Greece. One Finnish-ringed bird was recovered at Messolonghi in late April whilst the remaining five, ringed in Denmark (1), Poland (2), Finland (1) and Hungary (1) were recovered in autumn.

Paddyfield Warbler *Acrocephalus agricola*

Accidental

One bird seen at Almyros marsh, near Chania (Crete), on 16 April 1969 (M. Hodge) is the only confirmed record of Paddyfield Warbler (Handrinos 1994a).

Marsh Warbler *Acrocephalus palustris*

Scarce and local summer visitor, fairly common passage migrant

Marsh Warblers have a quite restricted and patchy breeding distribution. As far as is known up to now, they breed only in Macedonia and Thrace, in and around some of the major wetlands, from L. Mikri Prespa eastwards to the Evros Delta (*CFG*; Peterson *et al.* 1981). However, the exact limits of their breeding range are still poorly known and the total popu-

lation, probably numbering not more than a few hundred pairs, is difficult to assess. Even the habitat preferences of Marsh Warblers breeding in Greece are inadequately known. They have been seen alongside Reed Warblers in dense reedbeds but at L. Prespa they nest mainly in patches of brambles *Rubus*, reeds *Phragmites* and tall herbaceous plants alongside ditches within farmland.

The species seems to be fairly common as a passage migrant throughout the country, at least in the autumn. It is probably often overlooked, since most records come from ringing data. Spring passage is small, from late March (?) to late May but mainly from late April to mid May. In W Macedonia singing males first appear in late April. In autumn, Marsh Warblers are more numerous, with a passage from late July to late September or early October. Only adult birds are captured in late July and the first half of August. Later in August and in September many more Marsh Warblers have been captured and these are mainly juveniles. However, perhaps due to a peculiarity of Reed Warblers passing through Greece at this time of the year, these juveniles are difficult to distinguish from juveniles of the latter and thus the exact timing and volume of passage after mid August remains to be clarified.

Reed Warbler *Acrocephalus scirpaceus*

Common and widespread summer visitor and passage migrant

Reed Warblers have a widespread breeding distribution over the whole of the mainland and on the Ionian islands. There are still few definite breeding records from the islands of the Aegean Sea, presumably due to shortage of suitable nesting habitat. They definitely breed on Limnos and Lesbos and probably on Kos but there is still no evidence of breeding from Crete (*BoC*). As elsewhere in their breeding range, they occur almost exclusively in reedbeds, either of pure *Phragmites* or mixed with other tall marsh plants. The total Greek population probably amounts to 50,000–100,000 pairs. The species is often thought to be less numerous and widespread than Great Reed Warbler but this is probably a false impression deriving from the greater conspicuousness of the larger species. Birds begin to arrive in late March, with large numbers present from mid April onwards. Passage of through-migrants is heavy in both seasons. In spring, passage peaks in late April–early May and continues to mid or late May. In autumn, departures and passage take place mainly in August and up to late September, with a few birds as late as late October or even early November. Adults migrate first and almost only juveniles are seen or caught for ringing from late August onwards. There is strong evidence to suggest that locally breeding adults start departing already from mid July and are almost all gone by mid August. There are 14 ringing recoveries of Reed Warblers in Greece, ten of which had been ringed in Austria (mainly L. Neusiedler) and the remaining four in Hungary.

Great Reed Warbler *Acrocephalus arundinaceus*

Common and widespread summer visitor and passage migrant

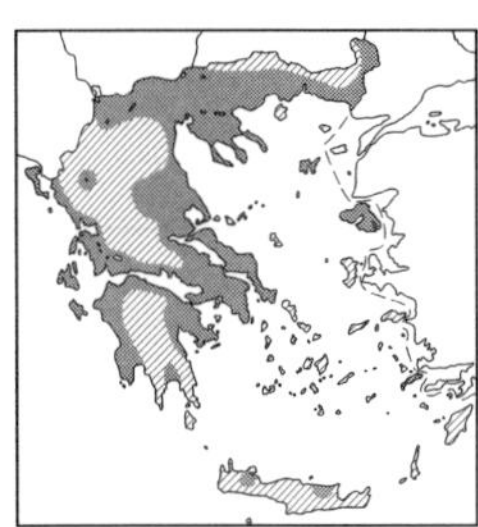

Great Reed Warblers have more or less the same breeding distribution as Reed Warblers, though they are slightly more restricted due to their special habitat requirements. Great Reed Warblers usually nest in flooded reedbeds and near open water whereas Reed Warblers are practically indifferent to the presence of surface water and thus may be found at drier sites than the larger species. In suitable areas Great Reed Warblers may reach high densities, e.g. *c.* 60 nests were found within *c.* 180 m along the shore of L. Koronia (Makatsch 1950). The total breeding population is probably in the order of 50,000–100,000 pairs or territorial males, since this is often a polygamous species. Some local declines have been noted due to habitat loss. A study of the diet of nestlings in east-central Greece showed the high dependence of the species on surface water, with a large proportion of the diet composed of aquatic insects such as adult and larval dragonflies (Odonata), water beetles (Dytiscidae) and flies (Diptera) (Akriotis 1988). However, breeding birds also regularly visit dry habitats within easy reach of their nest site, e.g. to feed on high densities of grasshoppers (Orthoptera) and dung beetles (Scarabaeidae, Geotrupidae).

The first Great Reed Warblers may arrive as early as mid March but maximum numbers are not attained until mid April, whilst passage of through-migrants continues until mid May. In autumn, birds leave from early August onwards. Significant numbers are still present up to mid September in suitable habitat (near open water) whereas reedbeds that dry up in the summer may be vacated any time from late June onwards. Adults leave first and only juveniles are present after early September. These presumably include a large proportion of birds on passage from breeding grounds further north. The last birds are usually recorded in late September. Both autumn and spring migrants are regularly seen (and even heard giving short bouts of song in the spring) away from reedbeds, e.g. in scrub, gardens and woodland. Up to now there are only five ringing recoveries of Great Reed Warblers, of birds ringed in Germany (1), the Czech Republic (2) and Hungary (2) and found on passage through Greece.

Olivaceous Warbler *Hippolais pallida*

Common and widespread summer visitor

Olivaceous Warblers are widely distributed, breeding over most of the mainland, including the Peloponnese, as well as on most of the islands in both the Aegean and the Ionian Seas. They are primarily low-altitude birds, commonest near sea level and up to *c.* 500 m, rarely found above 1000 m. Their breeding habitat includes any area with dense or sparse trees, especially olive groves, gardens, fruit orchards, Aleppo pine *Pinus halepensis* or oak *Quercus* woodland and humid zones along watercourses or at the margins of wetlands with tamarisks *Tamarix*, willows *Salix*, chaste tree *Vitex agnus–castus* etc. However, although they obtain much of their food on trees, they need some dense bushy vegetation in which to build their nests and thus are absent from areas such as intensively cultivated olive groves in which there are no bushes. The total Greek population almost certainly exceeds 100,000 pairs and may be as high as 300,000 pairs or more. The species has recently been reported as declining (Tucker & Heath 1994) but this does not appear to be the case in most parts of their range.

Olivaceous Warblers are among the latest arriving summer visitors. The first singing males are usually heard in late April, very rarely before 20 April and in some years not until the last few days of the month. Therefore, reports of the species before the middle of April must be treated as suspect. The birds also leave early, mainly between late July and late August and with a few late stragglers until mid September. Olivaceous Warblers breeding in Greece belong to race *H. p. elaeica*.

Booted Warbler *Hippolais caligata*

Accidental

Booted Warblers have been recorded twice in Greece: two males singing near Anatoli, Crete, in scrub at 600 m, on 1 April 1978 (*BoC*) and one seen at Cape Lakka, on the island of Paxoi, on 24 May 1992 (Vittery 1994).

Olive-tree Warbler *Hippolais olivetorum*

Fairly common and widespread summer visitor

Olive-tree Warblers have a reasonably widespread distribution both on the mainland and on the islands. On the mainland they occur mainly in warm and sunny coastal or low-lying zones, particularly in the Peloponnese, Sterea Hellas, Thessaly and Thrace, with a much more patchy distribution in Macedonia. Despite earlier reports (Pease 1940), the species does not breed on Crete (*BoC*) but it is a breeding bird on Lesbos, Skopelos, Paros and Naxos and, among the Ionian islands, on Kefallinia (A. Vittery) and possibly Zakynthos (P.F. Whitehead) and Corfu. The exact habitat requirements of Olive-tree Warblers are still poorly known and within their range they occur as small isolated populations with very large gaps in between. Despite their name, they are not confined to olive trees but very often occur in other orchard or open woodland habitats. In several areas (e.g. Thrace, Lesbos and the Peloponnese) they are more often found in dry park-like areas with scattered oaks (*Quercus macrolepis* or *Q. pubescens*) or almond trees *Prunus dulcis* and bushes. Owing to their irregular distribution, the total Greek population is difficult to assess; it is certainly not large and probably lies between 3,000 and 5,000 pairs or is perhaps a little larger. The timing of the movements of Olive-tree Warblers is still not well known. Spring arrivals mainly take place after the middle of April, though on Crete they have been recorded as early as late March (*BoC*). In autumn, departures probably begin in late July and most birds have left by early September.

Olive-tree Warbler

Icterine Warbler *Hippolais icterina*

Fairly common and widespread passage migrant

Icterine Warblers occur as passage migrants throughout the country. In spring they are on passage from mid April to late May or early June, with a rather late peak in early and mid May, whereas in autumn most birds are on passage from mid August (occasionally early August) to late September, with a peak in early September. During autumn migration they are fairly common but in spring they are rather scarce. However, their numbers vary considerably from day to day and from place to place. In autumn, large falls have been noted on small islands or coastal areas. The species is also a frequent prey of Eleonora's Falcons off NE Crete in autumn (Ristow *et al.* 1986). This pattern of occurrence suggests that in the autumn many birds overfly the country without landing or landing for only short periods unless forced by adverse weather. Although they may be found in any habitat with a mixture of trees and bushes, Icterine Warblers show a marked preference for thickets and areas with dense bushes, especially near water. Spring migrants often sing, and although a few records of singing males in suitable habitat in early June may indicate occasional breeding in northern Greece, there is as yet no concrete evidence for this. One Icterine Warbler ringed in Belgium, one ringed in Denmark and two ringed in Poland have been recovered in Greece.

Melodious Warbler *Hippolais polyglotta*

Accidental

One seen at Katelios, on Kefallinia, on 3 May 1990 after overnight westerly wind (Vittery 1994) is the only Greek record of Melodious Warbler fully supported with field notes so far. Three more records are currently not accepted due to lack of adequate documentation: one at Ermones, Corfu, on 3 September 1987 (C. Squires), one at Knossos, Crete, on 5 October 1991 and one on the island of Delos on 6 October 1991 (M. & F. Trubridge).

Marmora's Warbler *Sylvia sarda*

Rare and local resident (?)

The status of Marmora's Warbler in Greece is puzzling. The normal breeding range of the species is restricted to the Balearic islands, Corsica, Sardinia and the island of Pantelleria, off Sicily, and a proportion of the population of Corsica and Sardinia winters in Algeria, Tunisia and NW Libya (*BWP*). Compared with Dartford Warbler, which has a much wider breeding range and larger population, the number of records of Marmora's Warbler in Greece is surprisingly large. The first record of the species was at Vai (Crete) on 1 October 1980 (Pasquali 1981), followed by a record of a pair at a nest at Chersonisos (Crete) on 12 April 1981 (*BoC*) and a single at Matala (Crete) on 17 May 1981 (Pasquali 1982). Three years later, breeding was reported on the island of Naxos (Cyclades), with three pairs seen between 22 June and 8 September 1984 and two pairs between 13 May and 8 August 1985 (Magioris 1988, 1992b). Additional records, all of singles from Crete, are: a male at Arkadi on 10 May 1989, Georgioupolis on 4 and 6 October 1989 and between Georgioupolis and Kournas on 4 October 1989 (*BoC*). Unfortunately, none of these records is supported by detailed descriptions and the status of the species remains unclear. The possibility of confusion with Sardinian Warblers cannot be ruled out, especially for records between mid May and mid September, when dark immature Sardinian Warblers may be involved. It has been suggested that Marmora's Warblers may have recently colonised Crete (*BoC*). In view of the low probability of true vagrancy this proposition (which would also apply to the Cyclades) seems the only likely alternative to misidentification. Further records accompanied by adequate field descriptions or photographs will be needed before the status of the species becomes clear.

Dartford Warbler Sylvia undata

Accidental

There are two records of Dartford Warbler: one female collected on the island of Andros on 2 September 1934 (Bird 1935) and one at Kommeno, near Arta, in January 1967 (*CFG*).

Spectacled Warbler *Sylvia conspicillata*

Rare and irregular passage migrant

Spectacled Warbler was recorded as early as the 19th century (Mühle 1844; Erhard 1858; Lindermayer 1860) but all these old records were doubtful and rejected by later authors (Reiser 1905; *CFG*). More recently, the species was recorded again at Porto Lagos on 8 May 1960 (Raines 1962) and since then there have been 20–25 additional records, of which 14–15 are acceptable. Only two records are from inland sites, L. Prespa in May 1964 (Sage 1966) and Delphi on 8 September 1960 (Raines 1962), all the rest being from coastal sites or islands in both the Aegean and the Ionian Seas. All records are from April–May and August–October, except for one in late November, clearly suggesting birds on passage.

Interestingly, a pair feeding 2–3 recently fledged young was seen near Cape Agia Aikaterini, on the island of Corfu, between 15 and 19 May 1991 (K. & M. Claydon). The site is very close to S Italy, the nearest breeding area of the species (*BWP*), and this adds support to the validity of the record and may also indicate a high probability of future colonisation of the Ionian islands.

Subalpine Warbler *Sylvia cantillans*

Common and widespread summer visitor

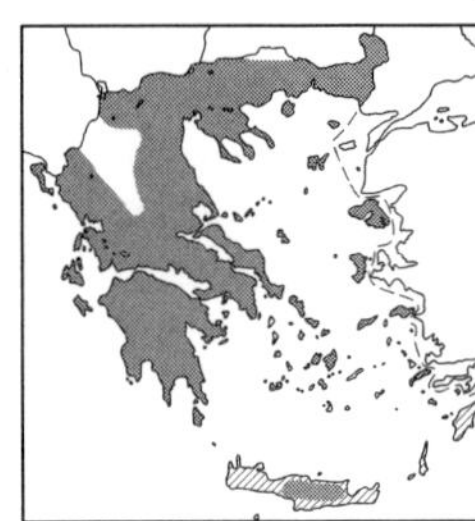

Subalpine Warblers are widely distributed both on the mainland and on several of the islands in the Aegean and the Ionian Seas. However, their abundance varies considerably from place to place, ranging from very scarce (e.g. on Crete) to locally very common (e.g. in parts of the mainland or the island of Lesbos). The total breeding population probably exceeds 200,000 pairs and may be as high as 500,000 pairs. Subalpine Warblers breed in a variety of bushy or open woodland habitats, including maquis, scrub, areas of low Kermes oak *Quercus coccifera* or *Cistus,* open Aleppo *Pinus halepensis* and Calabrian pine *P. brutia* woodland and areas of scattered Valonia oaks *Quercus macrolepis* with a dense undergrowth of bushes, from sea level up to 1200 m. Their habitat preference largely overlaps that of Sardinian Warbler and the two species are loosely separated altitudinally and geographically. Generally speaking, Subalpine Warblers tend to occupy more humid and often more wooded habitats, steeper slopes and higher elevations, and are generally commoner in the north than in the south, the opposite of Sardinian Warbler. It is possible that the breeding areas of Subalpine Warblers are too cold or snowy in winter for the largely sedentary Sardinian Warblers and the migratory Subalpine are able to settle there with reduced competition.

In spring, the first Subalpine Warblers arrive in mid March, with the main period of arrivals from late March to mid April. Some through-passage occurs until early May. As the breeding season comes to a close (around mid July) birds spread to a wider variety of habitats. They become fairly common in olive groves, orchards, gardens and farmland with scattered trees at low altitude and are especially attracted to figs *Ficus carica*, ripe mainly from early August to mid September. This applies more to juveniles than to adults, which seem to migrate earlier. Numbers begin to decline noticeably from late August and the last birds are usually seen in late September. The species is commonly recorded as a prey of Eleonora's Falcons off NE Crete in autumn (Ristow *et al.* 1986). The Greek population of Subalpine Warblers belongs to race *S. c. albistriata*.

Sardinian Warbler *Sylvia melanocephala*

Very common and widespread resident

Sardinian Warbler is one of the most familiar Greek passerines. It occurs in all types of maquis, phrygana, olive groves, open woodland with bushes, vineyards, hedges in farmland and sometimes in large gardens, from sea level up to about 700 m. The highest densities occur in low altitude maquis, dominated by such evergreen bushes as lentisc *Pistacia lentiscus*, Kermes oak *Quercus coccifera* or Phoenicean juniper *Juniperus phoenicea*. Locally, they breed at higher elevations and even up to 2000 m on Crete (*BoC*). Although common and familiar over most of the country, they are absent or extremely rare in many inland parts of Ipeiros, Macedonia and Thrace. The total Greek population is in the order of 500,000–1,000,000 pairs.

As a rule, Sardinian Warblers are sedentary, with dispersal (especially of immatures) to a wider variety of habitats during the non-breeding season and some temporary altitudinal movements at times of severe winter weather. However, in most parts of Macedonia and Thrace they are virtually absent in winter. In the absence of ringing recoveries the winter quarters of these birds remain unknown. There is evidence of a small scale migration in the area of Crete (*BoC*) and Karpathos (Kinzelbach & Martens 1965). The species is rare as a prey of Eleonora's Falcons off NE Crete in autumn (Ristow *et al.* 1986) but it appears that peak migration of Sardinian Warblers is after the end of the observation period at the falcons' colonies (up to the middle of October). On the islet of Dragonada, in 1974, larger numbers of migrant Sardinian Warblers were seen between 7 and 23 October than in September (*BoC*). In spring 1987 the first birds to be seen in Thrace were on 22 March at Porto Lagos and on 26 March in the Evros Delta (WIWO 90). Sardinian Warblers breeding on Crete, Karpathos and Rhodes are smaller and darker than those of the mainland (or other parts of southern Europe). These are sometimes distinguished as race *S. m. pasiphaë* (*BoC*) but the difference is small and clinal and in *BWP* they are not separated from the nominate race.

Rüppell's Warbler *Sylvia rueppelli*

Fairly widespread and locally common summer visitor

One of the few Mediterranean endemic species, Rüppell's Warblers have a distinctly southeastern distribution. On the mainland they occur sporadically from southern Thessaly southwards and in the Ionian they have possibly bred on Corfu (Böhr 1962) and Kefallinia (1994) (J. Mellett & L. Logothetis). In the Aegean they breed north to Lesbos and also on Chios, Samos and the Cyclades but they are generally scarce and local in all these areas. It is in the Dodecanese and Crete that they reach their highest density. On some islands of the Dodecanese (e.g. Kos and Nissyros) they are very common and may almost completely replace Sardinian Warblers. However, even here they are peculiarly absent from some areas. For example, whilst breeding has been recorded on Rhodes, the species was not recorded there during atlas censusing in 1988 (Scharlau 1989a). Throughout their breeding range Rüppell's Warblers are found mainly on

Rüppell's Warbler

dry, hilly ground with maquis, dominated by such bushes as Kermes oak *Quercus coccifera*, lentisc *Pistacia lentiscus* and *Calycotome villosa*, from sea level up to at about 1000 m. They probably compete with Sardinian Warblers and in some places tend to occur either at higher altitude or on steeper slopes than the more widespread species in the same general area. The total Greek population probably amounts to a minimum of 3,000 pairs and may be almost as high as 10,000 pairs.

Rüppell's Warblers are migratory. They are one of the first migrants to arrive in spring, with the first birds sometimes arriving in early March whilst the majority of males are defending territory by late March. Up to mid May, singing males are easy to locate. They sing intensively, usually sat on top of bushes and often performing their song-flight, rising vertically upwards and then parachuting downwards on slowly beating wings. In the south and at low altitude nest-building begins in late March and there is one exceptional record from Crete of a nest with young as early as 8 April (*BoC*). The timing of departures in autumn is not precisely known but the last birds are usually seen in mid September.

Orphean Warbler *Sylvia hortensis*

Widespread but scarce summer visitor

A widespread breeding species over much of the mainland and on most of the islands in both the Aegean and the Ionian Seas, Orphean Warblers are nowhere very numerous. They prefer taller vegetation than Sardinian Warblers, such as well-grown maquis with 1–3 m tall bushes, patches of tall bushes or hedges within agricultural land, deciduous scrub and olive groves or open woodland with plenty of bushy undergrowth, often in fairly cool and humid situations in ravines or by streams, from sea level up to about 1000 m. The total Greek population is in the order of 5,000–10,000 pairs.

Even accounting for its comparative scarcity, the species is relatively little known. It is migratory, arriving from late March onwards and with some through-passage until about early May. In autumn, departures of local breeders and passage from further north take place between mid August and mid September. The Greek population belongs to race *S. h. crassirostris*, distinguished among other characters by its thrush-like song.

Barred Warbler *Sylvia nisoria*

Rare and local summer visitor, scarce passage migrant

One of the least known passerine species in Greece, Barred Warblers have a restricted and patchy breeding distribution. They are reported as having bred in Attica in 1875 (Makatsch

1950). In recent years nesting was confirmed in the area of Dadia, Evros, in 1967 and 1968, with odd pairs also near L. Mikri Prespa and possibly at Delphi (*CFG*; Bauer & Hodge 1970). The hilly area west and northwest of Alexandroupolis (e.g. around the villages of Dadia, Aisymi and Makri) appears to be the stronghold of the species but even there it is very scarce. However, it is not unlikely that more pairs breed elsewhere in northern parts of the country. The total Greek population is tentatively estimated at 50–200 pairs. The precise habitat requirements of Barred Warbler in Greece are not well known but as elsewhere in southeastern Europe they seem to prefer semi-open habitats, with tall bushes or hedges, scattered oaks *Quercus*, elms *Ulmus* or other deciduous trees and open spaces such as small cornfields or grass meadows.

Barred Warblers are not often recorded on passage either, perhaps partly because of their skulking habits. Small numbers were identified among prey remains at nests of Eleonora's Falcons, off NE Crete in autumn 1977 (Ristow *et al.* 1986).

Lesser Whitethroat *Sylvia curruca*

Fairly common but local summer visitor, locally common passage migrant

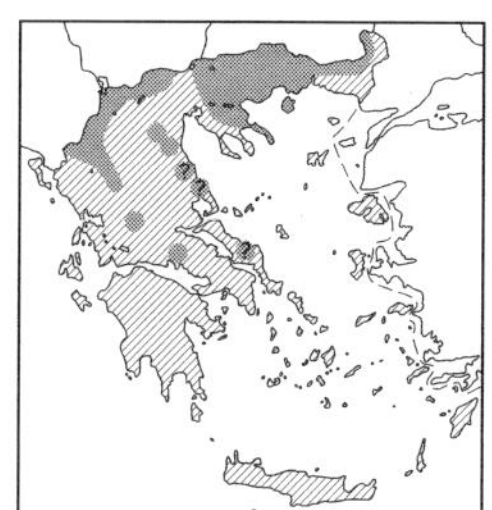

Lesser Whitethroats breed only in Thrace, Macedonia and along the northern and central part of the Pindos range, with odd pairs recorded from isolated mountains, e.g. Mt Olympos, Mt Ossa and Mt Parnassos (Peterson *et al.* 1981). In the islands breeding is known only from Thasos (Peterson *et al.* 1981) and is probable on Lesbos and Limnos. There is also an old breeding record (confirmed?) from Rhodes (*CFG*). Within their mainland range Lesser Whitethroats are very thinly distributed and even in suitable habitat they are rather scarce. They breed in upland and mountainous areas, in oak *Quercus*, beech *Fagus* or mixed pine *Pinus* and oak scrub, in open woodland and in upland areas with *Juniperus oxycedrus*, hawthorn *Crataegus* or other deciduous bushes, from 100 to 1600 m but more often between 700 and 1200 m. The total Greek population probably lies in the 5,000–20,000 pairs range.

Lesser Whitethroats occur throughout the country on passage. However, they are common only in northeastern parts of the country, i.e. Thrace and the islands of the northeastern Aegean (Chios, Lesbos, Limnos and Samothraki), and scarce in the all other areas. Spring passage and arrival of local breeders takes place between late March and early May whilst in autumn departures and passage occur from mid August to mid October. Lesser Whitethroats breeding in Greece were formerly treated as race *S. c. curruca* (Watson 1964; *CFG*) but more recently (*BWP*) they have been assigned to *S. c. caucasica*. This is an intermediate form between the nominate *S. c. curruca* of most of Europe and *S. c. althaea* of west–central Asia, differing from *curruca* in having a darker grey crown, the remainder of the upperparts greyer and less silky-white, more extensively buff mid underparts. Birds of the nominate race presumably occur on passage. There are seven ringing recoveries of Lesser Whitethroat, all ringed abroad and found in Greece: two had been ringed in Britain, two in Germany and singles in Denmark, Sweden and the Czech Republic. Significantly, one was recovered in the Peloponnese and the other six in northeastern parts of the country, i.e. near Alexandroupolis and on the islands of Chios and Lesbos.

Whitethroat *Sylvia communis*

Common and widespread summer visitor and passage migrant

The breeding range of Whitethroats spans the largest part of the mainland and many of the larger islands in both the Aegean and the Ionian Seas. It is a species of hedges, scrub, Kermes oak *Quercus coccifera* maquis, patches of bramble *Rubus* or other bushes in or around farmland or pasture and stony areas stunted with bushes at or just above the treeline. Whitethroats are typical of the deciduous and transitional vegetation zones. They are generally absent from

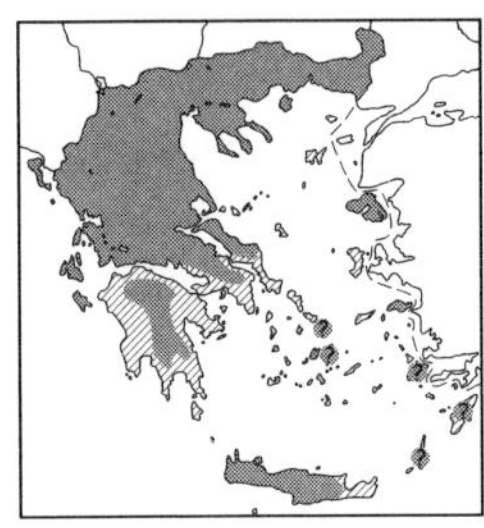

hot, dry, pure Mediterranean-type vegetation, and in southern parts of the country they prefer moderate to high altitudes or the vicinity of streams and irrigated areas. However, they are not so restricted as other similar species and even on Crete they breed down to sea level (*BoC*). The total Greek population probably lies between 100,000 and 300,000 pairs.

Whitethroats are one of the most numerous *Sylvia* species on passage throughout the country in both seasons. In spring, passage usually peaks in mid April but the first birds arrive in late March and migration continues up to mid May, when local birds are already nesting. Autumn passage is from mid August to late October, peaking in early and mid September. The species is also the commonest *Sylvia* warbler among prey remains of Eleonora's Falcons off NE Crete in autumn (Ristow *et al.* 1986). Whitethroats breeding in northern Greece belong to the nominate race, *S. c. communis,* but those of the Peloponnese and the Aegean islands grade into the west Asian *S. c. icterops*, which is greyer on the upperparts, whiter on the underparts and slightly larger (*BWP*). The seven ringing recoveries of Whitethroat in Greece available up to now are of birds ringed in Sweden (2), Finland (4) and Germany (1).

Garden Warbler *Sylvia borin*

Rare and local summer visitor, fairly common passage migrant

As a breeding species Garden Warbler is one of the rarest and least known species of *Sylvia.* So far, nesting has been reported from only a few localities, mainly in the north. However, the first breeding record was of one brooding female collected on the island of Naxos on 16 June 1959, feeding on mulberries *Morus* in high Kermes oak *Quercus coccifera* maquis in the south of the island (Watson 1964). This is a remarkable record on account of the unlikely habitat and isolation from the main breeding grounds of the species in central and northern Europe. Garden Warblers have also been recorded as possibly nesting in Chalkidiki and Corfu (*CFG*). If Garden Warblers breed regulary anywhere in the country, the most likely areas would be in the montane region of northern Ipeiros, Macedonia and Thrace. The total Greek population probably does not exceed 100 pairs.

The species is more numerous on passage, especially in autumn, but even then it is not common. Passage is from late March to mid May and from mid August to mid October, with largest numbers in mid and late September. In August and early September Garden Warblers are often seen feeding on figs *Ficus carica* but the main passage is after the end of the main fig season. Birds on passage are widespread in all kinds of habitats with bushes and some trees but show a slight preference for moist woodland and riverside vegetation. Garden Warblers breeding in and passing through Greece belong to the nominate race, *S. b. borin* (*CFG*; *BWP*). Birds of the slighty greyer and larger eastern race *S. b. woodwardi* or intermediates probably also occur on passage (Watson 1964). There are five ringing recoveries of the species in Greece: one had been ringed in Sweden, two in Finland, one in Poland and one in Russia.

Blackcap *Sylvia atricapilla*

Common and widespread resident

Although the term 'resident' may be used to describe the year-round presence of Blackcaps in Greece, the species in fact makes complex movements, as yet not fully clarified, apparently with different populations breeding, wintering and passing through. Its breeding range is fairly wide, covering mainly the northern half of the mainland (Thessaly and Ipeiros northwards), where it is locally fairly common. Breeding is increasingly local farther south but extends to the southern Peloponnese (Hölzinger 1990a). The species is far less widespread on the islands in both the Aegean and the Ionian Seas, with nesting confirmed only on Thasos, Samothraki

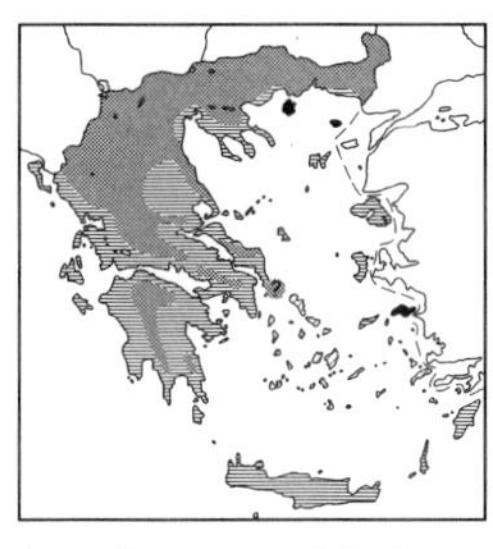

and Samos (Peterson *et al.* 1981). Breeding Blackcaps are absent from pure Mediterranean-type vegetation. They are found mainly in open coniferous (e.g. fir *Abies* or pine *Pinus)* and deciduous (e.g. oak *Quercus*, beech *Fagus* or sweet chestnut *Castanea sativa*) woodland or scrub, with an abundance of bushes. Thus they occur at medium to fairly high altitudes (500–1800 m) in the south but locally down to sea level in Macedonia and Thrace. In the lower zones of their altitudinal range, Blackcaps often breed in tall maquis with scattered trees, usually on moist and cool north-facing slopes, shady ravines or streamside vegetation. The total breeding population probably numbers between 5,000 and 20,000 pairs.

The movements of Blackcaps breeding in Greece are not well known but they certainly vacate the majority, if not all, of their breeding areas in winter. The species is a common passage migrant and winter visitor. Autumn passage is from early September to about mid October, with a peak in late September, whereas spring passage probably begins in early March and continues to late April, peaking from late March to mid April. Some very late migrants may rarely be seen up to late May away from breeding areas. Numbers decline slightly after the peak of autumn migration but quite large numbers of birds remain all through winter. It is not yet known with certainty whether winter visitors arrive and depart at the same time as passage migrants, but some retrap data of ringed birds suggest that they are present at least from the beginning of October to early April. Wintering birds are concentrated in southern and western parts of the mainland and some of the islands, where they are the commonest wintering warbler, usually outnumbering Sardinian Warblers. They are primarily found in olive groves and maquis with fruiting bushes (e.g. lentisc *Pistacia lentiscus* or wild olives), as well as orchards of any kind, parks and gardens. They are one of the most important olive-eating species. In the earlier part of autumn they also regularly feed on pomegranates *Punica granatum* and in gardens in midwinter on berries remaining on *Pyracantha* bushes. Wintering birds also frequently occur in reedbeds and especially use them for roosting, coming in from surrounding dry habitats. Blackcap has the largest number of ringing recoveries of all *Sylvia* warblers in Greece. The ringing places of the 50 recoveries available so far range west to Britain, north to Sweden and Norway, east to Rumania and south to Slovenia. Among these, Sweden comes top, with 16 recoveries, followed by the Czech Republic (8) and Austria (7).

Male Blackcap

Arctic Warbler *Phylloscopus borealis*

Accidental

There are three records of Arctic Warbler in Greece, with singles seen at Delphi in April 1965, Chasia Mts in April 1967 (*CFG*) and Dion, Pieria, on 3 October 1993 (Dennis 1993).

Yellow-browed Warbler *Phylloscopus inornatus*

Accidental

There are three records of Yellow-browed Warbler in Greece. Two were seen flycatching in a tree by the fortress of Rethymno on 16 April 1976 (*BoC*), four at Gerakas, Zakynthos, on 10 August 1991 (P.F. Whitehead) and one near Longos, on the island of Paxoi, on 19 May 1992 (Vittery 1994).

Dusky Warbler *Phylloscopus fuscatus*

Accidental

One seen and heard in reeds and ground vegetation at a river mouth by Gouna, near Kolympari, Crete, on 8 April 1978 (*BoC*) is the only record of the species.

Bonelli's Warbler *Phylloscopus bonelli*

Fairly widespread and locally fairly common summer visitor and passage migrant

Bonelli's Warbler has a restricted breeding range in Greece. So far, breeding has been recorded only north of 39°N, particularly in Macedonia and Thrace. In the 19th century, breeding was also recorded on the mountains of central Peloponnese, at Delphi and on Mt Arakynthos (Reiser 1905), but there are no recent breeding cases from these areas. The species has possibly bred on the island of Lesbos (Löhrl 1965) and it has recently been reported as breeding on Mt Parnassos and Mt Oiti (Hallmann 1985b, 1985c). Although it used to breed in the hilly area around L. Prespa, it appears to have disappeared from there in recent years (Catsadorakis 1989). Bonelli's

Warblers breed mainly in montane forest, from about 200 m (in Thrace) up to 1800 m but primarily between 800–1200 m (Bauer & Hodge 1970; Bauer & Böhr 1987; Schmid & Reichenecker 1988). Most often they occur in deciduous (beech *Fagus* or oak *Quercus*) but also mixed or pure coniferous (e.g. black pine *Pinus nigra*) forest. They are thinly distributed and the total breeding population is tentatively estimated at less than 10,000 pairs.

In spring, Bonelli's Warblers occur as scarce passage migrants throughout the country, from late March to late April and rarely to early May. Breeding birds are singing on their territories from mid April onwards. Autumn passage is in even smaller numbers, from mid August to early October. A very late record is of one near Gouves Lagoon on 20 October 1987 (*BoC*). Bonelli's Warblers breeding in Greece, belong to the eastern race *P. b. orientalis*. This form is distinct in the field on account of both its greyish and silky-white plumage and of its commonest call, a Crossbill-like 'chup'.

Wood Warbler *Phylloscopus sibilatrix*

Rare and local summer visitor, common passage migrant

Wood Warblers were first discovered nesting in Greece in the Rodopi Mts in 1971 (Bauer & Böhr 1987) and up to now this remains the only area where breeding of the species has been confirmed. Breeding pairs and singing males were found between 1070 and 1260 m in mixed forests dominated by beech *Fagus*, black pine *Pinus nigra*, silver birch *Betula pendula* and oak *Quercus*.

In spring, Wood Warblers are common on passage, from early April to mid May but in largest numbers in mid and late April. Although (as with most migrants) numbers vary considerably from year to year and from day to day, overall they are the commonest *Phylloscopus* warbler on spring passage. On the contrary, in autumn they are usually rather scarce and far outnumbered by Willow Warblers. Autumn passage takes place from late August to early October. The species has been seen in the Peloponnese already in late July (CP) and there are rare cases when birds have stayed up to mid November. There are two winter records of questionable validity, from Mt Varassova on 4 February 1897 (Reiser 1905) and from Athens on 3 February 1966 (*CFG*). The only two ringing recoveries from Europe are of a bird ringed in June in Latvia and found on the island of Paxoi in the autumn and of a late August bird from Switzerland found on the island of Kefallinia in April. There is an additional recovery of a bird ringed in Nigeria in August and found in Greece in May (*BWP*).

Chiffchaff *Phylloscopus collybita*

Fairly common but local summer visitor, common and widespread winter visitor

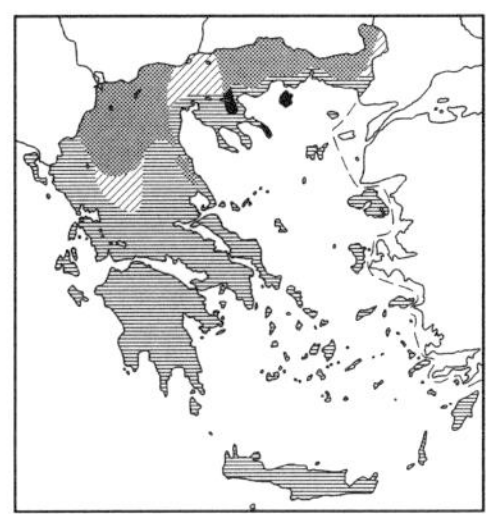

The breeding range of Chiffchaffs is even more restricted than that of Bonelli's Warblers. Their stronghold is the mountains of northern Greece, from the northern Pindos east to the higher hills of Thrace. They reach south to Mt Mavrovouni in SE Thessaly, parts of Chalkidiki and the island of Thasos (Peterson *et al.* 1981). Within this range they are thinly distributed, with a total population tentatively estimated in the order of 5,000–10,000 pairs. Their exact nesting habitat requirements are inadequately known but they occur in deciduous, coniferous or mixed woodland (e.g. oak *Quercus*, beech *Fagus*, pines *Pinus* and fir *Abies*), from about 300 m (e.g. in Thrace) up to the treeline, at *c.* 2000 m (e.g. on Mt Olympos and western Macedonia).

The species is much more widespread and numerous in winter, from mid October to about early April. Numbers decline already from mid March but some birds are occasionally observed in non-breeding areas up to early May. However, from late March onwards numbers often vary strongly from day to day, suggesting that most birds seen then are passing through, rather than being late-departing winter visitors. In winter, Chiffchaffs are fairly common in lowland areas, in cultivated land, lowland pine *Pinus* woodland, olive groves, wetlands and around human habitation. Surprisingly for a species at the northern limit of its winter range, they regularly occur as high as 1000 m in milder parts of the country and can often be seen in areas with long-lasting snow on the ground. Nevertheless, they either suffer heavy mortality or migrate at times of exceptionally cold and snowy weather. For example, in the winter of 1991 the species was practically exterminated from eastern Sterea Hellas after a few days of sub-zero temperatures and deep snow. Chiffchaffs breeding and many of those wintering in Greece belong to the nominate race *P. c. collybita*. According to the literature, *P. c. abietinus* occurs as a winter visitor and during migration (*CFG*). Birds with a characteristic call and greyer plumage, probably *abietinus*, occur especially in late March and April but also through the winter. There are two unconfirmed sightings of single *P. c. tristis* in the Evros and Nestos deltas in January and February 1965 respectively (*CFG*). Chiffchaffs ringed in Lithuania (1), Austria (1), the Czech Republic (2) and Slovenia (1) have been recovered in Greece.

Willow Warbler *Phylloscopus trochilus*

Very common and widespread passage migrant

Willow Warblers are the most numerous passage migrant in autumn, rivalled only by Swallows and Yellow Wagtails. They are then very common almost throughout the country, especially in habitats with at least some bushes or trees, including urban and suburban areas, but may be seen even in treeless low phrygana or saltmarshes, from sea level up to at least 2000 m. The first birds usually make their appearance between 15 and 25 August and passage peaks around 10 September, numbers declining thereafter. The last birds are normally seen in early October, rarely up to early November. The species is (by number) the most important prey of Eleonora's Falcons in the Aegean (Walter 1979; Ristow *et al.* 1986).

Spring passage occurs from late March to early May, with a peak in mid April. The volume of this passage represents only a small fraction of the large numbers passing through in autumn. There is a breeding record from near Thirea in the Evros district (date not given), where a pair with a nest containing four eggs was discovered in an area of oak *Quercus* and beech *Fagus* scrub (Hölzinger 1990c). Among the 26 ringed Willow Warblers recovered in Greece up to now, 18 had been ringed in Finland, one in Denmark, five in Sweden and two in Russia. The subspecific status of the passage migrants has not been clarified. Birds handled for ringing include some very long-winged individuals, with less green and yellow in their plumage than other short-winged ones, suggesting that a proportion of the migrants are of the north European race, *P. t. acredula*. Most of the ringing recoveries also come from within the breeding range of *acredula* but mainly from the western parts of the range of this form (e.g. Sweden and Finland), where it is not very clearly differentiated from the nominare race (*BWP*).

Goldcrest *Regulus regulus*

Fairly common but local resident, common and widespread winter visitor

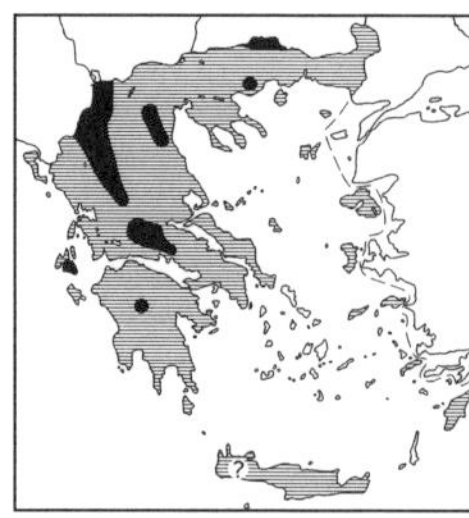

The least common of the two *Regulus* species in Greece, Goldcrests have a restricted and patchy distribution predominantly on central and northern mountains. Small breeding populations occur regularly in suitable habitat from Mt Parnassos northwards, but further south and on the islands the occurrence of the species is sporadic. It is fairly common as a breeding bird on Mt Ainos (Kefallinia) (A. Vittery) and probably breeds in Samaria Gorge on Crete (*BoC*). It has also been seen on Mt Mainalon in the Peloponnese in June 1966 (*CFG*). In most areas Goldcrests overlap with the range of Firecrests. However, unlike the latter they are more restricted to high altitude, mainly above 1000 m and up to the treeline. In this high-altitude zone they frequent conifers such as black *Pinus nigra*, white bark *P. heldreichii* and Scots pine *P. sylvaticus*, Greek *Abies cephalonica* and King Boris' fir *A. borisii–regis*, and (in the Rodopi Mts) Norway spruce *Picea abies*. On Crete they have also been recorded in cypresses *Cupressus sempervirens* at 1400 m on Mt Ida (*BoC*). The total breeding population probably does not exceed 10,000 pairs.

In winter, Goldcrests are fairly widespread at low altitude, from late September to early April but mainly from late October to mid March. Their abundance varies from year to year. They may be common in 'invasion' years but in most years they are rather scarce. Where coniferous trees are available, either planted or naturally growing (e.g. Aleppo pine *Pinus halepensis* woodland), they are preferred but the species is also frequently observed in olive groves, maquis and orchards or gardens with a mixture of trees or bushes. Wintering Goldcrests regularly occur in mixed flocks with Firecrests. There is one recovery of a bird ringed in Finland and found on the island of Myconos in late September.

Firecrest *Regulus ignicapillus*

Fairly common and widespread resident

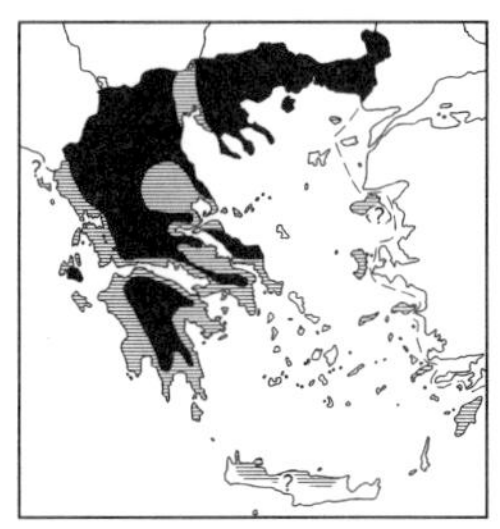

Firecrests have a widespread breeding distribution over much of the mainland, including the Peloponnese. In the Ionian they breed only on Mt Ainos (Kefallinia) and possibly Corfu whilst in the Aegean they probably breed locally on Lesbos and in central Crete (*BoC*). They typically breed in extensive areas of woodland and often at a relatively high altitude. Locally they breed down to sea level though they are more regular from about 400 m up to the treeline. They may sometimes be found in deciduous woodland (e.g. beech *Fagus* or oak *Quercus*) but they show a marked preference for conifers of any kind. On southern mountains they are fairly common in fir *Abies* forest and in the north in black pines *Pinus nigra*. However, they are locally not uncommon in Aleppo pine *P. halepensis* woodland at lower altitudes and in the northern suburbs of Athens they freely occur in cedars *Cedrus* or other exotic conifers. The species is much more numerous than Goldcrest, with a total population tentatively estimated at 20,000–100,000 pairs.

In winter, Firecrests make short-distance or altitudinal movements, and although some stay at altitudes of up to about 1000 m, they become much more widespread at low altitudes. They are most regularly seen in pines but locally they also occur in olive groves, tall maquis, hills with scattered junipers *Juniperus* or other evergreens. Their movements through Greece are very poorly understood and it is not known to what extent birds from further north move into the country for winter. A very small number of birds have been recorded as prey of Eleonora's Falcons off NE Crete in early autumn (Ristow *et al.* 1986), suggesting very little migration across the Aegean Sea before the middle of October (the end of the sampling period).

Brown Flycatcher *Muscicapa daurica*

Accidental

A first-year bird seen in the Nestos Delta on 4 September 1993 (A.G. Gosler, C.M. Jackson-Houlston & D. Mervyn-Jones) is the only confirmed record of Brown Flycatcher. There are two more undocumented records of singles at Porto Lagos on 22 April 1985 (J. Wittbrodt & D. Förnzlar) and at Kouvaras in Attica in September 1993 (A. Kyrkos).

Spotted Flycatcher *Muscicapa striata*

Widespread and locally common summer visitor, very common passage migrant

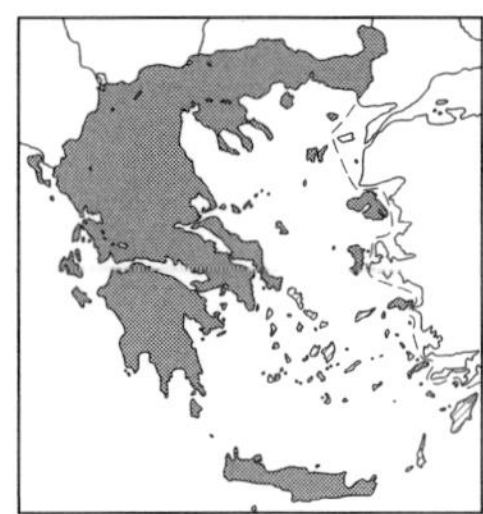

Spotted Flycatchers are the commonest of all flycatchers in Greece, with a widespread breeding range over much of the mainland and on some of the larger and more well vegetated islands in both the Aegean and the Ionian Seas. They occur in open woodland, both deciduous and coniferous, particularly areas with scattered large trees, clearings within dense forest, parks and large gardens, orchards and olive groves. They are generally commoner in parts of the country with a cooler and moister summer, i.e. in the north and at moderate or high elevations in the south. At low altitude in the south and on the islands they are often found along watercourses with tall trees. Their total breeding population is in the order of 20,000–50,000 pairs.

Spotted Flycatchers are very common on autumn passage, from about late August to mid October. Small numbers are regular until the end of October and occasionally birds may be seen up to mid November. On average, peak numbers occur in late September and large 'falls' may occur then or in October, when the weather is more variable than in the earlier part of the migration period. More than 2,000 birds were estimated on just a few plane trees *Platanus orientalis* near Aigion, NW Peloponnese, on 10 October 1987 (CP). Spotted Flycatcher have also been found to be one of the commonest prey of Eleonora's Falcons (Walter 1979, Ristow *et al.* 1986). In contrast to *Ficedula* flycatchers, they are less numerous in spring than in autumn. In N Africa the reverse is the case (*BWP*), with more birds stopping there in the spring, and thus it seems that in the spring many birds overfly Greek territory or stop only very briefly, after a more lengthy stay in N Africa. Nevertheless, during periods of unsettled weather very large numbers can be seen also in spring, e.g. for several days in mid May 1992 at least 10,000 Spotted Flycatchers were present on the island of Paxoi (Vittery 1994). The first spring arrivals may sometimes be noted as early as or even before 10 April but the main body of migrants passes through from late April to early May, with some still on the move up to late May. The 40 ringing recoveries of Spotted Flycatchers found in Greece up to now include 23 of birds that had been ringed in Finland, seven in Sweden, four in Poland and singles in Britain, Denmark, Latvia and Lithuania. The remaining two were ringed in the spring on Capri (Italy); one of them was recovered in the Aegean a few months later, in autumn of the same year, and the other was recovered on Kefallinia in spring of the following year. The subspecific status of Spotted Flycatchers breeding in Greece is still not fully clarified. They seem to be intermediate between *M. s. striata* and *M. s. neumanni* (Watson 1964; *BWP*). Both races probably occur on passage.

Red-breasted Flycatcher *Ficedula parva*

Rare and local summer visitor, scarce passage migrant

The first indication of Red-breasted Flycatchers breeding in Greece was in 1985, in the dense primeval forests of the Central Rodopi Mts (Bauer & Böhr 1987). The first nest was found in this area on 6 May 1988, among beech *Fagus sylvatica* and Norway spruce *Picea abies* at 1760 m (Hölzinger 1993b). In 1992 territorial males were seen also in beech forest on Mt Smolikas, at 1840 m, and on Mt Grammos, at 1670 m (Hölzinger 1993b). The species is more numerous as a passage migrant, from (early?) mid April to mid May and from mid August to mid October. There is a late record from Crete on 17 November 1980 (*BoC*). On average, larger numbers occur in autumn than in spring, but in both seasons 'waves' of migrants are obvious and the total volume of passage also varies from year to year.

Semi-collared Flycatcher *Ficedula semitorquata*

Fairly common but local summer visitor, widespread passage migrant

A poorly known species, Semi-collared Flycatchers are rather thinly and patchily distributed during the breeding season. They are mainly found in the north of the country, from Ipeiros and Thessaly northwards. Breeding in Sterea Hellas has not yet been confirmed, though it is likely and some suitable habitat exists there. There is no indication that the species breeds or has ever bred in the Peloponnese (CP). In fact, existing literature and unpublished sources give only a handful of definite nesting localities for the whole country, suggesting a very small breeding population (Curio 1959; *CFG*; Benussi & Brichetti 1983). The total breeding population probably numbers between 1,000–5,000 pairs and the species has been reported as locally declining (Tucker & Heath 1994). Semi-collared Flycatchers have been found nesting in mature beech *Fagus* and mixed beech and pine *Pinus* forest, as well as in old riparian stands of plane *Platanus orientalis* at lower altitude. Nesting within villages has also been reported (Curio 1959; Benussi & Brichetti 1983; Tucker & Heath 1994; Y. Roussopoulos). Curio (1959) searched large areas of likely habitat around Thessaloniki and in Chalkidiki and found breeding Semi-collared Flycatchers only on high ground, in mature beech forest with tall, bare trunks, closed canopy, little undergrowth and a reasonable population of woodpeckers to provide nest-holes. Overall, breeding has been recorded from almost sea level to about 1400 m.

The species is widespread though not common on passage. As is the case with all *Ficedula* flycatchers, it is much more numerous in spring than in autumn and its abundance fluctuates strongly from year to year. Furthermore, in most cases only adult males in the spring can be identified easily and females or birds of all ages in autumn plumage may often be overlooked. On spring passage through Crete, Semi-collared Flycatchers are generally scarce but 'occasionally fairly common' (*BoC*). Contrary to the situation in all other areas, in the NW Peloponnese the species is reported as intermediate in abundance between Collared and Pied Flycatchers (CP). In spring, passage takes place from late March to early May, with a peak in mid April, and in autumn from late August to late September.

Semi-collared Flycatcher

Collared Flycatcher *Ficedula albicollis*

Common and widespread passage migrant

Collared Flycatchers migrate through Greece in fluctuating numbers from year to year. In spring they range from scarce to common. Passage is from late March to mid May, with a peak usually in mid April. At this time of the year they are more numerous than Pied Flycatchers on average. There are indications that larger numbers are recorded in eastern parts of the country, including many of the Aegean islands, than in the west and the Ionian. Large 'falls' may occur

in appropriate weather conditions, when very high densities may be recorded over broad areas, probably involving thousands of birds. Migrating Collared Flycatchers may be found in any kind of habitat with some trees, and on small treeless islands may be seen even perching on low shrubs within phrygana. Often they may be seen in larger numbers along streams lined with tall trees, where they seem to be attracted by emerging mayflies (Ephemeroptera). In autumn they are very scarce, from late August to late September, with a peak in early September. There is one ringing recovery of a bird ringed as a chick in Sweden and found near Karditsa in September of the same year.

Pied Flycatcher *Ficedula hypoleuca*

Common and widespread passage migrant

As with Collared Flycatchers, Pied Flycatchers occur as passage migrants, mainly in spring, but unlike the former they are not so rare (though still uncommon and in varying numbers) in autumn. Spring passage takes place between late March and early May, with a peak in mid April, averaging a few days later than Collared Flycatchers. Autumn passage is from late August to early October, with a peak in early September. Small numbers of Pied Flycatchers were recorded among prey remains of Eleonora's Falcons at a colony off NE Crete in autumn (Ristow *et al.* 1986). In the same study, the relative abundance of Pied to Collared Flycatchers was 16:5. The majority of adult male Pied Flycatchers on passage through Greece in the spring are a dark chocolate brown on the upperparts and are thus quite different from the mostly black-and-white birds of western Europe. There are five recoveries of foreign-ringed Pied Flycatchers found in Greece: two had been ringed in Finland, two in Germany and one in Switzerland.

Bearded Tit *Panurus biarmicus*

Fairly common but local resident

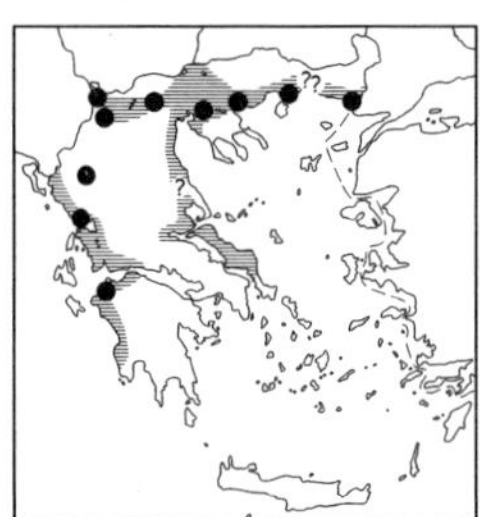

Bearded Tits have a restricted breeding range, mainly in the major wetlands of Macedonia and Thrace, from L. Mikri Prespa eastward to the Evros Delta. Nesting has also been recorded in the Louros Delta and at the Kalogria Lagoon in the Peloponnese (CP). Possibly the species also nests, at least occasionally, in other parts of the country too, e.g. in the Spercheios Delta or at L. Ioannina. As elsewhere in the Western Palearctic, Bearded Tits are confined to extensive *Phragmites* reedbeds or similar dense marsh vegetation (e.g. reedmace *Typha*) with small patches of open water. Thus they are absent from reedbeds that dry up during the summer. They occur both in coastal brackish wetlands and at inland freshwater sites. The highest breeding locality of the species is L. Mikri Prespa at 853 m. The total Greek population of Bearded Tit is tentatively estimated at a maximum of 5,000 pairs.

Local breeders probably undertake short dispersive movements to adjacent wetlands outside the breeding season. In addition, birds of unknown provenance appear in non-breeding wetlands (e.g. of southeast mainland) in winter in such numbers that indicate immigration from abroad. The number of winter visitors and the extent of the wintering range of the species vary strongly from year to year. The Greek population of Bearded Tits belongs to the nominate race, *P. b. biarmicus,* but with characters tending towards the east–central European and Asian *P. b. russicus* (*BWP*). The latter may occur in winter (*CFG*).

Bearded Tit

Long-tailed Tit *Aegithalos caudatus*

Fairly common and widespread resident

Throughout their breeding range in Greece, Long-tailed Tits are thinly distributed and they are generally not very common. They are more numerous and regular in suitable habitat in northern Greece, becoming less common and more localised in the south. Among the islands, breeding has been confirmed only on Lesbos, where they are locally common, and on Samos. There is a winter record from Corfu (19th century) (Drummond-Hay 1843a) but no records from any other islands. Long-tailed Tits are most often seen in coniferous, deciduous and mixed forest with plenty of bushy undergrowth and deciduous or mixed deciduous/evergreen scrub, thickets or maquis. Although occurring from sea level up to about 2000 m, they are commonest in hilly areas and at moderate altitudes, from 200 to 1000 m. The total Greek population is estimated at 20,000–50,000 pairs and probably nearer the lower end of this range. Long-tailed Tits breeding in Greece belong to two races: *A. c. macedonicus* on the mainland and *A. c. tephronotus* (grey-backed) on Lesbos and Samos (*CFG*; *BWP*). *A. c. europaeus* has been identified in the field in winter whilst *A. c. caudatus* (white-headed) may also occur exceptionally as a winter visitor (*CFG*). There is a remarkable ringing recovery of a Long-tailed Tit ringed on 2 March 1936 (winter visitor?) in Belgium and found on the island of Chios on 20 November 1937.

Marsh Tit *Parus palustris*

Fairly widespread and locally common resident

Marsh Tits are primarily birds of the deciduous and transitional Mediterranean vegetation zones. They are thus restricted to parts of the central and northern mainland, reaching as far south as Mt Parnassos. The only island on which they occur is Thasos. They seem to generally prefer oak *Quercus* and beech *Fagus* woodland, the former often richly mixed with other deciduous trees, the latter with high-altitude conifers. However, locally they also occur in riverside deciduous trees, tall maquis and even pure conifers, such as on Mt Parnassos where they are a scarce resident of fir *Abies* forest. Although mainly found at medium and, very locally, low altitude, small numbers have been recorded up to the treeline, e.g. up to 1850 m on Mt Orvilos (Bauer & Böhr 1987) and 2200 m on Mt Olympos (Malakou 1985). In the Rodopi Mts Marsh Tits have been recorded in very small numbers, mainly between 1100 and 1500 m, i.e. avoiding the highest altitudes favoured by Willow Tits (Bauer & Böhr 1987). The total Greek population probably amounts to 5,000–20,000 pairs. Marsh Tits appear to be chiefly sedentary and are very rarely recorded away from breeding areas.

Sombre Tit *Parus lugubris*

Widespread but scarce resident

A species near endemic to the E Mediterranean, Sombre Tits have a fairly widespread distribution over much of the mainland, including the Peloponnese, and on a few of the islands. They are absent from the Ionian islands, except Corfu, where a few recent records exist (K.S. Bovey, A.W. Martin & M. Mitchell), suggesting a very small breeding population. In the Aegean they breed on Lesbos, Samos (F. Johansson, D. Papandropoulos, F. Katsigiannis) and Kythira (*CFG*). Their status on Crete is unclear but perhaps the species is a very rare and local resident (*BoC*). Throughout their range Sombre Tits are generally thinly distributed and tend to be missing from very large areas of apparently suitable habitat. They occupy a range of diverse habitats in a way that makes it difficult to evaluate their precise requirements. They occur from sea level up to almost 2000 m and generally prefer more open and dry habitats than the other *Parus* species, avoiding dense woodland. Typical habitats include dry hillsides with scattered Kermes oak *Quercus coccifera* or wild olives, open olive groves, open deciduous oak *Quercus* woodland, terraced cereal fields with scattered small trees (e.g. almond pear *Pyrus amygdaliformis*, carob *Ceratonia siliqua* or Valonia oak *Quercus macrolepis*), non-intensive or neglected orchards (e.g. almond *Prunus dulcis*), subalpine pastures with scattered low trees or tall bushes and Aleppo pine *Pinus halepensis* woodland interspersed with clearings or small fields. Locally, Sombre Tits may be fairly common. Their entire breeding population is estimated at a minimum of 10,000 pairs and may be as high as 30,000 pairs.

As a rule, they are strictly sedentary, making only very short dispersive and altitudinal movements. Sombre Tits of the mainland were formerly treated as *P. l. lugens* (Watson 1964; *CFG*) but the species varies clinally in size, darkness of cap and bib, and paleness of underparts within its European range, with *lugens* representing the smallest birds with the least black cap and bib (*BWP*). Thus race *P. l. lugens* is not considered as valid any more and all mainland birds are now assigned to *P. l. lugubris* (*BWP*). Birds of the island of Lesbos (and presumably also Samos) belong to the Asia Minor form, *P. l. anatoliae*, which has a very dark cap and bib, relatively white underparts, dark mantle and small body (*CFG*; *BWP*).

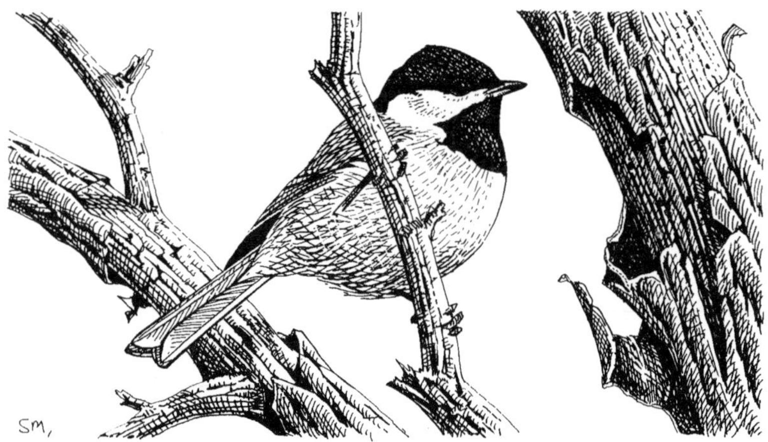

Sombre Tit

Willow Tit *Parus montanus*

Rare and local resident

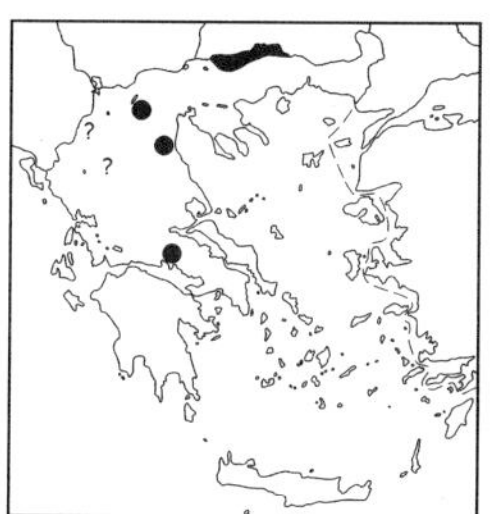

A very poorly known species, Willow Tit is the rarest of all Greek species of *Parus*. Breeding was first confirmed in 1973, in the Rodopi Mts (Bauer & Böhr 1987). Since then more records have come mainly from mountains in northern parts of the country west to Mt Vermion. Isolated populations apparently exist on Mt Olympos (Malakou 1985) and Mt Parnassos (*CFG*). In the Rodopi Mts Willow Tits were reported as not rare from 1270 m upwards and mainly above 1500 m, up to the treeline at 1920 m. They appeared clearly associated with the Norway spruce *Picea abies* (Bauer & Böhr 1987). On Mt Olympos, Willow Tits have been recorded at 800–1800 m, in mixed deciduous–coniferous forests, as well in pure coniferous and pure deciduous forests (mainly beech *Fagus sylvatica*). The total Greek population probably numbers between 200 and 1,000 pairs and is largely sedentary. Willow Tits breeding in Greece were formerly classified as race *P. m. transsylvanicus* (*CFG*) but this form is now treated as part of the nominate *P. m. montanus* (*BWP*).

Crested Tit *Parus cristatus*

Scarce and local resident

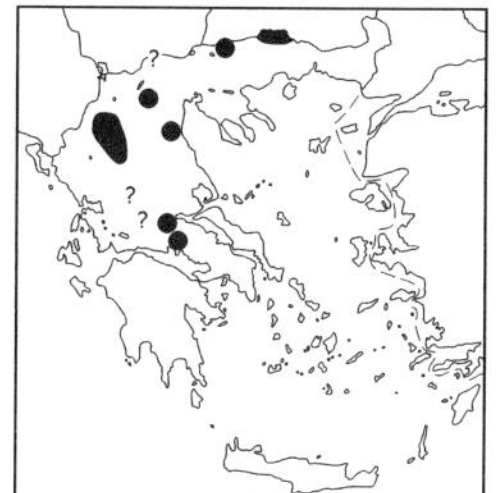

Crested Tits have a restricted and discontinuous range, with nesting so far confirmed in only a few mountainous regions of Macedonia, Ipeiros and Thessaly, i.e. the northern Pindos range, Mt Vermion, Mt Olympos and the Rodopi range. Isolated populations breed on Mt Parnassos and Mt Oiti (T. Nilsson), though on grounds of habitat availability further populations may exist in the still relatively little known parts of the central and southern Pindos. Throughout their breeding range Crested Tits are confined to high-altitude coniferous forest, e.g. of Norway spruce *Picea abies* in the Rodopi Mts, Greek fir *Abies cephalonica* and black pines *Pinus nigra* on Mt Parnassos and black pines *Pinus nigra* on Mt Olympos (Makatsch 1950; Bauer & Böhr 1987). They normally occur from about 1000 m upwards to the treeline, as high as 2300 m on Mt Olympos (V. Hatzirvassanis). The total Greek population is certainly small and probably in the order of 2,000–5,000 pairs. There is no information on the movements of the species in Greece but it is presumed to be sedentary as throughout its European range (*BWP*). The Crested Tit population of the southern Balkan peninsula is currently (*BWP*) separated as *P. c. bureschi*, a form which is greyer on the upperparts and paler on the underparts than western European races but not very different from the nominate *P. c. cristatus* of eastern and northern Europe.

Coal Tit *Parus ater*

Common and widespread resident

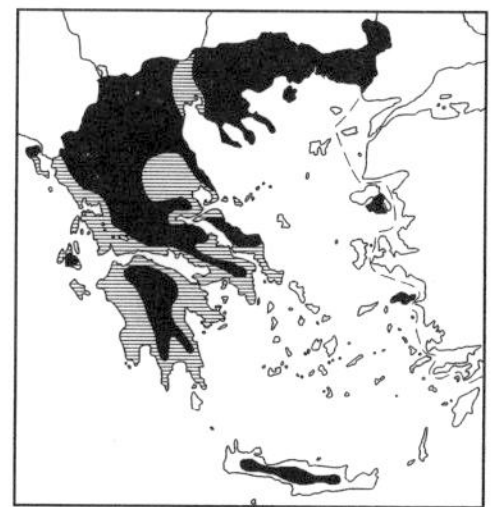

Coal Tits have a widespread distribution over much of the mainland and the Peloponnese but they occur on only a few of the islands: in the Ionian Sea they are common on Mt Ainos in Kefallinia (A. Vittery) and on Corfu whereas in the Aegean they are known to breed locally only on Lesbos and Samos. Their status on Crete is still uncertain (*BoC*) but they possibly breed locally (C. Vagliano). Throughout the mainland, Coal Tits reach their highest densities in montane coniferous forests, from about 500 m up to the treeline. However, they locally occur down to sea level, e.g. in Aleppo *Pinus halepensis* or Calabrian pine *P. brutia*. In northern Greece they also occur in very small numbers in oak *Quercus* and beech *Fagus* forest (Watson 1964). The total Greek population probably lies between 100,000 and 500,000 pairs. Although Coal Tits are largely sedentary, they probably make altitudinal movements. In winter the species is fairly common in lowland conifers and it is not unlikely that some winter visitors also arrive from the north.

Blue Tit *Parus caeruleus*

Very common and widespread resident

Blue Tits are widespread throughout the largest part of the mainland and most islands of both the Aegean and the Ionian Seas. As a breeding species they are missing from the hot and dry low-lying areas of the southern mainland as well as from many Aegean islands due to lack of suitable habitat. As elsewhere in Europe, they reach their highest densities in mature deciduous oak *Quercus* woodland, whether it is *Q. pubescens*-dominated at low altitude, *Q. frainetto*-dominated at medium altitude or other mixed types. They are less numerous but still very common in other deciduous and mixed deciduous/coniferous woodlands, including pure beech *Fagus* and streamside planes *Platanus*, willows *Salix*, alders *Alnus* and white poplar *Populus alba*. They are also common in the small patches of broadleaved evergreen woodland (characterised by the presence of the holm oak *Quercus ilex*) existing especially in western Greece. Sometimes they occur in montane coniferous forest (e.g. black pine *Pinus nigra* or Greek fir *Abies cephalonica*) but usually not far from some broadleaved trees. In some areas (e.g. western Greece and eastern Aegean islands) they are common in olive groves, a habitat from which they are entirely absent in other parts of the country. Their upper altitudinal limit may locally extend to nearly 2000 m but more often it coincides with the upper limit of deciduous trees, at about 1200–1500 m. The total Greek population of Blue Tits is difficult to estimate because although absent from some areas, in many habitats they are the commonest bird species. It is likely to be in the order of 1,000,000–5,000,000 pairs and the species probably vies with Chaffinch for the title of the most numerous breeding bird in Greece.

Blue Tits are apparently partly sedentary. Throughout the country they become common in the lowlands in winter and it seems likely that some immigration occurs from the north, though probably the majority of birds in the lowlands are altitudinal migrants since densities decline in most of the higher breeding areas. Winter visitors to the lowlands arrive from early to late October. On rare occasions dispersing juveniles appear in these areas already from mid July. Departures from the lowlands start around mid February, with few birds observed after mid March. Blue Tits breeding in Greece are regarded as belonging to two races: *P. c. caeruleus* in northern and central Greece and *P. c. calamensis* in the Peloponnese, Cyclades, Crete and Rhodes (*BWP*). The latter is slightly smaller and paler than the nominate form but even birds in northern Greece are paler than *P. c. caeruleus* from Scandinavia, though similar in size.

Great Tit *Parus major*

Common and widespread resident

The most widespread tit species in Greece, Great Tits are common throughout the country, on both the mainland and the islands. They are ubiquitous and have adapted to a wider range of habitats than any other tit species. They occur almost wherever trees are present, from sea level up to the treeline, and are equally at home in olive groves at sea level and in cool coniferous forest on high mountains. In many lowland habitats (e.g. olive groves, Aleppo pine *Pinus halepensis* woodland, fruit orchards and gardens) they are usually the only species of tit present. However, they never reach the high densities attained by Blue or Coal Tits in appropriate habitats and are missing from several Aegean islands, many of which (e.g. Rhodes) apparently offer perfectly suitable habitat. The total breeding population is probably in the order of 500,000–2,000,000 breeding pairs. At low altitude the breeding season of Great Tits is quite early, with egg-laying usually starting in late March. Fledglings have been observed as early as late April but more often appear in early May. Second broods appear to be uncommon, with fledglings observed in the second half of June and early July. Singing males may be heard on sunny days from mid January onwards.

Great Tits breeding in Greece are largely sedentary, with some altitudinal movements from the highest elevations to lower ground in winter. A proportion of the winter population of central and southern Greece is of brightly-coloured and comparatively large birds, suggesting immigration either from northern parts of the country or from further north. In the past (Watson 1964; *CFG*), Great Tits breeding in Macedonia, Thrace, Thessaly, Ipeiros and the Ionian islands were assigned to *P. m. major* and those of southern Greece, Peloponnese and the Aegean islands (including Crete) to *P. m. aphrodite*, distinct on account of its pale buff-ish-yellow underparts and smaller body. *BWP* now further separates the even smaller birds of the Cretan population as *P. m. niethammeri*.

Krüper's Nuthatch *Sitta krueperi*

Rare and local resident

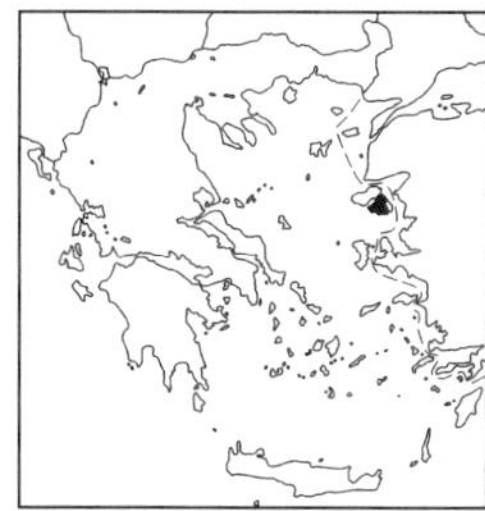

Krüper's Nuthatches were first discovered in Greece in the late 1950s (Kumerloeve 1961). They occur only on the island of Lesbos, where they are confined to the area of Mt Olympos. The species is found almost exclusively in or near Calabrian pines *Pinus brutia* and is thought to feed predominantly on the seeds of this tree (Löhrl 1988). During the breeding season it occupies high ground, usually above 400 m. Nest sites may be on pines or sweet chestnut *Castanea sativa* and old nest-holes of Middle-spotted Woodpeckers are sometimes used. Krüper's Nuthatches are frequently seen drinking and bathing, a habit which may related to their dry-seed diet, as happens with many finches. Therefore, one reason for their scarcity may be that throughout the summer season they may require a permanent supply of drinking water, which is generally scarce in a Mediterranean habitat—unlike finches they do not normally make long-distance flights so would require drinking water close at hand. On Lesbos, eggs have been found in mid April and young fledge from early May onwards (Löhrl 1988). The total breeding population of Lesbos is estimated at 50–100 pairs. However, the species is quite unobtrusive even during the breeding season and it is possible that the actual figure may be higher.

It appears the Krüper's Nuthatches are quite strictly sedentary and outside the breeding sea-

Krüper's Nuthatch

son do not wander very far. In late summer and the winter half of the year they are frequently observed in pines at sea level but they never leave their Calabrian pine habitat and even within Lesbos there are still no confirmed records away from the extensive woodlands of the southeast part of the island. There is an extraordinary record of one near Thessaloniki in October 1955 (*CFG*).

Nuthatch *Sitta europaea*

Fairly widespread and locally common resident

Nuthatches are quite widely distributed over the mainland, including the Peloponnese, but are absent from all islands, even those close to the mainland, with the exception of Lesbos. They are nowhere very numerous and local populations become increasingly sporadic and isolated towards the south. From Ipeiros and Thessaly southwards they are missing from the greater part of lowland areas. Reasonable densities are observed only in deciduous woodland, whether in the extensive tracts of oak *Quercus* or beech *Fagus* in northern parts of the mainland or in smaller patches of these or other deciduous species anywhere in the country (e.g. in the small relict Forest of Fraxos with *Fraxinus angustifolia* and elm *Ulmus* in the Acheloos Delta). Rarely (e.g. on Mt Parnassos) small numbers may occur in pure conifers, such as black pine *Pinus nigra* and Greek fir *Abies cephalonica* whereas in parts of western Greece Nuthatches are an uncommon bird of dry hillsides at low altitude with scattered large Valonia *Quercus macrolepis* or white oaks *Q. pubescens*. This is also their habitat on Lesbos, where it is interesting to note that they are peculiarly absent from the small area of sweet chestnuts *Castanea sativa* at higher altitude. The total Greek population of the species is estimated at 10,000–50,000 pairs and is sedentary, remaining within or near breeding areas all year round. Nuthatches breeding on the mainland belong to *S. e. caesia* (*CFG*; *BWP*). Those of Lesbos presumably belong to race *S. e. levantina*, the western Asia Minor race.

Rock Nuthatch *Sitta neumayer*

Fairly widespread and locally common resident

On the mainland, Rock Nuthatches and Nuthatches largely have a complementary distribution, Rock Nuthatches being common in southern and central parts and much more scarce or even absent from large parts of Macedonia and Thrace. The status of Rock Nuthatches on the islands is still not well known. In the Aegean they occur only on Lesbos despite much suitable habitat on many other islands and in the Ionian they occur on Corfu, Lefkada and Zakynthos. There are only two to three records from Crete, in April and October (*BoC*), and none from the Cyclades (Magioris 1994). Rock Nuthatches occur in all types of rocky habitats, particularly on limestone. Where they are numerous, a small rock outcrop may suffice as a nest-site and the birds may feed on surrounding boulder-strewn hillsides. At times they also visit or even breed in ruins or on old stone buildings or other human structures. Although typical birds of low hills and generally absent above about 800 m, locally they may reach up to 1600 m (e.g. in the Peloponnese). In suitable habitat they are common, and although often difficult to see due to the nature of their habitat, they are easy to detect by their loud ringing calls, used freely throughout the year. The total Greek population probably is in the order of 5,000–20,000 pairs. As a rule the species is sedentary but birds nesting on high ground may make short altitudinal movements in winter. Rock Nuthatches breeding on the mainland belong to the nominate race, *S. n. neumayer*, but those of the island of Lesbos presumably belong to the slightly smaller and paler *S. n. zarudnyi* of western Asia Minor (*BWP*).

Wallcreeper *Tichodroma muraria*

Scarce and local resident

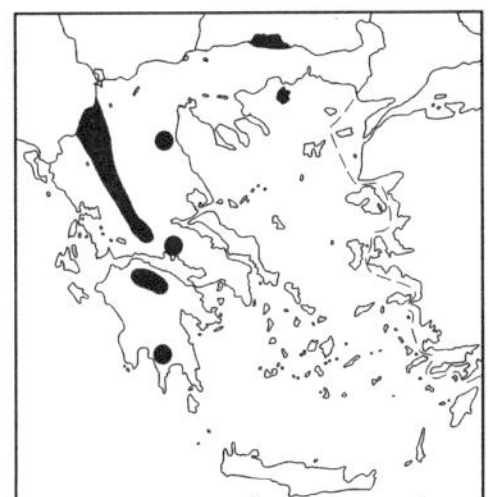

Owing to their specialised habitat, Wallcreepers occur sporadically as a breeding species in parts of mainland Greece. Their main breeding range spans the alpine zones of the Pindos range, south to Mt Parnassos, with isolated populations farther east and south, on Mt Olympos, eastern Macedonian mountains and, surprisingly, Mt Ypsarion on the island of Thasos (Hölzinger 1989a). Recently they have also been discovered breeding on three mountains of the Peloponnese, south to Mt Taygetos, where their breeding habitat lacks running or falling waters, a feature characteristic of the habitat of the species in other parts of Europe (Hölzinger 1989a). Mt Taygetos is the southernmost distribution limit of the species in the Western Palearctic. In the Peloponnese and in Sterea Hellas (Mt Parnassos) Wallcreepers frequent the upper alpine zone near the summits, between 1900 and 2400 m, whereas further north they also occur at lower altitude, down to about 500 m. The total Greek population is tentatively estimated at 100–300 pairs.

A number of records of Wallcreeper from outside the breeding season (October–March) suggest some altitudinal and short-distance movements in winter. These include observations at Delphi, the Acropolis of Athens, Mt Parnitha, Argos, Nafplion, Monemvasia, Mystras, Pylos, Mt Varassova (near Messolonghi) and the islands of Corfu and Zakynthos in the Ionian and of Kythira and Chios in the Aegean (Reiser 1905; Lamberton & Rotroff 1985; Spinthakis *et al.* 1993; D. Papandropoulos, Y. Roussopoulos, I. Schogolev).

Wallcreeper

Treecreeper *Certhia familiaris*

Scarce and local resident

Treecreepers have a much more restricted and localised range than Short-toed Treecreepers. So far, they have been found breeding only in the Pindos range and on some of the mountains of the northern mainland, east to the Rodopi Mts. The southernmost locality of the species and the only one in Sterea Hellas is Mt Parnassos (*CFG*) but there are no recent records from this area and confirmation of their presence there is needed. Short-toed Treecreepers do occur on Mt Parnassos and are fairly common up to the treeline so the possibility of misidentification cannot be ruled out. An outlying population is reported from Mt Ainos on Kefallinia (A. Vittery). The species has also been recorded on Corfu in June 1953 (Flach 1959) but the record is not documented and if it is valid, it seems more likely to refer to a wandering individual rather than a permanent population there. Treecreepers generally occur at high altitudes, not normally below 800–1000 m and usually from 1200 m up to the treeline. They have been recorded in a variety of mainly dense mature forests, particularly conifers (e.g. fir *Abies* or pines *Pinus*) but also pure beech *Fagus* and, in the Rodopi Mts, Norway spruce *Picea abies*. The size of the Greek population is very difficult to assess but probably lies between 1,000 and 10,000 pairs and appears to be sedentary. In view of the possibility of confusion with Short-toed Treecreeper, records of Treecreepers from the lowlands should be supported by sufficient details in order to be acceptable.

Short-toed Treecreeper *Certhia brachydactyla*

Fairly common and widespread resident

By far the commonest of the two species of *Certhia* in Greece. Short-toed Treecreepers breed practically over the whole mainland and on most of the larger islands in both the Aegean and the Ionian Seas, including Corfu, Kefallinia, Paxoi (A. Vittery), Crete, Lesbos, Thasos, Ikaria and Samos. They are thinly distributed, never attaining high densities, but breed widely in all types of woodland, olive groves, orchards, plantations and parks and gardens, provided there are some old trees with suitable cracks and crevices to provide nest sites. Their nearly ubiquitous occurrence almost parallels that of Great Tits and Chaffinches. Altitudinally, they may be found from sea level up to the treeline and thus entirely overlap the range of Treecreepers. The total Greek population probably numbers 30,000–100,000 pairs. Outside the breeding season Short-toed Treecreepers spread to adjacent habitats with trees but which are unsuitable for nesting (e.g. young orchards). The first juveniles disperse from breeding sites already from mid June but the species becomes even more widespread from early September up to about late March, perhaps due to some altitudinal movements. Short-toed Treecreepers breeding on the mainland, Crete and the Ionian islands belong to nominate race *C. b. brachydactyla,* but those of the eastern Aegean islands may be attributable to the Asia Minor race, *C. b. harterti.*

Penduline Tit *Remiz pendulinus*

Fairly widespread and locally common resident

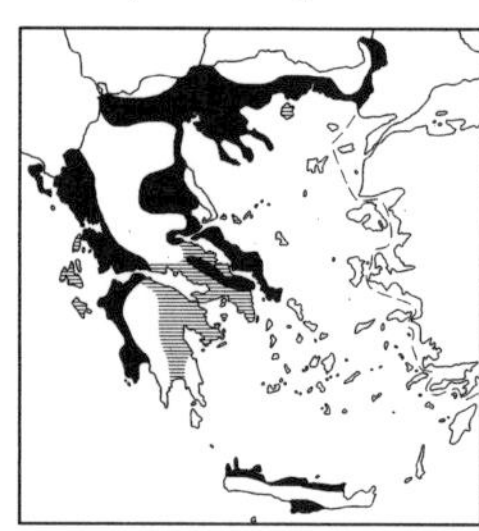

Breeding Penduline Tits occur over a large part of the mainland but due to their specialised habitat requirements within this area populations are discontinuous and often relatively isolated. In suitable habitat they breed throughout the central and northern parts of the mainland, south to the SW Peloponnese. The species is a recent colonist on Crete. The first nests were discovered there in 1984 and 1986 and now it is a regular though scarce breeding species (*BoC*). Penduline Tits are absent from all remaining islands, except for Corfu, where they have been found breeding in the past (Böhr 1962) and probably still do so. Penduline Tits nest in a variety of wetland habitats, from sea level up to 850 m, at L. Mikri Prespa. These include patches of tamarisks *Tamarix* in river deltas, patches of marshy woodland (with e.g. elm *Ulmus,* poplars *Populus* or narrow-leaved ash *Fraxinus angustifolia*), riverside woodland, willow *Salix* scrub on lake shores or along canals and ditches and beds of reed *Phragmites* or reedmace *Typha*. On rare occasions they also breed in clumps of trees outside wetlands. They normally build their nests over water, suspending them from overhanging branches of tall bushes or trees. Although elsewhere in their range they have been found suspending nests from reed stems (*BWP*), they do not seem to do so regularly in Greece. Thus, breeding birds are excluded from reedbeds or other marshy vegetation with no trees. The total Greek population of the species is tentatively estimated at 5,000–30,000 pairs.

In winter, Penduline Tits are usually seen in small loose parties of up to 5–10, particularly favouring extensive reedbeds. They appear more numerous and widespread than in summer and thus some immigration may take place from the north. In late winter and early spring (early February to late March) they regularly visit almond *Prunus dulcis* groves in blossom to feed on nectar and possibly pollen or insects as well. In pure reedbeds birds disappear around late March or early April at the latest and reappear as family parties with juveniles in early July. Also in early July or a little later wandering individuals or small parties may be seen on the move through atypical habitats (e.g. olive groves), presumably moving from breeding sites (which may have dried up by this time of the year) in search of suitable areas. There is only one ringing recovery of Penduline Tit in Greece, of a bird ringed in Bulgaria on 6 October 1977 and found at L. Koronia eight days later.

Golden Oriole *Oriolus oriolus*

Fairly common and widespread summer visitor and passage migrant

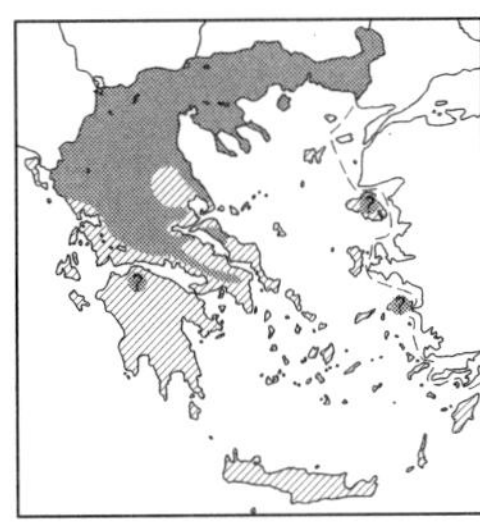

Golden Orioles are largely confined to northern and central parts of the mainland as a breeding species. Isolated pairs or small populations exist in pockets of suitable habitat in Ipeiros, Thessaly and Sterea Hellas but higher densities distributed in a more uniform manner may be seen only in the uplands of western Macedonia and parts of eastern Macedonia and Thrace. There are still no definite breeding records from the Peloponnese, though, possibly, odd pairs may nest in the north (CP). Similarly, there is no definite proof of breeding on any of the islands, except Thasos (D. Atter) and perhaps occasional odd pairs on Lesbos and Samos. A large proportion of alleged breeding records in southern parts of the mainland and the islands almost certainly refer to late migrants.

Golden Orioles occur at low and moderate altitudes, up to 1000–1200 m. They breed in a variety of woodland or open park-like habitats with scattered trees. They have a preference for mature and fairly open deciduous woodland, usually dominated by oaks *Quercus*. They are also common in patches of riparian forest and in poplar (*Populus* x *canadensis*) plantations whilst on rare occasions they have been recorded in coniferous woodland. During the breeding season they show a strong attraction to cherry trees, both cultivated and wild *Prunus avium*, and a less strong one to mulberries *Morus*. The total breeding population is tentatively estimated at 5,000–30,000 pairs.

Outside the breeding season, Golden Orioles occur throughout the country as passage migrants in both seasons. They are fairly common in spring, either singly or in flocks of up to ten (rarely 30 or more), from late March to late May, with a peak in early May. At least in central and northern parts of the mainland they are extremely rare before the last few days of April but on Crete they apparently occur from late March (*BoC*). Males regularly sing on passage. On autumn passage Golden Orioles are less common, from mid August to early October. Passage peaks in early September and on Crete there are rare records up to early November. Golden Orioles were formerly a quarry species and large numbers were shot in autumn but illegally also in spring, during the Turtle Dove shooting season, from 15 April to 15 May. There are 31 ringing recoveries of foreign-ringed Golden Orioles found in Greece. Four of these are of birds ringed presumably on spring passage in Italy (Capri), S France and Corsica and were recovered on autumn (3) or spring passage in a later year (1) in Greece. A further one ringed in May 1955 at Cap Bon (Tunisia) was recovered in September 1957 in Greece. The remaining 26 recoveries are of birds ringed during the breeding season in central and eastern Europe: Germany (3), Poland (4), Latvia (1), the Czech Republic (3), Slovakia (1), Hungary (10), Rumania (1) and Yugoslavia (3).

Isabelline Shrike *Lanius isabellinus*

Accidental

An adult male Isabelline Shrike was observed in the Evros Delta on 28 September 1995 (F. Hendrick). The bird was reported as nominate *L. i. isabellinus*, with a pale plumage. There

are two more records from Crete, of an adult on 4 October 1988 and a juvenile on 6 October 1988, both rejected due to lack of details (*BoC*).

Red-backed Shrike *Lanius collurio*

Common and widespread summer visitor and passage migrant

Probably the most numerous of the shrikes breeding in Greece, Red-backed Shrikes are nevertheless missing from large parts of the mainland and most islands. In most areas they are typical birds of the uplands, occurring mainly between about 500 m and 1500 m. Occasionally they reach higher up, as on Mt Chelmos, at up to 1700 m (CP) or the Katara Pass, at 1600 m. In most of Thrace and locally elsewhere they may occur down to sea level. Red-backed Shrikes breed in a variety of fairly open habitats with bushes or widely spaced trees, including hedges in non-intensive farmland, mountain slopes with scattered junipers *Juniperus* or stunted pines *Pinus*, not too dense maquis and clearings on wooded slopes. The total Greek population probably numbers 20,000–50,000 pairs.

The species is very common on autumn passage, mainly from mid August to mid October. On Crete, passage starts in late July (*BoC*). Quite often late birds may be seen up to early November. Only a minority (10–30%) of autumn migrants (as judged by sightings and ringing data) are adults and these mainly pass through in the first half of the season, up to mid September, though some have also been recorded among the latest birds in late October and early November. Red-backed Shrikes are the commonest, after Willow Warbler, prey species of Eleonora's Falcons in the Aegean during autumn migration (Walter 1979; Ristow *et al.* 1986). Radio tracking of six birds on the island of Karpathos showed a southeast on-going direction (Biebach *et al.* 1983). Red-backed Shrikes also used to be a popular autumn quarry of hunters in some parts of the country and many were shot or captured with traps or on lime up to the mid 1980s, when they became protected. Spring passage takes place from early April (more often late April) to late May, with a peak in early May. This passage is much smaller than in autumn and the species may then be described as scarce to fairly common, depending on weather conditions and the part of the country: it tends to be more numerous in the north, including islands such as Lesbos and Limnos, than in the south. Red-backed Shrike has the largest number of ringing recoveries of all bird species in Greece, with 117 up to now. All were ringed abroad and found in Greece, the vast majority in autumn (former shooting season). The birds had been ringed in 19 countries, from Britain, Belgium, Germany, Switzerland, Slovenia, and Yugoslavia in the west to Finland, Latvia, Poland, Slovakia and Rumania in the east. The largest numbers are from Sweden (31), Germany (28), Finland (10) and the Czech Republic (10).

Lesser Grey Shrike *Lanius minor*

Fairly widespread but scarce summer visitor and passage migrant

Lesser Grey Shrikes have a rather discontinuous breeding range from the extreme NW Peloponnese and Sterea Hellas northwards. They breed on only a few islands: Corfu in the Ionian and Lesbos and probably Thasos, Samothraki and Samos in the Aegean. A nest with two eggs was also found on the island of Naxos in 1862 (Krüper 1863). Within this range the species is very thinly distributed and even in extensive areas of suitable habitat breeding pairs

tend to be widely scattered. Their typical breeding habitat is open areas with cereal fields, meadows or dry stony grassland with patches of bushes and trees. They occur from sea level up to at least 1000 m and occasionally higher. The total Greek population probably does not exceed 2,000–3,000 pairs and is reported as declining (*BWP*; Tucker & Heath 1994). However, it seems that Lesser Grey Shrikes were never very common. For example, earlier this century Harrison & Pateff (1937) described them as 'not uncommon, though somewhat locally distributed' in Thrace, and Makatsch (1950) as 'not so common, missing from many areas where one would expect to find them' in Macedonia.

During migration, Lesser Grey Shrikes are much more widespread, though still not very common. They are scarce in spring and more numerous, sometimes fairly common, in autumn. They usually arrive in mid April and passage continues to mid or late May. In autumn they pass through from mid August to late September, with a peak around the end of August. Small numbers, much smaller than of Red-backed Shrike, have been recorded as prey of Eleonora's Falcons off NE Crete in autumn (Ristow *et al.* 1986). In another study at the same colony they were listed as the fifth commonest prey, comprising 6% of all prey remains (by number) (Walter 1968). It is probable that the latter study was carried out at a time when the species was still relatively common, before the sharp decline of European populations in the period 1970–1990 (Tucker & Heath 1994). Ringing recoveries of Lesser Grey Shrikes in Greece, all in autumn, include birds ringed in Germany (1), Hungary (3) and Kenya (1).

Great Grey Shrike *Lanius excubitor*

Fairly widespread but rare winter visitor

Great Grey Shrikes are winter visitors to Greece. They were formerly (before the 1960s) more widespread and although not very common, they were an important quarry, well known to hunters. During the last decades, they have become scarce or even rare, reflecting declines over much of their breeding range in Europe (*BWP*; Tucker & Heath 1994). In recent years the species has been recorded from most parts of the country but mainly from the northeastern mainland, with fewer in central and southern parts. There are no confirmed records from Crete (*BoC*) or the Ionian islands and there is only one record from the Cyclades from the 19th century (Magioris 1994) and a record of three seen together on the island of Kythira (Kominos 1995). There is little information on arrival and departure dates but most records have been between late October and mid March. There is no evidence of passage through Greece and although many August and September records exist, almost all clearly involve misidentified Lesser Grey Shrikes, especially juveniles. Great Grey Shrikes were seen during the breeding season in the Pindos National Park in 1985 (Tsounis 1988) but with no further evidence of breeding. Great Grey Shrikes belonging to race *L. e. homeyeri* (or intermediates with *L. e. excubitor*) have been identified with certainty in Greece (*CFG*). According to *CFG* and Makatsch (1950) *L. e. excubitor* (from western, central and northern Europe) may also occur. This suggestion is supported by the only ringing recovery available, of a bird ringed in Finland in September 1978 and found near Kozani in February 1980.

Woodchat Shrike *Lanius senator*

Common and widespread summer visitor

Woodchat Shrikes occur over much of the mainland and on most of the larger islands in both the Aegean and the Ionian Seas. They are the most widespread shrike in Greece but probably the second most numerous, after Red-backed. They occur in all types of lowland open terrain with scattered trees and bushes such as open olive groves, orchards and open oak *Quercus* or Aleppo pine *Pinus halepensis* woodland. They are most numerous in the lower foothills and

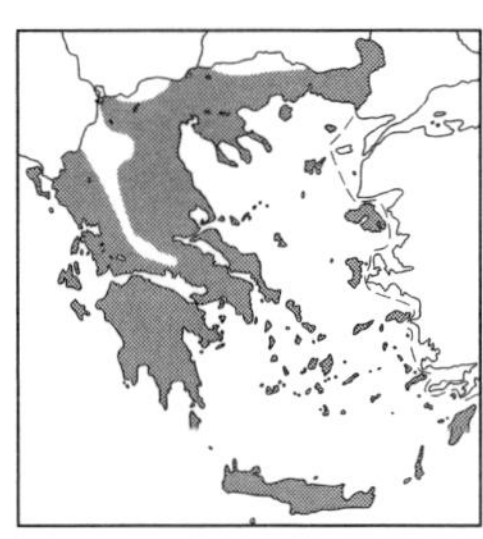

coastal plains, up to about 500 m, but rarely they may be found at up to 1000 m on the mainland or, on Crete, up to 1300 m (*BoC*), with one recorded case there at 1600 m (Watson 1964). The total Greek population probably lies in the 10,000–30,000 pairs range. The species has been reported as declining (Tucker & Heath 1994) though it is still quite numerous and it has certainly not declined as much as Lesser Grey Shrike.

On the mainland, Woodchat Shrikes begin arriving in late March and are present in numbers from mid April onwards. Most fledglings appear in mid to late June. Departures probably begin around late July. Adults are scarce after the middle of August and only a few juveniles remain after the beginning of September. The last birds are usually seen in late September or early October. On Crete, arrivals have been noted already in mid March and records extend till mid November, though autumn passage takes place mainly in August and early September (*BoC*). In Thrace, in the spring of 1987, the first birds were seen in early April and a large passage took place in early May (WIWO 90). Thus there seems to be a significant lag of spring arrivals from the southernmost to the northernmost areas of the country. In both seasons there is a perceptible through-passage of small numbers of Woodchat Shrikes throughout the country, more evident in spring than in autumn. Woodchat Shrikes have been recorded as prey of Eleonora's Falcons off NE Crete in autumn, but in even smaller numbers than Lesser Grey Shrikes (Ristow *et al.* 1986), presumably because of their early departure. The only ringing recovery of Woodchat Shrike is of a bird ringed as a chick in central Italy in May 1935 and recovered in Attica in early October of the same year. The direction of movement and the lateness of the recovery date strongly indicate a misidentified Red-backed Shrike.

Masked Shrike *Lanius nubicus*

Scarce and local summer visitor

Apparently more widespread in the 19th century (e.g. breeding in Attica, Reiser 1905), Masked Shrikes are today confined to the northeast mainland (from Asprovalta eastwards), the larger islands of the northeastern Aegean (Thasos, Samothraki, Limnos, Lesbos, Chios and Samos) and southeastern Thessaly. Possible nesting was also reported from Kos in 1986 (C. Wormwell). Masked Shrikes breed at low altitude, in areas of small fields with tall hedges and many trees, in open woodland, scrub and olive groves with bushes or bordering on maquis. They spend more of their time hidden within vegetation and the lower branches of trees and prefer an overall more

Masked Shrike

densely vegetated habitat than other shrikes. The total Greek population has been variously estimated from a few tens of pairs (*BWP*) to as many as 600–2,000 pairs (Tucker & Heath 1994) but probably does not exceed 1,000 pairs.

Most Masked Shrikes arrive in Greece in mid and late April and depart from mid August to early October. There are very few records away from known breeding areas: three from Crete, April–May (*BoC*), one from the Cyclades (Magioris 1988), one from Kozani (*CFG*) and two stuffed specimens from the island of Kythira (Kominos 1995). There are no records as yet from the Ionian islands, Ipeiros or the Peloponnese.

Jay *Garrulus glandarius*

Widespread and locally common resident

In suitable habitat, Jays are common throughout the mainland, as well as on almost all the major islands in both the Aegean and the Ionian Seas. They occupy a wide variety of open or dense woodland habitats and locally dense and tall maquis (e.g. with holm oak *Q. ilex*), orchards and olive groves. As is characteristic of the species in general, they are quite closely associated with oaks *Quercus* and reach their highest densities in fairly open, mature deciduous oak woodland. The association with oaks applies even to large bushes or trees of the normally low-growing evergreen Kermes *Q. coccifera* and holm oaks. Nevertheless, Jays are also quite common in beech *Fagus*, sweet chestnut *Castanea sativa* and upland conifers such as black pine *Pinus nigra* and fir *Abies*, but are generally absent from low-altitude Aleppo pines *Pinus halepensis*, except where there is some admixture with oaks. The overall altitudinal range of Jays is from sea level to about 1800 m but mainly between about 300 and 1200 m. In most areas they are scarce and local near sea level with the exception of some islands. Probably partly due to persecution, in Greece Jays tend to occur at higher altitudes or in denser forest than e.g. in Asia Minor (Watson 1964). On the islands, they are either common (e.g. on Lesbos, Chios and Samos) or quite local, restricted to specialised habitat types, e.g. upland Kermes oak on Crete, sessile oak *Q. petraea* on Samothraki or holm oak on Rhodes (Watson 1964; *BoC*). The total Greek population probably amounts to 20,000–50,000 pairs.

Jays are chiefly sedentary but become more widespread and conspicuous in winter, perhaps with some immigration of northern birds. A number of races occur in Greece, belonging to two distinct groups: *G. g. glandarius* (head streaked with black) and *G. g. atricapillus* (black crown). The former group is represented by three races: *G. g. albipectus* on the Ionian islands, *G. g. graecus* on the mainland and *G. g. cretorum* on Crete. The latter is represented by two races: *G. g. anatoliae* (= *krynicki*) on Lesbos, Chios, Rhodes and Kos and *G. g. samios* on Samos and Ikaria (Watson 1964; *BWP*).

Magpie *Pica pica*

Common and widespread resident

Magpies breed commonly over almost the whole mainland but, for no obvious reason, they are contrastingly absent from both the Aegean and Ionian islands, except Corfu, Kos and probably Lefkada (J.B. Andersen, F. Pergantis). Their population density varies greatly. They are commonest in agricultural land with mixed crops and scattered trees or bushes (including olive groves), at the edges of villages and towns and in partly wooded (e.g. with tamarisks *Tamarix* or willows *Salix*) wetland areas. They are normally absent from closed woodland, maquis or phrygana, except near farm buildings, shepherds' huts and sites of permanent human presence. High densities are often found along main roads, where they exploit road casualties, and near rubbish dumps. They occur from sea level up to about 800 m and occasionally at up to 1500 m, according to the availability of suitable habitat. In many areas, particularly those with extensive flat and treeless arable land, Magpies have adapted to nesting on electricity pylons, like Hooded Crows. The total breeding population of Magpies is in the order of 10,000–50,000 pairs.

Magpies are strictly sedentary and though some dispersion may occur after the breeding season, especially of juveniles, they rarely reach the islands. There are only three records from Crete (*BoC*), two from the Cyclades (Magioris 1994) and none from Chios (Spinthakis *et al.* 1993) or Lesbos. In winter they often form loose flocks, roosting communally in suitable patches of dense vegetation, e.g. tamarisks *Tamarix* in wetlands and patches of conifers elsewhere. The population of Magpies breeding in Greece belongs to the nominate race *P. p. pica* (*BWP*) but it has been suggested that it approaches *P. p. bactriana* (Watson 1964), the east European/west Asian form.

Nutcracker *Nucifraga caryocatactes*

Rare and local resident

The first indication of Nutcrackers breeding in Greece was in May 1966 in the Rodopi Mts, north of Drama (*CFG*). From the early 1970s onwards the species was found to breed quite commonly in the mountains along the Greece–Bulgaria border in much of the Rodopi range, east to Mt Orvilos (Bauer & Böhr 1987). In the primeval forest of the central Rodopi Mts north of Paranesti, Nutcrackers were found breeding at 1200–1920 m but particularly above 1500 m (Bauer & Böhr 1987). The total breeding population probably does not exceed 50–100 pairs.

Away from this area, singles have been seen at 860 m on Mt Kallidromon on 10 May 1981 (Hölzinger 1990d), flying overhead in the western suburbs of Athens on 20 October 1981 (F. Pergantis) and on Mt Olympos, in black pines *Pinus nigra*, between 800 and 1600 m in 1985 (Malakou 1985). Although no real invasion-type movements have ever been recorded in Greece, it is not unlikely that these records in the southern half of the country may be connected to invasions of the eruptive Siberian race *N. c. macrorhynchos* into other parts of Europe. The 1985 record does indeed coincide with such an invasion (*BWP*) but the two 1981 records do not. There is also an observation of one bird in Samaria Gorge (Crete) on 25 April 1984 (M.I. McDonald) but this record has been rejected due to lack of supporting details.

Alpine Chough *Pyrrhocorax graculus*

Fairly widespread and locally common resident

Alpine Choughs have a widespread breeding distribution that spans most of the higher elevations on the mainland, from the high mountains of the northern Peloponnese and Mt Parnassos northwards along the Pindos range, as well as on Mt Olympos, Mt Voras and from Mt Orvilos to Mt Pangaion. In the past the species has also reported from Mt Taygetos (*CFG*) but it has not been recorded there or elsewhere in the southern Peloponnese in recent times (Adamakopoulos *et al.* 1988). The species also occurs on Crete, where it is more local than Chough, breeding only on Lefka Ori and Mt Idi (Scharlau 1989b; *BoC*). In the past it was reported as locally very common on Mt Dirfys (Watson 1964) but it has not been seen there since the mid 1970s (though flocks of Hooded Crows which could have been mistaken for Alpine Choughs in the distance have been seen). During the breeding season Alpine Choughs are confined to the upper zones of high mountains, primarily on limestone, feeding in areas with short vegetation, usually heavily grazed and stony. Their total breeding population is hard to estimate but probably lies between 2,000 and 10,000 pairs.

Alpine Choughs make altitudinal movements in winter, sometimes down to sea level, according to snow conditions, but even then they are usually only a few minutes' flight away from their breeding grounds. An interesting observation is of a flock of *c.* 10 flying in from the sea over Aegion Lagoon, on 8 November 1995, presumably coming from the mountains of Sterea Hellas and heading towards the high peaks of the northern Peloponnese (CP). This suggests that sometimes birds move over longer distances and that populations on neighbouring mountains are not completely isolated.

Chough *Pyrrhocorax pyrrhocorax*

Fairly widespread but scarce resident

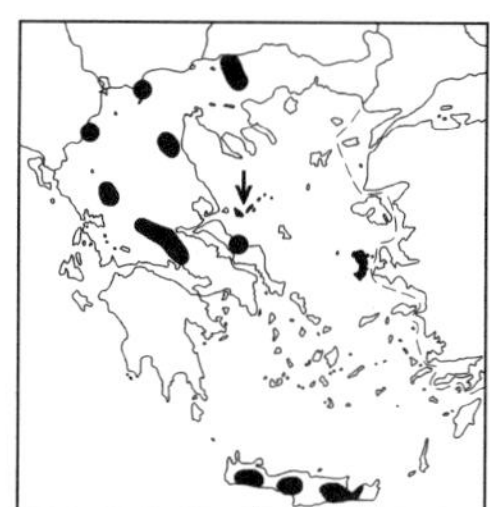

On the mainland, Choughs have a much more localised distribution than Alpine Choughs: they occur only on the highest massifs, from Sterea Hellas northwards and eastwards to eastern Macedonia. However, they are not restricted to the highest altitudes like the latter. They breed on the islands of Skopelos and Alonnisos (*CFG*, Androukaki & Adamantopoulou 1992, G. Kondylis). Breeding was confirmed on the island of Chios in 1971 (Bauer *et al.* 1973) though the species is not listed there by a more recent work (Spinthakis *et al.* 1993). Choughs also breed on Crete, where they are much more numerous and widespread than Alpine Choughs and reach a higher density than on the mainland (*BoC*). They are now absent from the Peloponnese, where they were recorded in the past (Reiser 1905; Niethammer 1943b). Choughs are most often seen above 400 m on the mainland and above 1000 m on Crete and in all regions they reach up to the highest altitudes. They prefer rocky, bare open areas with gorges, cliff faces and other suitable nest sites. On Crete they are common between 1000 and 2300 m (at one site down to 650 m); there are colonies of up to 100 pairs and feeding flocks of up to 100 birds, occasionally 250, may be seen; in autumn large numbers roost in caves (e.g. the Idean Cave) and in winter they usually descend to lower areas, particularly during bad weather (Watson 1964; *BoC*). The total Greek population of Choughs probably numbers between 500 and 2,000 pairs and belongs to race *P. p. docilis.*

Jackdaw *Corvus monedula*

Common and widespread resident

Jackdaws are widespread over much of the mainland but their distribution in southern Sterea Hellas and the Peloponnese, as well as in the Aegean and the Ionian islands is much more patchy. Prior to 1959 there were only two colonies on Crete (Watson 1964) but since then they have become more widespread and they are now a fairly common resident on the island (*BoC*). Jackdaws are most numerous at low altitude (below about 1000 m), nesting in ruins and abandoned buildings, whether isolated in the countryside or in villages and towns, and also at natural sites such as rocky gorges and cliffs, both coastal and inland. For feeding they prefer arable land, orchards, pastures and other fairly open habitats. Locally they are common at rubbish tips, though less so than Hooded Crows, and in central and northern parts of the country they are quite common in large towns (e.g. Thessaloniki), feeding on scraps of food in parks and streets. Their total breeding population probably numbers between 20,000 and 50,000 pairs. Outside the breeding season Jackdaws often form large flocks, usually mixed with Hooded Crows and Rooks. Jackdaws breeding in Greece belong to the eastern race, *C. m. soemmerringii* (*BWP*), but birds of the central European *C. m. spermologus* may also occur in winter (*CFG*).

Rook *Corvus frugilegus*

Former breeding species, now fairly widespread and locally very common winter visitor

Rooks formerly bred in parts of Macedonia such as the Axios Delta and L. Koronia (Makatsch 1950). They were listed as breeding in eastern Macedonia and Thrace until the 1960s, with 'only a few colonies known' (*CFG*). Although breeding may still occur in parts of northern Greece, there has been no confirmed breeding record since the 1960s.

The species is a regular and fairly widespread winter visitor to northern Greece, where it is locally numerous. It is very scarce south of the plains of Thessaly and west of the Pindos range. However, since the mid 1980s increasing numbers have been recorded in winter as far south as Aitolia (e.g. Agrinion and Messolonghi) and in the northern Peloponnese (CP), an indication of a possible range expansion. Wintering birds occur mainly in lowland agricultural areas and pastures with scattered trees, poplar plantations or patches of woodland. They are also quite common near villages and other rural human settlements. In suitable areas and especially during hard winter weather huge flocks may be seen, often mixed with other corvids, e.g. 20,000–25,000 were seen moving to roost in the Aliakmon Delta on 14 January 1986. One Rook ringed as a chick in the southern Ukraine was recovered at Serres in its first winter.

Hooded Crow *Corvus corone*

Very common and widespread resident

The most widespread and probably the most numerous corvid in Greece, Hooded Crows breed commonly throughout the mainland and on practically all of the main islands in both the Aegean and the Ionian Seas. They are ubiquitous, occurring almost everywhere from sea level up to the alpine zones of most mountains, in cultivated land, pastures, olive groves, open woodland, wetlands, sea coasts and in and around villages and towns. They have been recorded nesting even on small offshore islets, moving freely to and from the mainland or larger islands to feed. No Hooded Crows have been seen on the island of Kythira during the last 30 years, except for three spring records of presumed migrants (Kominos 1995). The species is also missing from Karpathos, Ikaria and Fournoi (*CFG*). In common with other corvids, some gaps in their distribution may at least in part be explained by the effect of past persecution. The total breeding population of the species probably lies within the 30,000–100,000 pairs range.

Outside the breeding season Hooded Crows gather in large flocks, often mixing with Rooks and Jackdaws to form impressive flocks. There is very little information on their movements but it seems likely that some immigrants arrive in Greece in winter. Hooded Crows nesting in Greece belong to the black-and-grey *C. c. cornix* group and though until recently classified as *C. c. sardonius*, they are now treated as *C. c. sharpii* (*BWP*). So far, there are 10–15 alleged records of all-black individuals of the nominate *C. c. corone* (= Carrion Crow), mainly from northern Greece and in winter or early spring. However, at least some of these records seem to refer to Rooks or have otherwise been misidentified. The occurrence of *C. c. cornix* from NE Europe is much more likely in winter but this form has never been positively identified.

Raven *Corvus corax*

Fairly common and widespread resident

Small numbers of Ravens occur throughout the mainland, including the Peloponnese, and on most of the main islands in both the Aegean and the Ionian Seas. In the late 1950s even some of the smallest Aegean islands had a breeding pair (Watson 1964) and, despite persecution, many of them still do so (Magioris 1994; CP). With the exception of extensive dense forests,

Ravens may be seen almost everywhere from sea level up to the highest summits. They are commonest in areas of low or open vegetation with large numbers of grazing stock and with rocky outcrops, where they may find nest sites. In many areas they regularly visit rubbish dumps. At certain sites (e.g. in Crete and Mt Parnassos) aggregations of 100–200 birds are not uncommon, particularly outside the breeding season. The total population of Ravens is estimated at a 3,000–10,000 pairs and appears to be stable. Most birds are sedentary, with local, mainly altitudinal, movements in winter. Greek Ravens are divided into two races, differing slightly in measurements and plumage gloss: the nominate *C. c. corax* on most of the mainland and *C. c. laurencei* in Thrace, Crete and the Aegean islands (*BWP*).

Starling *Sturnus vulgaris*

Fairly common but local resident, very common and widespread winter visitor

As a breeding species, Starlings have a rather restricted range: they breed only on the mainland, particularly in Macedonia, Thrace and Thessaly and very locally and rather irregularly in Ipeiros, Sterea Hellas and perhaps north–central Peloponnese (CP). They nest in semi-open habitats, such as orchards, open farmland with scattered trees or patches of woodland and in the outskirts of villages and towns, from sea level up to about 1300 m Their total breeding population is tentatively estimated at 3,000–5,000 pairs.

Outside the breeding season and particularly in winter Starlings are widespread and locally abundant. Though numbers vary annually, they are among the commonest winter visitors. Wintering Starlings frequent every type of agricultural habitat but they show a strong preference for olive trees. Very large numbers congregate in the main olive-growing areas of southern and western Greece, roosting in town parks and reedbeds. Roosts of 10,000–20,000 birds are quite common and regularly attract birds of prey, especially Sparrowhawks, Peregrines and Buzzards. Occasionally 1,000,000 or more birds are present in some of the larger coastal plains such as the Axios Delta and the areas of Messolonghi and Kotychi Lagoon. In many areas Starlings are regarded as pests of olives and are shot to protect the crop. They are peculiarly rare on Lesbos in most winters, despite the extensive olive groves covering more than a quarter of the island. Wintering birds begin to arrive in mid October and become widespread and numerous by early November, at about the time olives are ripe and begin to fall to the ground. Departures take place from late February to late March or early April. A few birds (perhaps passage migrants) may be seen in non-breeding areas up to late April or later. The large flocks observed in olive-growing areas in autumn greatly decline in numbers from early winter (December to early January) onwards, presumably due to the gradual disappearance of olives. This early winter decline is obvious on the mainland and on Crete (*BoC*) but it is not known whether it is the result of emigration, high mortality or simply dispersal to other habitats in neighbouring areas. Nineteen ringed Starlings have been recovered in Greece. Six had been ringed in Russia, four in Bulgaria, three in the Ukraine, three in Poland and singles in Britain, Estonia and Rumania.

Spotless Starling *Sturnus unicolor*

Accidental

Spotless Starlings have been recorded three times: on the island of Corfu, in May 1857 (Powys 1860), at R. Geropotamos, Crete, in May 1967 (*CFG*) and at Longos, on the island of Paxoi on 23 May 1992 (Vittery 1994). It is very probable that the species occurs more often but it is overlooked among the much more numerous Starlings.

Rose-coloured Starling *Sturnus roseus*

Irregular breeding species, widespread passage migrant

Rose-coloured Starlings have always been rather erratic visitors to Greece. There are several 19th-century records, mainly from central and southern Greece (Attica, Peloponnese, Evvoia and Corfu) (Reiser 1905), and several records from the earlier part of the 20th century. Rose-coloured Starlings seem to have been familiar birds in older times and they were associated with invasions of locusts, as testified by their two common Greek names: 'Agiopouli' means Bird of the Saint and 'Diavolopouli' means Bird of the Devil, presumably depending on whether they were regarded as destructors or harbingers of locusts. The species has been recorded more frequently in recent years, perhaps due to a genuine increase though certainly also due to increased observer activity. Records span the period from mid May to mid August but the vast majority are in late May and early June. There is one winter record, of a single at Kamares, Achaia, on 3 December 1988 (CP). On passage, Rose-coloured Starlings are usually seen in flocks of 5–40 birds and single birds are relatively rare. Flocks of migrants tend to be constantly on the move, not normally staying at any one site for more than a day. They are often attracted to white mulberries *Morus alba* which ripen in June.

Rose-coloured Starlings possibly nested at Koutsochero (Thessaly) in 1980 (Bruch 1992). The first confirmed breeding was in 1985, when *c.* 500 pairs nested at Vafiochori, Kilkis

Rose-coloured Starling

(Bruch 1992; Prigann 1992). In 1987, *c.* 2,000 pairs nested again at Vafiochori and a further *c.* 3,000 pairs at Drymos, near Thessaloniki (Limbrunner 1987). In 1988, *c.* 3,500 pairs nested near Kavala (Hölzinger 1992c). There were no breeding records between 1989 and 1994 (though wandering flocks were reported in all these years) but in 1995 large numbers nested again at Vafiochori. In view of the variability and unpredictability of their breeding it is very likely that the species has nested on several more occasions, both in the distant past and in more recent times. In all cases, colonies were formed in stone or marble quarries (both disused and active), with the nests being built mainly between stones and boulders. Pellets collected from the Kavala colony on 12 June 1988 contained mulberry seeds *Morus* (54% by frequency), remains of bush-crickets (Tettigonidae, mainly *Decticus albifrons)* (33%) and shells of the land snail *Helicella pappi* (13%) (Hölzinger 1992b).

House Sparrow *Passer domesticus*

Very common and widespread resident

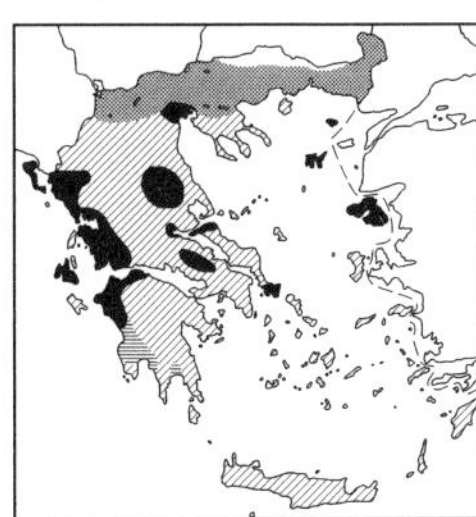

One of the commonest Greek birds, House Sparrows occur throughout the mainland and on practically all inhabited islands. They are numerous in villages and towns as well as on farmland from sea level up to about 1000 m, or the upper limit of permanent human habitation. As a rule they do not appear to be able to exist in purely natural areas but they are far less anthopophilous than in western or northern Europe. When available, they nest in holes in buildings of all kinds, whether in villages or towns or isolated structures such as bridges, silos and barns in the countryside. They also frequently build nests on the side of White Stork nests and, when no better choice is available, they build domed nests, like those of Spanish Sparrows, in suitable dense and thorny trees, such as false acacia *Robinia pseudacacia* and almond pear *Pyrus amygdaliformis*. The total breeding population of House Sparrow is likely to be in the order of 200,000–1,000,000 pairs but it is even more difficult to estimate than for most other species due to the concentration of large populations at relatively few sites.

Already as early as the end of June juveniles start forming flocks that roam the countryside during the day and in the evening gather into large roosting assemblages to spend the night in tall trees (especially *Eucalyptus* and poplars *Populus*) in towns. Roosts of this kind build up in size towards the end of summer as more and more juveniles and adults that have finished breeding join them. The flight of flocks early in the morning and back again in the evening, which may be non-stop for distances of more than 10 km, may be mistaken by the unwary for migratory movements. The species is not known to undertake any real migration, though some Cretan birds may occasionally wander or migrate to Egypt (Watson 1963).

'Italian Sparrow': Sparrows that can be referred to *italiae* occur on Crete. A subject of hot taxonomic debate for years, these have been variously classified as *P. domesticus italiae* (Vaurie 1959; Watson 1964) or *P. hispaniolensis italiae* (Summers-Smith 1980, 1988) but in either case accepted as a stabilised hybrid population between *P. domesticus* and *P. hispaniolensis*. Cretan birds though rather variable in plumage (*BoC*) bear on average a much more clear resemblance to those found in Italy, than to 'Italian Sparrow'-like birds elsewhere in the Aegean, e.g. of Rhodes and Karpathos (Watson 1964; *BWP*). At least two records of 'Italian Sparrow' exist from NW Peloponnese in spring and autumn (CP).

Spanish Sparrow *Passer hispaniolensis*

Widespread and locally very common resident and summer visitor

Spanish Sparrows have a much more restricted breeding range than House Sparrows. They breed most abundantly in Macedonia and Thrace but in the rest of the mainland they have a very patchy and discontinuous range, with breeding records from only a few widely spread areas (see also Peterson *et al.* 1981). They have recently been found breeding locally on the islands of Kefallinia (A. Vittery) and Corfu and a small population now breeds in the NW Peloponnese (Achaia and Ileia) (CP). Their breeding range in the Aegean is very limited and

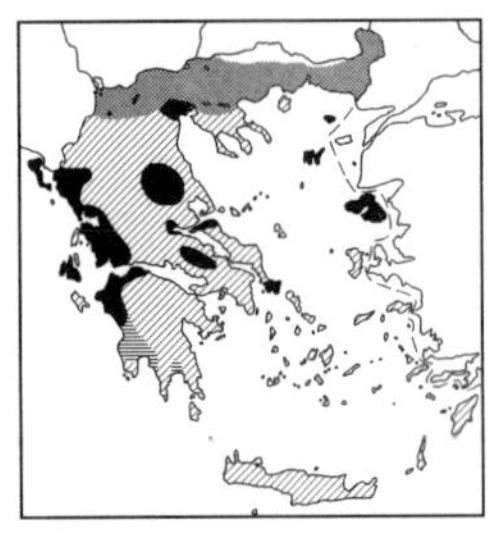

they are known to breed only on Samothraki, Limnos and Lesbos (Watson 1964; *CFG*). Spanish Sparrows tend to be found in more fertile areas than House Sparrows, nesting e.g. in patches of riparian woodland, orchards, lines or groves of poplar *Populus* or copses of willow *Salix*, usually amidst rich arable land or rice fields. Regularly they form small colonies in the stick structure of large occupied nests of White Storks or large birds of prey, whether on telegraph poles or in trees. The total breeding population almost certainly exceeds 50,000 pairs and may be as high as 200,000–300,000 pairs.

After breeding and up until the early autumn Spanish Sparrows often form huge flocks of thousands or tens of thousands of birds, e.g. to feed on ripening rice. Birds breeding in northern Greece appear to be mainly migratory and impressive movements of migrating flocks have been observed in various parts along the N Aegean coast, the eastern Aegean islands and the Cyclades (*CFG*), usually from late September to late October and, in smaller numbers, from late March to early May. Spanish Sparrow is a fairly common passage migrant on Crete (*BoC*) and it is common in prey remains of Eleonora's Falcons off NE Crete in autumn (Ristow *et al.* 1986). On the other hand, birds breeding in southern and central Greece may stay near their breeding grounds all year round and birds from northern Greece or the northern Balkans may also winter in southern parts of the mainland and the Aegean.

Spanish Sparrow

Dead Sea Sparrow *Passer moabiticus*

Accidental

A flock of about 20 birds seen on tamarisks *Tamarix* near Kallithea on the island of Rhodes in the first week of October 1972 is the only Greek record but also the first record of the species in Europe (Harrestrup-Andersen 1989).

Tree Sparrow *Passer montanus*

Widespread and locally common resident

The least common of the genus *Passer* breeding in Greece, Tree Sparrows have a restricted range, whose limits are very poorly known. However, they are certainly more widespread than previously (*CFG*) thought and they now seem to occur as local populations in many parts of the mainland. Tree Sparrows are found on farmland, town suburbs and the surroundings of villages, around farm buildings, in open olive groves or orchards and other similar habitats providing suitable nest-holes in trees and open areas for feeding. Near Chalkis, where they are common, they have been found to take readily to nestboxes and small colonies may form in this way within a couple of years. Altitudinally they range from sea level to about 900 m (L. Prespa area). The total breeding population is probably between 5,000 and 30,000 pairs.

In the non-breeding season Tree Sparrows form loose flocks or appear as scattered individual in mixed flocks of House Sparrows, finches or buntings. The Greek population seems to be sedentary, birds being present near their breeding grounds all year round. It is likely that a certain number of wintering birds arrive here from the north, though existing information is too limited to confirm this. The species is listed as an accidental visitor to Chios (Spinthakis *et al.* 1993) and as a passage migrant in small numbers on Crete, where it has become more regular since 1980 (*BoC*).

Rock Sparrow *Petronia petronia*

Fairly widespread but scarce resident

A poorly known species and though with a fairly wide overall distribution, Rock Sparrows tend to be found in small isolated populations. They are very sparsely distributed or even absent from large parts of northern and western Greece and the Peloponnese and occur on only a few of the islands. They are listed as accidental visitors to Crete, with four records (*BoC*), and there are no documented records from the Ionian islands but the species nests on several of the other Aegean islands, e.g. Chios (Spinthakis *et al.* 1993), some of the Cyclades, Samos and Lesbos. Rock Sparrows prefer low-altitude hilly country with phrygana and dry fields or pasture, nesting in colonies on cliffs, rock outcrops, disused quarries and ruins. On a few occasions they have been found in old olive groves with widely spaced trees, nesting in hollows in the trees (Pergantis 1981). They are sedentary, not wandering far away from their breeding sites all year round. They are always gregarious and breeding colonies or flocks of feeding birds are noisy and conspicuous. The total breeding population of Rock Sparrows probably lies between 2,000 and 5,000 pairs.

Rock Sparrows

Snowfinch *Montifringilla nivalis*

Rare and local resident

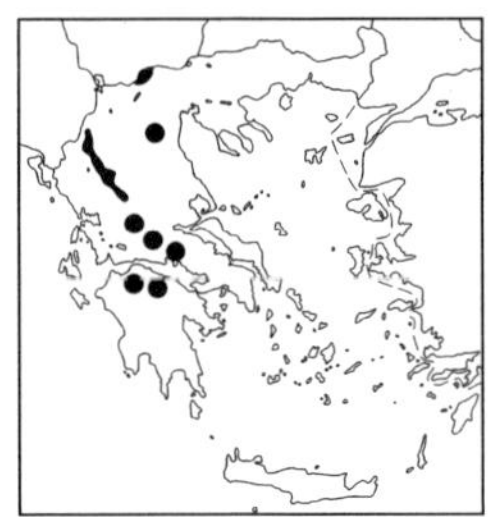

Snowfinches breed in an almost continuous belt on mountain tops along the Pindos range, from Mt Smolikas in the north, south to Mts Parnassos and Vardousia, as well as on more isolated mountains, i.e. Mt Voras, Mt Olympos, and Mt Kyllini. Individual populations are small and total *c.* 100 pairs (Hölzinger 1993c). Nesting habitat ranges between 1980 and 2530 m and is dominated by rocky alpine areas with crags, flat rocky plateaus, screes and alpine meadows (Hölzinger 1993c). There are extremely few records outside the breeding season, and even these are generally close to breeding areas (e.g. Delphi). This suggests that the Greek population is sedentary, undertaking only small scale altitudinal movements.

Chaffinch *Fringilla coelebs*

Very common and widespread resident and winter visitor

Chaffinches are widely distributed, breeding over almost the whole mainland and on most of the larger islands. They breed from sea level to as high as trees will grow, e.g. to 2000 m on Crete (*BoC*) or 2200 m on Mt Olympos (Malakou 1985). Their breeding habitat and altitudinal range vary geographically: in northern Greece they are very widespread, down to sea level, in deciduous or coniferous woodland and on cultivated land with rows of trees, copses or thickets; in the southern mainland they are more or less restricted to woodland and orchards and they are rare below about 200 m; finally on many of the islands they breed down to sea level (e.g. Lesbos, Crete), including lowland olive groves, a habitat from which they are absent in the southern mainland. The entire breeding population is probably between 1,000,000 and 3,000,000 pairs.

In winter, Chaffinches are very widespread and numerous and although no census of the wintering population has ever been made, one would not hesitate to say that they are clearly the most abundant bird species in Greece in winter. They begin arriving in late September and numbers peak by the end of October, large flocks forming in all kinds of open habitat and especially on ploughed and fallow fields. In the evening they gather in large roosts, sometimes involving thousands or tens of thousands of birds, in pine *Pinus* woodland or other dense evergreens. Presumably flocks of winter visitors from abroad are joined by birds breeding at higher altitudes but their is some evidence from ringing data and field observations that birds breeding at lower altitude stay near their summer territories all through the winter. Single Chaffinches ringed in the Ukraine and Russia have been recovered in Greece. The Greek breeding population of Chaffinches belongs to the nominate race *F. c. coelebs* (*BWP*), including the Cretan population which was formerly classified as *F. c. schiebelli* (*CFG*).

Brambling *Fringilla montifringilla*

Fairly common and widespread winter visitor

Bramblings are regular winter visitors from mid October to the end of March, mainly from the end of October to early March. They are most often seen on ploughed fields in large mixed flocks with Chaffinches and other seed-eating birds but they also occur in other open habitats and in deciduous woodland, especially beech *Fagus*, feeding on the mast, as is characteristic of the species in winter (*BWP*; Newton 1972). Their numbers vary from year to year and since it is well known that the species concentrates in the winter in various parts of Europe wherever there is a good beech-mast crop, it is not surprising that they arrive in Greece in varying numbers but rather that they are so regular and predictable in their appearance. In good years the ratio of Bramblings to Chaffinches in mixed flocks may reach 1:4 to 1:2 in central Greece. Overall, they tend to be less numerous in southern parts of the country than in the north and centre. There is one recovery of a bird ringed in Switzerland in winter, found wintering in Greece three years later.

Red-fronted Serin *Serinus pusillus*

Rare and irregular winter visitor

Red-fronted Serins have been recorded mainly on the island of Chios. Records obtained from local limers and trappers in the southern part of the island (areas of Volissos, Dotia, Kontari etc.) include two captures in October 1977 and at least 10–15 captures in October 1988 and 1989 (Handrinos 1994a; Spinthakis *et al.* 1993). Sightings from Chios (October–January) have been reported in 1963, 1976, 1979, 1980, 1990 and 1991 but the exact numbers involved are not known (Spinthakis *et al.* 1993). There are only two other records of the species. A male was seen caged in a shop at Chalkis on 19 February 1977; this bird was said to have been caught locally a few days previously (apparent from the good condition of its plumage). One pair was seen west of Antissa, on the island of Lesbos, on 15 May 1994 (R. Brooks).

Serin *Serinus serinus*

Fairly common and widespread resident

During the breeding season, Serins are widely distributed over much of mainland Greece, including the Peloponnese, but they tend to be rather thinly spread and often localised. They are scarce on the islands, where breeding has been confirmed only on Corfu, Lesbos, Chios (Spinthakis *et al.* 1993), Thasos and Samos. Serins probably breed on Crete (*BoC*) and perhaps locally on other islands. In late spring and summer they are most often seen in open woodland, orchards, olive groves and in more open habitats with scattered bushes or trees. Over the whole country they range from sea level up to 2200 m but this varies in different parts of the country. In most of the south they are regular near the treeline and often venture even higher up to feed in treeless areas, but they are rare below about 300 m. In the north and locally in the west they are not uncommon at low altitude and rare above 1500 m. The size of the breeding population is difficult to estimate but it is certainly not large and is very unlikely to exceed 30,000 pairs.

Birds of the Greek population move lower down the mountains in winter and are joined by immigrants from the north from early or mid October onwards. Three birds ringed in Austria and Hungary have been recovered in Greece in winter. Flocks of 5–20 and sometimes exceeding 100 birds occur on saltmarshes, weedy fields and vineyards, usually in the company of Linnets. These flocks begin to break up towards the end of February and have completely disappeared by the end of March. Odd wandering individuals may still be seen until mid April.

Greenfinch *Carduelis chloris*

Common and widespread resident

One of the most familiar finches in Greece, Greenfinches breed commonly throughout the mainland and on most of the islands in both the Aegean and the Ionian Seas. Breeding birds are usually found in orchards, olive groves, farmland with scattered trees, large gardens and open woodland, from sea level up to *c.* 1200 m and rarely even higher, e.g. at up to 1600 m on Crete (Watson 1964). More than any other Greek finch they stay close to human settlements and cultivated land, frequently nesting in garden and street trees. Their total breeding

population probably numbers between 50,000 and 200,000 pairs.

The Greek population is presumably mainly sedentary but in winter the total population increases significantly with the arrival of immigrants from the north. Wintering birds are present mainly from mid October to mid April. There appears to be some through-passage both in autumn and in spring. Throughout the year Greenfinches depend largely on weed and crop seeds for their food supply, with the exception of seeds of saltmarsh plants which are important in some parts of the country in winter. During April, May and June they rely heavily on the seeds of the milk thistle *Silybum marianum*, growing on manured ground, and on cabbage or cauliflower seeds, ripening after the autumn/winter harvest of the crop, whilst later in the summer they are often attracted to other large thistles such as *Onopordum* and *Cirsium*. A total of 19 birds ringed in Poland (1), Czechoslovakia (1), Hungary (14) and the Balkans (2) has been recovered in Greece and one bird ringed in Greece in winter was controlled in Hungary the following spring. Formerly, Greenfinches breeding in Greece were classified as race *C. c. aurantiiventris* (Watson 1964; *CFG*) but more recently (*BWP*) only those of western Greece are treated as belonging to this race, those of all other regions of Greece being assigned to *C. c. muehlei*. Birds of the nominate *C. c. chloris* occur both in winter and on passage.

Goldfinch *Carduelis carduelis*

Common and widespread resident

Goldfinches are widely distributed and quite numerous throughout the country, including most of the islands. They occur in a wide variety of open habitats, generally at low or medium altitude but often up to 2000 m, in olive groves, orchards, scrub, open oak *Quercus* or pine *Pinus* woodland, farmland with scattered trees and any other habitat which provides thistle (or other weed) seeds, trees for nesting and drinking water. They often start breeding quite early and fledged young have been observed following their parents to feed on Roman nettles *Urtica pilulifera* (when thistle seeds are still unavailable) as early as 3 April. In late August and September, when most dry land thistles have shed their seeds, they often gather in marshy areas, forming flocks that may exceed 200 birds to feed on the seeds of *Cirsium creticum* ripening at that time of year. The total breeding population of Goldfinches probably lies between 100,000 and 500,000 pairs.

The Greek population of Goldfinches is probably mainly sedentary but in winter (October–April) it is slightly augmented by immigrants from the north. There are eight ringing recoveries of birds ringed in the Balkans, Austria, Hungary and Czechoslovakia and found in Greece. Goldfinches breeding in Greece belong to two races: *C. c. hiediecki* in the Dodecanese and *C. c. balcanica* on all other islands and on the mainland (*BWP*), though other authors consider all Greek birds intermediate between these two forms, though closer to the former (Watson 1964). Birds of the nominate race *C. c. carduelis* occur in Greece in winter or as passage migrants (*CFG*).

Siskin *Carduelis spinus*

Rare and local resident, fairly common and widespread winter visitor

As a breeding species, Siskins are the rarest of the *Carduelis* finches in Greece, with a very restricted and discontinuous distribution. They have been found breeding on only a few mountains, mainly in the northern part of the Pindos range and in the Rodopi Mts. They have also been reported as breeding on Mt Parnassos and Mt Parnitha in the past (*CFG*), though recent records from the former are lacking (Hallmann 1985c) and on grounds of habitat suitability it is unlikely that they breed, at least regularly, south of Thessaly and Ipeiros. Breeding birds have been found from 550 to 1250 m (Schmid & Reichenecker 1988) in both coniferous and deciduous/mixed forest. The total Greek population is tentatively

estimated at 100–1,000 pairs.

The species is much more widespread and numerous in winter, from mid October to early April, mainly late October to mid March. The numbers arriving to winter vary greatly from year to year in cycles, in some years being scarce and in others very common. In invasion years it is difficult to miss the small groups that are on the move in the second half of October and in early November, looking for suitable feeding opportunities for the months to come. After such winters it is very likely that odd pairs may nest in suitable habitat throughout the country, including some islands. Wintering birds can be found in all kinds of woodland, in orchards and in olive groves but they concentrate especially on streamside or town and village plane trees *Platanus orientalis* (and the much less common alder *Alnus glutinosa*), feeding on their seeds. Siskins are favourite cage birds and although the practice is illegal and gradually dying out, many are still trapped and kept in captivity. Occasional single birds are seen in unlikely breeding habitat in southern Greece during the summer, particularly after invasion years, and these may well be escaped individuals caught during the previous winter. There are 12 ringing recoveries of Siskins ringed in Belgium, Norway, Finland, Switzerland, Germany, Hungary and the Czech Republic and recovered in Greece.

Linnet *Carduelis cannabina*

Common and widespread resident

Linnets are distributed throughout the mainland and the Peloponnese and they also breed on most of the islands in both the Aegean and the Ionian Seas. They tend to be uncommon and local in the northern mainland and commoner and more widespread towards the south and east, e.g. they have been reported as rare on the mainland (Watson 1964) or scarce in northern Greece (*CFG*) but locally common on some of the islands, e.g. Crete (*BoC*), though they are nowhere abundant. Their total breeding population probably is in the order of 50,000 to 200,000 pairs. During the breeding season they occur from sea level up to the alpine zone, preferring stony pastures, phrygana, open maquis and dry grassland.

Most Linnets in Greece probably make only short-distance movements in winter, depending on food availability. Upland breeding areas are vacated in winter and large flocks form in the lowlands, particularly in open farmland and saltmarshes, from about mid October to early–mid April. It is not rare to see flocks of 300–500 or even 1,000 birds in large saltmarshes, feeding on the seeds of *Arhtrocnemum* and perhaps other saltmarsh plants. Such flocks almost certainly contain immigrants from the north. Linnets breeding in Greece belong to race *C. c. mediterranea* (*BWP*), winter visitors probably include birds of the nominate race.

Crossbill *Loxia curvirostra*

Fairly widespread but scarce resident, common and widespread in invasion years

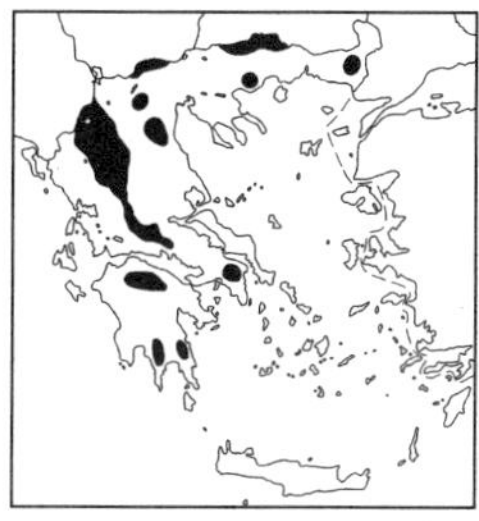

Crossbills have a fairly widespread breeding distribution in Greece, though within their range they are quite local with populations often widely scattered. Permanent populations exist on most of the mountains of the mainland including the Peloponnese (this distribution shown on the map). They seem to be absent from the islands, though breeding was recorded on Crete in 1984 (Massa 1984) and they have been reported as perhaps breeding on Lesbos, Samos, Ikaria and on Thasos (Watson 1964; *CFG*; I. Schogolev & M. Dimaki). Breeding may well occur wherever there are conifers after invasion years but observers should be aware that breeding of Crossbills does not necessarily take place in the spring but all through the year, depending on food availability (Newton 1972).

Permanent populations appear to rely mainly on upland pines (*Pinus nigra*, *P. sylvestris*, *P. heldreichii*), whose cones are small, so that they can be opened when closed in the autumn and winter, and retain seeds almost throughout the year (cf. Newton 1972). They thus usually occur at altitudes of 500–1500 m but exceptionally they may reach up to 2200 m (Malakou 1985; Schmid & Reichenecker 1988). They are usually absent from firs *Abies*, whose seeds are available only for the summer months, e.g. on Mt Parnassos they are absent from the extensive fir forest but are regularly present in a relatively small area of *Pinus nigra* on the northern slopes. They are also usually absent from the lowland *Pinus halepensis* and *P. brutia* forests for two reasons. Firstly because their cones are very large and hard to open when closed in winter and secondly because the birds need easily accessible supplies of drinking water, which are usually lacking from these lowland forests during the hot summer months. However, they seem to be able to survive at least temporarily in these lowland pine forests if water is available, such as near towns and villages and near irrigated farmland. It is interesting to note that in such a situation there is a permanent population in the northern suburbs of Athens and Mt Penteli (V. Vousvaros), where they probably also exploit various exotic conifers. The total breeding population of Crossbills in non-invasion years is estimated at 2,000 to 10,000 pairs.

Local populations tend to be resident or make short-distance movements. Invasions take place every few years and then birds may be much more widespread. The largest recent invasion occurred in 1990, the birds beginning to arrive in July and soon spreading to virtually the whole of the mainland, from sea level upwards, wherever suitable conditions existed, even in gardens and street conifers (e.g. at Messolonghi, Chalkis, Thiva, Athens). Movements of flocks were very evident in the summer and early autumn, gradually dying out after November, with the odd bird on the move until the end of February 1991. An adult bird ringed in Germany on 7 August 1930 was recovered in Greece on 28 September of the same year. This was during a very large invasion into southern and western Europe (*BWP*).

When compared with birds from northern Europe, Crossbills breeding in Greece tend to be smaller, the males duller and yellowish, with only a small percentage of red individuals, and females greyer, less greenish than northern birds (Watson 1964; V. Vousvaros). They have been classified as race *L. c. curvirostra* grading, however, into *L. c. guillemardi* of Turkey and Cyprus (*BWP*). Northern *L. c. curvirostra* with bright red males occur during invasions.

Trumpeter Finch *Bucanetes githagineus*

Accidental

There are seven records of Trumpeter Finch, mainly in April and all but one, of single birds. Five of the records are from the southern Aegean, particularly SW Crete and the island of Gavdos. Outside this area, a male (probably first-summer) was seen and photographed at Cape Lakka on the island of Paxoi, between 19 and 24 May 1992 (Vittery 1994) and one was seen at Olynthos, Chalkidiki, on 29 April 1977 (C.N. Arnold).

Scarlet Rosefinch *Carpodacus erythrinus*

Accidental

Scarlet Rosefinches have been recorded mainly from the island of Chios, with one female in October 1988 and one male and three females in October 1990. In both cases birds were caught on lime in the southern part of the island (Handrinos 1994a; Spinthakis *et al.* 1993). In addition, a singing male was seen at Molyvos (Lesbos) on 22 May 1991 (Brooks 1995) and an adult male was seen at Aposelemis mouth, Crete, on 12 September 1994 (J. & C. Henshall). A recent record of an adult from the Acropolis in Athens on 22 April 1995 (*per*

R. Lamberton), though probably genuine, lacks supporting details.

Bullfinch *Pyrrhula pyrrhula*

Scarce and local resident and winter visitor

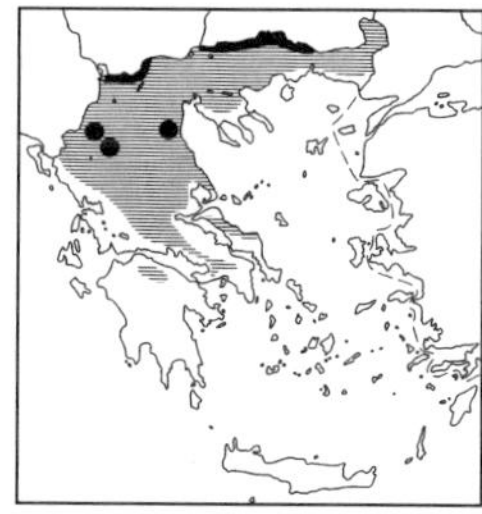

Bullfinches have a very limited breeding range: along the massifs of Mt Voras and Mt Tzena and possibly on adjacent mountains of NW Macedonia as well as farther east in the mountains along the Greece–Bulgaria border, i.e. Mt Kerkini, Mt Orvilos, Mt Kouskouras (an extension of Mt Orvilos) and the Rodopi Mts (*CFG*; Bauer & Hodge 1970; Bauer *et al.* 1973; T. Naziridis). A small isolated population breeds on Mt Olympos (*CFG*) and a few pairs also nest in the valley of R. Voidomatis in Ipeiros (Schmid & Reichenecker 1988) and in the Pindos National Park (Malakou *et al.* 1985). Breeding Bullfinches have been found mainly in beech *Fagus* forest, at altitudes of 680 to 1600 m but on Mt Olympos they occur in Black Pines *Pinus nigra*. The total Greek population is tentatively estimated at 500–1,000 pairs.

The species is more widespread in winter, the local population probably augmented by immigrants from northern countries. It is still an uncommon and local bird, mainly of northern and central parts of the mainland. In these areas wintering birds occur in scrub and open woodland, often at a fairly high altitude, and are commonly attracted to the seeds of the flowering ash *Fraxinus ornus*. South of Sterea Hellas, Bullfinches appear exceptionally, with only a couple of records from the northern Peloponnese. There is one 19th-century record from the Cyclades (Erhard 1858) and no confirmed records from Crete or the other Aegean and Ionian islands. However, one must bear in mind that Bullfinches are probably overlooked due to their secretive habits and montane habitat and may well be more regular and numerous than records suggest.

Hawfinch *Coccothraustes coccothraustes*

Fairly widespread but scarce resident, widespread and locally common winter visitor

As a breeding species, Hawfinches are thinly distributed over much of the central and northern mainland. So far, no breeding records have been reported from the Peloponnese or from the Aegean or Ionian islands, except for Lesbos where one or two birds were seen in June 1982 (P. Heck). During the breeding season Hawfinches prefer pure deciduous woodlands dominated by oak *Quercus* or beech *Fagus* but are not averse to an admixture of conifers. Locally they occur down to almost sea level but are more usually found between 200 and 1000 m and may reach up to the limit of deciduous forest, e.g. to 1800 m on Mt Olympos (Malakou 1985). In summer they are very often attracted to trees of cultivated or wild cherry *Prunus avium*. The total breeding population probably amounts to 5,000–30,000 pairs.

Hawfinches are much more widespread and numerous in winter, with presumably large numbers of immigrants arriving from the north. They are locally common south to Sterea Hellas but rather scarce (though regular) in the Peloponnese and on most Aegean islands. At this time of year they are found in all kinds of open woodland, scrub, orchards and farmland with hedges and trees. They concentrate in areas where there are abundant food sources and here they form loose flocks, usually of up to a dozen birds. In winter they are often seen feeding on the seeds of *Paliurus spina–christi* in northern Greece and on the seeds of *Pistacia terebinthus*, almonds *Prunus dulcis*, locally pine nuts *Pinus pinea* and perhaps olive stones in southern parts of the country and the islands. A small passage is reported for Crete (*BoC*), the Peloponnese (CP) and Kefallinia (A. Vittery), but the nature of their movements is not yet clear. Since the species does not winter in significant numbers south of the Mediterranean (*BWP*) it seems more likely that such movements refer to rather small scale wanderings in search of food sources. The arrival of wintering birds begins in early October, with the main body arriving in the second half of the month, and departures begin in the end of February and most birds have left by about 20 March, with the odd straggler until the end of April.

Pine Bunting *Emberiza leucocephalos*

Accidental

There are three records of Pine Bunting, all from the island of Chios and all of birds trapped or limed in the southern part of the island: a male in October 1977, a pair in November 1980 and a male in November 1981 (Handrinos 1994a; Spinthakis *et al.* 1993).

Yellowhammer *Emberiza citrinella*

Fairly common but local resident, locally common winter visitor

Yellowhammers have a restricted breeding range in Greece in two main areas on the mainland: along the Pindos range, as far south as Mt Parnassos, and on the Rodopi Mts, along the Greece–Bulgaria border (*CFG*; Bauer *et al.* 1973; Bauer & Hodge 1970; Bauer & Böhr 1987). A record of a male at L. Stymfalia in late August 1987 (CP) may refer to a bird from an isolated population in the northern Peloponnese or from Sterea Hellas. Yellowhammers nest in upland areas, always above 800–900 m altitude, usually between 1200–1600 m and sometimes even higher (e.g. at up to 1800 m on Mt Parnassos). Such areas correspond to both the montane coniferous and the deciduous (beech *Fagus*, oak *Quercus*) forest zones, and here they are found in clearings and other open areas with bushes and scattered trees. The total breeding population is probably in the order of 1,000–5,000 pairs.

Most Yellowhammers breeding in Greece presumably move to lower altitudes in winter. Overall numbers increase significantly in winter, particularly during severe weather. However, even then they are restricted to the north and parts of the central mainland. They are rare elsewhere: there is only one record from Crete, on 6 April 1979 (*BoC*), no records from most other Aegean and Ionian islands but surprisingly, presumably erroneously, the species is listed as a common autumn migrant (September–October) on Chios (Spinthakis *et al.* 1993). Wintering Yellowhammers form flocks with other seed-eating birds in open lowland areas, farmland, the margins of coastal wetlands and other open habitats.

Cirl Bunting *Emberiza cirlus*

Common and widespread resident

One of the commonest *Emberiza* species in Greece, Cirl Buntings breed over most of the mainland and the larger islands in both the Aegean and the Ionian Seas. For breeding they seem to like especially areas where small fields or stony pasture are mixed with scattered bushes and small trees. They also regularly occur in open maquis and in not too intensively cultivated open olive groves or orchards but they are practically absent from both extensive treeless farmland and closed woodland. Breeding takes place from sea level up to the treeline but populations are most dense below 1200 m and in southern parts they prefer middle altitudes, being largely or entirely absent below about 100 m. On Crete, Cirl Buntings breed from 400 to 1500 m but mainly at 700–1200 m (*BoC*) and on Kefallinia as high as 1300 m but mainly at lower altitudes (A. Vittery). The total breeding population almost certainly exceeds 50,000 pairs and may well be up to 200,000 pairs.

In winter, Cirl Buntings spread to farmland, where they are common, but they do not normally mix with the large flocks of Skylarks, Corn Buntings or Chaffinches that form on large ploughed fields, preferring to stay near the edge of the fields, close to bushes or trees. The Greek population seems to be resident as a rule, birds making only altitudinal movements to lower areas in winter. Additionally, there is probably an influx of immigrants from northern countries at this time of the year. Birds of either origin appear in non-breeding areas mainly from mid October to late February or early March.

Cirl Bunting

Rock Bunting *Emberiza cia*

Fairly widespread but scarce resident

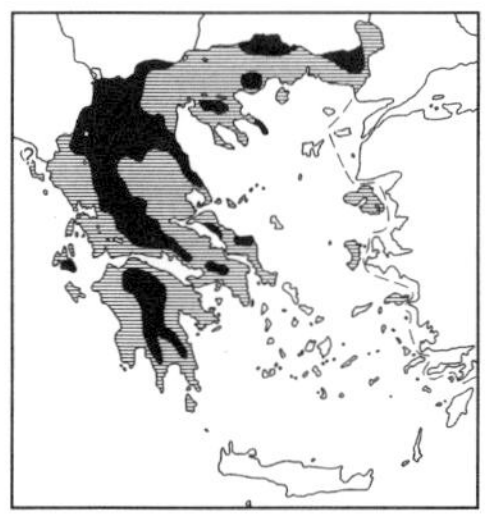

A rather poorly known species, Rock Bunting has a widespread but discontinuous breeding range over most of the mainland. Existing data show that they do not breed on any of the islands, except Kefallinia (F. Pergantis) and perhaps Corfu (*CFG*), despite statements to the contrary by some authors (e.g. Tucker & Heath 1994). In the past the species has been listed as breeding on Crete (Vagliano 1984) but more recently it was revealed to be only an accidental visitor there, with only a handful of records (*BoC*). Rock Buntings are generally birds of middle and higher altitudes, usually occurring at or just above the treeline, in rocky areas with scattered stunted trees, or lower down in clearings, felled areas and other open patches among denser woodland. When in or near woodland, they seem to prefer coniferous species (fir *Abies*, pine *Pinus* or juniper

Juniperus), perhaps because of the rather dry, rocky ground usually associated with these trees, and seem to avoid broadleaved woodland with dense undergrowth and meadow-like clearings with tall grass. They frequently sing from the top of quite tall trees, unlike most other greek buntings, except Black-headed. The total Greek population is probably in the order of 5,000–20,000 pairs.

In winter, Rock Buntings move to lower elevations and are not uncommon on coastal plains, especially in the vicinity of high mountains. They are quite hardy, frequently staying as near their breeding grounds as they can, and are only temporarily forced to lower ground by deep snow. Birds seen in the lowlands may well include some immigrants from the northern Balkans.

Cinereous Bunting *Emberiza cineracea*

Rare and local summer visitor

Cinereous Buntings were first discovered breeding in Greece in 1960 (Watson 1964). So far, they have been found to breed in three distinct populations. By far the largest population is found in the western part of Lesbos, with a minimum estimate of 100 and perhaps as many as 250 pairs. A few pairs have also been found nesting on Chios, where they were first discovered in 1971 (Bauer *et al.* 1973) and seen again in 1991, 1992 and 1993 (Hölzinger 1995; M.J. Taylor). A further small population was discovered much further west, on the island of Skyros in 1994, with one pair feeding young at one site in the north of the island and two singing males at another site in the south of the island (Hölzinger 1995). Thus, although no accurate census of the total Greek population has ever been made, the estimate of Tucker & Heath (1994) at 50–100 pairs is certainly too low. Cinereous Buntings are a poorly known species. On Lesbos they breed in dry, open hilly country with low phrygana and scattered boulders. Their breeding habitat is similar on Skyros and Chios, though in the latter widely spaced Calabrian pines *Pinus brutia* have been reported. They are present on their breeding grounds from early April to at least late July or early August. There are only two records from the rest of the country: a single was seen on Kos in May 1986 (C. Wormwell) and there is a remarkable sighting of two or three birds on Corfu from 7–9 June 1991 (D. Jackson).

Cinereous Buntings are not always easy to see, perching among boulders or on top of low stones or bushes, but once one has learnt their distinctive song they are relatively easy to locate in spring. On Lesbos, in areas where Cinereous Buntings occur in largest numbers, Cretzschmar's Buntings are either absent or scarce, whereas the latter are very common in similar habitat in nearby areas, suggesting a high degree of active or passive interspecific competition. On Lesbos, Cinereous Buntings seem to rely largely on the often abundant bush-crickets (Tettigonidae) that occur in the phrygana in late spring. Similarly, an adult were seen carrying a large 'grasshopper' on Chios (M.J. Taylor).

Ortolan Bunting *Emberiza hortulana*

Widespread and locally common summer visitor

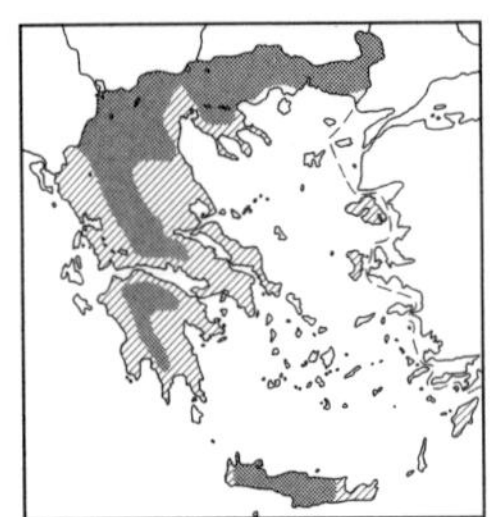

Ortolan Buntings breed over most of the mainland, including the Peloponnese but their status on the islands is not well known; they breed on Crete, where they are locally common (*BoC*) and perhaps on Samothraki. In the past they have been recorded possibly breeding on Rhodes, Naxos, Zakynthos and Corfu (*CFG*), though there exist no recent breeding records from any of these areas, and although reported as breeding on Chios (Spinthakis *et al.* 1993) this seems unlikely on grounds of habitat availability. Ortolan Buntings are an upland species in much of the country, found e.g. usually over 800 m on Mt Chelmos (CP), above the treeline on Samothraki (Watson 1964) and on Mts Vardousia and Parnassos, but they occur down to almost sea level in Macedonia and Thrace. They are thus separated altitudinally and latitudinally from

Cretzschmar's Buntings. On Crete, where Cretzschmar's Buntings are absent, Ortolans breed from sea level up to 1200 m, being commonest between 400 and 1000 m (*BoC*). Breeding takes place in a variety of semi-open habitats, particularly plateaus and bushy rocky slopes with scattered trees, patches of cultivated land within woodland or small scale fields with hedges and trees. The total breeding population lies within the 20,000–50,000 range.

In spring, there is a passage of birds heading for breeding grounds further north. This is on a small scale in most of the country, though the species is reported common on spring migration on Crete (*BoC*). Arrivals and through-passage are from late March to mid May and departures seem to take place mainly from late July to late August, with only a small number of records up to the end of September. Autumn passage is practically non-existent.

Cretzschmar's Bunting *Emberiza caesia*

Fairly widespread and locally common summer visitor

A Mediterranean endemic, Cretzschmar's Buntings are common in coastal southern and central Greece, but in the northern part of the country they breed only in Chalkidiki and Thasos and here they are rather local. They also breed in the Ionian islands and throughout the Aegean but surprisingly not on Crete or Karpathos, though a few May records exist from both islands (Broggi & Willi 1993; *BoC*). Southeastern Greece and the Aegean region hold the densest populations, being rather scarce in the west. Their total breeding population is in the order of 5,000–20,000 pairs.

In spring and early summer, Cretzschmar's Buntings are a characteristic species of bare rocky hills with phrygana or low, open maquis, from sea level up to about 1000 m. In the phrygana of southern Greece and many islands they are usually the most numerous species and on April mornings their song echoes on the bare hills, accompanied by that of the occasional Black-eared Wheatear, Sardinian Warbler or Stonechat. After breeding they frequently spread to farmland or other open habitats, even the edges of wetlands. They usually first appear around the middle of March, with most arrivals from about 20 March to 5 April, and leave from late July to late August.

Rustic Bunting *Emberiza rustica*

Accidental

There are two records of Rustic Bunting, both of ringed birds recovered in Greece: one ringed on Fair Isle on 12 June 1963, recovered on Chios on 15 October 1963 (Spencer 1964), and another ringed at Gozo, Malta, on 13 October 1976 and recovered on Rhodes on 24 October 1976 (Spinthakis *et al.* 1993).

Little Bunting *Emberiza pusilla*

Accidental

One bird seen in the Amvrakikos on 1 February 1964 (Hoffmann *et al.* 1964) is the only record of this species.

Yellow-breasted Bunting *Emberiza aureola*

Accidental

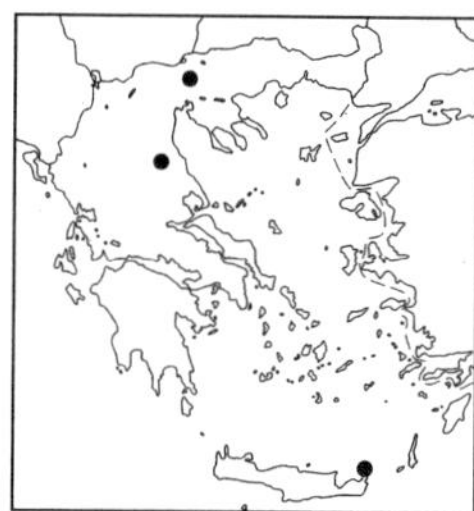

There are four records of Yellow-breasted Bunting, all of single birds: L. Artzan on 15 January 1956 (Flach 1956; Lambert 1957), near Larisa in May 1961 (Palsson & Flach 1962) and immatures ringed on the island of Dragonada, off NE Crete, on 5 September 1974 and 17 September 1976 (*BoC*).

Reed Bunting *Emberiza schoeniclus*

Scarce and local resident, common and widespread winter visitor

Reed Buntings have a very patchy breeding distribution, with confirmed breeding at a small number of sites in Thrace and Macedonia and with some scattered records of possible breeding in the central mainland (e.g. the Amvrakikos and Spercheios Delta). They breed mainly in reedbeds and *Tamarix* marshes both on the coast and at inland freshwater wetlands, from sea level up to 850 m, at L. Mikri Prespa. They are, however, nowhere common and the total Greek population is tentatively estimated at 300–500 pairs.

Reed Buntings breeding in Greece belong to the thick-billed race *E. s. reiseri* (*CFG*), which is presumably largely sedentary, but in winter the population is augmented by immigrants from the north, both of the thin-billed nominate race, *E. s. schoeniclus*, and of the intermediate-billed *E. s. intermedia*, and/or *E. s. stresemanni* and *E. s. ukrainae* (Makatsch 1950; *CFG*). Intermediate-billed birds are the most numerous, followed by thin-billed birds, whilst the thick-billed form is rather rare. Unfortunately, there are still no ringing recoveries to show the origin of wintering birds. Although much more widespread and locally common on the mainland in winter, they seem to rarely reach as far as the Cyclades or Crete. At this time of the year they occur in all kinds of marshy habitats but also occur in nearby farmland, joining flocks of other buntings and finches.Winter visitors arrive from the middle of October onwards and start leaving at the beginning of March, with some birds remaining almost to the end of the month.

Black-headed Bunting *Emberiza melanocephala*

Widespread and locally very common summer visitor

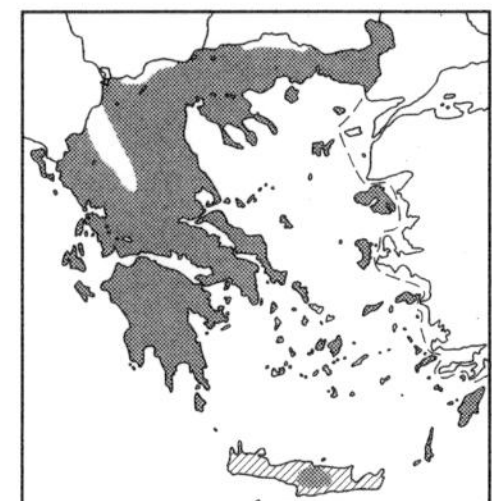

One of the most familiar birds of Greek farmland in summer, Black-headed Buntings have a widespread breeding distribution over most of the mainland and on most of the islands in both the Aegean and the Ionian Seas. However, they are not common on Crete (*BoC*) and due to shortage of suitable habitat are absent from most of the smaller islands. They are commonest in arable land with widely scattered bushes or trees and are often seen perched on telegraph wires and sometimes high up on top of tall trees. They also occur in other open low-lying areas, such as vineyards and open olive groves and range from sea level to 1200 m. Their total breeding population probably numbers 100,000–300,000 pairs. Although reported as declining in Greece (Tucker & Heath 1994), it is still a very common species in much of the country. Threats which may have caused local declines include habitat changes (especially the removal of trees and hedges from arable land), pesticides and illegal trapping for the pet trade. In spring, males arrive first, followed by females a few days later. Isolated individuals may be seen in late April but the large majority of males arrive in the first few days of May. In autumn, Black-headed Buntings leave early, from late July onwards and most are gone by the middle of August.

Black-headed Bunting

Corn Bunting *Miliaria calandra*

Very common and widespread resident

Apparently the commonest of the bunting species in Greece, Corn Buntings breed over virtually the whole of the mainland and on most islands in both Aegean and Ionian Seas. Throughout the year they occur in a variety of open habitats, treeless or with some hedgerows, scattered bushes or low trees, such as farmland (especially cornfields), dry pasture and meadows bordering wetlands, from sea level up to about 1600 m, though they are more usual below about 1200 m. Male Corn Buntings singing on telegraph wires are one of the commonest sights in the Greek countryside in spring. The total breeding population probably lies between 200,000 and 500,000 pairs. The species has been reported as declining (Tucker & Heath 1994) and although there is no hard evidence to justify this, it is very probable that intensification of agriculture affects them very adversely.

After breeding, Corn Buntings form flocks of 20–100 birds, frequently gathering in large numbers on lake shores to drink and bathe. The species is even commoner in winter, when the local population increases further with the arrival of winter immigrants. Large flocks are then present on arable land and sometimes gather in huge concentrations to roost in reedbeds.

APPENDIX A: ADDITIONAL ACKNOWLEDGEMENTS

The following also kindly responded to our request for information or photographic material, providing their notes from trips to Greece or slides.

R.C. Adsett
O. Armini
D. Atter
T.G. Ball
H.A.O. Baumann
G. Beale
G. Beaton
J.S. Bennett
J. Blincow
L. Bolund
P.R. Bono
S. Brehme
J.H.F. Brown
P.M. Burton
R. Butts
G. Clarke
D.G.F. Class
P.G. Crispin
R. Daalder
P. Dahmen
S. Davidson
F. Davis
R.J. Dean
P.K. Dedicoat
J.A. Dixon
C. Durdin
G. Elias
T. Elliot
F. Ellis
W. Emerson
J. Erritzoe
I.B. Evans
J. Faldborg
J. Fine
P. & J. Forbes
B.C. Forrester
D. Graham Bell
A.E. Green
P.G. Green
M.J. Hamzij
J. Hancox
B. Harden
P.R. Harrell
M. Helin
D. Hemingway
S. Hennig
P. Hess
G. Hewson
J. & H. Higgins
I. Hillery
B. Hinds
J.B. Holder
V. Hope
B. Husband
R.F. Jackson
M. Jahnel
W. & P. Jüttner
A. Kimber
R.G. King
H.R. Kirkwood
V. Knoke
B. Krause
V.D. Kuil
M. Lange
V. Larsen
H. Lege
J. Limberger
C.B. Linton
W. Lissak
A. Magnusson
D.C. Marsh
B. Massa
M.I. McDonald
R. & I. McGeorge
T. McGrath
H. Mendel
D. Miller
G.D. Mountain
R. Mundry
D. Murdoch
R.J. Mynott
I. Nörenberg
R.E. North
J.J. O'Connell
A. Onrubia
W.R. Palmer
R. Pasquali
R. Peterson
D. Pitman
R. Plowman
W. Preston
V. Radomski
A. Reed
G.D. Rees
J. Reichel
C.M. Richards
A. Rogers
H. Rosen
M. Roser
L. Rydell
L. Sandberg
R. Saranto
A. Schmidt
A.C. Selmar
R. Seppälä
M. Slater
J.H. Smart
V. Sperens
S. Squires
S.D. Stansfield
M. Stelzer
C. Stephenson
D. Stirling
W. Suter
Swan Hellenic Tours
J.P. Tavares
N. Tellbe
M. Townsend
R. Travis
L.R. Turner
H. Uhl
E. Vicks
C. & B. Viney
R. Vink
D. Warden
G. Wilson
R. Wittenberg
J.G. Wood
P. Yesou
T. Zorzenon

APPENDIX B: CHECKLIST OF GREEK BIRDS

Abbreviations

R	resident
PLM	partial migrant
SV	summer visitor (breeding)
PM	passage migrant
NBV	non-breeding visitor
WV	winter visitor
	(for all of the above: uppercase signifies that the species is common, lowercase that it is scarce)
Acc	Accidental
Ext	Extinct
Int	Introduced
FBr	Formerly breeding

More than one code may be used for many species, in order of importance.

1	Red-throated Diver	*Gavia stellata*	wv		
2	Black-throated Diver	*Gavia arctica*	WV		
3	Great Northern Diver	*Gavia immer*	Acc		
4	Little Grebe	*Tachybaptus ruficollis*	R		
5	Great Crested Grebe	*Podiceps cristatus*	WV	R	
6	Red-necked Grebe	*Podiceps grisegena*	wv	FBr	
7	Slavonian Grebe	*Podiceps auritus*	wv		
8	Black-necked Grebe	*Podiceps nigricollis*	WV	r	
9	Cory's Shearwater	*Calonectris diomedea*	SV		
10	Mediterranean Shearwater	*Puffinus yelkouan*	R		
11	Storm Petrel	*Hydrobates pelagicus*	sv		
12	Gannet	*Sula bassana*	wv	pm	
13	Cormorant	*Phalacrocorax carbo*	WV	R	
14	Shag	*Phalacrocorax aristotelis*	R		
15	Pygmy Cormorant	*Phalacrocorax pygmeus*	WV	r	
16	White Pelican	*Pelecanus onocrotalus*	sv	pm	
17	Dalmatian Pelican	*Pelecanus crispus*	R		
18	Bittern	*Botaurus stellaris*	wv	pm	r?
19	Little Bittern	*Ixobrychus minutus*	SV	PM	
20	Night Heron	*Nycticorax nycticorax*	SV	PM	
21	Squacco Heron	*Ardeola ralloides*	SV	PM	
22	Cattle Egret	*Bubulcus ibis*	nbv	sv	
23	Western Reef Heron	*Egretta gularis*	Acc		
24	Little Egret	*Egretta garzetta*	PM	R	
25	Great White Egret	*Egretta alba*	WV	r	
26	Grey Heron	*Ardea cinerea*	R		
27	Purple Heron	*Ardea purpurea*	PM	sv	
28	Black Stork	*Ciconia nigra*	sv	pm	
29	White Stork	*Ciconia ciconia*	SV	PM	
30	Glossy Ibis	*Plegadis falcinellus*	PM	sv	
31	Spoonbill	*Platalea leucorodia*	r		
32	Greater Flamingo	*Phoenicopterus ruber*	NBV	r?	
33	Mute Swan	*Cygnus olor*	WV	r	
34	Bewick's Swan	*Cygnus columbianus*	Acc		
35	Whooper Swan	*Cygnus cygnus*	wv		
36	Bean Goose	*Anser fabalis*	wv		

37	White-fronted Goose	*Anser albifrons*	WV		
38	Lesser White-fronted Goose	*Anser erythropus*	wv		
39	Greylag Goose	*Anser anser*	wv	r	
40	Brent Goose	*Branta bernicla*	Acc		
41	Red-breasted Goose	*Branta ruficollis*	wv		
42	Ruddy Shelduck	*Tadorna ferruginea*	plm		
43	Shelduck	*Tadorna tadorna*	WV	r	
44	Wigeon	*Anas penelope*	WV		
45	Gadwall	*Anas strepera*	WV	r	
46	Teal	*Anas crecca*	WV		
47	Mallard	*Anas platyrhynchos*	WV	r	
48	Pintail	*Anas acuta*	WV	PM	
49	Garganey	*Anas querquedula*	PM	sv	
50	Blue-winged Teal	*Anas discors*	Acc		
51	Shoveler	*Anas clypeata*	WV	PM	
52	Marbled Teal	*Marmaronetta angustirostris*	Acc	FBr	
53	Red-crested Pochard	*Netta rufina*	wv	r	
54	Pochard	*Aythya ferina*	WV	r	
55	Ferruginous Duck	*Aythya nyroca*	PM	sv	
56	Tufted Duck	*Aythya fuligula*	WV		
57	Scaup	*Aythya marila*	wv		
58	Eider	*Somateria mollissima*	nbv		
59	Long-tailed Duck	*Clangula hyemalis*	wv		
60	Common Scoter	*Melanitta nigra*	wv		
61	Velvet Scoter	*Melanitta fusca*	wv		
62	Goldeneye	*Bucephala clangula*	wv		
63	Smew	*Mergus albellus*	wv		
64	Red-breasted Merganser	*Mergus serrator*	WV		
65	Goosander	*Mergus merganser*	r		
66	White-headed Duck	*Oxyura leucocephala*	wv		
67	Honey Buzzard	*Pernis apivorus*	sv	pm	
68	Black-shouldered Kite	*Elanus caeruleus*	Acc		
69	Black Kite	*Milvus migrans*	wv	pm	r
70	Red Kite	*Milvus milvus*	wv	pm	
71	White-tailed Eagle	*Haliaeetus albicilla*	r		
72	Lammergeier	*Gypaetus barbatus*	r		
73	Egyptian Vulture	*Neophron percnopterus*	sv	pm	
74	Griffon Vulture	*Gyps fulvus*	R		
75	Black Vulture	*Aegypius monachus*	r		
76	Short-toed Eagle	*Circaetus gallicus*	sv		
77	Marsh Harrier	*Circus aeruginosus*	WV	PM	r
78	Hen Harrier	*Circus cyaneus*	wv	pm	
79	Pallid Harrier	*Circus macrourus*	pm		
80	Montagu's Harrier	*Circus pygargus*	PM	sv	
81	Goshawk	*Accipiter gentilis*	R		
82	Sparrowhawk	*Accipiter nisus*	WV	r	
83	Levant Sparrowhawk	*Accipiter brevipes*	sv	pm	
84	Buzzard	*Buteo buteo*	R	WV	
85	Long-legged Buzzard	*Buteo rufinus*	plm		
86	Rough-legged Buzzard	*Buteo lagopus*	wv		
87	Lesser Spotted Eagle	*Aquila pomarina*	sv	pm	
88	Spotted Eagle	*Aquila clanga*	wv		
89	Steppe Eagle	*Aquila nipalensis*	wv	pm	
90	Imperial Eagle	*Aquila heliaca*	r	wv	
91	Golden Eagle	*Aquila chrysaetos*	r		
92	Booted Eagle	*Hieraaetus pennatus*	sv	pm	
93	Bonelli's Eagle	*Hieraaetus fasciatus*	r		
94	Osprey	*Pandion haliaetus*	pm	FBr	

95	Lesser Kestrel	*Falco naumanni*	sv	pm	
96	Kestrel	*Falco tinnunculus*	R		
97	Red-footed Falcon	*Falco vespertinus*	PM		
98	Merlin	*Falco columbarius*	wv		
99	Hobby	*Falco subbuteo*	SV	PM	
100	Eleonora's Falcon	*Falco eleonorae*	SV		
101	Lanner	*Falco biarmicus*	r		
102	Saker	*Falco cherrug*	wv	pm	
103	Peregrine	*Falco peregrinus*	r	wv	
104	Barbary Falcon	*Falco pelegrinoides*	Acc		
105	Hazel Grouse	*Bonasa bonasia*	r		
106	Black Grouse	*Tetrao tetrix*	Acc?		
107	Capercaillie	*Tetrao urogallus*	r		
108	Chukar	*Alectoris chukar*	R		
109	Rock Partridge	*Alectoris graeca*	R		
110	Red-legged Partridge	*Alectoris rufa*	Int		
111	Black Francolin	*Francolinus francolinus*	Ext		
112	Grey Partridge	*Perdix perdix*	R		
113	Quail	*Coturnix coturnix*	SV	PM	r
114	Pheasant	*Phasianus colchicus*	r		
115	Water Rail	*Rallus aquaticus*	R		
116	Spotted Crake	*Porzana porzana*	pm	wv	
117	Little Crake	*Porzana parva*	PM	sv	
118	Baillon's Crake	*Porzana pusilla*	pm	sv?	
119	Corncrake	*Crex crex*	pm		
120	Moorhen	*Gallinula chloropus*	R		
121	Purple Gallinule	*Porphyrio porphyrio*	Acc	FBr	
122	Coot	*Fulica atra*	WV	R	
123	Crane	*Grus grus*	pm		
124	Demoiselle Crane	*Anthropoides virgo*	Acc		
125	Little Bustard	*Tetrax tetrax*	wv	pm	FBr
126	Houbara Bustard	*Chlamydotis undulata*	Acc		
127	Great Bustard	*Otis tarda*	Acc	FBr	
128	Oystercatcher	*Haematopus ostralegus*	WV	r	
129	Black-winged Stilt	*Himantopus himantopus*	PM	SV	
130	Avocet	*Recurvirostra avosetta*	R	WV	
131	Stone Curlew	*Burhinus oedicnemus*	sv	pm	
132	Cream-coloured Courser	*Cursorius cursor*	Acc		
133	Collared Pratincole	*Glareola pratincola*	SV	PM	
134	Black-winged Pratincole	*Glareola nordmanni*	pm		
135	Little Ringed Plover	*Charadrius dubius*	SV	PM	
136	Ringed Plover	*Charadrius hiaticula*	PM	wv	
137	Kentish Plover	*Charadrius alexandrinus*	R		
138	Greater Sand Plover	*Charadrius leschenaultii*	wv	pm	
139	Caspian Plover	*Charadrius asiaticus*	Acc		
140	Dotterel	*Charadrius morinellus*	pm	sv?	
141	Pacific Golden Plover	*Pluvialis fulva*	Acc		
142	Golden Plover	*Pluvialis apricaria*	WV		
143	Grey Plover	*Pluvialis squatarola*	WV	PM	
144	Spur-winged Plover	*Hoplopterus spinosus*	sv		
145	Sociable Plover	*Chettusia gregaria*	Acc		
146	White-tailed Plover	*Chettusia leucura*	Acc		
147	Lapwing	*Vanellus vanellus*	WV	r	
148	Knot	*Calidris canutus*	pm	wv	
149	Sanderling	*Calidris alba*	PM	wv	
150	Little Stint	*Calidris minuta*	PM	WV	
151	Temminck's Stint	*Calidris temminckii*	PM		
152	Long-toed Stint	*Calidris subminuta*	Acc		

153	Baird's Sandpiper	*Calidris bairdii*	Acc		
154	Curlew Sandpiper	*Calidris ferruginea*	PM		
155	Purple Sandpiper	*Calidris maritima*	Acc		
156	Dunlin	*Calidris alpina*	WV	PM	
157	Broad-billed Sandpiper	*Limicola falcinellus*	pm		
158	Ruff	*Philomachus pugnax*	PM	wv	
159	Jack Snipe	*Lymnocryptes minimus*	wv	pm	
160	Snipe	*Gallinago gallinago*	WV	PM	
161	Great Snipe	*Gallinago media*	pm		
162	Long-billed Dowitcher	*Limnodromus scolopaceus*	Acc		
163	Woodcock	*Scolopax rusticola*	WV	r	
164	Black-tailed Godwit	*Limosa limosa*	PM	wv	
165	Bar-tailed Godwit	*Limosa lapponica*	pm	wv	
166	Whimbrel	*Numenius phaeopus*	pm		
167	Slender-billed Curlew	*Numenius tenuirostris*	pm	wv	
168	Curlew	*Numenius arquata*	WV	PM	
169	Spotted Redshank	*Tringa erythropus*	PM	wv	
170	Redshank	*Tringa totanus*	R		
171	Marsh Sandpiper	*Tringa stagnatilis*	PM		
172	Greenshank	*Tringa nebularia*	PM	wv	
173	Lesser Yellowlegs	*Tringa flavipes*	Acc		
174	Green Sandpiper	*Tringa ochropus*	WV	PM	
175	Wood Sandpiper	*Tringa glareola*	PM		
176	Terek Sandpiper	*Xenus cinereus*	pm		
177	Common Sandpiper	*Actitis hypoleucos*	PM	sv	
178	Spotted Sandpiper	*Actitis macularia*	Acc		
179	Turnstone	*Arenaria interpres*	PM		
180	Red-necked Phalarope	*Phalaropus lobatus*	pm		
181	Grey Phalarope	*Phalaropus fulicarius*	Acc		
182	Pomarine Skua	*Stercorarius pomarinus*	Acc		
183	Arctic Skua	*Stercorarius parasiticus*	pm		
184	Great Skua	*Stercorarius skua*	Acc		
185	White-eyed Gull	*Larus leucophthalmus*	Acc		
186	Great Black-headed Gull	*Larus ichthyaetus*	nbv		
187	Mediterranean Gull	*Larus melanocephalus*	R		
188	Laughing Gull	*Larus atricilla*	Acc		
189	Little Gull	*Larus minutus*	PM	wv	
190	Black-headed Gull	*Larus ridibundus*	WV	r	
191	Slender-billed Gull	*Larus genei*	WV	PM	r
192	Audouin's Gull	*Larus audouinii*	r		
193	Common Gull	*Larus canus*	WV		
194	Lesser Black-backed Gull	*Larus fuscus*	pm	wv	
195	Herring Gull	*Larus argentatus*	wv		
196	Yellow-legged Gull	*Larus cachinnans*	R		
197	Iceland Gull	*Larus glaucoides*	Acc		
198	Great Black-backed Gull	*Larus marinus*	wv	pm	
199	Kittiwake	*Rissa tridactyla*	wv		
200	Gull-billed Tern	*Gelochelidon nilotica*	sv	pm	
201	Caspian Tern	*Sterna caspia*	nbv	r?	
202	Lesser Crested Tern	*Sterna bengalensis*	Acc		
203	Sandwich Tern	*Sterna sandvicensis*	WV	PM	r
204	Common Tern	*Sterna hirundo*	SV	PM	
205	Arctic Tern	*Sterna paradisaea*	Acc		
206	Bridled Tern	*Sterna anaethetus*	Acc		
207	Little Tern	*Sterna albifrons*	SV	PM	
208	Whiskered Tern	*Chlidonias hybridus*	PM	sv	
209	Black Tern	*Chlidonias niger*	PM	sv	
210	White-winged Black Tern	*Chlidonias leucopterus*	PM		

211	Pin-tailed Sandgrouse	*Pterocles alchata*	Acc		
212	Pallas's Sandgrouse	*Syrrhaptes paradoxus*	Acc		
213	Rock Dove	*Columba livia*	R		
214	Stock Dove	*Columba oenas*	wv	r	
215	Woodpigeon	*Columba palumbus*	R		
216	Collared Dove	*Streptopelia decaocto*	R		
217	Turtle Dove	*Streptopelia turtur*	SV	PM	
218	Rufous Turtle Dove	*Streptopelia orientalis*	Acc		
219	Laughing Dove	*Streptopelia senegalensis*	Acc		
220	Great Spotted Cuckoo	*Clamator glandarius*	sv	pm	
221	Cuckoo	*Cuculus canorus*	sv	PM	
222	Barn Owl	*Tyto alba*	R		
223	Scops Owl	*Otus scops*	PLM		
224	Eagle Owl	*Bubo bubo*	r		
225	Pygmy Owl	*Glaucidium passerinum*	r		
226	Little Owl	*Athene noctua*	R		
227	Tawny Owl	*Strix aluco*	R		
228	Long-eared Owl	*Asio otus*	R	WV	
229	Short-eared Owl	*Asio flammeus*	wv	pm	r?
230	Tengmalm's Owl	*Aegolius funereus*	r		
231	Nightjar	*Caprimulgus europaeus*	SV		
232	Swift	*Apus apus*	SV	PM	
233	Pallid Swift	*Apus pallidus*	SV		
234	Alpine Swift	*Apus melba*	SV	PM	
235	Little Swift	*Apus affinis*	Acc		
236	White-breasted Kingfisher	*Halcyon smyrnensis*	Acc		
237	Kingfisher	*Alcedo atthis*	WV	r	
238	Pied Kingfisher	*Ceryle rudis*	Acc		
239	Blue-cheeked Bee-eater	*Merops superciliosus*	pm		
240	Bee-eater	*Merops apiaster*	SV	PM	
241	Roller	*Coracias garrulus*	sv	pm	
242	Hoopoe	*Upupa epops*	SV	PM	
243	Wryneck	*Jynx torquilla*	PM	r	
244	Grey-headed Woodpecker	*Picus canus*	r		
245	Green Woodpecker	*Picus viridis*	r		
246	Black Woodpecker	*Dryocopus martius*	r		
247	Great Spotted Woodpecker	*Dendrocopos major*	r		
248	Syrian Woodpecker	*Dendrocopos syriacus*	R		
249	Middle Spotted Woodpecker	*Dendrocopos medius*	R		
250	White-backed Woodpecker	*Dendrocopos leucotos*	r		
251	Lesser Spotted Woodpecker	*Dendrocopos minor*	r		
252	Three-toed Woodpecker	*Picoides tridactylus*	r		
253	Dupont's Lark	*Chersophilus duponti*	Acc		
254	Calandra Lark	*Melanocorypha calandra*	R		
255	Bimaculated Lark	*Melanocorypha bimaculata*	Acc		
256	White-winged Lark	*Melanocorypha leucoptera*	Acc		
257	Black Lark	*Melanocorypha yeltoniensis*	Acc		
258	Short-toed Lark	*Calandrella brachydactyla*	SV	PM	
259	Crested Lark	*Galerida cristata*	R		
260	Woodlark	*Lullula arborea*	R		
261	Skylark	*Alauda arvensis*	WV	R	
262	Shore Lark	*Eremophila alpestris*	r		
263	Sand Martin	*Riparia riparia*	PM	SV	
264	Crag Martin	*Ptyonoprogne rupestris*	PLM		
265	Swallow	*Hirundo rustica*	SV	PM	
266	Red-rumped Swallow	*Hirundo daurica*	SV		
267	House Martin	*Delichon urbica*	SV		
268	Richard's Pipit	*Anthus novaeseelandiae*	pm		

269	Tawny Pipit	*Anthus campestris*	sv		
270	Tree Pipit	*Anthus trivialis*	PM	sv	
271	Meadow Pipit	*Anthus pratensis*	WV		
272	Red-throated Pipit	*Anthus cervinus*	PM	wv	
273	Water Pipit	*Anthus spinoletta*	WV	r	
274	Yellow Wagtail	*Motacilla flava*	SV	PM	
275	Citrine Wagtail	*Motacilla citreola*	pm		
276	Grey Wagtail	*Motacilla cinerea*	R	WV	
277	White Wagtail	*Motacilla alba*	WV	r	
278	Waxwing	*Bombycilla garrulus*	Acc		
279	Dipper	*Cinclus cinclus*	r		
280	Wren	*Troglodytes troglodytes*	R		
281	Dunnock	*Prunella modularis*	WV	r	
282	Alpine Accentor	*Prunella collaris*	r		
283	Rufous Bush Robin	*Cercotrichas galactotes*	sv		
284	Robin	*Erithacus rubecula*	WV	R	
285	Thrush Nightingale	*Luscinia luscinia*	pm		
286	Nightingale	*Luscinia megarhynchos*	SV		
287	Bluethroat	*Luscinia svecica*	wv	pm	
288	White-throated Robin	*Irania gutturalis*	Acc		
289	Black Redstart	*Phoenicurus ochruros*	WV	R	
290	Redstart	*Phoenicurus phoenicurus*	PM	sv	
291	Moussier's Redstart	*Phoenicurus moussieri*	Acc		
292	Whinchat	*Saxicola rubetra*	PM	sv	
293	Stonechat	*Saxicola torquata*	R		
294	Isabelline Wheatear	*Oenanthe isabellina*	sv		
295	Wheatear	*Oenanthe oenanthe*	SV	PM	
296	Pied Wheatear	*Oenanthe pleschanka*	pm	sv	
297	Black-eared Wheatear	*Oenanthe hispanica*	SV		
298	Desert Wheatear	*Oenanthe deserti*	Acc		
299	Finsch's Wheatear	*Oenanthe finschii*	Acc		
300	White-crowned Black Wheatear	*Oenanthe leucopyga*	Acc		
301	Black Wheatear	*Oenanthe leucura*	Acc		
302	Rock Thrush	*Monticola saxatilis*	SV	PM	
303	Blue Rock Thrush	*Monticola solitarius*	R		
304	White's Thrush	*Zoothera dauma*	Acc		
305	Ring Ouzel	*Turdus torquatus*	r	pm	wv
306	Blackbird	*Turdus merula*	R		
307	Black-throated Thrush	*Turdus ruficollis*	Acc		
308	Fieldfare	*Turdus pilaris*	WV	r?	
309	Song Thrush	*Turdus philomelos*	WV	r	
310	Redwing	*Turdus iliacus*	WV		
311	Mistle Thrush	*Turdus viscivorus*	R		
312	Cetti's Warbler	*Cettia cetti*	R		
313	Fan-tailed Warbler	*Cisticola juncidis*	R		
314	Grasshopper Warbler	*Locustella naevia*	pm		
315	River Warbler	*Locustella fluviatilis*	pm	sv?	
316	Savi's Warbler	*Locustella luscinioides*	PM	sv	
317	Moustached Warbler	*Acrocephalus melanopogon*	WV	r	
318	Aquatic Warbler	*Acrocephalus paludicola*	Acc		
319	Sedge Warbler	*Acrocephalus schoenobaenus*	PM	sv	
320	Paddyfield Warbler	*Acrocephalus agricola*	Acc		
321	Marsh Warbler	*Acrocephalus palustris*	PM	sv	
322	Reed Warbler	*Acrocephalus scirpaceus*	SV	PM	
323	Great Reed Warbler	*Acrocephalus arundinaceus*	SV	PM	
324	Olivaceous Warbler	*Hippolais pallida*	SV		
325	Booted Warbler	*Hippolais caligata*	Acc		

326	Olive-tree Warbler	*Hippolais olivetorum*	sv	
327	Icterine Warbler	*Hippolais icterina*	PM	
328	Melodious Warbler	*Hippolais polyglotta*	Acc	
329	Marmora's Warbler	*Sylvia sarda*	r?	
330	Dartford Warbler	*Sylvia undata*	Acc	
331	Spectacled Warbler	*Sylvia conspicillata*	pm	sv?
332	Subalpine Warbler	*Sylvia cantillans*	SV	
333	Sardinian Warbler	*Sylvia melanocephala*	R	
334	Rüppell's Warbler	*Sylvia rueppelli*	SV	
335	Orphean Warbler	*Sylvia hortensis*	sv	
336	Barred Warbler	*Sylvia nisoria*	pm	sv
337	Lesser Whitethroat	*Sylvia curruca*	SV	PM
338	Whitethroat	*Sylvia communis*	SV	PM
339	Garden Warbler	*Sylvia borin*	PM	sv
340	Blackcap	*Sylvia atricapilla*	R	
341	Arctic Warbler	*Phylloscopus borealis*	Acc	
342	Yellow-browed Warbler	*Phylloscopus inornatus*	Acc	
343	Dusky Warbler	*Phylloscopus fuscatus*	Acc	
344	Bonelli's Warbler	*Phylloscopus bonelli*	sv	pm
345	Wood Warbler	*Phylloscopus sibilatrix*	PM	sv
346	Chiffchaff	*Phylloscopus collybita*	WV	SV
347	Willow Warbler	*Phylloscopus trochilus*	PM	sv?
348	Goldcrest	*Regulus regulus*	WV	R
349	Firecrest	*Regulus ignicapillus*	R	
350	Brown Flycatcher	*Muscicapa daurica*	Acc	
351	Spotted Flycatcher	*Muscicapa striata*	PM	SV
352	Red-breasted Flycatcher	*Ficedula parva*	pm	sv
353	Semi-collared Flycatcher	*Ficedula semitorquata*	SV	PM
354	Collared Flycatcher	*Ficedula albicollis*	PM	
355	Pied Flycatcher	*Ficedula hypoleuca*	PM	
356	Bearded Tit	*Panurus biarmicus*	R	
357	Long-tailed Tit	*Aegithalos caudatus*	R	
358	Marsh Tit	*Parus palustris*	R	
359	Sombre Tit	*Parus lugubris*	r	
360	Willow Tit	*Parus montanus*	r	
361	Crested Tit	*Parus cristatus*	r	
362	Coal Tit	*Parus ater*	R	
363	Blue Tit	*Parus caeruleus*	R	
364	Great Tit	*Parus major*	R	
365	Krüper's Nuthatch	*Sitta krueperi*	r	
366	Nuthatch	*Sitta europaea*	R	
367	Rock Nuthatch	*Sitta neumayer*	R	
368	Wallcreeper	*Tichodroma muraria*	r	
369	Treecreeper	*Certhia familiaris*	r	
370	Short-toed Treecreeper	*Certhia brachydactyla*	R	
371	Penduline Tit	*Remiz pendulinus*	R	
372	Golden Oriole	*Oriolus oriolus*	SV	PM
373	Isabelline Shrike	*Lanius isabellinus*	Acc	
374	Red-backed Shrike	*Lanius collurio*	SV	PM
375	Lesser Grey Shrike	*Lanius minor*	sv	pm
376	Great Grey Shrike	*Lanius excubitor*	wv	
377	Woodchat Shrike	*Lanius senator*	SV	
378	Masked Shrike	*Lanius nubicus*	sv	
379	Jay	*Garrulus glandarius*	R	
380	Magpie	*Pica pica*	R	
381	Nutcracker	*Nucifraga caryocatactes*	r	
382	Alpine Chough	*Pyrrhocorax graculus*	R	
383	Chough	*Pyrrhocorax pyrrhocorax*	r	

384	Jackdaw	*Corvus monedula*	R	
385	Rook	*Corvus frugilegus*	WV	FBr
386	Hooded Crow	*Corvus corone*	R	
387	Raven	*Corvus corax*	R	
388	Starling	*Sturnus vulgaris*	WV	R
389	Spotless Starling	*Sturnus unicolor*	Acc	
390	Rose-coloured Starling	*Sturnus roseus*	PM	sv
391	House Sparrow	*Passer domesticus*	R	
392	Spanish Sparrow	*Passer hispaniolensis*	R	SV
393	Dead Sea Sparrow	*Passer moabiticus*	Acc	
394	Tree Sparrow	*Passer montanus*	R	
395	Rock Sparrow	*Petronia petronia*	r	
396	Snowfinch	*Montifringilla nivalis*	r	
397	Chaffinch	*Fringilla coelebs*	R	WV
398	Brambling	*Fringilla montifringilla*	WV	
399	Red-fronted Serin	*Serinus pusillus*	wv	
400	Serin	*Serinus serinus*	R	
401	Greenfinch	*Carduelis chloris*	R	
402	Goldfinch	*Carduelis carduelis*	R	
403	Siskin	*Carduelis spinus*	WV	r
404	Linnet	*Carduelis cannabina*	R	
405	Crossbill	*Loxia curvirostra*	r	
406	Trumpeter Finch	*Bucanetes githagineus*	Acc	
407	Scarlet Rosefinch	*Carpodacus erythrinus*	Acc	
408	Bullfinch	*Pyrrhula pyrrhula*	r	wv
409	Hawfinch	*Coccothraustes coccothraustes*	WV	r
410	Pine Bunting	*Emberiza leucocephalos*	Acc	
411	Yellowhammer	*Emberiza citrinella*	R	WV
412	Cirl Bunting	*Emberiza cirlus*	R	
413	Rock Bunting	*Emberiza cia*	r	
414	Cinereous Bunting	*Emberiza cineracea*	sv	
415	Ortolan Bunting	*Emberiza hortulana*	SV	
416	Cretzschmar's Bunting	*Emberiza caesia*	SV	
417	Rustic Bunting	*Emberiza rustica*	Acc	
418	Little Bunting	*Emberiza pusilla*	Acc	
419	Yellow-breasted Bunting	*Emberiza aureola*	Acc	
420	Reed Bunting	*Emberiza schoeniclus*	WV	r
421	Black-headed Bunting	*Emberiza melanocephala*	SV	
422	Corn Bunting	*Miliaria calandra*	R	

APPENDIX C: OMITTED SPECIES

The following 51 species have been recorded in Greece but all their records have been rejected. These records have either been published in the literature or, more recently, reported by birdwatchers visiting Greece. In most cases the reason for rejection is the lack of proper documentation, such as no field notes supplied or inadequate descriptions.

Great Shearwater *Puffinus gravis*: Three flying east, off Gouves, Crete, on 20 October 1987 (S. Coghlan).

Sooty Shearwater *Puffinus griseus*: 19th century, no date, Evvoia (?) (Lindermayer 1860, Reiser 1905).

Little Shearwater *Puffinus assimilis*: Two, off Gouves, Crete, on 20 October 1987 (S. Coghlan) and one, off Samos, in September 1988 (A. Ranner).

Leach's Storm Petrel *Oceanodroma leucorhoa*: 27 July 1984, Chersonisos, Crete (K. Mauer). Acoustic record of a bird flying inland from the sea at dusk.

Frigatebird *Fregata* sp.: One, flew past a tanker, during heavy seas, *c.* 15 miles southwest of Cape Tainaron, in late September 1966 (A. Tsatsaronis).

Yellow-billed Stork *Mycteria ibis*: 19th century, no date, Greece (Reiser 1905).

Sacred Ibis *Threskiornis aethiopicus*: 19th century, no date, Peloponnese, Aegean (?) (Reiser 1905).

Snow Goose *Anser caerulescens*: Four records: Winter of 1835 and 1841 both at Spercheios Delta (Reiser 1905), 'a large flock' in January 1846, in Macedonia (Drummond-Hay 1846), and a flying flock in the Ionian Sea, off Peloponnese in April 1955 (Bauer *et al.* 1969a).

Egyptian Goose *Alopochen aegyptiacus*: 19th century, no date, Messolonghi, Evvoia (Mühle 1844, Lindermayer 1860, Reiser 1905).

Wood Duck *Aix sponsa*: 19th century, no date, island of Kythira (Jameson 1837).

African Fish Eagle *Haliaeetus vocifer*: 19th century, no date, Greece (Reiser 1905).

Hooded Vulture *Necrosyrtes monachus*: 19th century, no date, Greece (Reiser 1905).

Rüppell's Vulture *Gyps rueppellii*: 19th century, no date, island of Mykonos (Erhard 1858) and island of Syros (?).

Lappet-faced Vulture *Torgos tracheliotus*: 19th century, no date, Peloponnese, Athens (Reiser 1905).

Dark Chanting Goshawk *Melierax metabates*: 19th century, no date, Greece (Reiser 1905).

Sooty Falcon *Falco concolor*: 19th century, no date, Evvoia, (?) Cyclades (Mühle 1844, Erhard 1858).

Barbary Partridge *Alectoris barbara*: 19th century, no date, Peloponnese, Aegean (Mühle 1844, Linderamayer 1860).

Helmeted Guineafowl *Numida meleagris*: 19th century, no date, Greece (Reiser 1905).

Button-Quail *Turnix sylvatica*: 19th century, no date, Greece (Reiser 1905).

Allen's Gallinule *Porphyrula alleni*: An adult found exhausted in a street in Athens on 16 April 1992 and taken to the Hellenic Wildlife Hospital (F. Dragoumis) is certainly an escape.

Siberian White Crane *Grus leucogeranus*: 'A large flock' seen in eastern Macedonia in January 1846 (Drummond-Hay 1846) is the only report of the species in Greece.

Black-headed Plover *Vanellus tectus*: According to Vaurie (1965) it is said to have occurred on Crete, but no other details are given.

White-rumped Sandpiper *Calidris fuscicollis*: One in the Evros Delta in September 1972 (Apalodimos 1983, 1993).

Bonaparte's Gull *Larus philadelphia*: One, in nearly adult plumage, at Platamonas beach on 2 January 1994, among Black-headed Gulls (C. Vagliano).

Roseate Tern *Sterna dougallii*: 19th century, no date, Greece (Mühle 1844).

Sooty Tern *Sterna fuscata*: One at L. Ismaris, 21 April 1985 (J. Wittbrodt & D. Förnzlar).

Brown Noddy *Anous stolidous*: 19th century, no date, island of Kythira (Jameson 1837).

Black-bellied Sandgrouse *Pterocles orientalis*: 19th century, no date, between Megara and Thiva and at Mesogeia (Attica) (Mühle 1844, Lindermayer 1860).

Ural Owl *Strix uralensis*: Acoustic record at Mavrolongos Valley on Mt Olympos, at 1700 m, between 15 and 18 June 1956 (Peus 1957).
Red-necked Nightjar *Caprimulgus ruficollis*: 19th century, no date, Greece (Reiser 1905).
Little Green Bee-eater *Merops orientalis*: 19th century, no date, Greece (Reiser 1905).
Desert Lark *Ammomanes deserti*: 19th century, no date, Tripolis (Mühle 1844), Corfu (Drummond-Hay 1843), Cyclades (Erhard 1858).
Hoopoe Lark *Alaemon alaudipes*: 19th century, no date, Greece (Mühle 1844), Cyclades (Erhard 1858), between Megara and Thiva and at Tripolis (Lindermayer 1860).
Lesser Short-toed Lark *Calandrella rufescens*: Two at Chersonisos, Irakleion, Crete between 28 and 30 April 1990 (R. D. Oades).
Thekla's Lark *Galerida theklae*: One bird near Elounda, Crete, on 7 May 1988 (J. Barker).
Temminck's Horned Lark *Eremophila bilopha*: 19th century, no date, Greek islands (Reiser 1905).
Common Bulbul *Pycnonotus barbatus*: Eggs (2 or 3) collected on Naxos in 1862 and 1863 were attributed to this species (Krüper 1863) but on later examination they were identified as those of the Black-headed Bunting (Reiser 1905).
Siberian Accentor *Prunella montanella*: One record from the island of Tinos in December 1965 (Bauer *et al.* 1969a). Considered valid by Hodge (1973).
Pied Stonechat *Saxicola caprata*: Two records, both from Corfu, on 29 April 1984 and 4 May 1984 (A. Falla).
Dusky Thrush *Turdus naumanni*: One on the island of Paros in March 1966 (Bauer *et al.* 1969a).
Graceful Prinia *Prinia gracilis*: Between 25 and 27 July 1986 at least six birds (four of them singing) near Rethymnon, Crete (T. Conzemius). This record was eventually published in Cramp (1977–94), but the original letter of the observer does not provide any supporting details and the species may well have been confused with Fan-tailed Warbler.
Desert Warbler *Sylvia nana*: In the 6th (1965) German edition of the Peterson *Field Guide* erroneously listed as 'accidental in Greece' (see note in Bauer *et al.* 1969a).
Citril Finch *Serinus citrinella*: One at Delphi in April 1965 (Bauer *et al.* 1969a) and two near Zakros Gorge, Crete, on 29 March 1978 (*BoC*).
Twite *Carduelis flavirostris*: 19th century, no date, Corfu (and other islands ?) (Drummond-Hay 1843).
Common Redpoll *Carduelis flammea*: 19th century, no date. Listed as common and 'appearing to nest' on Crete (Drummond-Hay 1865). Apparently confused with Linnet.
Parrot Crossbill *Loxia pytyopsittacus*: A young bird in the market of Syra, island of Syros, in 1855 (Erhard 1858) and two northeast of Drama on 31 July 1978 (Ritzel 1980).
Lapland Bunting *Calcarius lapponicus*: One at Delphi, in March 1957 (Hodge 1973).
Meadow Bunting *Emberiza cioides*: A female/immature at Kalodiki marsh, Ipeiros, among a flock of Cirl Buntings on 26 and 27 November 1994 (P. Harris).
House Bunting *Emberiza striolata*: 19th century, no date, Peloponnese (Reiser 1905).

APPENDIX D: INTRODUCED SPECIES AND ESCAPES

During the last 30 years a number species of exotic game bird have been released in various parts of Greece. These birds originate in captive-bred stock which was released in selected areas for hunting. Only one of these species, Red-legged Partridge, has become established (on the island of Alonnisos) and this is now included in the Greek list (Handrinos 1994). For all others, introductions have failed, and though small numbers are still kept at game-rearing stations and may be seen in the wild after recent releases, none of them has established a self-supporting population.

These species are:

California Quail *Callipepla californica*
Bobwhite *Colinus virginianus*
Reeves's Pheasant *Syrmaticus reevesii*
Golden Pheasant *Chrysolophus pictus*
Lady Amherst's Pheasant *Chrysolophus amherstiae*

One should bear in mind that Pheasants, Chukars and, to a much lesser extent, Grey Partridges are systematically released for hunting, even in areas or regions far away from their natural ranges. Therefore, all records of such species in unusual areas, e.g. Grey Partridge on the island of Kefallinia (Pasquali 1989), refer to captive-bred and released birds.

Since the mid 1980s there has been a significant increase in the number of exotic bird species imported into Greece for the pet trade. Ministry of Agriculture records show that these fall into two main categories: small parrot species (Psittaciformes) and colourful estrildid finches (Estrildidae).

Some of these birds inevitably escape, and though we have made no systematic or thorough search to record such occurrences, it is apparent that these are rather limited. Among these species, at least one, Ring-necked Parakeet *Psittacula krameri* is worth mentioning. Imported mainly from Pakistan and Hong Kong, it has been seen in the wild on at least seven occasions, particularly around Athens, as well as on Crete (*BoC*) and other parts of the country. A small flock was reported as having established a breeding colony at Glyfada, Athens, in 1991 (E. Tsirozidis) but we have not been able to confirm this.

Other species commonly in cages and often recorded as escapes include Cockatiel *Nymphicus hollandicus*, Common Waxbill *Estrilda astrild*, Zebra Finch *Poephila guttata* and Java Sparrow *Padda oryzivora*, as well as the 'classic' Budgerigar *Melopsittacus undulatus* and Canary *Serinus canarius*. The keeping of birds other than those that can easily be accommodated in a cage (waterfowl, raptors etc.) is virtually non-existent.

APPENDIX E: SPECIES WHICH REACH THEIR SOUTHERNMOST BREEDING LIMIT IN GREECE

Bird species for which Greece is the southernmost limit of their European or Western Palearctic breeding range.

1 Goosander *Mergus merganser*
2 Hazel Grouse *Bonasa bonasia*
3 Capercaillie *Tetrao urogallus*
4 Rock Partridge *Alectoris graeca*
5 Sandwich Tern *Sterna sandvicensis* (?)
6 Pygmy Owl *Glaucidium passerinum*
7 Tengmalm's Owl *Aegolius funereus*
8 Grey-headed Woodpecker *Picus canus*
9 Black Woodpecker *Dryocopus martius*
10 White-backed Woodpecker *Dendrocopos leucotos*
11 Three-toed Woodpecker *Picoides tridactylus*
12 Tree Pipit *Anthus trivialis*
13 Pied Wheatear *Oenanthe pleschanka*
14 Fieldfare *Turdus pilaris*
15 Rüppell's Warbler *Sylvia rueppellii*
16 Willow Tit *Parus montanus*
17 Wallcreeper *Tichodroma muraria*
18 Treecreeper *Certhia familiaris*
19 Nutcracker *Nucifraga caryocatactes*
20 Yellowhammer *Emberiza citrinella*

APPENDIX F: RINGING RECOVERY TOTALS BY COUNTRY OF ORIGIN

Below is a list of the totals of all foreign ringing recoveries in Greece available up to now by country of origin. The list is based on 1,379 recoveries: 1,322 from Europe and N Africa, 44 from Asia, and 13 from Africa south of the Sahara.

Region	Country	Totals
Europe & N Africa	Austria	45
	Belgium	21
	Bulgaria	25
	Croatia	20
	Czech Republic	76
	Denmark	34
	Estonia	15
	Finland	255
	France	12
	Germany	100
	Britain	28
	Hungary	99
	Italy	12
	Latvia	20
	Lithuania	13
	Malta	6
	Moldavia	2
	Netherlands	27
	Norway	9
	Poland	75
	Rumania	20
	Russia	52
	Slovakia	27
	Slovenia	9
	Sweden	151
	Switzerland	16
	Tunisia	1
	Ukraine	139
	Yugoslavia	13
Asia	Asiatic former USSR	40
	Cyprus	2
	Iran	1
	Israel	1
Sub-Saharan Africa	Mali	2
	Nigeria	10
	Kenya	1

APPENDIX G: BIRD SPECIES IN THE *RED DATA BOOK* OF THREATENED VERTEBRATES OF GREECE

E1: Endangered 1 (under immediate threat of extinction)

White Pelican
Dalmatian Pelican
Glossy Ibis
Spoonbill
Ruddy Shelduck
Black Kite
White-tailed Eagle
Lammergeier
Black Vulture
Montagu's Harrier
Imperial Eagle
Slender-billed Curlew
Gull-billed Tern

E2: Endangered 2 (threatened)

Pygmy Cormorant
Great White Egret
Black Stork
Lesser White-fronted Goose
Greylag Goose
Red-breasted Goose
Goosander
White-headed Duck
Spotted Eagle
Spur-winged Plover
Slender-billed Gull
Audouin's Gull

V: Vulnerable

Shag
Purple Heron
Shelduck
Ferruginous Duck
Egyptian Vulture
Griffon Vulture
Marsh Harrier
Lesser Spotted Eagle
Golden Eagle
Booted Eagle
Bonelli's Eagle
Lesser Kestrel
Lanner
Grey Partridge
Pheasant
Black-winged Stilt
Avocet
Stone Curlew
Collared Pratincole
Mediterranean Gull
Whiskered Tern
Black Tern
Roller
Emberiza schoeniclus reiseri

R: Rare

Storm Petrel
Greater Flamingo
Red-crested Pochard
Long-legged Buzzard
Capercaillie
Little Crake
Stock Dove
Great Spotted Cuckoo
Tengmalm's Owl
Grey-headed Woodpecker
White-backed Woodpecker
Three-toed Woodpecker
Isabelline Wheatear
Ring Ouzel
Moustached Warbler
Collared Flycatcher
Krüper's Nuthatch
Wallcreeper
Masked Shrike
Cinereous Bunting

I: Indeterminate

Red-necked Grebe
Bittern
Osprey
Saker
Hazel Grouse
Sandwich Tern

E: Extinct

Marbled Teal
Black Francolin
Spotted Crake
Crane
Great Bustard

K: Insufficiently known

Black-necked Grebe
Night Heron
Whooper Swan
Gadwall
Garganey
Pochard
Eleonora's Falcon
Peregrine
Quail
Oystercatcher
Dotterel
Broad-billed Sandpiper
Great Snipe
Chough
Caspian Tern
Fan-tailed Warbler
Savi's Warbler
Lesser Grey Shrike
Marsh Sandpiper

APPENDIX H: GREEK SPECIES OF GLOBAL CONSERVATION CONCERN

	Global	Europe	Greece
Dalmatian Pelican *Pelecanus crispus*	VU	V	E
Lesser White-fronted Goose *Anser erythropus*	VU	V	E
Red-breasted Goose *Branta ruficollis*	VU	L	E
Marbled Teal *Marmaronetta angustirostris*	VU	E	(Ex)
Ferruginous Duck *Aythya nyroca*	VU	V	V
White-headed Duck *Oxyura leucocephala*	VU	E	E
Spotted Eagle *Aquila clanga*	VU	E	E
Imperial Eagle *Aquila heliaca*	VU	E	E
Lesser Kestrel *Falco naumanni*	VU	(V)	V
Corncrake *Crex crex*	VU	V	-
Great Bustard *Otis tarda*	VU	D	(Ex)
Sociable Plover *Chettusia gregaria*	VU	E	-
Slender-billed Curlew *Numenius tenuirostris*	CR	-	E
Audouin's Gull *Larus audouinii*	CD	L	E
Aquatic Warbler *Acrocephalus paludicola*	VU	E	-

1 CR Critical, CD Conservation Dependent, VU Vulnerable (Collar *et al*. 1994)
2 E Endangered, V Vulnerable, D Declining, L Localised (Tucker & Heath 1994)
3 E Endangered, V Vulnerable, (Ex) Extinct (Handrinos 1992b)

APPENDIX I: SPECIES THAT MAY BE HUNTED IN GREECE

The following species may be hunted in Greece (as at 31 December 1995).

Wigeon
Teal
Mallard
Pintail
Garganey
Shoveler
Pochard
Tufted Duck
Chukar
Rock Partridge
Quail
Pheasant
Moorhen
Coot
Lapwing
Jack Snipe
Snipe
Woodcock
Rock Dove
Stock Dove
Woodpigeon
Turtle Dove
Skylark
Blackbird
Fieldfare
Song Thrush
Redwing
Mistle Thrush
Magpie
Jackdaw
Hooded Crow
Starling

APPENDIX J: SOME USEFUL ADDRESSES

Ministry of Agriculture
General Secretariat for Forests and the Natural Environment
Dept of Aesthetic Forests, National Parks and Wildlife Management
3–5, Ippokratous St.,
10164 ATHENS

Ministry of the Environment, Physical Planning and Public Works
Dept of Environmental Planning
Section of Natural Environment
36, Trikalon St.,
11526 ATHENS

Goulandris Natural History Museum
13, Levidou St.,
14562 KIFISSIA

Greek Biotope and Wetland Centre
14th km Thessaloniki/Mihaniona
57001 THERMI

Hellenic Bird Ringing Centre
P.O. Box 20006
11810 ATHENS

Hellenic Bird and Wildlife Hospital
42, N. Kazantzaki St.,
18010 AIGINA

Hellenic Ornithological Society
53, E. Benaki St.,
10681 ATHENS

Hellenic Society for the Protection of Nature
24, Nikis St.,
10557 ATHENS

WWF - Hellas
26, Filellinon St.,
10558 ATHENS

Zoological Museum
University of Athens
Dept of Biology
Panepistimioupolis
15784 ATHENS

BIBLIOGRAPHY

Titles are given in the original language except for those in more 'difficult' languages (including Greek), which are translated into English. Translated titles appear in brackets.

ADAMAKOPOULOS, T., & GATZOYIANNIS, S. (eds) (1994) [*Environmental Study for the Dadia Forest Reserve.*] WWF Greece, Min. of Environm. & Min. of Agriculture, Athens. [In Greek.]

ADAMAKOPOULOS, T., HATZIRVASSANIS,V., & MATSOUKA, P. (1986) [*The Mountains of Roumeli*]. Pitsilos Edit., Athens. [In Greek.]

ADAMAKOPOULOS, T., MATSOUKA, P., & HATZIRVASSANIS, V. (1988) [*The Mountains of Morias.*] Pitsilos Edit., Athens. [In Greek.]

AKRIOTIS, T. (1988) *Breeding Biology of Reed and Great Reed Warblers.* D.Phil. thesis, Dept. of Zoology, University of Oxford.

AKRIOTIS, T., & HANDRINOS, G. (1986) The first breeding case of the Storm Petrel in Greece. Pp: 31–38 *in* MEDMARAVIS & MONBAILLIU, X. (eds) *Mediterranean Marine Avifauna.* Springer Verlag.

ALKEMEIER, F., & HENNIG, V. (1988) Wintervögelbeobachtungen in Nordgriechenland. **Orn. Mitt.** 40: 163–168.

ALTNER, H,. & REGER, K. (1959) Ornithologische Frühjahrsbeobachtungen auf Kreta. **Anz. Orn. Ges. Bayern** 5: 224–234.

ANDROUKAKI, E., & ADAMANTOPOULOU, S. (1992) A proposal for an area-species diversity pattern for Northern Sporades Avifauna. **Biol. Gallo-hellen.** 19: 37–44.

ANON. (1964) [*Distribution of Forests in Greece.*] Ministry of Agriculture, Athens. [In Greek.]

ANON. (1986) Flamingos in Greece. **Nature, H.S.P.N. Bull.** 35: 44.

ANON. (1992) [*First National Inventory of Forests.*] Ministry of Agriculture, Athens. [In Greek.]

APALODIMOS, D. (1983) [*A Lexicon of Greek Bird Names.*] Goulandris Nat. Hist. Museum, Kifissia. [In Greek.]

APALODIMOS, D. (1993) *A Descriptive Lexicon of the Birds of Greece.* Goulandris Nat. Hist. Museum, Kifissia.

ARNOLD, E.N., BURTON, J.A., & OVENDEN, D.W. (1978) *Reptiles and Amphibians of Britain and Europe.* Collins, London.

ATHANASSIOU, H. (1987) *Past and Present Importance of the Greek Wetlands for Wintering Waterfowl.* Unpubl. Rep., IWRB, Slimbridge.

BALLANCE, D.K., & LEE, S.L.B. (1961) Notes on autumn migration at the Bosphorus and in the Aegean. **Ibis** 103: 195–204.

BAUER, W. (1970) [*Data for the Selection of Greek Wetlands as Sites of International Importance.*] Unpubl. Rep., H.S.P.N., Athens. [In Greek.]

BAUER, W., & BÖHR, H.J. (1987) Zur Kenntnis der südlichen Arealgrenzen einiger Vogelarten in den griechischen Rhodopen. **Vogelwelt** 108: 1–13.

BAUER, W., BÖHR, H.J., MATTERN, U., & MÜLLER, G. (1973) II. Nachtrag zum "Catalogus Faunae Graeciae, Pars Aves". **Vogelwelt** 94: 1–21.

BAUER, W., HELVERSEN, O.V., HODGE, M., & MARTENS, J. (1969a) Aves. *In* KANELLIS, A. (ed) *Catalogus Faunae Graeciae.* Thessaloniki.

BAUER, W., HELVERSEN, O.V., HODGE, M., & MARTENS, J. (1969b) Bemerkenswerte Brutnachweise aus Griechenland. **J. Orn.** 110: 79–83.

BAUER, W., & HODGE, M. (1970) I. Nachtrag zum "Catalogus Faunae Graeciae, Pars Aves". **Vogelwelt** 91: 96–105.

BAUER, W., & MÜLLER, G. (1969) Zur Avifauna des Ewros-Delta. **Beitr. naturkd. Forsch. SW- Deutschl.** 28: 33–52.

BELON. P. (1555) *L' Histoire de la Nature des Oyseaux, avec leurs Descriptions et Naifs Potraits, Retirez du Naturel.* Paris.

BENUSSI, E., & BRICHETTI, P. (1983) Osservazioni ornithologische nella Grecia settentrionale, dal 22 Aprile al 6 Maggio 1982. **Uccelli d' Italia** 8: 43–60.

BERG, VAN DEN, A. (1993) West palearctic reports. **Dutch Birding** 15: 180-185.

BERLIC, G. (1983) Contribution à l' étude de l' avifaune du Lac de Mikra Prespa. **Biol. Gallo-hellen.** 10: 345–355.

BEZZEL, E., & MÜLLER, G. (1964) Einige Notize zum Herbstzug in Nordgriechenland. **Anz. Orn. Ges. Bayern** 7: 190–196.

BIBER, J.-P. (1990) *Action Plan for the Conservation of the Western Lesser Kestrel* Falco naumanni *Populations.* ICBP Rep., Cambridge.

BIEBACH, H., DALLMANN, M., SCHUY, W., & SIEBENROCK, K.H. (1983) Die Herbstzugrichtung von Neuntötern (*Lanius collurio*) auf Karpathos (Griechenland). **J. Orn.** 124: 251–257.

BIJLEVELD, M. (1974) *Birds of Prey in Europe.* Macmillan, London.

BIRD, C.G. (1935) A visit to the Cyclades. Ibis (13) 5: 336–355.

BODENSTEIN, G., & KROYMANN, B. (1967) Die Ergebnisse der Mazedonien-Exkursion der Ornithologischen Gesellschaft in Bayern im Mai/Juni 1966. **Anz. Orn. Ges. Bayern** 8: 134–157.

BOEV, N., & SIMEONOV, S. (1985) Aves. Pp: 42–129 *in* BOTEV, B., & PESHEV, V. (eds) *Red Data Book of the People's Republic of Bulgaria, Vol. 2: Animals.* Bulgarian Acad. Sc., Sofia. [In Bulgarian.]

BÖHR, H.J. (1962) Zur Kenntnis der Vogelwelt von Korfu. **Bonn. Zool. Beitr.** 13: 50–114.

BONESS, M. (1959) Ornithologische Herbstbeobachtungen auf Korfu. **Bonn. Zool. Beitr.** 10: 387–397.

BREE, C.F. (1859–63) *A History of Birds of Europe, Not Observed in the British Isles.* 5 Vols.

BROGGI, M. (1993) Ornithologische Beobachtungen auf Karpathos (Dodekanes, Griechenland). **Ber. Bot. Zool. Ges. Liecht.** 20: 117–132.

BROGGI, M., & WILLI, G. (1986) Ornithologische Beobachtungen auf Naxos. **Ber. Bot. Zool. Ges. Liecht.** 15: 91–102.

BROGGI, M., & WILLI, G (1988) Ornithologische Beobachtungen auf Samothrake (Griechenland). **Ber. Bot. Zool. Ges. Liecht.** 17: 79–91.

BROOKS, R. (1995) *Birding in Lesbos*. Brookside Publishing, Fakenham, Norfolk.

BROSSELIN, M., & MOLINIER, M. (1968) *Visite au lac de Mikra Prespa (Grèce)*. Bureau MAR.

BRUCH, A. (1992) Rosenstar (Sturnus roseus) 1985 Brutvogel in bei Vafiohori, Nordgriechenland. **Kartierung mediterr. Brutvögel** 7: 9–10.

BRUCH, A., & STICKEL, W. (1965) Beiträge zur Vogelwelt Nordgriechenlands. **Vogelwelt** 86: 19–24.

CANT, G. (1978) Eleonora's Falcon reported wintering in the Southern Aegean. **Nature, H.S.P.N. Bull.** 15: 28–29.

CASEMENT, M. B. (1966) Migration across the Mediterranean observed by radar. **Ibis** 108: 461–491.

CATSADORAKIS, G. (1983) Some data on the avifauna of Naxos isl. and the migration over the Aegean. **Rapp. Comm. Int. Mer Médit.** 28(8): 123-124.

CATSADORAKIS, G. (1986) Notes on the avifauna of Lake Prespa National Park. **Biol. Gallo-hellen.** 12: 485–496.

CATSADORAKIS, G. (1989) [*Bird Communities in Prespa (Florina, NW Greece): Elements of Ecology and Biogeography*.] Ph.D. thesis, School of Biology, University of Athens. [In Greek.]

CATSADORAKIS, G. (1991) [Extinct birds and birds threatened with extinction in Lake Prespa Nat. Park.] **Nature, H.S.P.N. Bull.** 55: 21–25. [In Greek.]

CHASEN, F.N. (1921) Field notes on the birds of Macedonia. With special reference to the Struma plain. **Ibis** (11) 3: 185–227.

CHEYLAN, G. (1976) Le régime alimentaire de la chouette effraie (Tyto alba) en Europe Méditerranéenne. **Terre et Vie** 30: 565–579.

CHOREMI, J., & SPINTHAKIS, E. (1990) *Traditional Illegal Capture and Hunting of Migratory Birds on the Island of Chios, Greece*. Unpubl. Preliminary Rep., WWF Athens.

CHWALLEK, C., GOLZ, E., HECKENROTH, H., LUDESCHER, F.-B., & SCHAFER, C. (1981) Birds. Pp: 142-207 *in* SZIJJ, J. (ed) *Ecological Assessment of the Delta Area of the Rivers Louros and Arachthos in the Gulf of Amvrakia*. University of Essen and IUCN.

CLARKE, G.V.H. (1917) Nesting in Macedonia. **Ibis** (10) 5: 640–643.

COLLAR, N.J., CROSBY, M.J., & STATTERSFIELD, A.J. (1994) *Birds to Watch 2: the World List of Threatened Birds*. Birdlife Conserv. Series No 4. Birdlife Int., Cambridge.

CONRADTY, P. (1979) Ein weiterer Brutnachweis des Häherkuckucks (*Clamator glandarius*) in Griechenland. **Anz. Orn. Ges. Bayern** 18(2/3): 192.

CONRADTY, P,. & HOHLT, G. (1967) Zur Kenntnis der Vogelwelt Nordgriechenlands II. **Anz. Orn. Ges. Bayern** 8: 45–51.

COOK, A. (1988) Caspian Plover (*Charadrius asiaticus*). *In* HANDRINOS, G. *Three New Species to the Greek Avifauna*. **Nature, H.S.P.N. Bull.** 42: 34–35.

COOMBES, R.A.H. (1957) The Red-breasted Goose in Thrake. Pp: 265–267 *in* BANNERMAN, D.A. *The Birds of the British Isles*. Vol. 6. Edinburgh.

COSSON, F. (1985) Some recent data on the raptors of Rhodes (Greece). **Bull. W.W.G.B.P.** 2: 57–60.

CRAMP, S. (1983) Studies of W. Palearctic birds 185: White Pelican. **Brit. Birds** 76: 253–262.

CRAMP, S. (ed) (1977–94) *The Birds of the Western Palearctic*, Vol. I–IX. OUP, Oxford.

CRIVELLI, A. (1980) The importance of Greece for the conservation of two species of pelicans: *Pelecanus onocrotalus* (L) and *Pelecanus crispus* (Bruch). **Nature, H.S.P.N. Bull.** 23/24: 35–39.

CRIVELLI, A. (1984) European Pelican populations and their conservation. Pp: 123–127 *in* EVANS, P.R., HAFNER, H., & HERMITE, P.L. (eds) *Shorebird and Large Waterbird Conservation*. CEC, Brussels.

CRIVELLI, A. (1987) *The Ecology and Behaviour of the Dalmatian Pelican* Pelecanus crispus *Bruch: a World Endangered Species*. Unpubl. Rep., CEC, Brussels.

CRIVELLI, A., JERRENTRUP, H., & HALLMANN, B. (1988) Preliminary results of a complete census of breeding colonial wading birds in Greece spring 1985–1986. **H.O.S. Newsl.** 4: 31–33.

CRIVELLI, A., MITCHEV, T., CATSADORAKIS, G., & POMAKOV, V. (1991a) Preliminary results on the wintering of the Dalmatian Pelican *Pelecanus crispus* in Turkey. **Zool. in the Middle East** 5: 11–20.

CRIVELLI, A., LESHEM, Y., MICHEV, T., & JERRENTRUP, H. (1991b) Where do Palearctic Great White Pelicans (*Pelecanus onocrotalus*) presently overwinter? **Rev. Ecol. (Terre Vie)** 46: 145–171.

CRIVELLI, A., CATSADORAKIS, G., JERRENTRUP, H., HATZILACOS, D., & MICHEV, T. (1991c) Conservation and management of Pelicans nesting in the Palearctic. Pp: 137–152 *in* SALATHÉ, T. (ed) *Conserving Migratory Birds*. ICBP Techn. Publ. No. 12, Cambridge.

CRIVELLI, A., & VIZI, O. (1981) The Dalmatian Pelican (*Pelecanus crispus*, Bruch, 1832). A recently world-endangered bird species. **Biol. Conserv.** 20: 297–310.

CURIO, E. (1959) Beobachtungen am Halbringschnäpper, *Ficedula semitorquata*, im mazedonischen Brutgebiet. **J. Orn.** 100: 176–209.

DA PRATO, S.R.D. & DA PRATO, E. (1983) Densities of robins in north-east Greece in autumn. **Ringing Migr.** 4: 243–244.

DAFIS, S., PAPASTERGIADOU, E., PAPAGEORGIOU, M., & TSIAOUSSI, V. (1994) Greek Habitat project: the Directive 92/43/EEC on the conservation of natural habitats and of wild fauna and flora and its implementation in Greece. Proceed. Intern. Workshop Mediter. Biogeogr. Region. Segovia, Dec. 1994.

DANGEL, M. (1973) Ornithologische Beobachtungen am Dojran See. **Orn. Mitt.** 25: 73–75.

DATHE, H. (1950) Der Karla-See in Thessalien, ein Vogelparadies. **Natur und Volk** 80: 188–195.

DATHE, H., & PROFFT, J. (1940) Thessalien als Raststation für Kormorane. **Vogelzug** 11: 30.

DE JUANA, E., & VARELA, J. (1993) La poblacion mundial reproductora de la Gaviota de Audouin (*Larus audouinii*). Pp 71–75 *in* AGUILAR, J.S., MONBAILLIU, X., & PATERSON, A. (eds) *Status and Conservation of Seabirds -*

Ecogeography and Mediterranean Action Plan. Proceed. 2nd Mediterr. Seabird Symp. Calvia, 21–26 March 1989. SEO and MEDMARAVIS.

DE NOBEL, W.T. (ed) (1995) *Birds of the Messolonghi Wetlands. Eastern Mediterranean Wader Project, Spring 1990*. WIWO Rep. No 53. Zeist.

DENNIS, M. (1993) Arctic Warbler at Dion. **Birding World** 6: 393.

DESFAYES, M. (1987) Evidence for the ancient presence of the Bald Ibis (*Geronticus eremita*) in Greece. **Bull. Br. Orn. Club** 107(3): 93–94.

DEVILLERS, P., DEVILLERS-TERSCHUREN, J., & LEDANT, J.-P. (eds) (1991) *CORINE Biotopes Manual - Habitats of the EC, Vol. 3*. EC, Luxembourg.

DRAGOUMIS, F. (1984) Ornithological observations in Sifnos isl. **H.O.S. Newsl.** 1: 5–10.

DRUMMOND-HAY, H.M. (1843a) Catalogue of the birds found in Corfu and the other Ionian Islands also on the coast of Albania; from notes during a sojourn of four years. **Ann. Mag. Nat. Hist.** 12: 412–423.

DRUMMOND-HAY, H.M. (1843b) List of the birds of the island of Crete from observations made during a stay of nearly two months, from the 27 April to 18 June 1843. **Ann. Mag. Nat. Hist.** 12: 423–427.

DRUMMOND-HAY, H.M. (1846) List of the birds observed to winter in Macedonia; from notes made during a two months's shooting excursion in the interior during the winter of 1845–46. **Ann. Mag. Nat. Hist.** 18: 10–15.

DUBIN, M.S. (1993) *Trekking in Greece*. Lonely Planet, Hawthorn, Australia.

DYMOND, N., FRASER, P., & GANTLETT, S. (1989) *Rare Birds in Britain and Ireland*. T. & A.D. Poyser, Calton.

EBER, G. (1967) Wasservogelbeobachtungen im Marz 1967 auf Nordgriechenland und Südjugoslawien. **Anz. Orn. Ges. Bayern** 8: 158–165.

EGGERS, J. (1964) Rauhfusskauz und Zwergohreule am Olymp. **Vogelwelt** 85: 62.

ELWES, H.J., & BUCKLEY, T.E. (1870) A list of the birds of Turkey. **Ibis** (2) 6: 59–77, 188–201, 327–341.

ERHARD, ? (1858) Katalog der auf den Cycladen einheimischen und überwinternden oder nur durchziehenden Arten von Vögeln. **Naumannia** 8: 1–26.

FASOLA, M., BARBIERI, F., CANOVA, L., & SAINO, N. (1991) Important breeding populations of colonial waterbirds in the Arta Gulf. **Nature, H.S.P.N. Bull.** 52: 43.

FLACH, B. (1955a) En ornitologisk exkursion till floden Evros i Grekland. **Fauna och Flora** 50: 205–218.

FLACH, B. (1955b) Några fågelobservationer från Delfi och en exkursion på Parnassos. **Fauna och Flora** 50: 234–252.

FLACH, B. (1956) Från några Fågellokaler i Grekland. **Fauna och Flora** 51: 122–139.

FLACH, B. (1959) Einige Sommerbeobachtungen auf Korfu. **J. Orn.** 10: 303–306.

FLACH, B. (1960) Från två ornitologiska exkursioner till Grekland. **Fauna och Flora** 55: 229–263.

FLACH, B. (1961) Exkursionen till Grekland den 23 April - 10 Maj 1961. **Vår Fågelvärld** 29: 362–366.

FLINT, P.R., & STEWART, P.F. (1992) *The Birds of Cyprus*. B.O.U. Check-list No. 6 (2nd edn). B.O.U., Tring.

FOSSEY, A. (1988) First record of Baird's Sandpiper (*Calidris bairdii*) in Greece. **H.O.S. Newsl.** 4: 33.

FRIVALDSZKY, E. (1902) Über ornithologische Sammelreisen in der Türkei 1833–1836, 1841–1845. **Aquila** 9: 206–208.

GAETLICH, M. (1986a) [First record of the Blue-winged Teal (Anas discors) in Greece.] **H.O.S. Newsl.** 3: 8–9. [In Greek.]

GAETLICH, M. (1986b) [First sighting of the Blue-winged Teal Anas discors in Greece.] **Nature, H.S.P.N. Bull.** 34: 42–43. [In Greek.]

GAETLICH, M., & DRAGOUMIS, F. (1985) [Ecological importance and conservation problems of small wetlands.] **H.O.S. Newsl.** 2: 7–8. [In Greek.]

GEOFFROY SAINT-HILAIRE, I. (1832) Aves. Pp: 47–56 *in* BORY ST. VINCENT *et al. Expédition scientifique de Morée, Section des Sciences Phys*. Vol. 3. Paris.

GÉROUDET, P. (1962a) Notes d' ornithologie grecque: Delphes. **Nos Oiseaux** 26: 165–179.

GÉROUDET, P. (1962b) Notes d' ornithologie grecque: Le Parnasse. **Nos Oiseaux** 26: 205–209.

GÉROUDET, P. (1962c) Notes d' ornithologie grecque: Le lac Karla. **Nos Oiseaux** 26: 303–312.

GÉROUDET, P. (1963) Notes d' ornithologie grecque: Les Meteores. **Nos Oiseaux** 27: 136–139.

GÉROUDET, P. (1964) Notes sur le nid et les "collections" de la Sitelle des rochers. **Nos Oiseaux** 17: 272–276.

GÉROUDET, P. (1973) Micra Prespa, le lac des Pelicans. **Nos Oiseaux** 32: 145–167.

GÉROUDET, P. (1979) Nidification de l' hirondelle rousseline *Hirundo daurica* en Crete. **Alauda** 47: 39.

GHIGI, A. (1929) Riserche faunistiche nell'isole italiane dell'Egeo: Uccelli. **Arch. Zool. Ital.** 13: 25–30.

GLEGG, W.E. (1924) A list of the birds of Macedonia. **Ibis** (11) 6: 46–86.

GLUTZ VON BLOTZHEIM, U., & BAUER, K. (eds.) (1966–) *Handbuch der Vögel Mitteleuropas*. Vols. 1–13. Akademische Verlagsges., Frankfurt, and Aula Verlag, Wiesbaden.

GOODERS, J. (1970) *Where to Watch Birds in Britain and Europe*. Hamlyn, London.

GOODERS, J. (1988) *Where to Watch Birds in Britain and Europe*. Christopher Helm, London.

GOODERS, J. (1994) *Where to Watch Birds in Britain and Europe*. Hamlyn, London.

GOUTNER, V. (1980) [Conservation problems of rare birds nesting in the Evros Delta and management proposals.] **Nature, H.S.P.N. Bull.** 22: 31–33. [In Greek.]

GOUTNER, V. (1983a) [*Ecology of Breeding of the Avocet* (Recurvirostra avosetta) *and Oystercatcher* (Haematopus ostralegus) *in the Evros delta*.] Ph.D. thesis, School of Biology, University of Thessaloniki. [In Greek.]

GOUTNER, V. (1983b) The distribution of the waders (Charadrii) in the Evros delta (Greece) during the breeding season. **Sc. Annals, Fac. Sciences, Univ. Thessaloniki** 23: 37–78.

GOUTNER, V. (1986) Distribution, status and conservation of the Mediterranean Gull (*Larus melanocephalus*) in Greece. Pp 431–447 *in* MEDMARAVIS & MONBAILLIU, X. (eds) *Mediterranean Marine Avifauna*. Springer Verlag.

GOUTNER, V. (1988) The Lesser Crested Tern (*Sterna bengalensis*) in the Evros Delta (Greece): a case of pairing with the Sandwich Tern (*Sterna sandvicensis*)? **Kartierung mediterr. Brutvögel** 1: 7–11.

GOUTNER, V. (1991) Food and feeding ecology of Gull-billed Terns (*Gelochelidon nilotica*) in Greece. **Rev. Ecol. (Terre et Vie)** 46: 373–384.

GOUTNER, V. (1994) The diet of Mediterranean Gull (*Larus melanocephalus*) chicks at fledging. **J. Orn.** 135: 193–201.

GOUTNER, V., & HANDRINOS, G. (1990) The occurrence of Slender-billed Curlews (*Numenius tenuirostris*) in Greece. **Biol. Conserv.** 53: 47–60.

GOUTNER, V,. & ISENMANN, P. (1993) Breeding status of the Mediterranean Gull (*Larus melanocephalus*) in the Mediterranean basin. Pp: 59–63 *in* AGUILAR, J.S., MONBAILLIU, X., & PATERSON, A. (eds) *Status and Conservation of Seabirds - Ecogeography and Mediterranean Action Plan.* Proceed. 2nd Mediterr. Seabird Symp. Calvia, 21–26 March 1989. SEO and MEDMARAVIS.

GOUTNER, V., & JERRENTRUP, H. (1987) The destruction of the Drana lagoon in the Evros delta Ramsar wetland and its consequences for waterfowl. **W.S.G. Bull.** 50: 18–19.

GOUTNER, V., JERRENTRUP, H., KAZANTZIDIS, S., & NAZIRIDIS, T. (1991) Occurrence of the Cattle Egret (*Bubulcus ibis*) in Greece. **Riv. ital. Orn.** 61(3–4): 107–112.

GOUTNER, V., & KAZANTZIDIS, S. (1992) Shorebird populations in the Evros Delta, Greece. **Bios** 1: 65–94.

GREMPE, G. (1981) Auftreten und Durchzug von Raubmöwen in Schwarzmeergebiet und im ostmediterranen Raum. **Orn. Ber. Mus. Hein.** 5/6: 13–36.

GRETTON, A. (1991) *Conservation of the Slender-billed Curlew.* ICBP Monograph No 6. Cambridge.

GRIMMETT, R.F.A., & JONES, T.A. (1989) *Important Bird Areas in Europe.* ICBP Techical Publ. No 9. Cambridge.

GRIMMOND, R. (1993) Great Skua off Sitia, Crete. **Birding World** 6: 430.

GRISPOS, P. (1973) [*A History of Forestry in Modern Greece.*] Ministry of Agriculture, Spec. Publ. No 25, Athens. [In Greek.]

GROH, G. (1968) Ornithologische Reiseeindrücke aus Griechenland und der Türkei. **Mitt. Pollichia** (8) 15: 163–170.

GUYOT, I. (1993) Breeding distribution and numbers of Cory's Shearwater (*Calonectris diomedea*) in the Mediterranean. Pp: 25–35 *in* AGUILAR, J.S., MONBAILLIU, X., & PATERSON, A. (eds) *Status and Conservation of Seabirds - Ecogeography and Mediterranean Action Plan.* Proceed. 2nd Mediterr. Seabird Symp. Calvia, 21–26 March 1989. SEO and MEDMARAVIS.

HAENSEL, J. (1992) Zur Vogelwelt der griechischen Insel Kos (Dodekanes/Ägäis). **Kartierung mediterr. Brutvögel** 8: 21–28.

HAFEMANN, D. (1967) Beobachtungen zum Frühjahrs-Vogelzug auf Kreta (nebst einigen Bemerkungen zur Brutvogelwelt). **Bonn. Zool. Beitr.** 18: 221–233.

HAFNER, H., & HOFFMANN, L. (1974) Waterfowl counts in Northern Greece, January 1974. **IWRB Bull.** 37: 95–97.

HAFNER, H., & WALMSLEY, J.G. (1971) IWRB mission to Greece and southern Italy, January 1971. **IWRB Bull.** 32: 41–51.

HALLMANN, B. (1979) *Guidelines for the Conservation of Birds of Prey in Evros.* Unpubl. Rep., Ministry of Coordination / IUCN, Athens.

HALLMANN, B. (1980) Breeding bird census in Alyki. Pp: 24–28 *in* SEKLIZIOTIS, S., & KATSAOUNIS, A. *Report on the Environmental Impact of Proposed Housing Development at Alyki Lagoon, Pieria.* Unpubl. Rep., Ministry of Coordination, Athens.

HALLMANN, B. (1981) Notes on bird nesting and conservation in some Greek wetlands. **Nature, H.S.P.N. Bull.** 25: 44–48.

HALLMANN, B. (1982) *Preliminary List of Important Bird Areas in Greece.* ICBP/EC Working Group, Brussels.

HALLMANN, B. (1985a) Status and conservation problems of birds of prey in Greece. Pp: 55–59 *in* NEWTON, I. & CHANCELLOR, R. (eds) *Conservation Studies of Raptors.* ICBP Techn. Publ. No 5. Cambridge.

HALLMANN, B. (1985b) *The Fauna of Mount Oiti National Park.* Unpubl. Rep., Ministry of Agriculture, Athens.

HALLMANN, B. (1985c) *The Wildlife of Mount Parnassos.* Unpubl. Rep., Ministry of Agriculture, Athens.

HALLMANN, B. (1986) [A late nesting case of a Spur-winged Plover (*Hoplopterus spinosus*) pair.] **H.O.S. Newsl.** 3: 6–7. [In Greek.]

HALLMANN, B. (1989) Status and distribution of the Aquila in Greece. 4e Congrès Intern. de Zoogéographie et Ecologie de la Grèce et des Régions Avoisinantes. Kammena Vourla, Avril 1987. **Biol. Gallo-hellen.** 15: 171–176.

HALLMANN, B. (1992) Black Vulture Recovery Programme at Mount Olympus. **Nature, H.S.P.N. Bull.** 58: 36–37.

HANDRINOS, G. (1985a) Iceland Gull (*Larus glaucoides*): A new species to Greece. 2e Congrès Intern. sur la Zoogéographie et l'Ecologie de la Grèce et des Régions Avoisinates. Athens, 1981. **Biol. Gallo-hellen.** 10: 339–343.

HANDRINOS, G. (1985b) The status of vultures in Greece. Pp: 103–115 *in* NEWTON, I. & CHANCELLOR, R. (eds) *Conservation Studies of Raptors.* ICBP Techn. Publ. No 5. Cambridge.

HANDRINOS, G. (1987a) The Golden Eagle in Greece. Actes 1er Coll. Intern. Aigle Royal en Europe, Arvieux, June 1986. Pp: 18–22.

HANDRINOS, G. (1987b) The significance of Greece for wintering and migrating raptors. *In* "Rapaci Mediterranei III". **Suppl. Ric. Biol. Selvaggina** 12: 99–113.

HANDRINOS, G. (1987c) Greece five years after Thessaloniki. **Newsl. W.W.G.B.P.** 6: 5–6.

HANDRINOS, G. (1988) The present status of waterfowl wintering and migrating in Greece. Pp: 152–162 *in Wildfauna in Turkey and in the Balkan countries.* Proceed. Intern. Symp., Istanbul, 16–20 Sept. 1987. CIC-IGE-IWRB.

HANDRINOS, G. (1989a) The IWRB midwinter waterfowl counts in Greece. 1967–1987: A preliminary analysis of the populations of Anatidae. 4e Congrès Intern. de Zoogéographie et Ecologie de la Grèce et des Régions Avoisinantes. Kammena Vourla, Avril 1987. **Biol. Gallo-hellen.** 15: 219–236.

HANDRINOS, G. (1989b) Mid-winter numbers and distribution of Greater Flamingos (Phoenicopterus ruber roseus) in Greece. **F.W.G. Newsl.** 5: 15–17.

HANDRINOS, G. (1991) The status of geese in Greece. *In* FOX, A. D., MADSEN, J., & RHIJN, J. van (eds) *Western Palearctic Geese.* Proceed. IWRB Symp. Kleve, 1989. **Ardea** 79(2): 175–178.

HANDRINOS, G. (1992a) Wetland loss and wintering waterfowl in Greece during the 20th century: a first approach. Pp: 183–187 *in* FINLAYSON, C.M., HOLLIS, G.E., & DAVIES, T.J. (eds) *Managing Mediterranean Wetlands and their Birds.* Proceed. Symp. Grado, Italy, 1991. IWRB Spec. Publ. No 20. IWRB, Slimbridge.

HANDRINOS, G. (1992b) [Birds]. Pp: 123–243 *in* KARANDEINOS, M., & LEGAKIS, T. (eds) *The Red Data Book of Threatened Vertebrates of Greece.* Hellen. Zool. Soc. and Hellen. Orn. Soc., Athens. [In Greek.]

HANDRINOS, G. (1993a) The occurrence of the Marbled Teal in Greece. **IWRB Threatened Waterfowl Res. Group Newsl.** 3: 8–9.
HANDRINOS, G. (1993b) Midwinter numbers and distribution of Cormorants and Pygmy Cormorants in Greece. Pp: 135–147 *in* AGUILAR, J.S., MONBAILLIU, X., & PATERSON, A. (eds) *Status and Conservation of Seabirds - Ecogeography and Mediterranean Action Plan.* Proceed. 2nd Mediterr. Seabird Symp. Calvia, 21–26 March 1989. SEO and MEDMARAVIS.
HANDRINOS, G. (1993c) Bird recoveries at Chios isl.: 1930–1991. Pp: 65–69, 113–116 *in* SPINTHAKIS, E., CHOULIS, D., & CHOREMI, J. *The Birds of Chios Isl.* Municipality of Homeroupolis.
HANDRINOS, G. (1994a) Bird species new to Greece: 1969-1989. 5e Congrès Intern. de Zoogéographie et Ecologie de la Grèce et des Régions Avoisinantes. Iraklion, 16–20 Avril 1990. **Biol. Gallo-hellen.** 22: 77–89.
HANDRINOS, G. (1994b) Slender-billed Curlews *Numenius tenuirostris* in Greece. *In* Inst. Royal Sc. Natur. Bélgique. *Preparation d' un plan de sauvetage pour* Numenius tenuirostris. Final Rep. ACNAT Progr. 3010(92)7717, Vol. 2, Annex 9.
HANDRINOS, G. (1995) The White-headed Duck Oxyura leucocephala in Greece. **IWRB Threatened Waterfowl Res. Group Newsl.** 7: 6–7.
HANDRINOS, G. (in press) The numbers and distribution of swans wintering in Greece: an analysis of the IWRB counts (1963-1994). *ANATIDAE 2000.* Proceed. Conf., Strasbourg, 5–9 December 1994.
HANDRINOS, G., & AKRIOTIS, T. (1996) A bibliography of Greek ornithology. **Hellen. Zool. Arch.** 5: 1–36.
HANDRINOS, G., & GOUTNER, V. (1990) On the occurrence of the Lesser White-fronted Goose (*Anser erythropus*) in Greece. **J. Orn.** 131: 160–165.
HARRESTRUP-ANDERSEN, H. (1989) First European record of Dead Sea Sparrow. **Brit. Birds** 82: 380–381.
HARRISON, J.M. (1918) Bird notes from Macedonia. **Brit. Birds** 12: 14–18.
HARRISON, J.M. (1925) A contribution to the ornithology of Macedonia and the North Aegean area. Observations made during a commission in H.M.S. "M. 28", 26 January 1917 to February 1918. **Ibis** (12) 1: 422–442.
HARRISON, J.M., & PATEFF, P. (1937) An ornithological survey of Thrace, the islands of Samothraki, Thasos and Thasopulo in the North Aegean, and observations in the Struma Valley and the Rhodope Mountains, Bulgaria. **Ibis** (14) 1: 582–625.
HART, R. (1986) Laughing Gull in Greece in August 1984. **Dutch Birding** 2: 62–63.
HATZILACOU, D. (1992) [*The Breeding Biology and Feeding Ecology of the Great White Pelican* (Pelecanus onocrotalus) *L., 1758 at Lake Mikri Prespa (N.W. Greece).*] Ph.D. thesis, School of Biology, University of Athens. [In Greek.]
HATZILACOU, D. (1995) The distribution of pelicans in Greece: threats to their habitats and recommendations for protection. *Threats to Seabirds.* Proceed. 5th Intern. Seabird Group Confer., Glasgow, 24–26 March 1995. Pp: 24–25.
HATZISSARANTOS, C. (1953) [Let us know our gamebirds.] **Kynigetika Nea (Athens)** 265: 106. [In Greek.]
HATZISSARANTOS, C., & KANELLIS, A. (1947/48) [Check list of the birds of Greece, with their common names.] **To Vouno (Athens)**: 126–152. [In Greek.]
HATZISSARANTOS, C., & KANELLIS, A. (1959) La protection des oiseaux et mammifères rares en Grèce. Proceed. VII Congr. Intern. Prot. Nature. Athènes. **Nature, H.S.P.N. Bull.** 5: 74–76.
HELDREICH, T. V. (1878) *La Faune de la Grèce.* Exposition universelle de Paris. Athens.
HELLEBREKERS, W., ROS, J., & BOHR, H. J. (1969) Neue ornithologische Sommerbeobachtungen auf Korfu. **Bonn. Zool. Beitr.** 20: 437–440.
HENDRIKS, M.M., & MÖLIKER, C.W. (1982) Black-throated Diver in Greece in July 1981. **Dutch Birding** 4: 26.
HODGE, M. (1973) *The Birds of Greece: A Pocket Check-list.* Cyclostyled. Athens, Johannesburg and Washington.
HOFFMANN, L., OLNEY, P.J., & SWIFT, J.J. (1964) *IUCN-IWRB Expedition to Italy, Greece and Yugoslavia. January - February 1964.* Unpubl. Rep.
HOFFMANN, M. (1993) Ein Schwarzkelchen der nordkaspischen Unterart Saxicola torquata variegata in Griechenland. Limicola 7: 190–191.
HÖLZINGER, J. (1986a) Rasterkarten für die Darstellung der Vertikalen Verbreitung. **Ökol. Vögel** 8: 121–132.
HÖLZINGER, J. (1986b) Die Wacholderdrossel (*Turdus pilaris*) neuer Brutvogel für Grienchenland. **Ökol. Vögel** 8: 113–115.
HÖLZINGER, J. (1988a) Verbreitung der Ringdrossel (*Turdus torquatus alpestris*, C. L. Brehm, 1831) in Griechenland. **Kartierung mediterr. Brutvögel** 1: 13–15.
HÖLZINGER, J. (1988b) Vertikale Verbreitungmuster des Steinhuhns (*Alectoris graeca*) in verschiedenen Raumen Griechenlands als Abbild der Verfolgung durch den Menschen. **Kartierung mediterr. Brutvögel** 1: 25–28.
HÖLZINGER, J. (1989a) Verbreitung des Mauerläufers (*Tichodroma muraria*, Linnaeus, 1766) auf dem Peloponnes. **Ökol. Vögel** 11: 257–263.
HÖLZINGER, J. (1989b) Nonnensteinschmätzer (*Oenanthe pleschanka*, Lepechin, 1770) Brutvogel in Griechenland. **Vogelwelt** 110: 232–235.
HÖLZINGER, J. (1990a) Mönchsgrasmücke (*Sylvia atricapilla*) Brutvogel auf dem Peloponnes. **J. Orn.** 131: 167–171.
HÖLZINGER, J. (1990b) Weissrückenspecht (*Dendrocopos leucotos*, Bechstein, 1803). Brutvogel auf dem Peloponnes. **Kartierung mediterr. Brutvögel** 4: 19–22.
HÖLZINGER, J. (1990c) Fitis (*Phylloscopus trochilus*) Brutvogel in Griechenland. **Kartierung mediterr. Brutvögel** 4: 27-29.
HÖLZINGER, J. (1990d) Beobachtung eines Tannenhähers (*Nucifraga caryocatactes*) in Mittelgriechenland während der Brutzeit. **Kartierung mediterr. Brutvögel** 4: 31.
HÖLZINGER, J. (1990e) Frühbrut des Braunkelchens *Saxicola rubetra* auf Kithnos (Kykladen, Griechenland). **Orn. Beob.** 87: 257–258.
HÖLZINGER, J. (1991) Wetlands on the Greek island Limnos: a bird habitat of international significance. **Kartierung mediterr. Brutvögel** 6: 19–25.
HÖLZINGER, J. (1992a) Brutvorkommen des Wendehalses (*Jynx torquilla*) an seiner südlichen Arealgrenze in Griechenland. **Beih. Veröff. Naturschutz Landsch. Bad. Wurtt.** 66: 43–46.
HÖLZINGER, J. (1992b) Der Rosenstar (*Sturnus roseus*) 1988 Brutvogel bei Kavala (Nordgriechenland):

Beobachtungen zum Auftreten und zur Ernährung. **Kartierung mediterr. Brutvögel** 7: 3–8.

HÖLZINGER, J. (1992c) Der Rosenstar (*Sturnus roseus*) als Brutvogel in Griechenland - eine Zusammenfassung. **Kartierung mediterr. Brutvögel** 7: 17–25.

HÖLZINGER, J. (1992d) Südliche Arealgrenze und Vertikalverbreitung des Baumpiepers *Anthus trivialis* in Griechenland. **Orn. Beob.** 89: 231–234.

HÖLZINGER, J. (1992e) Schwarzhalstaucher *Podiceps nigricollis* brütet am Piklolimni, Nordgriechenland. **Kartierung mediterr. Brutvögel** 8: 29–30.

HÖLZINGER, J. (1993a) Zugwege und Winterquartier des Halsbandschnäppers *Ficedula albicollis* under besonderer Berücksichtigung des Frühjahrszugs durch den ägäischen Raum. **Orn. Beob.** 90: 267–282.

HÖLZINGER, J. (1993b) Brutvorkommen des Zwergschnäppers *Ficedula parva* an seiner südlichen Arealgrenze in Griechenland. **Vogelwelt** 114: 245–250.

HÖLZINGER, J. (1993c) Schneefink (*Montifringilla nivalis*) Brutvogel in Griechenland. **J. Orn.** 134: 405–411.

HÖLZINGER, J. (1994) Alpenbraunellen *Prunella collaris* fressen in Griechenland auf Schneefeld gestandete Blütenkäfer Omophus sp. **Orn. Beob.** 91: 206–207.

HÖLZINGER, J. (1995) The Cinereous Bunting *Emberiza cineracea* breeding on Skyros (Greece). **Zool. in the Middle East** 11: 31–36.

HÖLZINGER, J., & KÜNKELE, S. (1986) Beiträge zur Verbreitung des Weißstorchs (*Ciconia ciconia*) in Nordgriechenland (Mazedonien, Thrakien). **Beih. Veröff. Naturschutz Landsch. Bad. Wurtt.** 43: 173–179.

HÖLZINGER, J., & RÖSLER, M. (1990) Vorkommen des Auerhuhns (*Tetrao urogallus major* C. L. Brehm, 1831) am Athos (Griechenland). **J. Orn.** 131: 95–96.

H.O.S (1994) [*Important Bird Areas in Greece.*] H.O.S. Special Publ., Athens. [In Greek.]

IAPICHINO, C., & MASSA, B. (1989) *The Birds of Sicily.* B.O.U. Check-list No. 11. B.O.U., Tring.

ILES, D. (1988) Moussier's redstart: first record for Greece. **Nature, H.S.P.N. Bull.** 41: 38.

INSKIPP, T. (1979) Recent west Palearctic records of Citrine Wagtail. **Brit. Birds** 72: 44.

ISENMANN, P. (1975) Contribution a l' étude de la reproduction de la Mouette melanocéphale (*Larus melanocephalus*). **Nos Oiseaux** 33: 66–73.

ISENMANN, P., & GOUTNER, V. (1993) Breeding status of the Slender-billed Gull (*Larus genei*) in the Mediterranean basin. Pp: 65–70 *in* AGUILAR, J.S., MONBAILLIU, X., & PATERSON, A. (eds) *Status and Conservation of Seabirds - Ecogeography and Mediterranean Action Plan.* Proceed. 2nd Mediterr. Seabird Symp. Calvia, 21–26 March 1989. SEO and MEDMARAVIS.

JAMES, P.C. (1984) The status and conservation of seabirds in the Mediterranean Sea. Pp: 371–375 *in* CROXALL, J.P., EVANS, P.G., & SCHREIBER, R.W. (eds) *Status and Conservation of the World's Seabirds.* ICBP Techn. Publ. No 2, Cambridge.

JAMESON, R. (1837) Notes on the natural history and statistics of the Island of Cerigo and its dependencies. **Edinburgh New Philosophical J.** 22: 62–69.

JERRENTRUP, H. (1986) [The birds of Xanthi and Nestos.] **Thracian Chronicles** 41: 194–211. [In Greek.]

JERRENTRUP, H. (1988) Die Lachmöwe (*Larus ridibundus*) neuer Brutvogel für Griechenland. **Kartierung mediterr. Brutvögel** 1: 5–6.

JERRENTRUP, H. (1989) Vergleich zweier teil-population des Weissstorchs (*Ciconia ciconia*) im Nestos-Delta, Nordostgriechenland. Pp: 127–135 *in* RHEINWALD, G., OGDEN, J., & SCHULZ, H. (eds) Proceed. 1st Int. Stork Conserv. Symp. Walsrode, 14–19 October 1985 D.D.A.

JERRENTRUP, H., GAETHLICH, M., JOENSEN, A.H., NØHR, H., & BRØGGER-JENSEN, S. (1988) *Urgent Plan to Safeguard Three Endangered Species in Greece and EC: Pygmy Cormorant, Great White Egret and White-tailed Eagle.* Unpubl. Rep. Ornis Consult, Nat. Hist. Mus. Århus and Hell. Orn. Soc.

JERRENTRUP, H., & HALLMANN, B. (1989) The White-tailed Eagle (*Haliaeetus albicilla*) in Greece. **Nature, H.S.P.N. Bull.** 46/47: 35.

JERRENTRUP, H., & HANDRINOS, G. (1987) [The severe winter of 1984/85 in Greece and its impact on waterfowl.] **Nature, H.S.P.N. Bull.** 36: 9–12. [In Greek.]

JERRENTRUP, H., & RESCH, J. (1989) *Der Nestos: Leben Zwischen Fluss und Meer.* Verlag J. Resch, Radolfzell.

JOENSEN, A.H,. & JERRENTRUP, H. (1988) The Agios Mamas Lagoon, Halkidiki, Greece an area of international importance for breeding waders. **Natura Jutlandica** 22: 185–188.

JOENSEN, A.H., & MADSEN, J. (1985) Waterfowl and raptors wintering in wetlands of western Greece. **Natura Jutlandica** 21(11): 169–200.

JOENSEN, A.H., PREUSS, N.O., & HANSEN, P. (1987) Waterfowl and raptors wintering in Western Greece and the Peloponnese, 1986-1987. **Natura Jutlandica** 22(5): 89–100.

JOHNSON, A., & CARP, E. (1973) IWRB Mid-winter waterfowl census in Greece, with observations in Italy and Yugoslavia, January 1973. **IWRB Bull.** 35: 47–57.

JOHNSON, A., & HAFNER, H. (1970) Winter wildfowl counts in south-east Europe and western Turkey. **Wildfowl** 21: 22–36.

JUILLARD, M., BASSIN, P., HALLMANN, B., & LANGENEGGER, A. (1990) Un Guepier de Perse, Merops superciliosus, en Crète. **Nos Oiseaux** 40: 430–431.

KANELLIS, A. (1977) [Birds threatened with extinction.] Nature, H.S.P.N. Bull. 9: 3–5. [In Greek.]

KANELLIS, A. (1980) [*Greek Wetlands: their International Importance for Bird Conservation.*] Proceed. Conf. Protect. Flora, Fauna & Biotopes in Greece. Athens, October 1979. H.S.P.N. Pp: 158–163. [In Greek.]

KARANDEINOS, M., & LEGAKIS, T. (eds) (1992) *The Red Data Book of Threatened Vertebrates of Greece.* Hellen. Zool. Soc., Athens. [In Greek.]

KASSIOUMIS, K. (1990) Greece. Pp: 157–174 *in* ALLIN, C. (ed) *International Handbook of National Parks and Nature Reserves.* Greenwood Press, Connecticut.

KASSIS, K. (1980) [*The Folklore of the Inner Mani Peninsula.*] *Vol. 1*. Athens. [In Greek.]
KATSANOS, A. (1981) [*A World History of Forestry.*] Ministry of Agriculture, Spec. Publ. No 62, Athens. [In Greek.]
KATTINGER, E. (1934) Beiträge zur Vogelkunde Nordgriechenlands. **Verh. orn. Ges. Bayern** 20: 349–437.
KATTINGER, E. (1935) Beiträge zur Vogelkunde Nordgriechenlands. **Verh. orn. Ges. Bayern** 20: 483–537.
KATTINGER, E. (1938) *Erforschung des Gebiets Thasos und Samothraki.* Proceed. 9th Intern. Orn. Congr. Rouen. Pp: 187–198.
KAUTZKY, J. (1993) *Reiseführer Natur Griechenlands: Festland und Küste.* BLV, Munich.
KELHAM, H.R. (1922) Some Cretan birds. **Ibis** 11(4): 675–687.
KINZELBACH, R. (1969) Ornithologische Beobachtungen von der Peloponnes (Griechenland). **Bonn. zool. Beitr.** 20: 175–181.
KINZELBACH, R., & MARTENS, J. (1965) Zur Kenntnis der Vögel von Karpathos (Südliche Ägäis). **Bonn. zool. Beitr.** 16: 50–91.
KLOCKENHOFF, H., & KRAPP, F. (1978) Brut und Zugvögel auf Ostkreta in Frühjar 1976. **Bonn. zool. Beitr.** 28(3–4): 331–368.
KNIGHTBRIDGE, R.W.S., & AKRIOTIS, T. (1982) Greek tragedy. **B.T.O. News** 118: 10.
KNOTZSCH, G. (1965) Ornithologische Beobactungen aus Nordgriechenland. **Orn. Beob.** 62: 181–187.
KOMINOS, T. (1995) [*Kythira: on the Migratory Path of Birds.*] Etairia Kythiraikon Spoudon, Thessaloniki. [In Greek.]
KOTOULAS, D. (ed) (1989) [*Greek Forests.*] Goulandris Nat. Hist. Museum, Kifissia. [In Greek.]
KRAUS, M., & CONRADTY, P. (1965) Zur Kenntnis der **Vogelwelt** Nordgriechenlands. **Anz. Orn. Ges. Bayern** 7: 475–485.
KRAUS, M., CONRADTY, P., HOHLT, G., & BAUER, E. (1969) Zur Kenntnis der **Vogelwelt** Nordgriechenlands, III. **J. Orn.** 110: 83–89.
KROYMANN, B., & KROYMANN, L. (1992) Brutvorkommen des Fahlseglers (*Apus pallidus*) in Phokien, Mittelgriechenland. **Kartierung mediterr. Brutvögel** 7: 39–44.
KRÜPER, T. (1860) Über *Aquila bonelli* in Griechenland. **J. Orn.** 8: 442–447.
KRÜPER, T. (1862) Ornithologische Notizen über Griechenland. **J. Orn.** 10: 360–379, 435–448.
KRÜPER, T. (1863) Die Brutvögel von Naxos. **J. Orn.** 11: 402–407.
KRÜPER, T., & HARTLAUB, G. (1875) Zeiten des Gehens und Kommens und des Brütens des Vögel in Griechenland und Ionien. Pp: 155–330 *in* MOMMSEN, A. *Griechische Jahreszeiten.* Vol. 3
KUMERLOEVE, H. (1957) *Anthropoides virgo* (L.) in Griechisch-Macedonien. **Vogelwelt** 78: 65.
KUMERLOEVE, H. (1961) Zur Kenntnis der Avifauna Kleinasiens. **Bonn. Zool. Beitr. (Suppl.)** 12: 1–318.
KUMERLOEVE, H. (1977) Remarques sur l'avifaune de l'ile Kos. **Alauda** 45(2–3): 239.
KUMMER, J. (1964) Der Braunliest, *Halcyon smyrnensis*, in Europa. **J. Orn.** 105: 200.
KUMMER, J. (1981) Ornithologische Beobachtungen in der Ägäis. **Beitr. Vogelk.** 27(2): 57–69.

LAMANI, F., & ZEKO, I. (1985) L' Albanie, pays propre à l' hivernage des Anseriformes. 2e Congrès Intern. sur la Zoogéographie et l'Ecologie de la Grèce et des Régions Avoisinates. Athens, 1981. **Biol. Gallo-hellen.** 10: 333–337.
LAMBERT, A. (1957) A specific check-list of the birds of Greece. **Ibis** 99: 43–68.
LAMBERTON, R.D., & ROTROFF, S.I. (1985) *Birds of the Athenian Agora.* Amer. School of Classical studies. Athens and Princeton.
LAUBMANN, A. (1927) Zur Ornithologie der Ionischen Inseln. **Verh. orn. Ges. Bayern** 17: 291–376.
LENSCH, A. (1979) Vogelkundliche Beobachtungen auf der Insel Kos (Griechenland). **Orn. Mitt.** 31(11): 262–266.
LIMBRUNNER, A. (1979) Erstnachweis der Fortpflanzung des Häherkuckucks (Clamator glandarius) in Griechenland. **Anz. orn. Ges. Bayern** 18(1): 84–85.
LIMBRUNNER, A. (1987) Rosenstare (*Sturnus roseus*) brüteten 1987 in Nordostgriechenland. **Verh. orn. Ges. Bayern** 24: 541–542.
LINDERMAYER, A. (1843) Die Vögel Griechenlands. Isis 5: 321–364.
LINDERMAYER, A. (1855) Euboea. Eine naturhistorische Skizze. **Bull. soc. imp. nat. Moscou** 28: 401–451.
LINDERMAYER, A. (1860) Die Vögel Griechenlands. *Ein Beitrag zur Fauna dieses Landes.* Ber. naturw. Ver. Passau.
LÖHRL, H. (1988) *Etho-ekologische Untersuchungen an Verschiedenen Kleiberarten* (Sittidae). Bonner Zool. Monogr. No. 26.
LONDEI, T. (1991) Winter record of the Booted Eagle (*Hieraaetus pennatus*) and the Short-toed Eagle, (*Circaetus gallicus*) in Crete (Greece). **Riv. ital. Orn.** 61(3–4): 128–129.
LOTERIJMAN, J.A. (1968) Observation of *Streptopelia orientalis* in Southeast Europe. **Ardea** 56: 285–288.
LYNES, H. (1909a) Observations on the migration of birds in the Mediterranean II. Spring migration at Crete. Brit. Birds 8: 99–104.
LYNES, H. (1909b) Observations on the migration of birds in the Mediterranean III. Migration at sea. **Brit. Birds** 8: 133–150.

MACDONALD, D.W., & BARETT, P. (1993) *Mammals of Britain & Europe.* Harper Collins, London.
MAGERL, C., & FRANCIS, I. (1979) Notizen zur Vogelwelt Thraziens. **Orn. Mitt.** 31(2): 281–285.
MAGIORIS, S. (1987a) Check-list of the bird species that have been observed in Cyclades, Aegean, Greece, during 19th and 20th century. **Ecol. Mediterr.** 12(1/2): 15–22.
MAGIORIS, S. (1987b) Migration over the Cyclades, central Aegean. **Ringing Migr.** 8(2): 109–114.
MAGIORIS, S. (1988) Breeding birds of the island of Naxos (Cyclades, Greece). **Rapport C.I.E.S.M.** 31(2): 131.
MAGIORIS, S. (1989) Supplementary elements regarding the check-list of the bird species that have been observed in the Cyclades, Aegean Sea, Greece. **Ecol. Mediterr.** 15(1/2): 65–68.
MAGIORIS, S. (1992a) Mission dans l' île de Naxos 23 au 25 mars 1989. Mission dans l' île de Skopelos du 20 au 27 avril 1989. *In Inventaire de la Faune de Grèce. Milieux Humides Insulaires: Égée Occidentale et Centrale. Condensés des Rapports des Missions.* **Biol. Gallo-hellen.** 19: 104.
MAGIORIS, S. (1992b) Nidification des fauvettes Sarde (*Sylvia sarda*) et de Ruppell (*Sylvia rueppelli*) dans les îles

Cyclades en Mer Egée (Grèce). **Alauda** 60(2): 123.
MAGIORIS, S. (1994) The avifauna of the Cyclades (Aegean Sea). **Hellen. Zool. Arch.** 2: 1–16.
MAKATSCH, W. (1943a) [*Contribution to the Knowledge of the Avian World of Macedonia.*] Ph.D. thesis, Univ. of Thessaloniki. [In Greek.]
MAKATSCH, W. (1943b) *Aquila pomarina* C.L. Brehm als Brutvogel Macedoniens. **Orn. Monatsber.** 51: 94–95.
MAKATSCH, W. (1950) *Die Vogelwelt Macedoniens.* Leipzig.
MAKATSCH, W. (1952) Ein Beitrag zur Biologie der Brachschwalbe (*Glareola p. pratincola*). **Larus** 4–5: 89–98.
MAKATSCH, W. (1959) A propos de la protection des oiseaux en Grèce et en Turquie. Proceed. VII Congr. Intern. Prot. Nature. Athènes. **Nature, H.S.P.N. Bull.** 5: 77–80.
MAKATSCH, W. (1962) Einige Beobachtungen am Brutplatz des Spornkiebitzes (*Hoplopterus spinosus*). **J. Orn.** 103: 219–228.
MAKATSCH, W. (1963) Ornithologische Beobachtungen in Griechenland. **Zool. Abh. Mus. Tierk. Dresden** 26: 135–186.
MAKATSCH, W. (1968a) Die Möwen Griechenlands. **Nat. u. Museum** 98: 221–230.
MAKATSCH, W. (1968b) Beobachtungen an einem Brutplatz der Korallenmöwe (*Larus audouinii*). **J. Orn.** 109: 43–56.
MAKATSCH, W. (1968c) Wir Fanden die seltenste Möwe Europas. **Vogel Kosmos** 5: 112–116.
MAKATSCH, W. (1969a) Europe's rarest Gull? **Animals, Int. Wildl. Magazine** 4: 544–545.
MAKATSCH, W. (1969b) Studies of less familiar birds 154, Audouin's Gull. **Brit. Birds** 62: 230–232.
MAKATSCH, W. (1970) Die Limicolen Griechenlands. **Natur u. Museum** 100(4): 185–194.
MAKATSCH, W. (1978) Beobachtungen an einem Brutplatz des Cistensängers auf der Peloponnes. **Vögel der Heimat** 48: 194–203.
MAKATSCH, W. (1981) Ornithologische Beobachtungen in Griechenland. **Nature, H.S.P.N. Bull.** 19/20: 55–76.
MALAKOU, M. (1985) [*A Study of the Fauna of Olympos National Park.*] Unpubl. Rep., H.S.P.N., Athens. [In Greek.]
MALAKOU, M., & CATSADORAKIS, G. (1992) Past and present situation of the wetlands of Crete with special reference to their birds. **Biol. Gallo-hellen.** 19: 59–72.
MALAKOU, M., TSOUNIS, G., RAVASINI, M., & SFIKAS, G. (1985) [Pindos National Park.] **Nature, H.S.P.N. Bull.** 31: 3–19. [In Greek.]
MARGALEF, R. (1984) Le plancton de la Mediterranée. **La Recherche** 158: 1082–1094.
MARINKOVIC, S., & ORLANDIC, L. (1994) Census of the Griffon Vulture (*Gyps fulvus*) on Crete island. 6e Congrès Intern. de Zoogéographie et Ecologie de la Grèce et des Régions Avoisinantes. Thessaloniki, 5–6 Avril 1993. **Bios** 2: 295–300.
MARIOLOPOULOS, I. (1938) [*The Climate of Greece.*] Athens. [In Greek.]
MARIOLOPOULOS, I. (1953) [*Overview of the Climate of Greece.*] Athens. [In Greek.]
MARTEIJN, E., & MEININGER, P. (1988) Greater Flamingos in NE Greece, spring 1987. **Flamingo W.G. Newsl.** 4: 14–19.
MARTENS, J. (1966) Brutvorkommen und Zugverhalten des Weissstorchs (*C. ciconia*) in Griechenland. **Vogelwarte** 23: 191–208.
MASSA, B. (1982) Il gradiente faunistico nella Peninsola Italiana e nelle isole. **Atti Soc. ital. Sci. Nat.** 123: 353–374.
MASSA, B. (1984) Il Crociere (*Loxia curvirostra*) nidifica nell' isola de Creta. **Riv. ital. Orn.** 54(1–2): 102–103.
MATVEJEV, S. (1986) [The life and works of Dr O. Reiser, ornithologist of the Balkan lands.] **Larus** 36/37: 205–224. [In Serbo-Croat.]
MEIKLEJOHN, R.F. (1936) Nesting notes on Ruppel's Warbler and Black-headed Bunting. **Ibis** 13 (6): 377–378.
MEINERTZHAGEN, R. (1920) New birds from Crete: *Corvus, Garrulus, Oenanthe, Otus, Melanocorypha, Galerida, Anthus, Cisticola.* **Bull. Br. Orn. Club** 41: 10–25.
MEININGER, P. (1988) Citrine Wagtail in Greece, in April 1987. **Dutch Birding** 10: 90–91.
MEININGER, P. (ed) (1990) *Birds of the Wetlands in North-east Greece, Spring 1987.* WIWO Rep. No 20. Zeist.
MEININGER, P., & SØRENSEN, U. (1993) Egypt as a major wintering area of Little Bulls. Brit. Birds 86: 407–410.
MESCHINI, E., & FRUGIS, S. (eds) (1993) Atlante degli uccelli nidificanti in Italia. **Suppl. Ric. Biol. Selvaggina** 20: 1–344.
MEYBURG, D.U., SCHELLER, W., & MEYBURG, C. (1993) Satelliten-Telemetrie bei einem juvenilen Schreiadler (Aquila pomarina) auf dem Herbstzug. **J. Orn.** 134: 173–179.
MIGHELL, A. (1986) Third record of a Western Reef Heron (*Egretta gularis*) in Greece. **H.O.S. Newsl.** 3: 19.
MIKKOLA, H. (1983) *Owls of Europe.* T. & A.D. Poyser, Calton.
MILLON, D., PARENT, M., & ROLIN, G. (1988) Lesser Yellowlegs (*Tringa flavipes*). *In* HANDRINOS, G., *Three New Species to the Greek Avifauna.* **Nature, H.S.P.N. Bull.** 42: 36.
MITCHELL, K.D.G. (1968) Nightingale or Thrush Nightingale at 10,000 feet over Greece. **Brit. Birds** 61: 33–34.
MONVAL, J.-Y., & PIROT, J.-Y. (eds) (1989) *Results of the International Waterfowl Census 1967–1986.* IWRB Special Publ. No 8, Slimbridge.
MOREAU, R.E. (1953) Migration in the Mediterranean area. **Ibis** 95: 329–364.
MOREAU, R.E. (1960) Autumn migrants in Greece. **Ibis** 102: 473–475.
MOREAU, R.E. (1961) Problems of Mediterranean - Saharan migration. **Ibis** 103a: 373–427, 580–618.
MOREAU, R.E., & MOREAU, W. (1963) Aegean observations, autumn 1961. **Ibis** 105: 268269.
MÖRZER-BRUYNS, W.F., & VOOUS, K. (1965) Great Skuas (*Stercorarius skua*) in N. Indian Ocean. **Ardea** 53: 80–81.
MÜHLE, GRAF H. v.d. (1844) *Beiträge zur Ornithologie Griechelands.* Leipzig.
MÜLLER, G. (1980) The birds of Greece threats and measures of protection, Conclusions from 20 years of observations. Proceed. Conf. Protect. Flora, Fauna & Biotopes in Greece. Athens, October 1979. H.S.P.N. Pp: 147–155.

NATIONAL STATISTICAL SERVICE OF GREECE (1986) [*Distribution of the Country's Area by Basic Categories of Land Use.*] Athens. [In Greek.]
NATIONAL STATISTICAL SERVICE OF GREECE (1994) [*Statistical Yearbook of Greece.*] Athens. [In Greek.]
NAUMANN, J.F. (1905) *Naturgeschichte der Vögel Mitteleuropas.* Vol. X. E. Köhler, Gera.
NAZIRIDIS, T., JERRENTRUP, H., & CRIVELLI, A. (1992) Wintering herons in Greece (1964–1991). Pp: 73–75 *in*

FINLAYSON, C.M., HOLLIS, G.E., & DAVIES, T.J. (eds) *Managing Mediterranean Wetlands and their Birds.* Proceed. Symp. Grado, Italy, 1991. IWRB Spec. Publ. No 20. IWRB, Slimbridge.

NAZIRIDIS, T,. & PAPAGEORGIOU, N. (in press) The breeding biology of Pygmy Cormorants *Phalacrocorax pygmeus*, a vulnerable bird species, at L. Kerkini, N. Greece. **Colonial Waterbirds.**

NEWTON, I. (1972) *Finches*. The New Naturalist series, No. 55. Collins, London.

NIETHAMMER, G. (1943a) Über die Vogelwelt Kretas. **Ann. Nat. Hist. Mus. Wien** 53: 5–50.

NIETHAMMER, G. (1943b) Beiträge zur Kenntnis der Brutvögel des Peloponnes. **J. Orn.** 91: 167–238.

NISBET, I.C.T. (1967) Frühjahrs-Vogelzug auf Paros (Kykladen). **Bonn. Zool. Beitr.** 18: 234–252.

NISBET, I.C.T. (1975) Greece and the Greek islands. Pp: 285–296 *in* FERGUSON LEES, J., HOCKLIFFE, Q., & ZWEERES, K. (eds) *A Guide to Bird Watching in Europe*. Bodley Head, London.

NISBET, I.C.T., & SMOUT, T.C. (1956) Observations de la migration d' automne de *Larus melanocephalus* en Grèce et Turquie. **Alauda** 24: 306–307.

NISBET, I.C.T., & SMOUT, T.C. (1957) Autumn observations on the Bosphorus and Dardanelles. **Ibis** 99: 483–499.

NOESKE, A. (1987) Binnenlandvorkommen des Eleonorenfalken (*Falco eleonorae*) während der Heimzug und frühen Brutphase. **Limicola** 1: 91–95.

OGILVIE, M. (1978) *Wild geese*. T. & A.D. Poyser, Berkhamsted.

PAIN, D.J., & HANDRINOS, G. (1990) The incidence of ingested lead shot in ducks of the Evros Delta, Greece. **Wildfowl** 41: 167–170.

PALSSON, P.G., & FLACH, B. (1962) Ornithologiska observationer från Grekland 1961. **Fauna och Flora** 57: 196–199.

PAPACONSTANTINOU, C. (1991) [The Aegion Lagoon.] **Nature, H.S.P.N. Bull.** 55: 40–44. [In Greek.]

PAPACONSTANTINOU, C., OIKONOMIDOU, E., BOUSBOURAS, D., KARDAKARI, N., ZOGKARIS, S., TSIAKIRIS, R. & ROUSSOPOULOS, Y. (1995) [*Ecological Investigation in the Northern Dodecanese, HOS Expedition to the Islands and Islets of the North of Nomos Dodekanisos.*] H.O.S., Athens. [In Greek.]

PAPAEVANGELOU, E. (1980) General situation of the partridge species in Greece. *Partridges of the* Alectoris *Genus.* Proceed. Intern. Sympos., Athens, May 1979. CIC Paris. Pp: 71–77.

PAPAEVANGELOU, E., THOMAIDES, C., HANDRINOS, G., & HARALAMBIDES, A. (in press) *Status of Partridge Species in Greece.* Proceed. Partridges, Quail and Grouse Symposium, Paris, Oct. 1995.

PAPAGEORGIOU, N. (1992) [The present status and future of the Pheasant in the forest of Nestos Delta.] *Nestos: its Natural Environment and Problems.* Proceed. Conf. Kavala, Greece, 24–26 April 1991. Pp: 169–183. [In Greek.]

PAPAIOANNOU, J. (1953) [The forest of Kotza Orman]. **Eklogi (Athens)** 2: 55–64. [In Greek.]

PAPAIOANNOU, J. (1968) [The Tetraonidae in Greece]. **The Forest** 40/41: 23–35. [In Greek.]

PARROT, C. (1905) Eine Reise nach Griechenland und ihre ornithologischen Ergebnisse. **J. Orn.** 53: 515–556, 618–669.

PARROT, C. (1908) Über einige Vögel aus Calamata, Peloponnes. **Verh. orn. Ges. Bayern** 8: 27–28.

PARROT, J. (1977) The Fan-tailed warbler (*Cisticola juncidis*) in Crete. **Ibis** 119(4): 520–521.

PARROTT, J., COGHLAN, S., & GOODERS, J. (in press) *The Birds of Crete.* B.O.U. Check-list No ?. B.O.U., Tring.

PASQUALI, R. (1981) Osservazioni ornithologiche nell' isola di Creta (autunno 1980). **Riv. ital. Orn.** 51(3-4): 252–254.

PASQUALI, R. (1982) Osservazioni ornithologiche nell' isola di Creta. **Uccelli d' Italia** 4: 239–247.

PASQUALI, R. (1989) Osservazioni ornithologiche nelle Isole Ionie della Grecia. Corfu, Zacinto, Cefalonia. **Uccelli d' Italia** 14: 45–47.

PATERSON, A. (1993) The status of the Northern Gannet (*Sula bassana*) in the Mediterranean. Pp: 161–171 *in* AGUILAR, J.S., MONBAILLIU, X., & PATERSON, A. (eds) *Status and Conservation of Seabirds - Ecogeography and Mediterranean Action Plan.* Proceed. 2nd Mediterr. Seabird Symp. Calvia, 21–26 March 1989. SEO and MEDMARAVIS.

PEASE, H.J.R. (1940) Supplementary notes on Mr. C.M.N. WHITE'S "Contribution to the ornithology of Crete" (Ibis Jan. 1939). **Ibis** (14) 4: 99–106.

PERGANTIS, F. (1981) *The Distribution of Birds in Olive Groves and their Association with Olive Trees in Greece.* M.Sc. thesis, University College Wales, Bangor.

PERGANTIS, F., & AKRIOTIS, T. (1994) The breeding status of terns Sternidae in the Amvrakikos area. 5e Congrès Intern. de Zoogéographie et Ecologie de la Grèce et des Régions Avoisinantes. Iraklion, 16–20 Avril 1990. **Biol. Gallo-hellen.** 22: 179–184.

PERGANTIS, F,. & HANDRINOS, G. (1992) A preliminary check-list of the birds of the Messolonghi wetlands (1860–1986) with seasonal occurrence and population data. **Biol. Gallo-hellen.** 19: 5–28.

PERGANTIS, F., & ROUSSOPOULOS, J. (1994) Effects of pisciculture development on the breeding populations of the Black-winged Stilt (*Himantopus himantopus*) and of the Collared Pratincole (*Glareola pratincola*) in the Amvrakikos wetland area in W. Greece. 5e Congrès Intern. de Zoogéographie et Ecologie de la Grèce et des Régions Avoisinantes. Iraklion, 16–20 Avril 1990. **Biol. Gallo-hellen.** 22: 151–159.

PETERSON, R.T., MOUNTFORT, G., HOLLOM, P.A.D., KANNELLIS, A, & BAUER, W. (1981) [*The Birds of Greece and Europe.*] Golden Press, Athens. [In Greek.]

PETROU, N. (1994) *Images of Dadia.* Koan Publ., Athens.

PETROU, N. (1995) *Reflections on Kerkini.* Koan Publ., Athens.

PEUS, F. (1954) Zur Kenntnis der Brutvögel Griechenlands, I. *Bonn. Zool. Beitr.* **(Special Edition)** 5: 1–50.

PEUS, F. (1957) Zur Kenntnis der Brutvögel Griechenlands, II. **Mitt. Zool. Mus. Berlin** 33: 261–305.

PIEPER, H. (1977) Fledermäuse aus Schleiereulen-Gewöllen von der Insel Kreta. **Zeitschr. Säugetierk.** 42: 7–12.

PIEPER, H. (1981) Zur säugetiernahrung des Uhus (*Bubo bubo*) auf der griechischen Insel Lesbos. **Vogelwelt** 102: 55–56.

POIRAZIDIS, K. (1989) [*Study of the Distribution and Ecology of the Capercaillie* (*Tetrao urogallus*) in Greece.] Dissert., School of Geotechnic studies, University of Thessaloniki. [In Greek.]

POIRAZIDIS, K. (1990) [The Capercaillie (*Tetrao urogallus*) in Greek forests.] **Nature, H.S.P.N. Bull.** 48: 3–7. [In Greek.]

POLLARD, J. (1977) *Birds in Greek Life and Myth.* Thames and Hudson, London.

POLUNIN, O. (1980) *Flowers of Greece and the Balkans: a Field Guide*. OUP, Oxford.
POTTER, J. (1988) Barbary Falcon (*Falco pelegrinoides*). *In* HANDRINOS, G. *Three New Species to the Greek avifauna*. **Nature, H.S.P.N. Bull.** 42: 34.
POWYS, H.L.T. (=Lord LILFORD) (1860) Notes of the birds observed in the Ionian Islands and the provinces of Albania proper, Epirus, Acarnania and Montenegro. **Ibis** 2: 1-10, 133-140, 228- 139, 338-357.
POWYS, H.L.T. (=Lord LILFORD) (1862) On the Extinction in Europe of the Common Francolin, Francolinus vulgaris Steph. **Ibis** 4: 352-356.
PRIGANN, I. (1992) Rosenstar (*Sturnus roseus*) 1985 Brutvogel bei Vafiohori, Nordgiechenland. **Kartierung mediterr. Brutvögel** 7: 11–12.
PSILOVIKOS, A. (1990) [Changes in Greek wetlands during the 20th century: the case of Macedonian inland waters.] Pp: 182–195 *in* GERAKIS, P.A. (ed) *Conservation and Management of the Greek Wetlands*. Proceed. Workshop Thessaloniki, 16–21 April 1989. WWF, IUCN and Lab. of Ecology, School of Agronomy, Aristotelian University Thessaloniki. [In Greek.]
PYROVETSI, M. (1989) Foraging trips of White Pelicans (*Pelecanus onocrotalus*) breeding on Lake Mikri Prespa, Greece. **Colonial Waterbirds** 12(1): 43–50.

RAINES, R.J. (1962) The distribution of birds in northeast Greece in summer. **Ibis** 104: 490–502.
RAINES, R.J. (1971) The pied Wheatear in Greece. **Ibis** 113: 110.
RALFS, G. (1960) Ornithologische Beobachtungen auf Rhodos. **Vehr. Natw. Ver. Hamburg** 5: 7–18.
REIFFENSTUEL, W. (1958) Der Nachtreiher Brutvogel in Südmazedonien? **Vogelwelt** 79: 108–109.
REISER, O. (1905) *Ornis Balcanica. III. Griechenland und die Griechischen Inseln (Mit Ausnahme von Kreta)*. Wien.
RENZONI, A., & MASSA, A. (1993) Contaminants in Mediterranean seabirds. Pp: 207–212 *in* AGUILAR, J.S., MONBAILLIU, X., & PATERSON, A. (eds) *Status and Conservation of Seabirds - Ecogeography and Mediterranean Action Plan*. Proceed. 2nd Mediterr. Seabird Symp. Calvia, 21–26 March 1989. SEO and MEDMARAVIS.
RISTOW, D. (1975) Neue Ringfunde vom Eleonorenfalken (*Falco eleonorae*). **Vogelwarte** 28: 150–153.
RISTOW, D., CONRAD, B., WINK, C., & WINK, M. (1980) Pesticide residues of failed eggs of Eleonora's Falcon (*Falco eleonorae*) from an Aegean colony. **Ibis** 122: 74–76.
RISTOW, D., & WINK, M. (1980) Sexual dimorphism of Cory's Shearwater. **Il-Merill** 21: 9–12.
RISTOW, D., & WINK, M. (1985) Breeding success and conservation management of Eleonora's Falcon. Pp: 147–152 *in* NEWTON, I., & CHANCELLOR, R. (eds) *Conservation Studies of Raptors*. ICBP Techn. Publ. No 5. Cambridge.
RISTOW, D. & WINK, M. (1994) Distribution of non-breeding Eleonora's Falcon (*Falco eleonorae*). **Il-Merill** 28: 1–10.
RISTOW, D., WINK, C., & WINK, M. (1979) Site tenacity and pair bond of the Eleonora's Falcon. **Il- Merill** 20: 16–18.
RISTOW, D., WINK, C., & WINK, M. (1982) Biology of Eleonora's Falcon (*Falco eleonorae*): 1. Individual and Social defense behaviour. **Raptor Research** 16(3): 65–70.
RISTOW, D., WINK, C., & WINK, M. (1986) Assessment of Mediterranean autumn migration by prey analysis of Eleonora's Falcon. Proceed. 1st Conf. on Birds wintering in the Mediterranean Region. Aulla, 1984. **Suppl. Ric. Biol. Selvaggina** 10: 285–295.
RISTOW, D., SCHARLAU, M., & WINK, M. (1989) Population structure and mortality of Eleonora's Falcon (*Falco eleonorae*). Pp: 321–326 *in* MEYBURG, B.U., & CHANCELLOR, R.D. (eds) *Raptors in the Modern World*. W.W.G.B.P./Pica Press, Berlin.
RISTOW, D., FELDMANN, F., SCHARLAU, W., & WINK, M. (1990) Population structure, philopatry and mortality of Cory's Shearwater (*Calonectris d. diomedea*). **Vogelwelt** 111: 172–181.
RISTOW, D., FELDMANN, F., SCHARLAU, W., WINK, C., WINK M., (1991) Population dynamics of Cory's Shearwater (*Calonectris diomedea*) and Eleonora's Falcon (*Falco eleonorae*) in the Eastern Mediterranean. Pp: 199–212 *in* SEITZ, A., & LOESCKHE, V. (eds) *Species Conservation: a Population - Biological Approach*. Birkhauser Verlag, Basel.
RISTOW, D., HADRICH, J., BAUM, F., & WINK, M. (1992) Pesticide residues in Cory's Shearwater eggs (*Calonectris d. diomedea*). *In* FASOLA, M. (ed) *Management of Island and Coastal Ecosystems in the Mediterranean*. Proceed. MEDMARAVIS Sympos. Chios, Greece, 15–20 Sept. 1992. **Avocetta** 16: 102–104.
RITZEL, L. (1980) Beiträge zur **Vogelwelt** Nordgriechenlands. **Orn. Mitt.** 32(5): 115–124.
ROSE, P. (ed) (1995) *Western Palearctic and S.W. Asia Waterfowl Census 1994*. IWRB Publ. No 35.
ROUSSOPOULOS, Y. (1990) [*The Breeding Birds of the Messolonghi Wetlands*.] Dissert., Messolonghi Technical Institute. [In Greek.]
ROUSSOPOULOS, Y., & PERGANTIS, F. (1994) The decline of the Lesser Kestrel (*Falco naumanni*) in Aetolia, W. Greece. 5e Congrès Intern. de Zoogéographie et Ecologie de la Grèce et des Régions Avoisinantes. Iraklion, 16-20 Avril 1990. **Biol. Gallo-hellen.** 22: 161–170.
RÜGER, A., PRENTICE, C., & OWEN, M. (1986) *Results of the IWRB International Waterfowl Census 1967–1983*. IWRB Special Publ. No 6, Slimbridge.
RUTSCHKE, E. (1987) *Die Wildgänse Europas*. Aula Verlag, Wiesbaden.

SAGE, B.L. (1966) Récentes observations ornithologiques au lac Prespa, Macedoine (Yougoslavie). **Alauda** 34: 45-54, 120–132.
SALVADORI, T. & FESTA, E. (1913) Escursioni zoologiche del Dr. Enrico Fest nell' isola di Rodi. II. Uccelli. **Boll. Mus. Zool. Anat. Torino** 28: 1–23.
SCHARLAU, W. (1989a) Die Vogelwelt der Ägäis. Teil 1: Die Brutvögel von Rhodos. **Kartierung mediterr. Brutvögel** 3: 3-23.
SCHARLAU, W. (1989b) Die Vogelwelt der Ägäis. Teil 2: Die Brutvögel von Ostkreta. **Kartierung mediterr. Brutvögel** 3: 24–40.
SCHIEBEL, G. (1925) Ornithologische Briefe aus Kreta. I–III. **Orn. Monatsber.** 33: 76–78, 124–127, 145–147.
SCHIEBEL, G. (1926) Ornithologische Briefe aus Kreta. IV–VI. **Orn. Monatsber.** 34: 111–114, 142–144, 176–179.
SCHMID, W. (1992) Weitere Brutzeit-Feststellungen der Wacholderdrossel (*Turdus pilaris*) in Mittelgriechenland. **Kartierung mediterr. Brutvögel** 7: 49–51.
SCHMID, W., & REICHENECKER, H. (1988) Die Brutvögel des Vikos und Voidomatis Tals und dem Gebirgsstock

Astraka und Gamila im Pindusgebirge Bezirk Ioannina, Zentralgriechenland. **Kartierung mediterr. Brutvögel** 1: 17–24.
SEER, ? (1942) Ornithologische Notizen aus Kreta. **Orn. Monatsber.** 50: 173-174.
SEVASTOS, K. (1976) Greece: National Report. Pp: 97–103 *in* SMART, M. (ed.) Proceed. Intern. Conf. Conserv. wetlands and waterfowl. Heiligenhafen, F.R.G., December 1974.
SIBLET, J. (1986) Bird records from Greece, in August 1982. **Dutch Birding** 2: 65.
SIMMS, E. (1985) *British Warblers.* Collins, London.
SIMPSON, W.H. (1860a) Ornithological notes from Mesolonghi and south Aetolia. **Ibis** (1) 2: 279–296.
SIMPSON, W.H. (1860b) Further observations on some of the birds of Western Greece. **Ibis** (1) 2: 378–395.
SIMPSON, W.H. (1860c) Brief note on *Aquila bonellii* and *Pelecanus crispus.* **Ibis** (1) 2: 202.
SLADEN, A.G.L. (1917) Notes on birds recently observed in Macedonia. **Ibis** (10) 5: 429–433.
SLADEN, A.G.L. (1918) Further notes on the birds of Macedonia. **Ibis** (10) 6: 292–300.
SMIT, C. (1986) Waders along the Mediterranean. A summary of present knowledge. Proceed. 1st Conf. on Birds wintering in the Mediterranean Region. Aulla, 1984. **Suppl. Ric. Biol. Selvaggina** 10: 297–317.
SONNENSCHEIN, E. (1980) Ein Beitrag zur kenntnis der Vogelwelt der Insel Lesbos (Griechenland). **Vogelwelt** 101: 182–186.
SPENCER, R. (1964) Ringing report for 1963. **Brit. Birds** 57: 525–582.
SPERLING, R.M. (1864) Some accounts of an ornithologist's cruise in the Mediterranean. **Ibis** (1) 6: 268–290.
SPINTHAKIS, E., CHOULIS, D. & CHOREMI, J. (1993) *The Birds of Chios Isl.* Municipality of Homeroupolis.
STEINFATT, O. (1954/55) Vogelkundliche Beobachtungen in Attika., 96: 92–101. **J. Orn.** 95: 22–37, 254–262,.
STRESEMANN, E. (1942a) Frühlingsanfang in Attika. **Orn. Monatsber.** 50: 27–48.
STRESEMANN, E. (1942b) Winterbeobachtungen auf Kreta. **Orn. Monatsber.** 50: 1–5.
STRESEMANN, E. (1943) Überblick über die Vögel Kretas und den Vogelzug in der Ägäis. **J. Orn.** 91: 448–514.
STRESEMANN, E. (1944) Der Frühjajrsdurchzug einiger Vogelarten durch die Mittelmeerländer. **Orn. Monatsber.** 52: 29–44.
STRESEMANN, E. (1951) *Die Entwicklung der Ornithologie von Aristoteles bis zur Gegenwart.* Berlin.
STRESEMANN, E. (1956) Bausteine zu einer Ornithologie von Kreta. **J. Orn.** 97: 44–72.
SULTANA, J. (1993) *Important Seabird Sites in the Mediterranean.* Malta Orn. Soc., Malta.
SUMMERS-SMITH, D. (1980) Sparrows on Crete. **Il-Merill** 21: 17–18.
SUMMERS-SMITH, D. (1988) *The Sparrows.* T. & A.D. Poyser, Calton.
SZIJJ, J. (1980) The significance of the Louros and Arachthos Estuaries from the conservation point of view. **Nature, H.S.P.N. Bull.** 22: 43–46.
SZIJJ, J. (ed) (1983) *Ökologische Wertanalyse des Acheloos-Deltas (Westgriechenland).* Unpubl. Rep., Univ. of Essen.

TERRASSE, J.F., TERRASSE, M., & BROSSELIN, M. (1969) Avifauna d' un lac des Balkans: Mikra Prespa (Grèce). **L' Oiseau et R.F.O.** 39: 185–201.
THIBAUT, J.-C. (1993) Breeding distribution and numbers of Cory's Shearwater (*Calonectris diomedea*) in the Mediterranean. Pp: 25–35 *in* AGUILAR, J.S., MONBAILLIU, X., & PATERSON, A. (eds) *Status and Conservation of Seabirds - Ecogeography and Mediterranean Action Plan.* Proceed. 2nd Mediterr. Seabird Symp. Calvia, 21–26 March 1989. SEO and MEDMARAVIS.
THOMAIDES, C., & PAPAGEORGIOU, N. (1992) Nesting biology and habitat use of the Grey Partridge (*Perdix perdix*) in Northern Greece. *In* BIRKAN, M., POTTS, G.R., AEBISCHER, N.J., & DOWELL, S.D. (eds) *Perdix VI.* First Intern. Symp. on Partridges, Quails and Francolins. **Gibier Faune Sauvage** 9: 443–446.
THORPE, W.H., COTTON, P.T., & HOLMES, P.F. (1936) Notes on the birds of lakes Ohrid, Malik and Prespa and adjacent parts of Jougoslavia, Albania, and Greece. **Ibis** (13) 6: 557–580.
TORTONESE, E., & MOLTONI, E. (1947) Appunti ornitologici relativi all' isola di Rodi (Egeo), 1942–1943. **Riv. ital. Orn.** 17: 29–39.
TOURNEFORT, J.P. DE (1717) *Relation d' un Voyage du Levant, Fair par Ordre du Roy.* 3 Vols. Lyon.
TSOUNIS, G. (1984) Osservazioni ornitologiche nella Laguna di Messolonghi (Grecia Occidentale). **Riv. ital. Orn.** 54(3–4): 262–264.
TSOUNIS, G. (1987) Aspetti Faunistici del Parco Nazionale di Valia-Calda, Pindo. Pp: 44–47 *in* CRUCITTI, P. (ed) *Atti convegno di Zoologia Ellenica.* Roma, Maggio 1986. Soc. Romana Scienzi Naturali.
TSOUNIS, G. (1988) The Valia-Kalda National Park, Greece. **Oryx** 22: 25–29.
TSOUNIS, G. (1990) [The avifauna of the island of Lesbos.] **H.O.S. Newsl.** 6: 28–31. [In Greek.]
TSOUNIS, G., & DIMITROPOULOS, A. (1992a) Seasonal variation of the feeding of Barn Owl (*Tyto alba* Scopoli 1769) in Mount Hymettus, Attica, Greece. **Biol. Gallo-hellen.** 19: 29–36.
TSOUNIS, G., & DIMITROPOULOS, A. (1992b) The avifauna of the North-Eastern Aegean islands Lesvos and Chios: differences and similarities. **Biol. Gallo-hellen.** 19: 73–102.
TSOUNIS, G., & FRUGIS, S. (1987) Red list of Birds of Greece. **Nature, H.S.P.N. Bull.** 36: 29–34.
TSOUNIS, G., & FRUGIS, S. (1989) Considerations on Zoogeographical origins of the birds breeding in Greece. 4e Congrès Intern. de Zoogéographie et Ecologie de la Grèce et des Régions Avoisinantes. Kammena Vourla, Avril 1987. **Biol. Gallo-hellen.** 15: 117–128.
TSOUNIS, G., & SFIKAS, G. (1993) *Ecotouristic Guide to Greece.* General Secret. of Youth and H.S.P.N., Athens.
TUCKER, G.M., & HEATH, M.F. (1994) *Birds in Europe: their Conservation Status.* Birdlife Conserv. Series No 3. Birdlife Int., Cambridge.

UNEP/UNESCO/FAO (1988) *Eutrophication in the Mediterranean Sea: Receiving Capacity and Monitoring of Long Term Effects.* M.A.P. Technical Reports Series No. 21. UNEP, Athens.

VADER, W.J.M. (1965) The first nesting of Spur-winged Provers in Greece. **Brit. Birds** 58: 195–196.
VAGLIANO, C. (1977) Changes in bird populations due to the effects of an extensive campaign of aerial spraying against *Dacus oleae* in the plain of Messara, Crete. **Nature, H.S.P.N. Bull.** 10/11: 57–59.

VAGLIANO, C. (1981) Contribution au statut des rapaces diurnes et nocturnes nicheurs en Crète. *In "Rapaces Mediterranéens"*. **Annales du CROP. 1. Aix en Provence:** 14–16.
VAGLIANO, C. (1984) Les oiseaux observés en Crète. **Biol. Gallo-hellen.** 11: 111–127.
VAGLIANO, C. (1985) The continental and island migration route of the S.E. Mediterranean: problems and propositions. Pp: 263–269 *in* NEWTON, I., & CHANCELLOR, R. (eds) *Conservation Studies of Raptors*. ICBP Techn. Publ. No 5. Cambridge.
VASIC, V. (1994) Avian diversity of Balkan Peninsula. 6e Congrès Intern. de Zoogéographie et Ecologie de la Grèce et des Régions Avoisinantes. Thessaloniki, 5-6 Avril 1993. **Bios** 2: 325–332.
VAUGHAN, R. (1960) Notes on autumn migration in Greece and Crete. **Ibis** 102: 87–92.
VAUGHAN, R. (1961) *Falco eleonorae*. **Ibis** 103a: 114–128.
VAURIE, C. (1959) *The Birds of the Palearctic Fauna: Passeriformes*. Witherby, London.
VAURIE, C. (1965) *The Birds of the Palearctic Fauna: Non-Passeriformes*. Witherby, London.
VAVALEKAS, K., THOMAIDES, C., PAPAEVANGELOU, E., & PAPAGEORGIOU, N. (1993) Nesting biology of the Rock Partridge *Alectoris graeca graeca* in northern Greece. **Acta Orn.** 28: 97–101.
VITTERY, A. (1994) Unusual bird species in the Ionian Islands (1988–1993). **Nature, H.S.P.N. Bull.** 64: 40–41.
VLACHOS, C. (1989) [*The Ecology of the Lesser-spotted Eagle* (Aquila pomarina) *in the Dadia Forest, Evros.*] Ph.D. thesis, School of Geotechnic studies, University of Thessaloniki. [In Greek.]
VLACHOS, C. (1991) The ecology of the lesser spotted eagle *Aquila pomarina* in Thrace (Greece). **Newsl. W.W.G.B.P.** 14: 10–11.
VLACHOS, C., & PAPAGEORGIOU, N. (1994) Diet, breeding success and nest-site selection of the Short-toed Eagle (Circaetus gallicus) in Northeastern Greece. **J. Raptor Research** 28: 39–42.
VOIKLIS, G. (1990) [Toxic pesticides in our food.] **Oikotopia (Athens)** 10: 20–24. [In Greek.]
VOOUS, K. (1960) *Atlas of European Birds*. Nelson.

WALMSLEY, J. (1980) *Waterfowl Mission to Greece and Italy, Autumn 1980*. Station Biol. Tour du Valat.
WALTER, H. (1968) Zur Abhängigkeit des Eleonorenfalken (*Falco eleonorae*) vom mediterranen Vogelzug. **J. Orn.** 109: 323–365.
WALTER, H. (1978a) Eleonora's Falcon (*Falco eleonorae*) in Greece. **Nature, H.S.P.N. Bull.** 15: 30–32.
WALTER, H. (1978b) *Breeding Locations of* Falco eleonorae: *A World Directory*. Los Angeles (private publication).
WALTER, H. (1979) *Eleonora's Falcon: Adaptations to Prey and Habitat in a Social Raptor*. Univ.of Chicago Press, Chicago.
WARNCKE, K. (1995) Der Mornellregenpfeifer *Charadrius morinellus* wohl Brutvogel auf dem Peloponnes. **Orn. Verh.** 25: 239–240.
WARNCKE, K., & WITTENBERG, J. (1961) Beobachtungen am Eleonorenfalken auf den Nordlichen Sporaden. **Vogelwelt** 82: 48–54.
WATSON, G.E. (1960) Flamingos in Greece. **Ibis** 102: 135–136.
WATSON, G.E. (1961a) Aegean bird notes including two breeding records new to Europe. **J. Orn.** 102: 301–307.
WATSON, G.E. (1961b) Ausbreitung der Türkentaube in Griechenland und auf den griechischen Inseln. **J. Orn.** 102: 98–99.
WATSON, G.E. (1961c) Aegean Bird Notes I. Description of new subspecies from Turkey. **Postilla** 52: 1–15.
WATSON, G.E. (1962a) A revision of Balkan, Aegean and Anatolian Crested Larks. **Bull. Br. Orn. Club** 82: 9–18.
WATSON, G.E. (1962b) Three sibling species of *Alectoris* Partridge. **Ibis** 104: 353–367.
WATSON, G.E. (1962c) Sympatry in Palearctic *Alectoris* Partridges. **Evolution** 16: 11-19.
WATSON, G.E. (1962d) La fauvette des jardins *Sylvia borin* migratrice et nidificatrice sur les îles de la mer Egée. **Alauda** 30: 210–213.
WATSON, G.E. (1962e) A re-evaluation and redescription of a difficult Asia Minor *Phylloscopus*. **Ibis** 104: 347–352.
WATSON, G.E. (1963) *Passer rufipectus* Bonaparte in Crete. Bull. Br. Orn. Club 83: 63–65.
WATSON, G.E. (1964) *Ecology and Evolution of Passerine Birds on the Islands of the Aegean Sea*. Ph.D. thesis, Yale University, New Haven, Connecticut.
WATSON, G.E. (1968) Lindermayer's Greek specimen of White-eyed Gull, *Larus leucophthalmus*. **J. Orn.** 109: 133–134
WATSON, G.E. (1973) Sea-bird colonies in the Islands of the Aegean Sea. **Nat. Geogr. Soc. Res. Rep. Proj.** 1966: 299–305
WEBER, P. (ed) (1994) *Atlasul Provizoriu al Pasarilr Clocitoare din Romania*. Soc. Ornit. Romanae, Medias.
WEESIE, P.D.M. (1982) A Pleistocene endemic island form within the genus Athene: Athene cretensis n.sp. (Aves, Strigiformes) from Crete. **Proc. Kon. Nederlandse Akademie. B.** 85(3): 323–336.
WEESIE, P.D.M. (1987) *The Quaternary Avifauna of Crete, Greece*. Ph.D. thesis, Univ. of Utrecht.
WETTSTEIN, O.V. (1938) Die **Vogelwelt** der Ägäis. **J. Orn.** 86: 9–53.
WHITE, C.M.N. (1939) A contribution of the Ornithology of Crete. **Ibis** (14) 3: 106–136.
WIELOCH, M. (1991) Population trends of the Mute Swan *Cygnus olor* in the Palearctic. *In* SEARS, J., & BACON, P.J. (eds) Proceed. Intern. Swan Symp. Oxford, 1989. **Wildfowl (Suppl.)** 1: 22–32.
WIETFELD, J. (1981) Bird communities of Greek olive plantations in the breeding season. Pp: 127–128 *in* PURROY, F.J. (ed) *Bird Census and Mediterranean Landscape*. Léon University, Léon.
WINK, M., WINK, C., & RISTOW, D. (1982) Brutbiologie mediterraner Gelbschnabelsturmtaucher (*Calonectris diomedea diomedea*). **Seevogel (Suppl.)**: 127–135.
WINK, M., BIEBACH, H., FELDMANN, F., SCHARLAU, W., SWATSCHEK, I., WINK, C., & RISTOW, D. (1993) Contribution to the breeding biology of Eleonora's Falcon (*Falco eleonorae*). *Biology and Conservation of Small Falcons*. Proceed. Hawk and Owl Trust Confer., Kent, 6–8 Sept. 1991. London. Pp: 59–72.
WITT, H. (1977) Zur Biologie den Korallenmöwe *Larus audouinii* - Brut und Ernährung. **J. Orn.** 118: 134–155.
WOLFF, W.J. (1966) Spring and summer observations from Mesolonghion, Greece. **Ardea** 54: 68–75.

ZALIDIS, G., & MANTZAVELAS, A. (eds) (1994) [*Inventory of Greek Wetlands as Natural Resources (First Approximation).*] Greek Biotope/Wetland Centre, Thessaloniki. [In Greek.]

INDEX